CM0074241b

Harden's

Established 1991

LONDON 2024
restaurants

SURVEY DRIVEN REVIEWS OF 1.6K RESTAURANTS

Take your dining to the next level

Enjoy benefits at the UK's Best Restaurants

Join today at hardens.com

© **Harden's Limited 2023**

ISBN 978-1-9160761-6-7

British Library Cataloguing-in-Publication data:
a catalogue record for this book is available from
the British Library.

Printed in the UK by CPI Books

Assistant editors: Bruce Millar, Antonia Russell

Harden's Limited
Missionworks, 41 Iffley Road, London W6 0PB

Would restaurateurs (and PRs) please address
communications to 'Editorial' at the above address,
or ideally by email to: editorial@hardens.com

The contents of this book are believed correct at
the time of printing. Nevertheless, the publisher
can accept no responsibility for errors or changes in
or omissions from the details given.

No part of this publication may be reproduced or
transmitted in any form or by any means, electronically
or mechanically, including photocopying, recording or
any information storage or retrieval system, without
prior permission in writing from the publisher.

CONTENTS

RATINGS & PRICES

Ratings

Our rating system does not tell you – as most guides do – that expensive restaurants are often better than cheap ones! What we do is compare each restaurant's performance – as judged by the average ratings awarded by reporters in the survey – with other similarly-priced restaurants. This approach has the advantage that it helps you find – whatever your budget for any particular meal – where you will get the best 'bang for your buck'.

The following qualities are assessed:

F — Food

S — Service

A — Ambience

The rating indicates that, ***in comparison with other restaurants in the same price-bracket***, performance is…

5 — Exceptional

4 — Very good

3 — Good

2 — Acceptable

1 — Poor

Prices

The price shown for each restaurant is the cost for one (1) person of an average three-course dinner with half a bottle of house wine and coffee, any cover charge, service and VAT. Lunch is often cheaper. With BYO restaurants, we have assumed that two people share a £7 bottle of off-licence wine.

Map reference – *shown immediately after the telephone number.*

Full postcodes – *for non-group restaurants, the first entry in the 'small print' at the end of each listing, so you can set your sat-nav.*

Website, Instagram – *shown in the small print, where applicable.*

Opening hours – *unless otherwise stated, restaurants are open for lunch and dinner seven days a week.*

Credit and debit cards – *unless otherwise stated, Mastercard, Visa, Amex and Maestro are accepted.*

Dress – *where appropriate, the management's preferences concerning patrons' dress are given.*

Sustainability – *if a restaurant or group has a star rating from the Sustainable Restaurants Association, this is shown.*

HOW THIS GUIDE IS WRITTEN

Celebrating our 33rd year!

This guide is based on our annual poll of what 'ordinary' diners-out think of London's restaurants. The first such survey was in 1991 with a few over 100 people taking part. This year, the total number of reporters in our combined London/UK survey, conducted mainly online, numbered 2,500, and, between them, they contributed 30,000 individual reports. Last year, some aspects of the guide needed amendment in order to allow for the effects of the Covid pandemic: for example, presenting two years of openings in a single edition. As far as possible this year, the format and content have been arranged on the same basis as all previous years, on the presumption and hope that where we are now is the long-anticipated 'new normal'.

How intelligent is AI?

At a time when the credibility of online reviews and influencer posts are under ongoing scrutiny, there is an ever-greater need for trusted sources such as the Harden's annual national diners' poll. In particular, the active curation by humans that we provide. For – while obviously folks can attempt to stuff the Harden's ballot too – our high degree of editorial oversight, plus our historical data about both the restaurants and those commenting, makes it much harder to cheat. In this way Harden's can socially source restaurant feedback, but – vitally – curate it carefully. It is this careful curation that provides extra 'value-added' for diners.

How we determine the ratings

In general, ratings are arrived at statistically. We create a ranking akin to football leagues, with the most expensive restaurants in the top league and the cheaper ones in lower ones. Any restaurant's ranking *within its own particular league* determines its ratings.

How we write the reviews

The tone of each review and the ratings are guided by the ranking of the restaurant concerned, derived as described above. At the margin, we may also pay regard to the balance of positive votes (such as for 'favourite restaurant') against negative ones (such as for 'most overpriced'). To explain why an entry has been rated as it has, we extract snippets from user comments ("enclosed in double quotes"). On well-known restaurants, we receive several hundred reports, and a short summary cannot do individual justice to all of them. What we seek to do – *without any regard to our own personal opinions* – is to illustrate key themes in the collective feedback.

How do we find our reporters?

Anyone can take part. Register now at www.hardens.com if you have not already done so! In fact, we find that once people have taken part, they often continue to do so.

This is a tough time to be running a restaurant. Operators are dealing with the cost-of-living crisis, skyrocketing energy bills, supply chain disruptions and ongoing staffing issues – all while the impacts of Brexit and the pandemic still linger. At the same time, the climate crisis is at a breaking point. Talk of sustainability is everywhere, and restaurants are under increasing pressure from every direction to implement transparent and measurable sustainability practices.

As customers, we're feeling the pinch, too, and money is tighter in many of our households these days. When we do get out for a bite to eat, most of us want to know that we're supporting the right sort of business: one that makes a positive contribution to our world.

The number of environmental marks and green awards seems to grow by the moment, and it can be impossible to know which is the most meaningful. At The Sustainable Restaurant Association, we've been working directly with the hospitality industry since 2010, and we've poured all of this knowledge into creating a new edition of the Food Made Good Standard. Relaunched earlier this year, this is the only global sustainability accreditation built especially for restaurants and other hospitality businesses.

When you see a restaurant sporting the Food Made Good logo, you know they're committed to sustainability in a tangible, measurable and transparent way – we make a point of rewarding action over intention. Completing the Food Made Good Standard is rigorous and requires an ongoing commitment; the accreditation must be renewed every two years, and each time, the restaurant receives a tailored report outlining practical steps they can take to improve further. The FMG Standard is a significant step forward for any restaurant, one that better informs their practices and guides them in a process of continuous improvement.

Food Made Good also takes a holistic, big-picture view of sustainability efforts. While carbon is of critical importance, it's far from the only metric that needs to be measured. Sustainability is a much bigger story, and taking a 360-degree approach is a more meaningful way to have an impact. We focus on 10 key focus areas across three pillars (Sourcing, Society and Environment) to ensure that every part of a restaurant's operation is actively contributing towards a better future for both people and planet.

The people element of this is important. Society – the 'S' in ESG – is too often forgotten when it comes to sustainability; however, in an industry built on people and personality, it needs to be a key concern. Things like diversity and equity, work-life balance, career development, zero tolerance for bullying and harassment and reasonable compensation have not always been a given in this industry, but we believe they must play a role in any restaurant's sustainability ambitions. Because restaurants also provide spaces for people to come together and help to define culture on a local level, community engagement is central to what it means to be a sustainable restaurant.

There are lots of accreditations out there, but the Food Made Good Standard is the only one specifically tailored to fit the needs of the hospitality industry. We see where restaurants are now, we know where they need to go, and we provide clear, measurable and practical directions for how they can get there. Whether you're considering a fine dining restaurant or a cosy neighbourhood hangout for your next meal, ask if they've done the Food Made Good Standard. It's how you can rest assured that they're playing their part in building a more sustainable future for all of us.

Stay up to date with The Sustainable Restaurant Association and our latest Food Made Good accredited businesses.

Website: www.thesra.org   Instagram: @foodmadegood

HOW THIS GUIDE IS WRITTEN

Consequently, many people who complete the survey have done so before. With high repeat-participation, the end-result is really more the product of a very large and ever-evolving panel, or jury, than a random 'poll'.

Wouldn't a random sample be better?

That's a theoretical question, as there is no obvious way, still less a cost-efficient one, to identify a random sample of the guests at each of, say, 5,000 establishments across the UK, and get them to take part in any sort of survey. People steeped in statistical market research tend be most keen on this idea. Other folks accept that having someone stand with a clipboard at Oxford Circus asking random people their opinion on Le Gavroche is unlikely to glean useful data.

Do people ever try to stuff the ballot?

Of course they do! Sometimes with the aid of social media agencies. Many rogue entries are weeded out every year. But stuffing the ballot is not as trivial a task as some people seem to think: the survey results throw up clear natural voting patterns against which unfair 'campaigns' tend to stand out.

Aren't inspections the best way to run a guide?

This could be called the 'traditional' model of restaurant reviewing; and chefs seem particularly prone to tout this form of recognition as the one form of criticism that they will respect. And, doubtless the inspection model has its strengths. But a prime weakness is that it is so expensive it precludes too many visits. Take its most famous exponent: Michelin. The tyre man has not historically claimed to visit each entry listed in its guide annually. Even once! But cost alone is not the only reason to query the inspection model. Another vital issue: who are its inspectors? Often catering professionals, whose tastes may be at odds with the natural customer base. On any entry of note, however, Harden's typically has somewhere between dozens and hundreds of reports annually from the folks who keep the restaurant in business. We believe that such feedback, carefully analysed, is far more revealing and accurate than an occasional 'professional' inspection.

SURVEY MOST MENTIONED

These are the restaurants which were most frequently mentioned by reporters. (Last year's position is given in brackets.) An asterisk* indicates the first appearance in the list of a recently opened restaurant.

1 J Sheekey (1)
2 Scott's (2)
3 Chez Bruce (3)
4 Noble Rot (11)
5 The Wolseley (4)
6 Clos Maggiore (6)
7 The River Café (7)
8 Core by Clare Smyth (5)
9 Brasserie Zédel (8)
10 Medlar (24)

11 Bocca di Lupo (15)
12 The Delaunay (8)
13 Andrew Edmunds (13)
14 The Cinnamon Club (22)
15 Noble Rot Soho (20)
16 La Trompette (16)
17 The Ritz (21)
18 Sam's Riverside (30)
19 La Poule au Pot (23)
20 A Wong (12)

21 Gymkhana (14)
22 Bentley's (19)
23 Trinity (25)
24 The Five Fields (17)
25 The Anchor & Hope (-)
26 Rules (-)
27 Galvin La Chapelle (38)
28 Benares (-)
29 Wiltons (32)
30 Gordon Ramsay (26)

31 Pied à Terre (28)
32 Moro (-)
33 Sessions Arts Club (-)
34 The Ledbury (-)
35 Lorne (34)
36 Oxo Tower (Restaurant) (-)
37 Harwood Arms (-)
38 Caraffini (-)
39 The Ivy (18)
40 St John Smithfield (39)

SURVEY NOMINATIONS

Top gastronomic experience

1. Core by Clare Smyth (1)
2. Chez Bruce (2)
3. Bouchon Racine*
4. Pied à Terre (-)
5. The Ledbury (8)
6. The Five Fields (3)
7. Frog by Adam Handling (5)
8. The Ritz (7)
9. The River Café (-)
10. Medlar (10)

Favourite

1. Chez Bruce (1)
2. Sam's Riverside (10)
3. Bouchon Racine*
4. The Wolseley (2)
5. The River Café (3)
6. La Trompette (8)
7. Bocca di Lupo (-)
8. Medlar (-)
9. Hawksmoor (Group) (-)
10. J Sheekey (-)

Best for business

1. The Wolseley (1)
2. The Delaunay (3)
3. Hawksmoor (Group) (3)
4. Scott's (6)
5. Rules (-)
6. Coq d'Argent (4)
7. Galvin La Chapelle (8)
8. Cabotte (8)
8= The Dining Room, The Goring Hotel (10)
10. Bleeding Heart Bistro (-)

Best for romance

1. Clos Maggiore (1)
2. La Poule au Pot (2)
3. Andrew Edmunds (3)
4. Core by Clare Smyth (7)
5. Sessions Arts Club (5)
6. Galvin La Chapelle (-)
7. Medlar (-)
8. Chez Bruce (6)
9. Scott's (8)
10. Pied à Terre (-)

Best breakfast/brunch

1 The Wolseley (1)
2 Dishoom (2)
3 The Delaunay (4)
4 Granger & Co (5)
5 Breakfast Club (10)
6 Côte (3)
7 Caravan (7)
8 Megan's (8)
9 The Ivy Grills & Brasseries (6)
10 Claridges Foyer & Reading Room (-)

Best bar/pub food

1 Harwood Arms (1)
2 The Anchor & Hope (3)
3 The Anglesea Arms (4)
4 The Eagle (8)
5 Bull & Last (7)
6 The Wigmore, The Langham (5)
7 The Drapers Arms (-)
8 The Ladbroke Arms (-)
9 The Pelican (-)
10 The Red Lion & Sun (6)

Most disappointing cooking

1 Oxo Tower (Restaurant) (1)
2 The Ivy (2)
3 The Wolseley (-)
4 Dinner Mandarin Oriental (-)
5 Gordon Ramsay (3)
6 Mere (-)
7 Hot Stone (-)
8 Jacuzzi (-)
9 Rick Stein (5)
10 Skylon (-)

Most overpriced restaurant

1 The River Café (1)
2 Gordon Ramsay (5)
3 Oxo Tower (Restaurant) (4)
4 Sexy Fish (2)
5 Hélène Darroze, Connaught (3)
6 Dinner Mandarin Oriental (-)
7 J Sheekey (-)
8 Scott's (10)
9 Langan's Brasserie (-)
10 Estiatorio Milos (-)

SURVEY HIGHEST RATINGS

FOOD

SERVICE

£130+

FOOD	SERVICE
1 Endo at The Rotunda	1 Core by Clare Smyth
2 Core by Clare Smyth	2 Da Terra
3 Da Terra	3 Endo at The Rotunda
4 A Wong	4 The Five Fields
5 Sketch (Lecture Room)	5 Muse

£100–£129

FOOD	SERVICE
1 Chez Bruce	1 Charlie's at Brown's
2 SOLA	2 The Ritz
3 Otto's	3 Clarke's
4 Hutong, The Shard	4 Otto's
5 The Ninth London	5 Chez Bruce

£75–99

FOOD	SERVICE
1 BiBi	1 The Dysart Petersham
2 The Barbary	2 Theo Randall
3 Myrtle	3 Cornerstone
4 The Dysart Petersham	4 Myrtle
5 Brat	5 BiBi

£55–£74

FOOD	SERVICE
1 Sabor	1 Oslo Court
2 Jin Kichi	2 Café Spice Namaste
3 Bombay Bustle	3 Hereford Road
4 The French House	4 The French House
5 Berber & Q	5 Mazi

£54 or less

FOOD	SERVICE
1 Dastaan	1 Dastaan
2 Roti King	2 Monmouth Coffee Co
3 Supawan	3 Lupins
4 Manteca	4 Kiln
5 Kiln	5 Fish Central

AMBIENCE	OVERALL
1 Sketch (Lecture Room)	1 Sketch (Lecture Room)
2 Endo at The Rotunda	2 Endo at The Rotunda
3 Core by Clare Smyth	3 Core by Clare Smyth
4 The Ledbury	4 Da Terra
5 Da Terra	5 The Ledbury
1 Charlie's at Brown's	1 Charlie's at Brown's
2 The Ritz	2 The Ritz
3 Min Jiang	3 Hutong, The Shard
4 Galvin at Windows	4 Min Jiang
5 Hutong, The Shard	5 Otto's
1 Clos Maggiore	1 The Dysart Petersham
2 The Dysart Petersham	2 BiBi
3 The Barbary	3 The Barbary
4 Sam's Riverside	4 Cornerstone
5 The Cinnamon Club	5 Norma
1 Sessions Arts Club	1 Sabor
2 Andrew Edmunds	2 The French House
3 Cafe Cecilia	3 Cafe Cecilia
4 Sabor	4 Café Spice Namaste
5 The French House	5 Sessions Arts Club
1 Bar Italia	1 Trattoria Brutto
2 Trattoria Brutto	2 Dastaan
3 Maison Bertaux	3 Supawan
4 Granary Square Brasserie	4 Bar Italia
5 Casa do Frango	5 Kiln

SURVEY BEST BY CUISINE

These are the restaurants which received the best average food ratings (excluding establishments with a small or notably local following).

Where the most common types of cuisine are concerned, we present the results in two price-brackets. For less common cuisines, we list the top three, regardless of price.

For further information about restaurants which are particularly notable for their food, see the area overviews starting on page 262.

British, Modern

£75 and over	Under £75
1 Core by Clare Smyth	1 The French House
2 The Ledbury	2 Cafe Cecilia
3 Chez Bruce	3 The Plimsoll
4 Muse	4 12:51
5 The Five Fields	5 Lupins

French

£75 and over	Under £75
1 Sketch (Lecture Room)	1 Casse-Croute
2 La Dame de Pic London	2 Café du Marché
3 Otto's	3 Galvin Bistrot & Bar
4 The Ninth London	4 The Wells Tavern
5 Galvin La Chapelle	5 Petit Ma Cuisine

Italian/Mediterranean

£75 and over	Under £75
1 Norma	1 Pentolina
2 Theo Randall	2 Manteca
3 Murano	3 Padella
4 Luca	4 Bocca di Lupo
5 Enoteca Turi	5 Flour & Grape

Indian & Pakistani

£75 and over	Under £75
1 BiBi	1 Dastaan
2 Bombay Bustle	2 Café Spice Namaste
3 Gymkhana	3 Kricket
4 Trishna	4 Pure Indian Cooking
5 Tamarind	5 Lahore Kebab House

Chinese

£75 and over
1. A Wong
2. Hutong, The Shard
3. Min Jiang
4. China Tang
5. Hunan

Under £75
1. Three Uncles
2. Barshu
3. Master Wei
4. Mandarin Kitchen
5. Four Seasons

Japanese

£75 and over
1. Endo at The Rotunda
2. Dinings
3. Nobu Portman Square
4. Zuma
5. Nobu

Under £75
1. Jin Kichi
2. Oka
3. Akira at Japan House
4. Eat Tokyo
5. Sticks'n'Sushi

British, Traditional
1. The Ritz
2. St John Smithfield
3. Scott's

Vegetarian
1. Bubala
2. Apricity
3. Ragam

Burgers, etc
1. Burger & Lobster
2. MEATLiquor
3. Patty and Bun

Pizza
1. Santa Maria
2. Cinquecento
3. 50 Kalò di Ciro Salvo

Fish & Chips
1. Nautilus
2. Toff's
3. fish!

Thai
1. Supawan
2. Kiln
3. Smoking Goat

Steaks & Grills
1. Lurra
2. Goodman
3. Hawksmoor

Fish & Seafood
1. Cornerstone
2. The Oystermen
3. Bentley's

Fusion
1. Da Terra
2. Paladar
3. Scully

Spanish
1. Sabor
2. Brat
3. José

THE RESTAURANT SCENE

Headwinds continue to constrain growth

We recorded 123 new openings in the last 12 months. Like last year, this is the lowest level of openings since the 2012 edition. Yet again, the rate falls near the bottom of the range of 107-200 openings per annum since the year 2000.

By contrast, the rate of closures stands at 77, which – while not high – isn't a low rate either. Subtracting this figure from the openings gives net growth of 46, continuing the tame run of growth seen since 2018. London's quality restaurant scene nowadays is expanding at a rate more in keeping with the 1990s than the previous millennial trend. When you consider that the population today is over 30% higher than it was in 2000, it underlines the tepid nature of current activity.

Hold onto your hats!

One area of undoubted growth is restaurant bills! The average price of dinner for one at establishments listed in this guide is £75.65 (c.f. £69.28 last year). This represents an annualised increase of 9.2% in the past year: well above CPI growth of 6.4% for the 12 months to July 2022 (although food inflation in this period was higher).

Continuing a trend seen last year, the rise is most marked amongst the most pricey restaurants (those charging over £100 per head). In this group, the annualised growth rate is again higher than for restaurants generally, at 10.7% (down a fraction from 11.7% last year).

This last factor continues to produce ever-new, vertigo-inducing price points that would have seemed far-fetched in the capital barely five years ago. Last year, we noted that £100 per head is no longer enough for our highest price category (now redefined to £130+). Next year, we will have to redefine our top category at £150+.

Growth at the loftiest price-levels is particularly eye-catching: becoming more so the higher you move up the price scale. There are now 191 restaurants in the guide charging over £100 per head (up 24% from last year's 154); there are 54 restaurants charging over £150 per head (up 46% from last year's 37); above £200 per head, there are 27 establishments (up 59%) and above £250 per head now 11 (up 83% from 6 last year). And these figures do not include establishments such as those in Whitehall's new OWO hotel, flagged in the guide but not yet part of our stats.

Rich person's playground?

Beyond the global pressure on prices, it is tempting to look for other long-term trends that may account for shifting the price-landscape at the top of the London restaurant scene. In September 2023, London's *Evening Standard* ran a front page with the headline "London's 7-star gold rush" in which it charted the large number of über-luxe new hotel projects approaching completion. Pricewise, these establishments are seeking a room rate of £1000+ per night – breaking new ground for the capital. Many of London's splashiest new eateries operate from within such ventures.

Another factor adding to the top-end price category is the rise of luxury Japanese dining in London. Nearly half of the £250+ entries are Japanese omakase venues yet this is a category of eatery that barely existed in London 10 years ago. And many of the more expensive Modern European and fusion restaurants in the upper price categories ape this counter-based style of dining. It's a form of top-end meal that would not be recognisable to previous generations of Londoners: often based around a chef's table with the focus on foodie reverie rather than the traditional image of gilded chambers, candle-light, flunkies, gueridons, and napery.

It is tempting to conclude that the capital is becoming a playground for what used to be called "the jet set", with most of its own residents consigned to looking on enviously on Insta and in colour supplements. But historically one of the striking features of the London restaurant scene has been its lack of a top tier of splurgy, expensive destinations such as those that have long characterised top-end dining in Paris and Tokyo. Perhaps it is perverse to complain if London can now hold its own internationally.

Changing of the guard

Although this year has not been exceptional for closures, what has caught attention is the number of famous names and stalwart institutions that have given up the ghost.

Le Gavroche (open till January, but now booked solid on the news of its demise) is the most notable, with Michel Roux Jr now seemingly focusing purely on his media and consultancy commitments. In a similar vein, Marcus Wareing has also announced that he is stepping back this year.

The very venerable Simpsons Tavern (which dated from 1757), Julies, The India Club and Banners all chose to go this year, while Simpsons in the Strand (est. 1828) sold off its famous carving trollies and is to be relaunched with an as-yet-to-be-revealed new look.

Japanese most popular non-European cuisine

In terms of cuisines, this year's openings mirrored last year's. After Modern British (30) openings, Italian cuisine was next favourite (with 18 debuts), followed by Japanese cuisine (with 10 openings).

In terms of location, Central London remained dominant, with 50 arrivals. In the 'burbs, South London led the way for once (with 21 openings) boosted by the Battersea Power Station development. East London followed (with 19 openings); while West London equalled North London's rate of opening (with 16 apiece).

OPENINGS & CLOSURES

The listings below relate to the period from Autumn 2022 to Autumn 2023. In one or two cases (Le Gavroche, Marcus) we have anticipated a closure due shortly post-publication.

Only branches of small groups in the listings below contribute to the grand total figures. (It is beyond the scope of this book to track comings and goings at the large multiples.)

* temporarily closed as we to go to press.

Openings (123)

The Apollo Arms
Archway
ArtSpace Café, Claridge's
Attica
Audrey Green, NPG
Bancone *(SE1)*
Bao Battersea *(SW11, W1)*
Bar Kroketa
The Barley Mow
The Beefsteaks @ M. Manze
Berbere Pizza
Berenjak Borough *(SE1)*
Blacklock *(E14)*
Block Soho
Bone Daddies *(W8)*
Bouchon Racine
Boudica
Brooklands
Café Lapérouse, The OWO
Capri
Caravan *(WC2)*
Carlotta
Casa do Frango *(SW1, W1)*
Chet's, Hoxton Hotel
Chungdam
Cilantro Putney
Cinder *(NW8)*
Cinquecento *(W1, NW3)*
Claridges Restaurant
Contigo
Crisp Pizza, The Chancellors
The Devonshire
Diba *(SW3)*
Doppo
Dorian
Dorothy & Marshall
Dovetale by Tom Sellers
EDIT

081 Pizzeria, Peckham Levels
Eline
Emmanuelle
Empire Empire
Endo Kazutoshi, The OWO
Epicurus
Evernight
Fatto A Mano *(N1)*
Flat Iron *(W8)*
Freak Scene
La Gamba
Giacco's
Gouqi
The Gurkhas
Harvest
Hawthorn
Hicce Hart
Homies on Donkeys
Humo
Izakaya Nights
Kanada-Ya *(W5)*
Kapara by Bala Baya
Kettners
Kibako
Kima
Kuro Eatery
The Lanesborough Grill
Langosteria, The OWO
Lasdun, National Theatre
Lavo, The BoTree
Leo's
Lilienblum
Lina Stores *(SW4)*
Little Kudu
Little Pizza Hicce
Llama Inn, The Hoxton
Lusin
Maene
Maresco

OPENINGS & CLOSURES

Maria G's (SW6)
Masala Zone (W1)
Mauro Colagreco,
  The OWO
Mayha
Meet Bros
Midland Grand Dining
  Room
Miznon (W11)
Los Mochis (EC2)
Mount Street Restaurant,
  The Audley
Mountain
Mr Ji (NW1)
Nammos
1905
Noble Rot Mayfair
Noci (SW11, EC1)
Notto
Oak & Poppy
Ochre
The Orangery
Paper Moon, The OWO
Papi
The Parakeet
The Park
Pavyllon
Ploussard
The Portrait Restaurant by
  Richard Corrigan, NPG
Rasa Street
Sam's Kitchen
Sheesh
Shiro
64 Goodge Street
Souvlaki Street
Sticks n Sushi (W12, E1)
Sticky Mango Butler's
  Wharf (SE1)
Story Cellar
Studio Gauthier
Supa Ya Ramen (SE15)
Sushi Kanesaka
TAKU
Terra Moderna
Terra Rossa (EC4)
The eight Restaurant
Toba
Tofu Vegan (E1)

Tozi Grand Cafe (SW11)
Trinco
20 Berkeley
Uli Marylebone (W1)
Via Emilia (W1T)
Vori
The Waterman's Arms
The Wolseley City
Yaatra
Zapote
Zia Lucia (NW6, E14)

OPENINGS & CLOSURES

Closures (77)

Amethyst
Antillean
Aquavit
Attawa
Attimi
The Avenue
Banners
Bao Bar* (E8)
Bao Fitzrovia (W1)
Bermondsey Larder*
Black Radish
BOB's Lobster
Boiler & Co
Boudin Blanc
Bright
Celeste at The
  Lanesborough
Chameleon
Cincinnati Chilibomb
Dai Chi
Dumpling Shack x Fen
  Noodles
FENN
Fiend
Folie*
Le Gavroche
Giannino Mayfair*
Goddard & Gibbs
Grand Trunk Road
Ham
Hankies Marble Arch (W1)
Haugen
The Hero of Maida
Hood
India Club, Strand
  Continental Hotel
Isibani
Itaku
Joanna's
The Jones Family Affair
Julie's
Lino's
The Tent (at the End of the
  Universe)
M Restaurant Victoria
  Street (SW1)
Ma Goa

Made in Italy (SW19)
Marcus, The Berkeley
Mathura
Maya
Mike's Peckham
Miscusi (N1)
Mr Ji (W1)
Mr Todiwala's Petiscos
The Narrow
Native at Browns
Ngon
Nutshell
Off the Hook
Oklava (EC2)
Olivocarne
Oxeye
P Franco
Pizza East Portobello (W10)
Plateau
Rabot 1745
Radici
The Red Duck
The Residency
Sarap Filipino Bistro
SeaSons
7 Saints
Simpson's Tavern
Sparrow
St Martin's House
Stem & Glory (EC1, EC2)
Tatale
Tokyo Sukiyaki-Tei & Bar
Walter's
West 4th
Wun's (W1)

DIRECTORY

Comments in "double quotation marks" were made by reporters.

A Cena TW1 £79 443
418 Richmond Road   020 8288 0108   1–4A

With its "traditional tablecloths and a sense of comfort", this "really strong and inventive neighbourhood Italian" close to Richmond Bridge in St Margaret's appeals to a broad local constituency – "you can tell because it can be hard to get a table!". The food is "always a treat" – and "the menu changes regularly, which makes eating here frequently even more of a pleasure". / TW1 2EB; www.acena.co.uk; acenarestaurant; Tue-Sat 10 pm.

A Wong SW1 £252 522
70 Wilton Rd   020 7828 8931   2–4B

"Without a shadow of a doubt the very best Chinese restaurant in town" – Andrew Wong is "such a talent" and his "genius" cuisine inspires unending superlatives regarding his Pimlico HQ (previously run for decades by his parents as Kym's). "Exceptional craft is on display" in the preparation of the "exquisite dim sum" and other "clearly Chinese dishes" ("none of your fusion nonsense here!") and for some reporters it is "one of the most extraordinary culinary experiences ever". But since the award of a second Michelin star (the first ever for a Chinese establishment) a meal here risks becoming "prohibitively expensive", with minimum spends for lunch and tasting menus only in the evening. On most accounts it's "worth it despite the high cost", but the equation is more evenly balanced now, and the levels of service and ambience have struggled to keep up with the "hellish" bill. Even so, "there's scarce table availability even with the extension into the outer terrace". / SW1V 1DE; www.awong.co.uk; awongsw1; Wed-Sat, Tue 8.30 pm.

The Abingdon W8 £67 333
54 Abingdon Rd   020 7937 3339   6–2A

"A very special gastropub tucked away in a quiet street off Kensington High Street", which has been run for 25 years by the Staples family, who have remodelled what was built as a classic Victorian corner tavern into an "all-round reliable local restaurant" and bar fit for its chichi environs. / W8 6AP; www.theabingdon.co.uk; theabingdon; Mon-Sat 10 pm, Sun 9 pm.

Acme Fire Cult E8 £55 213
The Bootyard, Abbot Street   no tel   14–1A

"Don't be put off by what looks like a dodgy side street to get there", say fans of Andrew Clarke and Daniel Watkins's Dalston BBQ, who say that the "great food cooked with fire and flames" (and served "in the classic small plates style") justifies eating "in a tent! in January!" ("you get blankets… it's worth it and fun"). And there's "amazing vegetarian options as well as the fish and meat". But other diners in our annual poll are less sure. "Haphazard" or "too-cool-for-school" service is a recurrent theme. And overall ratings were dragged down by the minority who found the food itself to be "a real let down" ("considering everything is prepared over coals, it was not the charry interesting place we'd heard of, in fact somewhat bland"). / E8 3DP; www.acmefirecult.com; acmefirecult; Tue-Sat 10 pm, Sun 4 pm.

Afghan Kitchen N1 £37 322
35 Islington Green   020 7359 8019   9–3D

This "tiny hole in the wall with an even tinier kitchen" on Islington Green "delivers time and time again" with its tasty and good-value Afghan cooking. Top Menu Tip – "get the pumpkin curry". / N1 8DU; kubiti.blog/afghan-kitchen; afghankitchenldn; Wed & Thu, Sun 9.30 pm, Fri & Sat 10 pm.

Aglio e Olio SW10 £52 **3** **3** **2**
194 Fulham Rd   020 7351 0070   6–3B
"Spot-on pasta" is a key draw at this "excellent local Italian" near Chelsea & Westminster Hospital "that welcomes kids" and "always delivers with charming service". It's the sort of place regulars "go to at least once a month, love it!" – which means it's typically rammed. / SW10 9PN; www.aglioeolio.co.uk; Mon-Sun 11 pm.

Akari N1 £45 **4** **3** **3**
196 Essex Rd   020 7226 9943   9–3D
"Still a bit of a hidden gem, which is a real shame as this place should be packed" – this converted pub by Essex Road station is a longstanding fixture of the area. With its mix of sushi and other "enjoyable and very tasty" fare, fans say it serves "really wonderful izakaya dishes in a pretty chilled-out environment"; and that even if "it's not as cheap as it once was, it's still good value". / N1 8LZ; www.akarilondon.co.uk; akari_islington; Tue-Thu, Sun 10.30 pm, Fri 10 pm, Sat 11 pm.

Akira at Japan House W8 £74 **3** **3** **2**
101-111 Kensington High Street   020 3971 4646   6–1A
"Exquisite" (or "expensive"?) is the apposite word to describe a meal at the first-floor restaurant of the Japan House cultural centre on Kensington High Street, where tableware and presentation are given equal billing with the food. "The bento boxes are beautiful", too. / W8 5SA; www.japanhouselondon.uk; japanhouseldn; Tue-Sat 11 pm, Sun.

Akoko W1 £164 **4** **4** **3**
21 Berners Street   020 7323 0593   5–1A
Ayo Adeyemi is now at the stoves of Aji Akokomi's groundbreaking Fitzrovia West African, after the departure of Theo Clench in March 2022. Clench held a Michelin star at his previous gig (Bonham's) and was instantly awarded one at his new home (Cycene) so it's slightly puzzling why one was withheld from him here? Perhaps Ayo will eventually succeed where Theo did not? The intriguing cooking uses West African ingredients and spicing as inspiration for an 'haute' take on these cuisines, and though feedback was limited this year it seems to continue at the same "brilliant, creative and delicious" level set by his predecessor. Add in the vibey interior using a palette inspired by African village culture, and the establishment has helped move the goalposts of what can be expected in terms of sophistication for an African-inspired venture in London. BREAKING NEWS. In September 2023, Aji announced a spin-off venture in Borough Yards called Akara – also West African but in a cheaper, more accessible format. / W1T 3LJ; akoko.co.uk; akokorestaurant; Tue-Sat 9 pm.

Akub W8 £70 **2** **3** **4**
27 Uxbridge Street   07729 039206   7–2B
Fadi Kattan's three-floor Palestinian newcomer in Notting Hill inspires mixed reviews. Everyone agrees it's a "beautiful room" with a "bubbling" atmosphere; and welcomes the fact that its Middle Eastern menu is "just a bit different, with a nice twist on more familiar fare". But while some reporters (especially veggie ones) feel the cuisine is outstanding, too many feel it is "heavy handed" – "a baffling series of dishes, some of them good, some of them unappetising, with no coherent pattern of size or flavour". "I was so looking forward to this one – the service was great and so was the ambience but the food was disappointing". / W8 7TQ; www.akub-restaurant.com; akub.london; Tue-Thu 11 pm, Fri & Sat 11.30 pm, Sun 4 pm.

Al Duca SW1 £90 3 2 3
4-5 Duke of York St   020 7839 3090   3–3D
"Very well-presented Italian food" and "an atmosphere quiet enough for conversation" make this straightforward trattoria on a corner site in St James's a useful and reasonably priced option in an expensive part of town. / SW1Y 6LA; www.alduca-restaurant.co.uk; al_duca; Mon-Sat 11 pm.

Alain Ducasse at The Dorchester W1 £278 3 3 2
53 Park Lane   020 7629 8866   3–3A
"A perfect menu that will forever stay in the mind" is how some reporters remember this luxurious Mayfair outpost of France's most celebrated restaurateur, whose kitchen is run by chef-patron Jean-Philippe Blondet. Often indifferently rated in our survey over the years, it was more regularly acclaimed this year as offering "the very best of French cuisine" to match its Michelin three-star renown, although even those acknowledging the "impeccable food and service" sometimes note that "the room itself is a bit soulless and rather boring". And there remains an undercurrent in sentiment of the view that the performance is "uninspiring and poor value". Top Menu Tip – save yourself for the signature dish, which is rum baba, with Chantilly cream and rum. / W1K 1QA; www.alainducasse-dorchester.com; alainducasseattthedorchester.

Alex Dilling Café Royal W1 £212 5 4 3
68 Regent Street   020 7406 3333   4–4C
Ex-Greenhouse chef, Alex Dilling, "has hit the ground running" at this West End yearling, overlooking Regent Street: one of the highest quality arrivals of the last twelve months (for which he was awarded two Michelin stars in no seconds flat). Feedback is full of superlatives for his "exceptional cuisine" which is in a "classic" style rooted in tradition ("it was some of the most technically accomplished food I have ever been served…"). Overall it's an "elegant" experience, but the "dining room could do with a little refresh (staff indicated plans are in the pipeline for this)". / W1B 4DY; www.hotelcaferoyal.com; alexdillingcaferoyal; Tue-Sun 8.30 pm.

Alexandrie W8 £74 3 3 3
38C Kensington Church Street   020 7937 2244   6–1A
This relatively unsung Kensington outfit is worth knowing about, if on limited feedback, for its refined French-influenced Egyptian cooking – of the style enjoyed in sophisticated homes rather than in tourist traps. / W8 4BX; alexandrie_kensington; Wed-Sat 10 pm, Sun 9.30 pm.

Allegra E20 £95 3 2 2
The Stratford, 20-22 International Way   020 3973 0545   14–1D
Patrick Powell's "adventurous and well-crafted" cuisine on the 7th floor of this glossy design hotel (part of the Manhattan Loft Gardens apartment block) "is something far beyond other restaurants in the area, with real delicacy and touch, particularly in the fish cookery… if it were more central it would be constantly packed to bursting". On the downside, "despite the pleasant decor and the great view you can't quite shake the feeling that it's part of a hotel… which of course it is…" / E20 1GQ; www.allegra-restaurant.com; allegrarestaurant; Wed-Sat 10 pm, Sun 3 pm.

The Alma SE19 £69 3 3 4
95 Church Road   020 8768 1885   1–4D
This "lovely food-led pub" – a carefully modernised beauty from 1854 on Crystal Palace's thriving 'Triangle' – showcases chef David Yorkiston's "really great cooking – way, way above typical gastroboozer fare". "Controversially, it has banned kids under 10" but not everyone objects ("we think the atmosphere is all the better for it, even if it means we can't go there as often as we'd like"). / SE19 2TA; thealmapub.com; thealmacp; Mon-Sat 10 pm, Sun 9 pm.

Aloo Tama SW1 £47 4 3 2
18 Greencoat Place   020 7834 9873   2–4C
"Terrific Nepalese dishes in a basic setting" behind Victoria station. "The manager is exceptionally friendly and skillful – they were happy to make black lentils for us despite not being on the menu". They also have a lunchtime food truck at Merchant Square in Paddington. Top Tip – "BYO, so don't turn up empty-handed expecting a beer or glass of wine". / SW1P 1PG; www.alootama.com; alootamaofficial; Tue-Sat 10 pm, Sun 9 pm.

Alter E1 £34 4 3 2
15 Leman Street   no tel   10–2D
Within Leman Locke Hotel in Aldgate East, Andy Goodwin's modern dining room (with floor-to-ceiling windows looking out onto the nearby offices) aims to 'challenge the common perceptions of vegan cooking by drawing inspiration from global street food cultures'. Feedback on his interesting meat-free creations remains limited, but very enthusiastic. Top Tip – dip your toe in the water with the £28 early evening menu. / E1 8EN; www.alterldn.com; alter_ldn; Mon-Sat 10 pm.

Amaya SW1 £96 4 4 4
Halkin Arcade, 19 Motcomb St   020 7823 1166   6–1D
"Sophisticated flavours run through outstanding quality grill and tandoori dishes" – "beautiful" food from a "cleverly designed menu" using a wide variety of cooking techniques – at this Belgravia pioneer of Indian tapas (part of MW Eats, which owns Masala Zone, Chutney Mary, et al). With its stylish design, built around an open kitchen, it falls under the heading: "pricey but worth it". / SW1X 8JT; www.amaya.biz; amaya.ldn; Tue-Sat 10.30 pm, Sun 10 pm.

Amazonico W1 £144 2 3 4
10 Berkeley Square   020 7404 5000   3–3B
"If you feel like a party this is a good place to come" – this lavish, foliage-filled Mayfair haunt 'goes for it' with its "live music, nice cocktails and lively ambience" and provides a "great setting" (including for romance). Fans say "the food is as good as the music" and applaud a "superb overall experience". But there are also those – particularly who focus on the sushi and luxurious grills rather than the complete package – for whom it's just far too overpriced. / W1J 6EF; www.amazonicorestaurant.com; amazonicolondon; Mon-Sat 1 am, Sun midnight.

The American Bar, The Stafford SW1 £82 3 3 4
16-18 Saint James's Place   020 7493 0111   3–4C
The "great vibe" created by its tranquil St James's location and retro Americana helps create a feeling of luxurious nostalgia at this long-standing fixture. With the hotel catering now overseen by Northcote's Lisa Goodwin-Allen, the menu has been usefully re-imagined in recent times and has a heartier, more distinctive US spin (steaks, dogs, pastrami rolls) than it did of old. / SW1A 1NJ; thestaffordlondon.com; Sun-Wed midnight, Thu-Sat 1 am.

L'Amorosa W6 £67 4 4 3
278 King St   020 8563 0300   8–2B
This "lovely local Italian" near Ravenscourt Park tube is getting back into its stride after "a dreadful time with lockdown followed by a flood at the premises". Ex-Zafferano chef Andy Needham and his team offer a "really warm welcome and a beautifully executed short menu". Top Menu Tip – "excellent pasta and specials". / W6 0SP; www.lamorosa.co.uk; lamorosa_london; Thu, Sat 9 pm.

Ampéli W1 £93 3|3|2
18 Charlotte Street   020 3355 5370   2–1C
Opened a matter of weeks before Covid struck in 2020, photographer Jenny Pagoni's debut restaurant on Fitzrovia's foodie Charlotte Street was inspired by contemporary Athenian wine bars, and has a "very interesting all-Greek list" emphasising indigenous grape varieties, accompanied by a menu of eastern Mediterranean dishes. / W1T 2LZ; www.ampeli.london; ampeli.london; Tue-Sat 9.30 pm.

Amrutha SW18 £37 3|4|2
326 Garratt Lane   020 8001 4628   11–2B
"Vegan food that's as good as can be" – from a selection of broadly Asian choices – inspires devotees of this 'vegan soul food' venture in Earlsfield (now with a spin-off in Honor Oak Park) from school friends Arvin Suntaramoorphy and Shyam Kotecha. "Being able to ask for additional dishes until satisfied means you never leave disappointed". Guests are invited to BYO without charge, and to reduce the bill if they believe it is too high – while the truly hard-up can eat for free in return for a couple of hours' work. / SW18 4EJ; www.amrutha.co.uk; amruthauk; Tue-Sat 10 pm, Sun 9 pm.

The Anchor & Hope SE1 £69 4|3|3
36 The Cut   020 7928 9898   10–4A
"Still fantastic after all these years" – this celebrated foodie favourite near the Old Vic returned to being London's No.1 gastropub this year, in a dead heat with Fulham's Harwood Arms. "It's a bit insulting to call it bar/pub food as it's a level up from that" – "very strong, British traditional fare is made with added flair and style" from a "daily changing menu with lots of options" ("the shared roast and other meat dishes are quite unique and the eclectic wine list a joy"). And "nowadays they serve a well-priced lunch as well as its always-magnificent evening menu". / SE1 8LP; www.anchorandhopepub.co.uk; anchorhopecut; Mon & Tue 10 pm, Wed-Sat 10.30 pm, Sun 3.15 pm.

Andanza SE1 £54 4|3|3
66 Weston Street   020 7967 1972   10–4C
This "buzzing tapas bar, hidden away from the tourist traps of Borough Market", occupies a former bookies' in the shadow of the Shard, and offers some "great, non-standard" pintxo, pequeno and other options. If "the set-up's a little bit cramped, that does give it the feel of the tightest of tapas bars in Catalonia". / SE1 3QJ; www.andanza.co.uk; andanza.se1; Mon-Sun 11 pm.

The Andover Arms W6 £53 3|4|4
57 Aldensley Rd   020 8748 2155   8–1C
"Now under new management", this "small and friendly" pub – in the picturesque Hammersmith backstreets known as 'Brackenbury Village' – has gone from good to better. It has always been a "solid, welcoming local, with good food and well-kept beer" and its new incarnation is just that bit 'next-level': with its "well judged and executed seasonal menus and quality wines by the glass" it's "buzzing". / W6 0DL; www.theandoverarmsw6.com; theandoverarms; Mon-Sat 10 pm, Sun 9 pm.

Andrew Edmunds W1 £71 3|4|5
46 Lexington Street   020 7437 5708   4–2C
"If your date is going badly here, it's not destined to be" at this "gorgeous", candle-lit Soho townhouse – one of the capital's prime destinations "for a tête-a-tête lunch or smoochy dinner". "All bare wood, nooks, and snugs", it is "very tightly packed" and down-to-earth and for its legions of fans captures "just what I want from a restaurant. OK, the setting could be more comfy, but it has a superb vibe", "amenable" and "charming" service, and "British seasonal food with a twist" that's not aiming for fireworks but which is "always reliable". Crucially, all this is backed up by "a short wine selection that's second to none and at absolutely outstanding prices". Andrew

Edmunds himself unexpectedly passed away in September 2022, but the business (now run by his family) "continues to honour his legacy": "I've been coming here since the 90's and I'm so glad the team have carried on without Andrew – the place goes from strength to strength". / W1F 0LP; www.andrewedmunds.com; andrew.edmunds; Mon-Sun 10.30 pm.

Angelina E8   £72   5 3 4
56 Dalston Lane   020 7241 1851   14–1A
"Every time is a different experience thanks to the ever changing menu" at this "imaginative and wonderful" Dalston venture. "The food really is a mix of European and Japanese influences" and served in a tasting menu format (either the 10-course 'kaiseki' or 4-course 'omakase') that's "excellent, without feeling too fussy, and great value for money". The "dark and moody interior" creates a "pared-back but buzzy atmosphere, which makes this a perfect pick for a special dinner". / E8 3AH; angelina.london; angelina.dalston; Mon-Fri 10 pm, Sat 10.30 pm.

Angler,
South Place Hotel EC2   £118   3 4 2
3 South Pl   020 3215 1260   13–2A
"Fine fish, delicately cooked and served" is the speciality at this "smart modern restaurant on the top floor of a hotel" near Broadgate, from D&D London. Food of this standard is rare in the City, and "not even the dullest business chat can take the edge off the outstanding cooking and wines". It's a discreet place, too, "and the team knows when to shoot the breeze with diners and when to withdraw to let the serious negotiations take place". / EC2M 2AF; www.anglerrestaurant.com; angler_restaurant; Tue-Sat 9.15 pm; SRA-accredited.

The Anglesea Arms W6   £67   4 3 5
35 Wingate Rd   020 8749 1291   8–1B
A "favourite in West London" – this very popular hostelry sits on "a quiet tree-lined street" near Ravenscourt Park, and has a small, sunny outside terrace. Its legions of fans say it's "the perfect gastropub" thanks to its "continually brilliant food" over many years, its "perfectly informal service" and its "cosy and intimate" style. "It still feels like a pub and not a restaurant, but the cooking is better than practically any other pub and most restaurants". / W6 0UR; www.angleseaarmspub.co.uk; theangleseaarmsw6; Mon-Wed, Fri & Sat 11 pm, Sun 10.30 pm.

Anglo EC1   £111   5 4 3
30 St Cross Street   020 7430 1503   10–1A
"Surely the best restaurant in London without a Michelin star!" Chef Anthony Raffo provides "modern British cooking at its finest" at this "tiny" Farringdon venture, with "novel flavours and combinations, cleverly incorporating a perfect balance of umami and other tastes; all whilst using seasonal ingredients and looking incredible". Meanwhile, manager, Marie Danzanvilliers, presides "with great charm and hospitality". "The venue itself is quite hipster-cool but pretty low key. At the end of the day, it is all about the food offer and they absolutely nail that!". "It really is a hidden gem"… "No idea why the Tyre Man hasn't come calling." / EC1N 8UH; www.anglorestaurant.com; anglorestaurant; Tue-Sat 11 pm.

Anima e Cuore NW1   £59   4 3 2
129 Kentish Town Rd   07590 427171   9–2B
"Tucked away behind an ice-cream parlour" in Kentish Town, "this lovely local restaurant produces dishes that would shame a far more expensive West End place". Calabrian-born with Moroccan heritage, chef Mustapha Mouflih conjures up "exceptional real Italian cuisine" in a "no-frills" setting which is "reflected in the prices" – and "a bargain deal on corkage". / NW1 8PB; www.animaecuore.co.uk; animaecuoreuk; Tue-Sat 10.30 pm.

Anjanaas NW6 £39 342
57-59 Willesden Lane   020 7624 1713   1–1B
"Super southern Indian dishes at reasonable prices too" win a following for this family run Keralan in Kilburn. It's either "brilliant and low key" or "very good but with slightly disappointing surroundings" depending on your tastes. / NW6 7RL; www.anjanaas.com; anjanaaslondon; Mon, Wed & Thu 10.30 pm, Fri & Sat 11 pm, Sun 10 pm.

Annie's W4 £65 234
162 Thames Rd   020 8994 9080   1–3A
"A favourite local, always to be relied on" – this cosy, all-day fixture in Strand on the Green, from Lorraine Angliss, is still popular after 24 years. A branch in Barnes hit the buffers a while ago, but three other sister venues are still thriving – Little Bird in Battersea and Rock & Rose in Richmond and most recently Chiswick High Road. / W4 3QS; www.anniesrestaurant.co.uk; anniesrestaurant; Tue-Thu 9 pm, Fri & Sat 10 pm, Sun 5 pm.

L'Antica Pizzeria da Michele £65 432
44 Old Compton Street, W1   020 7434 4563   5–2A
199 Baker Street, NW1   020 7935 6458   2–1A
"Outstanding pizzas" live up to the highest expectations at the London outposts of a Neapolitan original going back five generations and 150 years (even if these days they merrily break late founder Michele Condurro's commandment that only two types of pizza are allowed, the Marinara and the Margherita). The Naples flagship became a place of post-divorce pilgrimage following Elizabeth Gilbert's 2006 bestseller 'Eat Pray Love'. / www.anticapizzeriadamichele.co.uk; anticapizzeriadamicheleuk.

The Apollo Arms SW4 NEW
13-19 Old Town   020 3827 1213   11–1D
Clapham pub, taken over by the operator behind Ganymede in Belgravia and The Hunter's Moon in South Kensington. It re-opened in May 2023, too late for survey feedback, but it looks worth knowing about, if for no other reason than its spacious terrace. / SW4 0JT; apolloarms.co.uk; theapolloarms; Mon-Sat 10 pm, Sun 9 pm.

Applebee's Fish SE1 £75 332
5 Stoney St   020 7407 5777   10–4C
This "reliable" fish specialist on the edge of Borough Market has raised its game in line with the location's emergence as a culinary mecca, and can accommodate guests year-round, either indoors or on its street terrace. The team has recently opened La Gamba tapas bar at the Southbank Centre. / SE1 9AA; www.applebeesfish.com; applebeesfishlondon; Mon-Thu 10 pm, Fri & Sat 11 pm, Sun 6 pm.

Apricity W1 £105 332
68 Duke Street   020 8017 2780   3–2A
Chantelle Nicholson's Mayfair yearling has "a menu balance that's the opposite way around to most restaurants, with an emphasis on vegetarian/vegan cooking, but also with a few meat/fish options". Although some more critical reviewers "were expecting more after reading the glowing reviews", even they said it was "perfectly good". And most feedback this year was uniformly positive, hailing it as an unqualified "winner": "there was no need to order any meat or fish: the vegetarian and vegan dishes we had were spectacular!". / W1K 6JU; www.apricityrestaurant.com; apricityrestaurant; Tue-Sat 9 pm.

Apulia EC1 £71 22**3**
50 Long Lane   020 7600 8107   10–2B
"In a great location opposite Smithfield Market", and "an excellent pre-theatre option near the Barbican" – this "cheap 'n' cheerful" Italian is "very popular" for its "decent, solid staples" (in particular "good – and huge – pizzas"). "Go hungry." / EC1A 9EJ; apuliarestaurant.co.uk; apuliarestaurant; Mon-Fri 10.30 pm, Sat 10.45 pm, Sun 10.15 pm.

Aqua Shard SE1 £115 22**4**
31 St Thomas St   020 3011 1256   10–4C
"Everyone is here for the view" on the 31st floor of the Shard, with "all diners glammed up to celebrate something special": "it's what you are paying for". "And boy are you paying!" – "when you consider the sky-high bills", the cuisine is somewhere between "decent enough" and "bog standard". In a similar vein, "service is fine, but could use some improvements… with views to attract the crowds anyway, perhaps management aren't super-worried about the service levels". Overall, though, it's a Faustian bargain many reporters are prepared to make, especially for afternoon tea or a date… or both! / SE1 9RY; www.aquashard.co.uk; aquashard; Sun-Thu 10 pm, Fri & Sat 10.30 pm.

Aquavit SW1 £114
St James's Market, 1 Carlton St   020 7024 9848   4–4D
A sense of nearly-but-not-quite hovers over this Scandi NYC-import, whose 1980s namesake is a legend of the Manhattan restaurant scene, but whose London branch (opened in 2016) has never really made waves. A location in the un-loved St James's Market development doesn't help, nor does the atmosphere which can appear gorgeous and glam but can also feel "sterile, despite the best attempts of expensive interior decor". Ultimately, the impression of there being more this place could give "probably comes down to the pricey, decent-but-not-brilliant food". BREAKING NEWS: in September 2023, the restaurant closed unexpectedly, although the owners of NYC Aquavit (who had no stake in the London spin-off) announced a desire to re-establish the brand in London. / SW1Y 4QQ; www.aquavitrestaurants.com; aquavitlondon; Tue-Thu 9 pm, Fri & Sat 10 pm.

Arabica £60 **3**3**3**
7 Lewis Cubitt Walk, N1   020 3747 4422   9–3C
3 Rochester Walk, SE1   020 3011 5151   10–4C
"The food is always a delight" at this "consistently high-quality" Levantine specialist "with an emphasis on inventive veg". Originally a market stall, it graduated to a restaurant inside a Borough railway arch, with a second branch in King's Cross. Top Menu Tips – "the stand-out cod dish with chunky flakes cooked just perfectly" and "the toasted flatbread that comes hot in rustling bags". / www.arabicalondon.com; arabicalondon.

The Araki W1 £398 4**5**3
Unit 4 12 New Burlington St   020 7287 2481   4–3A
When it first touched down in 2014 under founder Matsuhiro Araki, this nine-seat Mayfair venue broke the mould for London in the level of ambition for its top-end sushi omakase (gaining three Michelin stars in the bargain). When Master Araki returned to the Far East in 2019, his protégé, UK-born Marty Lau, took over and Michelin removed all three stars never to return any. Why always puzzled us, as little other than very good or outstanding meals are reported here. "You sit at the sushi bar, watching the chef produce the most incredible sushi ever, with the theatre of exceptional fish being filleted", and if there's a quibble it's that "even though the sushi is superb, it's hard not to wonder what it was like when Master Araki himself was still

here". There is also the issue that this genre of high-end sushi experiences have multiplied in the capital in recent years and so it is no longer unique in the way it was in the early days. / W1S 3BH; the-araki.co.uk; the_araki_london; Tue-Sat 9 pm.

Arcade Food Hall WC1 £35 222

103-105 New Oxford Street   020 7519 1202   5–1A

As a "buzzy venue for the young, after-work crowd", this JKS Restaurants food court at the foot of Centre Point does have its fans, who feel that as a "cheap 'n' cheerful" option it's "phenomenal, with such a great variety of street food to try all under one roof – ideal for big groups". Ratings are undercut, though, by those who just find it "very noisy", "pricey" and "average". (In July 2023, JKS launched a second Arcade in the new Battersea Power Station complex, mixing brands from the original together with a new selection of offerings.) / WC1A 1DB; www.arcade-london.com; arcadefoodhall; Tue-Sat 11.30pm, Sun 9.30 pm.

Archway SW8 NEW £70 444

Arch 65, Queen's Circus   020 3781 1102   11–1C

"This new spot under the railway arches by Battersea Power Station has some really good cooking" from ex-River Café chef, Alex Owens, to the extent that one early reporter thought it this year's "top opening". It helps too that it has a very attractive interior and "amazing service", led by the other woman behind the new place: owner and CEO Emily Few Brown, who launched the catering company Spook almost ten years ago. / SW8 4NE; www.archwaybattersea.co.uk; archwaybattersea; Wed-Sat midnight.

Ark Fish E18 £55 332

142 Hermon Hill   020 8989 5345   1–1D

"With a varied fish menu", "nice interior" and "very friendly staff", this spacious South Woodford chippy is "great for a family lunch". / E18 1QH; www.arkfishrestaurant.co.uk; ark_fish_restaurant; Tue-Thu 9.45 pm, Fri & Sat 10.15 pm, Sun 8.45 pm.

Aroma Buffet W12

First Floor, West 12 Shopping Centre   020 8746 7625   8–1C

All spent out at Westfield? Head for this large first-floor eatery within the much-less-glam'-looking West 12 Shopping Centre on the other side of Shepherd's Bush Green. Reports on the all-you-can-eat £15 pan-Asian buffet are few, but The Guardian's Grace Dent in late 2022 was a fan, describing a "vast" array of "feisty flavours" (with diverse dishes from as far afield as Canton and West Sumatra) whose "pleasing" prices spark "joy through dark times and ransacked wallets". / W12 8PP; www.aromabuffet.co.uk; aromabuffetw12; Mon, Fri-Sun 10.30 pm.

Arros QD W1 £100 232

64 Eastcastle Street   020 3883 3525   3–1D

No-one, it seems, told star Spanish chef Quique Dacosta (whose Alicante restaurants hold three Michelin stars) that you don't launch an ambitious foodie venue just off the shopping hell of Oxford Street. This impressive-looking four-year-old – complete with a large open kitchen – offers high quality grills, with the speciality being a selection of paella dishes. Feedback remains quite limited (not helped by its location) – neither huge criticism, nor huge praise is present. / W1W 8NQ; www.arrosqd.com; arrosqd; Mon-Sat 11 pm, Sun 3 pm.

L'Artista NW11 £52 2 3 3
917 Finchley Rd   020 8731 7501   1–1B
*Celebrating its 40th anniversary next year, this "big, bustling old favourite in
the heart of Golders Green" (occupying a railway arch by the tube) has itself
hosted more than its fair share of birthdays over the years thanks to a
crowd-pleasing combination of "generous portions of pasta and pizza" at
"very reasonable prices". / NW11 7PE; www.lartistapizzeria.com; lartistalondon;
Mon-Sun midnight.*

**ArtSpace Café,
Claridge's W1** NEW
Brook's Mews   020 7409 6424   3–2B
*Jet-set living for the price of a (admittedly relatively expensive) croissant and
a coffee? That's the promise of this new café within Claridge's, serving up
toasties, crepes and cakes in a new space with a small art gallery attached
designed by John Pawson. / W1K 4HR; www.claridges.co.uk; claridgeshotel; Mon-Fri
6 pm, Sat & Sun 4 pm.*

Artusi SE15 £61 3 3 2
161 Bellenden Rd   020 3302 8200   1–4D
*As it celebrates its tenth anniversary, this small Peckham Italian – named
after Pellegrino Artusi, author of nineteenth-century classic 'La Scienza in
Cucina' – is "still a destination" for its dedicated southeast London fans.
/ SE15 4DH; www.artusi.co.uk; artusipeckham; Tue-Thu 9.30 pm, Fri & Sat 10 pm, Sun
4 pm.*

Assaggi W2 £90 4 5 3
39 Chepstow Pl   020 7792 5501   7–1B
*"A classic that's every bit as good as when it first started", claim fans of
Nino Sassu's quirky Italian, which has occupied this room above a Bayswater
pub for over 25 years. Compared to its glory days – when it was the talk of
the town – feedback is nowadays very limited. But its diehard fan club are
unanimous regarding this "perennial favourite" and its "incredible, genuine
dishes": "it feels very special to take the family there and everyone is always
greeted with such warmth". / W2 4TS; www.assaggi.co.uk; assagginottinghill; Tue-Sat
10 pm.*

L'Atelier Robuchon W1 £140
6 Clarges Street   020 8076 0570   3–4C
*As Le Comptoir Robuchon (RIP), this Mayfair outpost of the famous French
chef's global empire (which opened after his death) has never been a huge
talking point for the fooderati. This was despite it providing a "top
gastronomic experience" combining a very elegant interior with traditional
Gallic fare that's "worth the price". Now, from September 2023, it's being re-
jigged to sit under the group's international, flagship 'Atelier' brand – so
creating a successor to the erstwhile Covent Garden site of that name that
closed in 2018. Chef Andrea Cofini will be at the stoves, and doubtless
aiming to put it on a par with its siblings in Hong Kong, Miami, Taipei, Vegas
and Geneva, each of which holds at least one Michelin star (and most two or
three). / W1J 8AE; www.robuchonlondon.co.uk; lecomptoirrobuchon; Mon-Sat 11 pm.*

The Atlas SW6 £54 3 4 4
16 Seagrave Rd   020 7385 9129   6–3A
*This "traditional backstreet pub – wood-panelled and with a walled garden"
– is a good find in the thin area surrounding West Brompton tube and
makes a cosy winter destination or – in summer – "the terrace is a great
sun trap in the afternoon". Its Med-inspired cuisine is a cut-above typical
gastropub standards. / SW6 1RX; www.theatlaspub.co.uk; theatlaspub; Mon-Sat
9.30 pm, Sun 8.30 pm.*

Attica EC1 NEW £58 2|3|3
56-60 Rosebery Ave   020 7837 8367   10–1A
Like Jay Rayner of The Observer, reporters in our annual diners' poll remember this Clerkenwell site from its days as The Kolossi Grill (RIP), which for decades provided a good, post-work piss-up, but which has faded from view in recent years. In early 2023 it was relaunched (first under the old Kolossi flag, then changing its name to Attica). But our diners disagreed with Jay's upbeat April 2023 assessment. He found Greek cuisine that's "so much better than [revelatory]… the essentials done with due care and attention" making it "a venerable restaurant that has found a way to avoid decline and start afresh". Our early reporters feel that "despite glowing press reviews we found the food between average to disappointing"… "a shadow of the former taverna experience"… "nice people, but not a great meal". / EC1R 4RR; Tue-Sat 9.15 pm.

The Audley W1 £57 3|2|4
43 Mount Street   020 3840 9862   3–3A
"Fantastic looking, cleaned up and with an amazing ceiling by the late Phyllida Barlow" (who completed the work shortly before she died in March 2023) – ArtFarm's newly relaunched "posh boozer" in Mayfair has five storeys (with the Mount Street Restaurant on the first – see also – and with the upper floors dedicated to art events supporting Hauser & Wirth's roster of artists). Aside from "loads of interesting art and a good backstory", the traditional British grub (pint of prawns, oysters, shepherd's pie, fish finger sarnie, Chelsea bun…) is pricey but "decent". / W1K 3AH; theaudleypublichouse.com; audleypublichouse; Mon-Fri 11.30 pm, Sat midnight, Sun 10.30 pm.

**Audrey Green,
National Portrait Gallery WC2** NEW
St Martin's Place   020 3822 0246   2–2C
After being closed for several years for a major refurbishment, the NPG re-opened in June 2023 (too late for our survey), with a new all-day café on the ground floor and in the intriguing vaulted basement. The latter was always a surprisingly attractive, but completely undiscovered feature of the West End – now it's to be better publicised as 'Larry's Bar', with a late-night bar and small-plates menu. / WC2H 0HE; www.npg.org.uk; Mon & Tue, Sun 5.30 pm, Wed-Sat 10.30 pm.

Augustine Kitchen SW11 £68 3|2|3
63 Battersea Bridge Rd   020 7978 7085   6–4C
"Just the job for a simple, casual supper" – this bistro in an "unlikely spot" just south of Battersea Bridge is inspired by the cuisine of Evian in the French Alps, hometown of patron Franck Raymond, who is "completely invested in making sure you have a great experience". / SW11 3AU; www.augustine-kitchen.co.uk; augustinesw11; Tue-Sat 9 pm.

Aulis London W1 £236 5|4|3
16a St Anne's Court   020 3948 9665   4–1D
"If you can't make it to Cartmel to visit L'Enclume, enjoy Simon Rogan's innovative cuisine here in London in a strange combination of chef's table and culinary laboratory: a unique gastronomic and social experience in all respects!". From May 2023, the star chef's Soho outpost grew (a little) in size to seat 12 guests (up from the original 8) together with a complete refurb. But fans say "they didn't need to bother with the decor when the food (from executive head chef Oli Marlow and head chef Charlie Tayler) is this spectacular"; and they hail it as "the top spot in the capital for those who want to focus on what's on the plate" (for which the ingredients are

*primarily sourced from 'Our Farm' – Simon's Lake District property).
Compared with the culinary pyrotechnics and inventiveness, the "wine list is
quite simple by comparison". / W1F 0BF; aulis.london; aulissimonrogan; Tue-Sat
11.30 pm.*

Authentique Epicerie & Bar NW5   £54   3 3 3
114-116 Fortess Road   020 3609 6602   9–2C
*800+ wines by the bottle and a selection of 75 craft beers are the USP of
this intriguing Tufnell Park showcase for regional French drinks and produce.
The menu changes every six weeks with a different region moving into focus
– it's short and in a supporting role to all the delicious grog, but good value.
/ NW5 5HL; authentique-epicerie.com; authentiquelondon; Tue-Sat 11 pm, Sun 8 pm.*

Avanti W4   £53   2 2 3
South Parade   020 8994 9444   8–1A
*"The mixture of tapas and pizzas works well for a family meal" at this
handy local on the edge of Bedford Park in Chiswick, where "the ambience is
nice, particularly out on the terrace on a warm evening". If there's a
complaint, it's that standards can be "a bit hit 'n' miss". / W4 1LD;
avantichiswick.com; avantichiswick; Mon-Sun 10 pm.*

Ave Mario WC2   £67   3 3 4
15 Henrietta Street   no tel   5–3C
*"We all loved it – especially the kids", is the most popular view of this vast
and OTT mock-Italian operation in Covent Garden from French group Big
Mamma, whose "funky interior, fun staff and really positive vibe" create a
jolly backdrop to some "surprisingly good and cheaply priced food" – mainly
pizza and pasta. Moaning "shame about the Instagramming teenagers"
rather misses the point of the whole enterprise, although the odd 'off' report
suggests that the joke can fall flat on a bad day – "indifferent service, a
quiet atmosphere and disappointing grub: what went wrong? They had
something but blew it!". / WC2E 8QG; www.bigmammagroup.com; bigmamma.uk;
Sun-Wed 10.30 pm, Thu-Sat 10.45 pm.*

L'Aventure NW8   £80   4 5 4
3 Blenheim Terrace   020 7624 6232   9–3A
*This "consistently fabulous restaurant" in St John's Wood has a "special and
romantic atmosphere" thanks to its "charming" French owner Catherine
Parisot, who has run it for 42 years and ensures the "service is so good and
personal" that "you can't fail to feel boosted by a visit". The classic 'cuisine
bourgeoise' hits the spot every time, too. / NW8 0EH; www.laventure.co.uk;
Mon-Sat 11 pm.*

Awesome Thai SW13   £39   3 3 2
68 Church Rd   020 8563 7027   11–1A
*With its "above-average food and friendly staff" this "fine, family-run Thai"
is a "popular Barnes local that also delivers" – and that takes full advantage
of its prime position directly opposite the Olympic Studios indie cinema.
("The menu has remained the same for a long while – some new dishes
wouldn't harm!") / SW13 0DQ; www.awesomethai.co.uk; Mon-Sat 10.45 pm, Sun
10 pm.*

Le Bab   £61   4 3 2
Top Floor, Kingly Court, W1   020 7439 9222   4–2B
4 Mercer Walk, WC2   020 7240 9781   5–2C
Battersea Power Station, SW11   020 7864 354   11–1C
408 Coldharbour Lane, SW9   020 7864 354   11–2D
130 Kingsland High Street, E8   020 3877 0865   14–1A
231 Old Street, EC1   020 3456 7890   13–1A
*"Tasty kebabs and sides" that "offer a modern twist on traditional Middle
Eastern cuisine" make this "brilliant" Carnaby Street outfit "a must-visit", "in*

the lovely setting of Kingly Court". The Battersea branch is "an absolute gem", and there are now half a dozen outlets around town, including at the Market Halls in Oxford Street and Canary Wharf. See also Kebab Queen. / www.eatlebab.com; eatlebab.

Babur SE23 £58 443
119 Brockley Rise 020 8291 2400 1–4D
To its many fans, this "small place" off the gastronomic track in Honor Oak Park "remains the best Indian in South London", and its "engaging staff" delivering "very different food with panache and skill", "after almost 40 years". "Unless you're local, it's not entirely easy to get to, but it's well worthy of a journey." / SE23 1JP; www.babur.info; baburrestaurant; Mon-Sat 11 pm, Sun 10.30 pm.

Bacchanalia W1 £189 224
1 Mount Street 020 3161 9720 3–3B
"A complete circus!" – Richard Caring jovially sticks two fingers up to good taste at his willfully opulent and theatrical riff on Mayfair-meets-Roman-orgy, where staff are clad in togas, and winged statues and nymphs flying around in the ceiling murals look down on you as you eat. Compared to the "OTT" riot of the decor, it's easy to overlook the luxurious menu, which is Italian- and Greek-accented, with a bit of caviar thrown in for good measure. There's the odd report of "appalling service" ("trying to hurry us to meet their deadline") or dishes that misfire badly, but savage put-downs are absent from reports; even while acknowledging that it is "crazily expensive" and "full of selfie takers" (obvs!). / W1K 3NA; bacchanalia.co.uk; bacchanalialdn; Mon-Sat 12.30 am, Sun midnight.

Bacco TW9 £74 332
39-41 Kew Rd 020 8332 0348 1–4A
"An excellent venue for a meal before a performance at Richmond Theatre" – this "good value" Italian restaurant near the station has long been a mainstay of the area. Top Tips – set menus are a feature for lunch and pre-theatre, and the wine list is extensive. / TW9 2NQ; www.bacco-restaurant.co.uk; Mon-Sat 9.30 pm.

Bageriet WC2 £21 422
24 Rose St 020 7240 0000 5–3C
"Cakes to die for!" say fans of this tiny Scandi café in a cute Covent Garden cut-through, with a handful of seats outside in summer. Top Menu Tip – Prinsesstårta (a Swedish cake, layering sponge, cream and marzipan). / WC2E 9EA; www.bageriet.co.uk; bageriet_london; Mon-Fri 6.30 pm, Sat 6 pm.

Bala Baya SE1 £74 433
Old Union Yard Arches, 229 Union Street 020 8001 7015 10–4B
Former Ottolenghi chef Eran Tibi showcases his accomplished take on modern Israeli cuisine at this fun Tel Aviv-style venue in a Southwark railway arch, on which all reports were upbeat this year. / SE1 0LR; balabaya.co.uk; bala_baya; Mon-Sat 11 pm, Sun 10 pm.

Balham Social SW12 £38 342
2 Station Parade Road, Balham High Road 020 4529 8222 11–2C
The latest opening from the team behind Putney's popular Chook Chook 'Indian Railway Kitchen' is a flamboyant Balham hangout in the former premises of long-serving Lamberts (RIP). A café by day, it switches in the evening to 'high-end' modern cuisine with an "interesting South Indian influence", under head chef Imran Mansuri, whose Mayfair-heavy CV takes in Jamavar, Tamarind and Annabel's. / SW12 9AZ; balhamsocial.com; balham.social; Mon-Sun 10.30 pm.

Balthazar WC2 £85 1 2 3
4-6 Russell Street   020 3301 1155   5–3D
"Like being in an old fashioned Parisian brasserie", this big venue, *"centrally located by Covent Garden Piazza"*, provides a *"hectic but impressive"* backdrop to a meal. Many reporters feel *"it has a whole lot going for it"*, but even they often acknowledge either *"seriously poor"* cooking, or the trade-offs that a visit entails: *"Yes it's on the pricey side and the food is average really, but it's still a tradition that we enjoy."* / WC2B 5HZ; www.balthazarlondon.com; balthazarldn; Mon-Sat 10.45 pm, Sun 9.45 pm.

Baluchi,
Lalit Hotel London SE1 £79 3 3 4
181 Tooley St   020 3765 0000   10–4D
"Hints of the Raj" at the Lalit Hotel Group's flagship property in the UK (the group has sites across India), occupying *"the old hall of a former grammar school"* near City Hall (a big property, designed by the architect of the Old Bailey). Reports are not huge in number, but cite *"attentive service"* and *"refined dishes from across the subcontinent"*. / SE1 2JR; www.thelalit.com; thelalitlondon; Mon-Sun 10 pm.

Bancone £59 2 3 3
10 Lower James Street, W1   020 3034 0820   4–3C
39 William IV Street, WC2   020 7240 8786   5–4C
Borough Yards, Stoney Street, SE1   no tel   10–4C **NEW**
"Elevating accessible pasta to another level" and *"at fair prices"* has won a huge fan club for these pasta pit-stops, which – in July 2023 – added a Borough Yards location to their outlets in Soho and off Trafalgar Square. It's the *"narrow"* WC2 branch that's best known, and, despite the weight of custom, *"helpful staff do their best"* and it delivers *"lots of atmosphere"*. The food rating dipped this year, though, due to a few refuseniks who say *"it used to be good, but is becoming a victim of its own success"*. / www.bancone.co.uk; bancone.pasta.

Bang Bang Oriental NW9 £44 3 2 2
399 Edgware Road   no tel   1–1A
"The Oriental food hall of your dreams" – this gastro-warehouse in Colindale offers a vast choice. *"The quality ranges extremely widely between the various stalls"*, but choose carefully and you'll be well fed. / NW9 0AS; www.bangbangoriental.com; bangbangoriental; Sun-Thu 9.30 pm, Fri & Sat 10 pm.

Bao £40 3 4 4
53 Lexington St, W1   07769 627811   4–2C
56 James St, W1   no tel   3–1A **NEW**
4 Pancras Square, N1   no tel   9–3C
13 Stoney Street, SE1   020 3967 5407   10–4C
Battersea Power Station, SW11   no tel   11–1C **NEW**
1 Redchurch Street, E2   no tel   13–1B
"A first-choice Asian restaurant" – say fans of this *"friendly, buzzy"* chain serving *"delicious"* Taiwanese filled buns that can constitute *"a quick bite for lunch, or a longer meal with friends"*. Launched as a street-food stand in 2012 by Erchen Chang, her husband Shing Tat and his sister Wai Ting Chung, the group is now backed by the all-conquering JKS Restaurants and opened its sixth venue in Battersea Power Station in 2023. Top Tip – *"beef with black pepper sauce and rice is a must-order at King's Cross"*. / baolondon.com; bao_london.

Baozi Inn £37 3 2 2
24 Romilly Street, W1 020 7287 3266 5–3A
34-36 Southwark Street, SE1 020 8037 5875 10–4C
Northern Chinese fare including "authentic and tasty dumplings and noodles" make either of Wei Shao's duo (Borough Market and Soho) "a great standby for a quick and fun meal". "A Chinese that's worth a visit for an evening bite and not just for dim sum – and which doesn't break the bank – is a rare find in London." / baoziinn.com.

Bar des Prés W1 £129 2 4 3
16 Albemarle Street 020 3908 2000 3–3C
This 'Franco-Japanese fusion' – a two-year-old Mayfair spin-off from TV chef Cyril Lignac's Paris restaurant St Germain des Prés – excites contradictory responses (and relatively little feedback overall). For fans, "the fusion of Japanese food with French expertise has resulted in an excellent dining experience". For the odd critic, though, it's nothing more than a "flash, cramped and noisy Euro place with prices that reflect the name of the celebrity French chef and the fancy crowd". / W1S 4HW; bardespres.com; bardespres; Mon-Sat 11 pm, Sun 10 pm.

Bar Douro SE1 £55 3 3 4
Arch 35b, 85b Southwark Bridge Rd 020 7378 0524 10–4B
"Fresh, pungent sharing plates", "cooked in front of you", backed up by "good wine options" – win praise for this tiled bar in a railway arch near Borough Market (founded by Max Graham, from the Churchill's port family), which does "just what Portuguese tapas should do". "Characterful service" contributes to a "wonderfully relaxed" atmosphere. / SE1 0NQ; www.bardouro.co.uk; bardouro; Tue-Sat 10 pm, Sun 9 pm.

Bar Esteban N8 £61 3 4 4
29 Park Rd 020 8340 3090 1–1C
This Crouch End spot has built a strong local name over more than a decade, and is known for its superior tapas and a "really good selection of Spanish wine, by the glass or bottle". Founder Stephen ('Esteban') Lironi is a Glasgow-born music producer and sherry aficionado, while Barcelona-born chef Pablo Rodriguez arrived via Barrafina. / N8 8TE; www.baresteban.com; bar__esteban; Fri & Sat 11 pm, Tue-Thu 10 pm.

Bar Italia W1 £42 2 4 5
22 Frith St 020 7437 4520 5–2A
This "Soho institution" stands for "tradition and location", offering "the best coffee 24/7" along with "the most atmospheric counter seating in London". Founded in 1949 by the Polledri family, who still own it, it is a rare survivor of Soho's once-thriving Italian community. / W1D 4RF; www.baritaliasoho.co.uk; Mon-Sun 5 am.

Bar Kroketa W1 NEW
21 Beak Street 0203 954 8888 4–2B
With 'croquetas at its core', this small, December 2022 newcomer, south of Carnaby Street, promises to bring 'Spanish bar culture with regional sensibilities to Soho'. Run by Brindisa, it's a non-branded attempt at a funkier outlet for their Hispanic produce and wines. No survey feedback as yet, but in a March 2023 review, The Independent's Lucy Thackray hailed a "cosy, convivial Spanish hangout" that's "a potentially chemistry-crackling date place" – "the spelling may be gimmicky but the food is not". / W1F 9RR; www.kroketa.co.uk; bar.kroketa; Mon-Sun 11 pm.

The Barbary WC2 — £83 — 5 4 4
16 Neal's Yard   no tel   5–2C

"Stunning in every respect" – this "tiny, dark, smoky, and cool" North African-inspired venue in Neal's Yard is "a superb place where they really make use of the counter service to engage you in the cooking". "No matter how many times I go I always need the menu explained" – "beautifully spiced" small plates ("a bit salty at times") plus "great, unusual wines" all served by "enthusiastic staff". / WC2H 9DP; www.thebarbary.co.uk; the barbary; Mon-Sat 10 pm, Sun 9 pm.

The Barbary Next Door WC2 — £49 — 4 3 2
16a Neal's Yard   no tel   5–2C

This "fab, tiny little counter bar" next door to its grown-up sibling in Neal's Yard, Covent Garden, offers "superb" Middle Eastern/Moroccan food accompanied by biodynamic wines. "Sooo sad they stopped doing breakfast!". The site's previous occupant was the much-loved Jacob the Angel (RIP). / WC2H 9DP; thebarbarynextdoor.co.uk; thebarbarynextdoor; Mon-Sat 11 pm.

Barbican Brasserie, Barbican Centre (fka Osteria) EC2 — £53 — 3 3 3
Level 2 Silk Street   020 7588 3008   10–1B

"The restaurant formerly known as Osteria has recently re-emerged from a makeover as the Barbican Brasserie, but still operated by catering company Searcy's"; and still with a vaguely Italian spin on its selection of modern European dishes. It's "a smart venue overlooking the lake", which this year was more often "recommended for reasonably priced dinner" – especially prior to a show within the centre. / EC2Y 8DS; osterialondon.co.uk; searcyslondon; Mon-Wed, Sat 7 pm, Thu & Fri 9 pm.

La Barca SE1 — £90 — 3 3 3
80-81 Lower Marsh   020 7928 2226   10–4A

"From a bygone era, and all the better for it!" – this family-run Italian restaurant behind Waterloo station set sail almost 50 years ago, offering "a combination of excellent traditional dishes, lively atmosphere and attentive service from staff, many of whom have worked there for years". / SE1 7AB; www.labarca-ristorante.com; labarca1976; Mon-Sat 10.30 pm.

Barge East E9 — £68 — 4 3 5
Sweetwater Mooring, White Post Lane   020 3026 2807   14–2C

"It's so fun being on board a boat!" – this 120-year-old barge is moored in Hackney Wick, near the Olympic stadium, and is also surrounded by gardens providing an alternative backdrop to a meal. All reports agree on its "fantastic food and atmosphere": there are a variety of menus, including tasting and group options, all featuring imaginative modern British dishes. / E9 5EN; www.bargeeast.com; bargeeast; Wed-Sun midnight.

The Baring N1 — £85 — 4 3 3
55 Baring Street   020 7359 5785   14–2A

"It's probably unfair to call it pub food though it is food in a pub!" – Re-opened in 2022, this revamped Islington boozer has built a major following thanks to offering "an all-round five-star experience" that's very superior for the gastropub genre. Staff who are "charming, friendly and fast" provide "simple"-sounding yet "fabulous" and "sustainably sourced" dishes ("the almond financier made me smile so much the chef came over to see what was entertaining me"). "The only downside is the slightly out-of-the-way location" that's "hard to get to on public transport". / N1 3DS; www.thebaring.co.uk; thebaring; Tue-Sat 9.30 pm, Sun 4 pm.

The Barley Mow W1 NEW   £98   3 3 3
82 Duke Street   020 7730 0070   3–2A
"All of the Cubitt's pubs are class acts", and this recent (2022) addition to their glossy tribe is a gentrified Mayfair boozer with fine period features. In culinary terms, it fits the "pricey but good quality" DNA of the group – in fact, it's at the upper level of achievement in that respect. There's a bar downstairs and a more formal restaurant on the first floor. / W1K 6JG; www.cubitthouse.co.uk; cubitthouse; Mon-Sat 10 pm, Sun 5 pm.

Barrafina   £70   5 4 4
26-27 Dean Street, W1   020 7813 8016   4–1D
10 Adelaide St, WC2   020 7440 1456   5–4C
43 Drury Lane, WC2   020 7440 1456   5–2D
Coal Drops Yard, N1   0207 440 1486   9–3C
2 Dirty Lane, SE1   0207 440 1486   10–4C
"It's a great show to watch the chefs at work", perched on a stool at the counter of the Hart Bros' "incredibly busy and buzzy" bars – their hyper-successful homage to Barcelona's Cal Pep. "The tapas is always first rate" with "succulent grilled seafood all prepared in front of your very eyes" a highlight. "Staff are friendly and efficient and take such pride in the dishes and their presentation". (In April 2023, executive chef Angel Zapata Martin left the group after six years, leaving Antonio Gonzales Milla minding the central Barrafina locations, and Francisco Jose Torrico in charge of Coal Drops Yard and Borough). / www.barrafina.co.uk.

Barshu W1   £71   5 3 2
28 Frith St   020 7287 6688   5–3A
"Spicy, authentic Sichuan cuisine" makes this Chinatown destination "worth hunting out" – it's "way above the bog-standard fare nearby", with "amazing taste sensations including a lot more besides the fragrant heat of the eponymous Sichuan pepper". And "friendly staff made choosing from the huge menu easier". Top Tip – find a table downstairs if you can, to avoid the "weak ambience on the first floor". / W1D 5LF; www.barshurestaurant.co.uk; barshurestaurant; Sun-Thu 10 pm, Fri & Sat 10.30 pm.

Base Face Pizza W6   £38   4 4 3
300 King Street   020 8617 1092   8–2B
"A true find" – jazz bassist Tim Thornton's lockdown pizza project-gone-permanent goes from strength to strength, serving "top sourdough pizzas" at his original pizzeria on King Street in Hammersmith and a more recent addition across the river in Barnes. "Lovely staff and a great atmosphere" add to the package. / W6 0RR; www.basefacepizza.com; base.face.pizza; Tue-Sat 10 pm, Sun 9 pm.

Bayleaf N20   £25   4 3 3
1282 High Road   020 8446 8671   1–1B
Established on the foundation of a long-running takeaway business, this highly rated Whetstone curry house serves "high-quality" food with a focus on "super-dramatic presentation" of dishes, with "steam rising from the table". / N20 9HH; www.bayleaf.co.uk; bayleafofficial; Mon-Sun 10 pm.

The Beefsteaks @ M. Manze N1 NEW
74 Chapel Market   no tel   9–3D
Due to open in the second half of 2023 – this historic Islington pie 'n' mash shop in Chapel Market closed in 2018 but has been rescued by Alex Pashby of street-food trader The Beefsteaks ('An exclusive 18th Century London steak club reimagined as inclusive 21st Century street food'). At first it will operate as a low-intervention wine bar serving British small plates – as it takes off, the hope is for the food offering to expand. / N1 9ER; thebeefsteaks.

Behind E8 £140 [5][4][3]
20 Sidworth Street no tel 14–2B
"Wow!" "Andy Beynon continues to produce superb, good-value cuisine in a relaxed and intimate setting" at his small venue, near London Fields: "an immersive experience, where the chefs prepare the food around you as you sit at the bar". "There are no waiters: the chefs cover service, chat about the food and ferry each new course from the nearby open preparation areas"; and the team gives the impression of being "super keen and far from weary, jaded or sitting on their laurels". "Sustainable fish is the clear focus here, and everything is on point in each exceptional dish". / E8 3SD; www.behindrestaurant.co.uk; behindrestaurant; Wed-Sat 11 pm.

Bellamy's W1 £80 [3][4][4]
18-18a Bruton Place 020 7491 2727 3–2B
"A haven of calm in an ever-changing world": "they cater for the most conservative of palates (and the deepest pockets)" at Gavin Rankin's "old-school, brasserie-style restaurant in Mayfair" (which had the rare privilege of hosting the late Queen Elizabeth on a couple of occasions). Its Anglo-French fare is "super reliable, if not exciting" and service "immaculate". "If you like the kind of place where you still need to dress up a bit, this is it", but "the ambience is set by its older, quietly-spoken crowd: don't visit if you are planning a loud-laughing night!". Top Menu Tip – "good value lunch menu; and staples such as iced lobster soufflé, smoked eel mousse and steak tartare". / W1J 6LY; www.bellamysrestaurant.co.uk; bellamysmayfair; Mon-Fri 10.30 pm, Sat.

Bellanger N1 £58
9 Islington Green 020 7226 2555 9–3D
"Evoking a big Parisian brasserie", this Wolseley Group venture on Islington Green has had a chequered history. Opened in 2015, when Corbin & King owned the business, they closed it again in 2019 saying "we just couldn't make it the success we aspired to". But then, in 2020 – having failed to sell the property – they re-opened and had a second run at making a go of it. With Corbin & King then forced to exit the business in 2022, we are now going around again under the new owners. In June 2023, after our survey had completed, the restaurant re-opened yet again after a complete refit of the vast space and a new menu. Though brighter, the decor is still in the traditional brasserie mould. When it comes to food: out go the retro 'tarte flambées' and the chicken schnitzel – in comes the focaccia and – according to the PR – an 'evolving seasonal menu… taking inspiration from the southern Mediterranean coastal regions'. Er, except it also includes very un-Mediterranean dishes like Dressed Dorset Crab, Loch Duart Salmon with jersey royals and a watercress velouté and Flat Iron Steak Frites. The weekend brunch – with its pancakes and Eggs Benedict – also owes little to Spain, Italy and Greece. Other novelties are a new cocktail bar, and a DJ booth (the latter of which really risks 'Dad dancing' for this kind of venue). Our pre-revamp feedback suggested the same rather 'OK but not particularly distinguished' performance of old. But we've left it unrated on the basis of the latest changes, as this sounds like a case of 'outlook negative'. / N1 2XH; www.bellanger.co.uk; bellanger_n1; Mon-Sat 10 pm, Sun 9 pm.

Belvedere W8 £72 [3][3][4]
off Abbotsbury Rd in Holland Park 020 7602 1238 8–1D
Is it London? It doesn't feel like it at this enchanting, 17th-century ballroom adjoining Holland House, and surrounded by the tranquility of Holland Park. As a restaurant, it's had many ups and downs over the years (there's always a temptation here to coast on the location), and its latest incarnation was launched without fanfare in December 2022 by George Bukhov-Weinstein and Ilya Demichev, of Goodman, Burger & Lobster and Wild Tavern. True to the DNA of these other offerings, it's been handsomely revamped and now

serves an Italian-influenced menu centred on luxe casual dining – raw seafood, USDA steak, plus fancy pizza and pasta. In a February 2023 review, Giles Coren of The Times decried it as akin to "the second-best Italian restaurant in Dubai" whose unifying principle is "expensive" not Italian. Our initial reports are less sniffy: "an amazing meal with attentive service, and good ambience even if the decor is a bit overdone for my taste and the food is on the pricey side for what it is". / W8 6LU; www.belvedererestaurant.co.uk; belvedere_holland_park; Mon-Sat 10.30 pm, Sun 9.30 pm.

Benares W1 £94 4️⃣3️⃣2️⃣

12a Berkeley Square House, 020 7629 8886 3–3B

"Outstandingly good Indian fine dining, curated by head chef Sameer Taneja, whose forte is a tasting menu with a strong seafood offering" wins strong approval for this "sophisticated" nouvelle Indian, located in a large first-floor space above Berkeley Square, whose "helpful service" offsets the "rather soulless" decor. Top Tip – "their bottomless thali lunchtime meal deal is amazing value for a Michelin-starred restaurant. Not to be missed!!" / W1J 6BS; www.benaresrestaurant.co.uk; benaresofficial; Mon-Sat 10.30 pm, Sun 9.30 pm.

Bentley's W1 £106 3️⃣4️⃣4️⃣

11-15 Swallow St 020 7734 4756 4–4B

"Owner Richard Corrigan is often around and the food is always good" at this "iconic" fish and seafood "classic" – 107 years old (est. 1916) – which is to be found in a side street, near Piccadilly Circus. It offers two distinct experiences: "upstairs for very elegant fine dining, or in the bar downstairs for top-notch seafood with less formality – both excellent" (although the latter gets many people's vote, as "there is always a good buzz in the bar area with a few famous faces sometimes"). "Possibly the best oysters in town (and the best shuckers too)" number alongside "top crab" and "the notably good fish pie" as its best menu options, all in a "reassuringly good-but-expensive" mould ("comfort seafood at West End prices"). Service that's "very attentive and kind" from long-serving staff is intrinsic to the performance. / W1B 4DG; www.bentleys.org; bentleysoysterbar; Mon-Sat 9.30 pm, Sun 9 pm.

Berber & Q £61 5️⃣4️⃣3️⃣

Arch 338 Acton Mews, E8 020 7923 0829 14–2A
Exmouth Market, EC1 020 7837 1726 10–1A

"Never had a bad trip here!" – a common experience at these impressively consistent hipster grills where the "great and tasty mezze and flatbreads" are inspired by North Africa and the eastern Med: "delicious dishes with explosive flavours" that are "well-priced and extremely fresh tasting". They "can get very noisy" ("it was as easy to talk as sitting in a rock concert!") "but an excellent meal is your reward!" / www.berberandq.com; berberandq.

Berbere Pizza NW5 NEW £42 4️⃣3️⃣3️⃣

300 Kentish Town Road 020 3417 7130 9–2C

"Really good Calabrian pizza made with sourdough" is winning attention for this Kentish Town newcomer, which opened in November 2022, with a mix of standard and unusual toppings, such as 'Orange Crush' (creamed butternut squash, leeks, olives, chilli and peanut butter). It also has an often overlooked Clapham sibling (not listed), that's been open for three years; and is part of a wider genuinely Italian chain with branches in numerous cities, founded in Bologna in 2010. / NW5 2TG; www.berberepizzeria.co.uk; berberepizzeria_ldn; Sun-Thu 10 pm, Fri & Sat 10.30 pm.

Berenjak £64 544
27 Romilly Street, W1   020 3319 8120   5–2A
1 Bedale Street, SE1   020 3011 1021   10–4C NEW
"Sit at the counter and watch the magic", say fans of Kian Samyani's "rammed-to-the-rafters" charcoal grill in Soho, which aims (with the help of JKS Restaurants) to bring to London the childhood tastes of his Iranian upbringing. The result: "delicious food, super friendly front-of-house staff, and a great atmosphere, especially at the counter" (although there is also a more conventional seating area). It now has a similar Borough Market spin-off too, on the two-storey site of the short-lived Flor (RIP), which scores highly, but is slightly less venerated than its more established sibling: "there is no doubting that the food is excellent here too. But the price for a lamb or chicken kebab is more Salt Bae than Efes!" / berenjaklondon.com; berenjaklondon.

The Berners Tavern W1 £107 345
10 Berners Street   020 7908 7979   3–1D
"The impressive room is good as it looks in the photos" and "the bar is one of the most beautiful in central London" at Jason Atherton's sparkling venue: a converted banking hall that's part of a glam (Ian Shrager-designed) hotel, north of Oxford Street. With its "big and well-spaced tables" it's "sure to wow your customers", catch the attention of your date or set the scene for a "lovely special occasion". Historically, other aspects of the performance have played second fiddle to the surroundings here, but this year it won all-round praise for its "excellent" luxury brasserie cuisine and "knowledgeable" service too. / W1T 3NP; www.editionhotels.com; bernerstavern; Mon-Sat 9.45 pm.

Best Mangal £52 442
619 Fulham Rd, SW6   020 7610 0009   6–4A
104 North End Rd, W14   020 7610 1050   8–2D
A handy "cheap 'n' cheerful" option – these traditional Turkish venues, near West Kensington tube and on Fulham Broadway are a favourite stop-off for a freshly BBQ'd kebab. (The West Ken branch is not to be confused with 'Best Mangal 1996' – a similar venture at 66 North End Road). / www.bestmangal.com.

Bibendum SW3 £225 333
81 Fulham Rd   020 7589 1480   6–2C
"The lovely Michelin building is so cool", and its "well-spaced, light and airy dining room" is perhaps the late Sir Terence Conran's most enduring contribution to London's restaurant scene (best visited at lunch, when all the natural daylight makes it serene and "romantic"). Under Claude Bosi, its foodie renown has grown, and fans say he is "still setting the bar for outstanding contemporary French cooking in the capital" (for which he's held two Michelin stars since 2017). Its ratings blipped rather this year, however – as at a number of other top restaurants coping with the cost of living crisis, it can now just seem "too expensive" ("used to be great – recently disappointing"). / SW3 6RD; www.claudebosi.com; claudebosiatbibendum; Tue-Sat 9.30 pm.

Bibendum Oyster Bar SW3 £87 334
Michelin House, 81 Fulham Road   020 7581 5817   6–2C
The "plateau de fruits de mer takes some beating" at Claude Bosi's oyster bar, downstairs from his grand – and rather more expensive – flagship restaurant, in the foyer of Chelsea's iconic Michelin building. (Some hot alternatives to the cold luxurious seafood bites were introduced a couple of years ago.) / SW3 6RD; www.claudebosi.com; claudebosiatbibendum; Mon-Sun 9.30 pm.

BiBi W1 £87 **5** **5** **4**
42 North Audley Street   020 3780 7310   3–2A
"Creative and fascinating riffs on classic Indian cooking" by chef Chet
Sharma inspire another year of rapturous reviews (*"quite simply the best
Indian food I have ever eaten"*) for this JKS Restaurants property in Mayfair;
on the (somewhat *"narrow"*) site that was Truc Vert (RIP). *"The friendly,
charming team makes the experience a true delight, and there's a cracking
playlist as well!"* Caveats? *"It's another case of a restaurant going set menu
only in the evenings"*, which limits a less expensive à la carte option to lunch.
/ W1K 6ZR; www.bibirestaurants.com; bibi_ldn; Wed-Sat 9.30 pm.

Bibida W8 £45 **3** **4** **2**
1 Hillgate Street   020 7221 0151   7–2B
This *"great local Korean"* close to Notting Hill Gate tube station offers a
"good variety of dishes" – including Japanese sushi and *"super lunchtime
bento boxes"*. *"It can get very busy, so booking is advised"*. / W8 7SP;
www.bibida.co.uk; Mon-Sat 10.30 pm, Sun 10 pm.

**Bibo by Dani García,
Mondrian Hotel EC2** £86 **2** **2** **3**
45 Curtain Road   020 3146 4545   13–1B
Star chef Dani Garcia opened his first UK venture in Shoreditch's Mondrian
Hotel a couple of years ago, to mixed reviews. This up-and-down sentiment
continues in feedback to date – some reporters think the Spanish cuisine –
paellas, roast and grilled fish and meat, tapas – is *"very good"* (but
encountered *"an empty room on a Sunday lunch"*); other well-travelled types
thought it *"underwhelming compared to the wonders of his native
Andalusian restaurants"*. / EC2A 4PJ; www.sbe.com; bibo_shoreditch; Sun-Wed 9 pm,
Thu-Sat 10 pm.

Big Easy £72 **2** **2** **3**
12 Maiden Ln, WC2   020 3728 4888   5–3D
332-334 King's Rd, SW3   020 7352 4071   6–3C
Crossrail Pl, E14   020 3841 8844   12–1C
"BBQ, live music, decent cocktails and craft beer" channel the spirit of the
American South at this *"buzzy"*, long-running spot in Chelsea and its more
recent spin-offs in Covent Garden and Canary Wharf. The food is *"more
about quantity than quality"*, although the *"great-value lunch deals"* are
popular: *"£10 meat taster is unbeatable"*. / www.bigeasy.co.uk; bigeasylondon.

Big Fernand SW7 £43 **3** **3** **2**
39 Thurloe Place   020 3031 8330   6–2C
"French… and have to admit pretty good" – London's outpost of this Gallic
'Maison du Hamburgé' chain (that's 50-strong over the Channel) is to be
found in South Kensington's 'Little France' and gets a consistent thumbs up.
The addition of lashings of different French regional cheeses is key to
distinguishing its menu options. / SW7 2HP; www.bigfernanduk.com;
bigfernand_uk; Mon-Sun 10 pm.

The Bird in Hand W14 £56 **3** **3** **3**
88 Masbro Road   020 7371 2721   8–1C
"Great food and drink, especially pizza" makes it worth remembering this
stylish (if sometimes noisy) Olympia pub-conversion, a few minutes' walk
from Brook Green (part of the Oak group). / W14 0LR;
www.thebirdinhandlondon.com; thebirdw14; Tue-Fri 11 pm, Sat & Sun 10 pm.

Bistro Union SW4 £64 **3** **3** **2**
40 Abbeville Rd 020 7042 6400 11–2D
"Good food, leaning towards the hearty end of the spectrum rather than the refined", is enjoyed by most reporters at this 'Abbeville village' bistro from star Clapham chef Adam Byatt. If there's a grumble, it is that it can seem "disappointing given its link to Trinity", his flagship across the Common. / SW4 9NG; www.bistrounion.co.uk; bistrounionclapham.

Black Bear Burger £48 **4** **3** **2**
11-13 Market Row, SW9 020 7737 3444 11–2D
Canada Square, E14 020 7737 3444 12–1C
2-10 Bethnal Green Road, E1 no tel 13–2B
17 Exmouth Market, EC1 020 7837 1039 10–1A
"Smoky, flavourful, moist, DEELICIOUS – the burger is so well done, I go back again and again", chorus fans of this five-year-old independent with five outlets around London. Some hail the burgers – made from high-welfare native breed grass-fed West Country beef, dry-aged on the bone – as "the best in town". Founders Liz & Stew dreamt up the project while working ski seasons in Canada – hence the name. / blackbearburger.com; black_bear_burger.

The Black Book W1 £54 **3** **4** **4**
23 Frith Street 020 7434 1724 5–2A
Snug Soho bar, whose superior wine list belies its founding by two Master Sommeliers: Gearoid Devaney and Xavier Rousset. To help soak up the vino: well-rated small plates, cheese and charcuterie. Top Tip – head here in the wee hours: it's open till 3am later in the week. / W1D 4RR; blackbooksoho.co.uk; theblackbooksoho; Tue, Wed 1 am, Thu-Sat 3 am.

Black Dog Beer House TW8 £57 **3** **3** **3**
17 Albany Road 020 8568 5688 1–3A
"Great, hearty gastro-food" with "no pretensions" along with an "excellent array of beers" (14 from the keg, five real ales, 50 bottled or canned) leave guests spoilt for choice at this "very welcoming" backstreet free house in Brentford. Landlord Pete Brew (sic) even has his own in-house nano-brewery, Fearless Nomad. Top Menu Tip – "the fantastic salt-beef sandwich". / TW8 0NF; www.blackdogbeerhouse.co.uk; blackdogbeerhouse; Mon, Wed-Sat 11 pm, Sun 10.30 pm.

The Black Lamb SW19 £60 **3** **2** **2**
67 High Street 020 8947 8278 11–2B
"The cooking is interesting, vegetable heavy, but accessible to all", say fans of the Gladwin family's field-to-fork yearling (supplied by their Sussex farm), which has proved to be one of their more commented-on recent openings. But even those who feel it's "a great addition to the dining choices in Wimbledon Village" say "the food is perhaps not always as good as they think it is (some portions are tiny)". And it does also attract one or two really harsh critiques: "as a replacement for The White Onion (RIP) – an outstanding local – The Black Lamb is a disappointment and can be totally lacking in atmosphere". / SW19 5EE; www.theblacksheep-restaurant.com; theblacklamb_resto; Wed-Fri 10.30 pm, Tue 10 pm, Sat 11.30 pm, Sun 8.30 pm.

Black Salt SW14 £49 **4** **4** **3**
505-507 Upper Richmond Road West 020 4548 3327 11–2A
"Oh, you lucky punters of East Sheen… rejoice!" – this "unexpected" two-year-old is a spin-off from Ewell's legendary Dastaan, and is praised in numerous reports for chef Manish Sharma's "extraordinary Indian cuisine at fair prices": "big, complex punches of flavour but all nicely balanced". On the downside, ratings are capped by the odd reporter who feels it's "OK, but not quite as good as its reviews and reputation would suggest". / SW14 7DE; blacksaltsheen.com; blacksaltsheen; Tue-Thu 10 pm, Fri & Sat 10.30 pm, Sun 9 pm.

Blacklock £54 3 4 4

24 Great Windmill St, W1   020 3441 6996   4–3D
16a Bedford Street, WC2   020 303 4139   5–3C
5 Frobisher Passage, E14   020 3034 0230   12–1C NEW
28 Rivington Street, EC2   awaiting tel   13–1B
13 Philpot Lane, EC3   020 7998 7676   10–3D

"Absolutely delicious grilled meats with equally tasty accompaniments, all in a buzzy and fun setting" inspire many loyalists for Gordon Ker's *"go-to"* chain, which in May 2023 added a fifth branch in Canary Wharf's North Dock. *"Hawksmoor every week could be financially ruinous, but this never disappoints, be it lunch or dinner, for half the money".* Top Tips – *"Butchers Block Monday prices, and regular £10 corkage. Get in!"* Also the *"all-in"* meat-fest of lamb and pork chops, steak and bacon: *"it uses cheaper cuts and preparation is basic, but juices drip over the plate, and the peppercorn sauce is delicious!"* / theblacklock.com; blacklockchops.

Blanchette W1 £82 3 3 2

9 D'Arblay St   020 7439 8100   4–1C

"Excellent, stylish Gallic fare" sets the tone at this *"friendly"* bistro, run by a trio of French brothers who named it after their mother, that has notched up a decade in Soho. *"I'm already planning my next visit!".* The only real complaint is that *"in true Gallic style, the settings can be a bit cramped".* / W1F 8DS; www.blanchettesoho.co.uk; blanchettelondon; Mon-Sat 11 pm.

Blandford Comptoir W1 £75 3 4 3

1 Blandford Street   020 7935 4626   2–1A

Sommelier Xavier Rousset is behind this *"wonderful and quiet little restaurant"* and wine bar in Marylebone, *"serving delicious, serious food"* – mostly inspired by Italy – and *"an outstanding Rhône-specialist wine list".* Service is notably *"friendly, with a relaxed vibe".* / W1U 3DA; blandford-comptoir.co.uk; blandfordcomptoir; Tue-Sat 11 pm.

Bleecker Burger £29 4 2 2

205 Victoria St, SW1   no tel   2–4B
The Balcony, Westfield White City, W12   020 3582 2930   1–3B
Unit B Pavilion Building, Spitalfields Mkt, E1   07712 540501   13–2B
Queen Victoria Street, EC4   awaiting tel   10–3C

"Still the best burger in town in my opinion" is a widely shared view of this independent chain with four sit-down and three delivery-only kitchens. *"No matter how many burgers I try in London, I can't beat Bleecker"* – *"they get the simple stuff right: quality of meat, how the patty is made, doneness, ratio of meat to bread, and it adds up to a serious burger".* Zan Kaufman, a former New York corporate lawyer, launched her brand from the back of a truck 12 years ago, naming it after a Greenwich Village street. / www.bleecker.co.uk; bleeckerburger.

Bleeding Heart Bistro EC1 £64 3 3 4

Bleeding Heart Yard   0207 2428238   10–2A

This *"impressive French-inspired bistro"* is cutely tucked away in a historic yard on the fringe of the City, and thrives on its *"simple typically Gallic cooking with good ingredients"*, its high-quality wine list, and its *"attentive and friendly service".* *"It's not quite what it was"* when the adjoining buildings held a posher sister restaurant, but *"a reliable mainstay that's still well worth a visit"*, and which is still a go-to business entertaining venue. Top Tip – large and very attractive terrace for the summer months; and *"the set menu isn't bad value either".* / EC1N 8SJ; www.bleedingheart.co.uk; bleeding_heart_restaurants; Mon-Sat 9 pm.

Block Soho W1 NEW £53 222

Clarion House, 2 Saint Anne's Court   020 3376 9999   4–1D

On a cute, pedestrianised Soho cut-through, this year-old chop-house has seen lots of restaurants come and go over the years (most recently, Zelman Meats, RIP). Many reporters went in days of the 50%-off soft launch offer, and said they "would not pay the full price" due to inept service and either "too much char, char, char" or – conversely – "a lack of the flavour you'd expect from somewhere promoting itself by reference to its flame-grilled dishes". Post-launch comments veer in the other direction: "excellent meat… but wow the prices!" / W1F 0AZ; www.blocksoho.com; blocksoho; Sun-Thu midnight, Fri & Sat 12.30 am.

Blue Boar Pub,
Conran London St James SW1 £80 222

22-28 Broadway   020 3301 1400   2–3C

This stab at a 'modern British pub' from a posh Westminster hotel has not really convinced reporters, despite the appointment of high-profile chef, Sally Abé, from Fulham's brilliant Harwood Arms (she also runs the hotel's flagship restaurant, The Pem). "There isn't a lot of choice round this way" but BB is "expensive for what it is and full of a combination of mid-ranking politicians and journalists" – ouch! / SW1H 0BH; blueboarlondon.com; blueboarpub; Mon-Sun 11 pm.

Bluebird SW3 £93 213

350 King's Road   020 7559 1000   6–3C

It has a "very attractive site" – a landmark 1920s car showroom on King's Road Chelsea, with a "trendy vibe" – but is perennially "let down by a tired menu which is not well executed" and mediocre service. Why D&D London have never sorted this place out is a bit of a mystery – it could be so good. / SW3 5UU; www.bluebird-restaurant.co.uk; bluebirdchelsea; Mon-Wed, Fri, Thu, Sat 10.30 pm, Sun 9.30 pm; SRA-accredited.

Bob Bob Ricard £91 244

1 Upper James Street, W1   020 3145 1000   4–2C

Level 8, 122 Leadenhall Street, EC3   020 3145 1000   10–2D

The 'Press for Champagne' button has become an Instagram classic – made famous by the original Soho branch of Leonid Shutov's decadent diners, which provide luxurious treats like caviar and beef Wellington all served in a sumptuous environment, whose dark wood and polished surfaces evoke the deco glam of a trip on the Orient Express. "A fun place for a celebration" or romance, they are also notably "overpriced" – a factor harder to overlook in the era of straitened post-Covid expense accounts, when splashy business dining (for which they are a favourite) has been reined in. Perhaps that's why the renamed 'Bob Bob Cité' – a "nightclub-like space" occupying a floor of the City's Cheesegrater – has failed to make waves, and generates very few (albeit positive) reports. In August 2023, the group (celebrating its fifteenth year) started a new, 56-seat spin-off, a few doors down from the original, called 'Bébé Bob': the offering here will shoehorn champagne and caviar into a more dressed-down offering, alongside rotisserie chicken as the main event.

Bocca di Lupo W1 £67 443

12 Archer St   020 7734 2223   4–3D

"Jacob Kenedy's terrific Italian restaurant in the heart of the West End hasn't lost its edge in 15-plus years" (est. 2008) and is one of the most popular London destinations in our annual diners' poll. It serves "inspired, regional-Italian dishes" – "lots of interesting choices from an original, constantly-changing, seasonal menu" – all at notably "sensible prices". "The sommelier will assist you to navigate a marvellous Italian list and introduce you to some new wines; and service generally is both professional yet very friendly". Many diners "prefer sitting at the counter" watching the chefs to

the "more formal" tables at the back, "but you always get a good meal either way". "It is deafeningly loud, but that's the price you pay for such a buzzy atmosphere". Top Tip – "wonderful ice cream shop opposite which they also own". / W1D 7BB; www.boccadilupo.com; bocca_di_lupo; Mon-Sat 11 pm, Sun 9.30 pm.

Bocconcino Restaurant W1 £116
19 Berkeley St   020 7499 4510   3–3C
"You can't fail to impress with the food, vibes and service", according to fans of this Moscow-based chain, whose Mayfair offshoot is not short on glam. It provoked less feedback this year, though, in our annual diners' poll (too limited for a rating), but expansion is coming in the second half of 2023 with a new branch, below the Strand Palace Hotel. / W1J 8ED; www.bocconcinorestaurant.co.uk; bocconcino_london; Mon-Sat 12.30 am, Sun 10.30 pm.

Boisdale of Belgravia SW1 £111 ②③③
15 Eccleston Street   020 7730 6922   2–4B
The Scottish roots of Ranald Macdonald (the eldest son of the 24th chief and captain of Clanranald) help explain the approach of this Belgravian stalwart, which – since 1986 – has majored in a menu of Scottish-sourced beef and burgers (plus lobster and a few other dishes); backed up by an 'old school' wine list informed by Ranald's original career in the wine trade; and topped off with a huge range of whiskies. "Live music helps make it fun" and there's also a cigar terrace. On the downside, although harsh critiques are absent, its overall rating suggests it is fully priced. (For traditional expense-accounters, though, it's tailor-made.) / SW1W 9LX; www.boisdale.co.uk; boisdale_uk; Mon, Sat, Tue-Fri 1 am, Sun 4 pm.

Boisdale of Canary Wharf E14 £83 ③③③
Cabot Place   020 7715 5818   12–1C
"If you are not planning a return to the office, the largest selection of whisky ever seen" helps round off a business lunch at this Canary Wharf branch of Ranald Macdonald's Caledonian group. "The restaurant prides itself on good Scottish ingredients… shellfish in season… excellent fillet steak" and "tables are sufficiently spaced for private conversation". Top Tip – "regular visitors may join a club which gives discounts on wines and they host musical events in the evenings". / E14 4QT; www.boisdale.co.uk; boisdale_restaurants; Tue, Wed 11 pm, Fri & Sat 2 am, Thu 1 am, Sun 4.30 pm.

Bombay Brasserie SW7 £94 ③③③
Courtfield Road   020 7370 4040   6–2B
This grand Indian near Gloucester Road tube station was famous in the late 1980s, and nowadays has achieved a respectable semi-obscurity. Now owned by India's swish Taj Hotels group, all reports rate it well, and fans say it's been "year-in, year-out enjoyable" for four decades. / SW7 4QH; www.bombayb.co.uk; bombaybrasseriesw7; Tue-Thu, Sun 10 pm, Fri & Sat 10.30 pm.

Bombay Bustle W1 £79 ⑤③④
29 Maddox Street   020 7290 4470   3–2C
"Imaginative dishes", which deploy "authentic and distinct spicing with just the right kick", "make for a cracking experience" at Samyukta Nair's "smartly decorated room on the edge of Mayfair, with memories of Old Bombay". It's "the casual little sister of Jamavar" and "almost as good as its more expensive sibling" – while probably more "fun". Top Menu Tip – "Jalebi cheesecake". / W1S 2PA; www.bombaybustle.com; bombaybustle; Mon-Sat 10.30 pm, Sun 9.30 pm.

Bombay Palace W2   £69   **4 4 2**
50 Connaught St   020 7723 8855   7–1D
"Don't be fooled by the 1990s looks – standards are right up to snuff!" This "old-fashioned, well-spaced, very comfortable" Indian near Edgware Road has – for decades – won surprisingly high scores for its "consistently good, traditional dishes of high quality served by knowledgeable waiters". It remains "highly recommended" but its ratings have been a bit more up-and-down since the pandemic; and the odd report says "a bit more consistency would be appreciated: the food can be excellent but can also be mediocre". / W2 2AA; www.bombay-palace.co.uk; bombaypalacelondon; Mon, Thu, Tue, Wed, Sun 10 pm, Fri & Sat 10.30 pm.

Bone Daddies   £46   **3 2 2**
Nova, Victoria St, SW1   no tel   2–4B
30-31 Peter St, W1   020 7287 8581   4–2D
46-48 James St, W1   020 3019 7140   3–1A
1 Phillimore Gardens, W8   020 3668 5500   8–1D **NEW**
24 Old Jamaica Road, SE16   020 7231 3211   10–4D
22 Putney High St, SW15   020 8246 4170   11–2B
The Bower, 211 Old Street, EC1   020 3019 6300   13–1A
These funky (and noisy) 'rock 'n' roll ramen' bars shook up the capital's Japanese fast-food scene when the first outlet opened in Soho 11 years ago, spawning a small group now reaching as far as Richmond. Their "super ramen" is served with 20-hour pork bone broth cooked these days at a kitchen on Bermondsey's 'beer mile'. But the business has not been immune to the industry's difficulties: a Putney spin-off only lasted a year before closing, and a long-touted outlet in the old Eurostar terminal at Waterloo has yet to eventuate. / www.bonedaddies.com; bonedaddies.

Bonoo NW2   £63   **3 3 3**
675 Finchley Road   020 7794 8899   1–1B
"A great local Indian, with tapas-style Indian dishes full of fresh, zingy flavours" – this family-run operation in Childs Hill is "definitely not your traditional curry house" and has proved a "really welcome addition to North London". / NW2 2JP; www.bonoo.co.uk; bonoo.indian.tapas; Mon-Sun 10.30 pm.

Booking Office 1869,
St Pancras Renaissance Hotel NW1   £87   **2 3 5**
Euston Road   020 7841 3566   9–3C
"The scene is set for romance before you even step through the door" at this "very impressive and spectacular" yearling, with its location "next to Paul Day's sculpture of a couple kissing at St. Pancras International". Set inside the station's former ticket office (nowadays part of a glossy five-star hotel), "the majesty of the architecture is set off by elegant palm trees and it's a calm and wonderful oasis" (complete with a 22m bar). The only potential shortcoming is the all-day brasserie menu: even some fans concede it's "pricey" and there is the odd report of "really disappointing" dishes here. Top Menu Tip – "it's always been a stunning space and – now it's a restaurant – it's the perfect place to crash a hotel breakfast!"; "beautifully executed afternoon tea" too. / NW1 2AR; www.booking-office.co.uk; bookingoffice; Mon-Sun 10 pm.

The Boot & Flogger SE1 £69 ③③④
10-20 Redcross Way   020 7407 1184   10–4C
"Traditional, old favourites" characterise the British cooking at this "relaxed" and very atmospheric wine bar and dining room, just south of Southwark Street and the railway arches that ultimately run over nearby Borough Market. It has a "great atmosphere and good wine list" – like so much of the 15-strong Davy's wine bar chain, of which this was the original, opening in 1965. / SE1 1TA; www.davy.co.uk; davysoflondon; Tue-Sat 11 pm, Mon 10 pm, Sun 6 pm.

Il Bordello E1 £61 ③③④
Metropolitan Wharf, 70 Wapping Wall   020 7481 9950   12–1A
This neighbourhood Italian of almost 30 years' standing in a Wapping warehouse conversion "never disappoints" with its food and service, but "it's the lively atmosphere that really sells it", drawing a "great mix of local families and couples just getting together". / E1W 3SS; www.ilbordello.com; ilbordellorestaurant; Mon-Sat 11 pm, Sun 10.30 pm.

Borough Market Kitchen SE1 £66 ④②②
Jubilee Place   020 7407 5777   10–4C
"If you like street food and quick relaxed eating", seek out this three-year-old covered street-food area adjoining the famous market that's winning a consistent thumbs up; you can choose from about 15 different stands and there's a fair amount of communal seating. It used to be a car park! / SE1 9AG; www.applebeesfish.com; boroughmarket; Mon-Thu 10 pm, Fri & Sat 11 pm, Sun 9 pm.

Il Borro W1 £132 ②③③
15 Berkeley Street   020 3988 7717   3–3C
Owned by the Ferragamo fashion family and named after their Tuscan wine estate, this Mayfair two-year-old in the former premises of Nobu Berkeley (RIP) is certainly "a bit bling", but has won over a constituency of fans who say "it seems to be right for the occasion, whether business or pleasure". Plus points include "some fine dishes – including wonderful fish and vegetables" – and "a pleasant buzz". The big drawback, if you're footing the bill, is "the insane price point". / W1J 8DY; ilborrotuscanbistro.co.uk; tuscanbistrolondon; Sun-Thu midnight, Fri & Sat 1 am.

Bossa W1
4 Vere Street   020 3062 5844   3–1B
Opened in May 2023, just as our latest annual diners' poll was concluding, the debut of this Marylebone newcomer from Brazilian World's 50 best chef Alberto Landgraf has so far made remarkably few waves. It's clear from the pics that he's spent a packet on the svelte interior, but the menu – with mains for £30-£40 – has few distinguishing Latino inflections (e.g. a sample main – 'Pork Loin Chop, Apple Purée, Savoy Cabbage, Black Pudding'). Ignored in its initial months by the newspapers, including The Standard – reports please! / W1G 0DG; www.bossa.co.uk; bossa_uk; Tue-Sat 11 pm.

Bottle & Rye SW9 £62 ③④②
Ground Floor, 404-406 Market Row   no tel   11–2D
"Still dreaming about the anchovies on toast!" Robin and Sarah Gill's compact (28 covers) yearling aims to bring Parisian café culture to Brixton's Market Row. All feedback on the "daily changing menus of small and larger dishes" is upbeat: "a small place with a brilliant selection of options, good wine and drinks list. Staff are really on it, know the dishes inside out and steer you in the right direction for your order". / SW9 8LD; www.bottleandrye.com; bottleandrye; Tue-Sat 11 pm.

Bouchon Racine EC1 NEW £88 5 5 3
66 Cowcross Street   020 7253 3368   10–1A

A "fabulous successor to the legendary Racine" (which closed in Knightsbridge in 2015) and "an amazing, blazing return to the stove for Henry Harris" – this "very lively room, up steep stairs" above Farringdon's Three Compasses pub is the opening of the year and, despite all the hype, it doesn't disappoint. "There's lots of passion and skill that goes into this quintessential cooking" – "French classics (basics even) taken to another level". Service, overseen by co-founder Dave Strauss, is "pitch perfect": "charming and from people who clearly love what they do". "One leaves uplifted and feeling that all is well with the world… that is, in the unlikely event that you can get a table!". Top Menu Tip – "a spot-on and delicious tête de veau sauce ravigote". / EC1M 6BP; www.bouchonracine.com; bouchonracine; Tue-Sat 10 pm.

Boudica SW11 NEW
Boudica House, 12 Palmer Road   020 8017 3400   11–1C

On the fringes of the new developments around Battersea Power Station, this modern all-day-brasserie opened in April 2023 – too late to generate any survey feedback. Instagram-worthy foliage is a feature, both inside and on the terrace. Let's hope chef Luigi Vairo (who provides an international menu) doesn't take too much inspiration from the restaurant's name… the legendary queen of the Iceni, who burnt London to the ground…
/ SW11 4FQ; www.boudicalondon.com; boudica_london; Mon-Sat midnight, Sun 10 pm.

Boulevard WC2 £62 2 3 3
40 Wellington St   020 7240 2992   5–3D

A "Covent Garden staple" for 33 years, this "bustling French bistro with packed tables but speedy service" serves "good-value, reliably cooked traditional Gallic fare" that belies its somewhat touristy looks. Top Tip – "a wide-ranging menu and the set menus and special deals add to its appeal; and it's a good choice for families with children". / WC2E 7BD; www.boulevardbrasserie.co.uk; boulevardbrasseriewc2; Mon-Wed 11 pm, Thu-Sat 11.30 pm, Sun 10 pm.

Brackenbury Wine Rooms W6 £59 2 4 4
111-115 Hammersmith Grove   020 3696 8240   8–1C

This "cheerful" and "enjoyable" Hammersmith haunt carries a good selection of wines and its kitchen offers modern bistro food – but 'La Cave', its coffee house, generates the most feedback this year, for its "friendly staff", "superb coffee" and "the best chocolate brownies". / W6 0NQ; winerooms.london; wine_rooms; Mon-Sat 11 pm, Sun 4 pm.

Bradley's NW3 £78 2 2 2
25 Winchester Rd   020 7722 3457   9–2A

Simon & Jolanta Bradley's "efficient" veteran of 30 years' standing near Swiss Cottage station "never lets you down" and it's a "great option if going to the Hampstead Theatre around the corner". But while fans say "the quality of the food is such that it shouldn't be only for pre-theatre", there's also a view that "it can feel rather soulless" as a destination in itself. / NW3 3NR; www.bradleysnw3.co.uk; bradleysrestaurant; Wed-Sat, Tue 9 pm, Sun 2.30 pm.

La Brasseria £89 222

42 Marylebone High Street, W1   020 7486 3753   2–1A
290 Westbourne Grove, W11   020 7052 3564   7–2B

For a "solid menu, with a wide variety" of "reliable Italian" options, this duo have a broad fanclub – both the Marylebone five-year-old and its year-old Notting Hill sibling. Their ratings are undercut, though, by a feeling that they are "expensive (but isn't everything nowadays…")", and can "lack atmosphere when they're not busy". Top Tip – for some folks, "the most important thing is that they welcome both families and doggies!"
/ www.labrasseria.com; brasseria_nottinghill.

Brasserie Blanc £62 222

119 Chancery Lane, WC2   020 7405 0290   2–2D
Goldhurst House, Parr's Way, W6   020 8237 5566   8–2C
9 Belvedere Rd, SE1   020 7202 8470   2–3D
60 Threadneedle St, EC2   020 7710 9440   10–2C

"For a reasonable pre-theatre/concert meal" on the South Bank, the SE1 branch of this Gallic brasserie chain is "a useful option behind the Royal Festival Hall"; its City and Legal-land outlets are serviceable for a working lunch; and its W6 branch has a "classy" position on the river. Over time, though, it has "declined from being one of the better multiples" and is nowadays "very, very average indeed" – with the possible exception of Hammersmith, you wouldn't make them a destination in their own right.
/ www.brasserieblanc.com; SRA-3 stars.

Brasserie of Light W1 £81 234

400 Oxford Street   020 3940 9600   3–1A

"Who would have believed you are eating in a department store!" – Richard Caring's "glitzy but useful" second-floor brasserie has "a real buzz". "With huge windows, the decor is fabulously glamorous and Damien Hirst's stunning 'Pegasus' dominates the scene". The "Ivy-style menu" is "appealingly eclectic, if with rather average execution", but by-and-large comes at "fair prices". / W1A 1AB; www.brasserie-of-light.co.uk; brasserieoflight; Mon-Sat midnight, Sun 11 pm.

Brasserie Zédel W1 £60 124

20 Sherwood St   020 7734 4888   4–3C

"Transport yourself to an imaginary 1930s world of Parisian glamour, as might be imagined by Fitzgerald or Hollywood", when you visit this Art Deco basement, "bang in the heart of town", just seconds from Piccadilly Circus. "The vast (Grade I listed) room is a crowded symphony of marble and gold leaf, with an immense buzz" and is "a faithful facsimile of a traditional French brasserie", complete with an excellent American Bar. Fans say "if you want to impress without spending a fortune then this is the place to go" and since its founding (in 2015) it's become a byword for "affordable luxury", with most folks tolerating its "dull and unmemorable" Gallic staples for the overall package. Since changes in the group, however, the equation is beginning to shift and fears are growing that "the package all-round is not quite good enough". "Service in particular has fallen notably in the post-Jeremy King era" and for more critical types "the whole experience is rather underwhelming" ("it was busy, but instead of making the atmosphere vibrant, there was a tired feel to the experience"). That's not yet the dominant verdict though: most diners still "never tire of visiting… it always feels like a wonderful and extravagant treat". / W1F 7ED; www.brasseriezedel.com; brasseriezedel; Mon-Sat 11 pm, Sun 10 pm.

Brat E1 £87 **5** **4** **3**
First Floor, 4 Redchurch Street   no tel   13–1B
"Simple things are done very, very well on a smoking fire and every dish is a wow!" at Tomos Parry's Shoreditch superstar, which – now five years old – has proved "a superb addition to the London dining scene". "It's casual in style, but the truly original cooking" and "enthusiastic and informed staff" generate "a real buzz about the place" and create a "cosy" atmosphere in what might otherwise might seem a "somewhat lacklustre" and tightly packed space (on the first floor, above Smoking Goat downstairs). As well as the signature turbot for which the restaurant is named, many dishes here are praised in reports ("spider crab toast to die for…"; "clever duck rice, like paella…"; "beautifully flavoursome and light Basque cheesecake"). / E1 6JJ; www.bratrestaurant.com; bratrestaurant; Mon-Sun 10 pm.

Brat at Climpson's Arch E8 £101 **4** **3** **2**
Climpson's Arch, 374 Helmsley Place   020 7254 7199   14–2B
"Such a treat on a summer's day" – ace chef Tomos Parry's railway arch pop-up-turned-permanent in London Fields "feels like a (rather smoky) house party", serving "great grilled meat and fish in a tent" – "the only issue is trying to limit the number of dishes one orders, and the quandary of whether to have THAT turbot or try something else!". / E8 3SB; bratrestaurant.com; bratrestaurant; Wed-Sat 10 pm, Sun 9 pm.

Bravi Ragazzi SW16 £51 **4** **2** **2**
2a Sunnyhill Road   020 8769 4966   11–2D
"Excellent Neapolitan sourdough pizza" has carved a legendary reputation for Andrea Asciuti's cult Streatham pitstop, to which aficionados journey from far and wide. He also runs 081 Pizzeria – see also. / SW16 2UH; www.bravi-ragazzi.business.site; braviragazzipizzeria; Mon-Thu 10 pm, Fri 10.30 pm, Sat 11 pm, Sun 9.30 pm.

Brawn E2 £78 **5** **5** **4**
49 Columbia Road   020 7729 5692   14–2A
"Not missing a beat and at the very top of its game" – this culinarily renowned East End fixture, near Columbia Road flower market, scored highly all round in this year's annual diners' poll, putting any doubts about its staying power to one side. Its Med-influenced, superior bistro cuisine delivers "extraordinary flavours", service is very "charming" and all in all, it's "a delightful, unpretentious neighbourhood place". / E2 7RG; www.brawn.co; brawn49; Tue-Sat, Mon 10.30 pm.

Bread Street Kitchen EC4 £78 **2** **2** **3**
10 Bread Street   020 3030 4050   10–2B
"Well-located in the power station", the new Battersea branch of Gordon Ramsay's upscale brasserie chain has inspired more interest than some others in this expanding group (which also now incorporates the Limehouse riverside pub GR has owned for ages, fka The Narrow). With their generously spaced, comfortable and quite stylish interiors they can be a versatile choice – especially on business – but their resolutely MOR standards mean they hardly set the pulse racing. / EC4M 9AJ; www.gordonramsayrestaurants.com; breadstreetkitchen; Mon-Wed 11 pm, Thu-Sat midnight, Sun 10 pm.

Breakfast Club £45 **3 4 3**
Branches throughout London
"Plenty of yummy breakfast options" win praise for this "extremely well done" brunch specialist which launched 19 years ago in Soho and now has 13 self-described 'cafés', 10 of them around the capital, and another four bars and pubs. The fry-ups, pancakes and other comfort-food delights can be accompanied by cocktails if you fancy pushing the boat out early with a Breakfast Mai Tai. Any complaints? – "just the incredibly annoying queues". / www.thebreakfastclubcafes.com; thebrekkyclub.

Briciole W1 £69 **3 3 2**
20 Homer St 020 7723 0040 7–1D
According to a fair few reports, this "charming neighbourhood Italian" near Edgware Road tube station offers "authentically tasty small plates and delicious classics", although "you do need to put up with the noise". Top Tip – "they are very good with children here". / W1H 4NA; www.briciole.co.uk; briciolerestaurant; Mon-Sun 10.45 pm.

Brick Lane Beigel Bake E1 £9 **5 2 1**
159 Brick Ln 020 7729 0616 13–1C
"The original and the best", agree fans of this legendary East End Jewish deli, which is "well worth a detour any time, day or night" (thanks to its 24/7 opening) for its "fantastic" beigels (stubbornly spelt in the traditional European manner), stuffed with classic fillings including salt beef, lox and pickled herring. "Amazing value" too – it feels like they've forgotten to change the prices for the last 20 years. / E1 6SB; www.beigelbake.co.uk; bricklanebeigelbake; Mon-Sun midnight.

Brigadiers,
Bloomberg Arcade EC2 £71 **4 3 3**
Queen Victoria Street 020 3319 8140 10–3C
"Standards remain high" at JKS Restaurants' "Anglo-Indian sporting and military-themed eaterie" in the Bloomberg Arcade – "a go-to lunching spot (albeit that City lunching is significantly less prevalent than in days gone by)". The "amazing and different dishes" are "full of flavour and spices". Top Menu Tips – "the tandoori meats in particular are excellent" and "dum beef shin and bone marrow biryani is a must try!" / EC2R 8AR; brigadierslondon.com; brigadiersldn; Mon-Sat 10.30 pm.

The Bright Courtyard W1 £90 **3 2 2**
43-45 Baker St 020 7486 6998 2–1A
A "big Chinese restaurant" – the London outpost of a Shanghai group – which serves Cantonese fare that's "really good and not too pricey". It occupies part of an office block near Portman Square in Marylebone – a setting that "can seem a bit sterile". / W1U 8EW; www.lifefashiongroup.com; brightcourtyard; Mon-Sat 10.30 pm, Sun 9.30 pm.

Brinkley's SW10 £74 **2 3 3**
47 Hollywood Rd 020 7351 1683 6–3B
For its Sloane Ranger crowd, wine merchant John Brinkley's long-established brasserie is a "still-buzzing Chelsea legend where you can drink well at almost-retail prices". But, while most fans feel the food is "decent" too, others say "you pay too much for what you get and folks are starting to vote with their feet". There are spin-offs in Wandsworth Bridge Road and beside Wandsworth Common (see Brinkley's Kitchen). / SW10 9HX; www.brinkleys.com; brinkleysrestaurant; Mon-Sun 11 pm.

Brinkley's Kitchen SW17 £76 2️⃣2️⃣3️⃣
35 Bellevue Rd   020 8672 5888   11–2C
"Always busy local favourite" facing onto Wandsworth Common. It serves "competent modern British food" but what particularly helps keep its regulars coming back is a "keenly priced wine list" from owner John Brinkley, who has a string of wine-focused venues in southwest London. / SW17 7EF; www.brinkleys.com; brinkleyskitchen; Tue-Sat 11 pm, Sun 4 pm.

Brooklands SW1 NEW
1 Grosvenor Place   020 8138 6888   2–3A
When it opens in September 2023, this rooftop restaurant promises to be one of the capital's glossier debuts in recent times. It's on top of the Peninsular London – a branch of the landmark HK hotel, overlooking Hyde Park Corner (right next to The Lanesborough). The kitchen is under the culinary direction of Claude Bosi, the Lyon-born chef behind Bibendum in Chelsea, who will provide a contemporary European menu. Let's hope the cuisine really takes off… unlike the model of Concorde, which it is promised will soar above the heads of diners on the outside terrace. / SW1X 7HJ; www.peninsula.com; peninsulahotels; Mon-Sun.

Brookmill SE8 £56 3️⃣3️⃣3️⃣
65 Cranbrook Road   020 8333 0899   1–4D
If you find yourself near Brookmill Park, between Deptford and Lewisham, this "lovely and friendly" corner pub (with garden) is worth knowing about for its "reliable" standard of cooking. / SE8 4EJ; www.thebrookmill.co.uk; brookmillse8; Sun & Mon 9 pm, Tue-Sat 10 pm.

The Brown Dog SW13 £63 3️⃣3️⃣4️⃣
28 Cross Street   020 8392 2200   11–1A
This "unspoilt, cosy and simply furnished" late-Victorian pub, "tucked away down a side street" in the cute 'Little Chelsea' enclave of Barnes, is "a joy to visit for its competently cooked food and excellent beer" – "not surprisingly it has loyal local support". Top Tip – sweet garden in summer. / SW13 0AP; www.thebrowndog.co.uk; browndogbarnes; Tue, Wed 11 pm, Thu-Sat 10 pm, Sun 6 pm.

Brown's Hotel,
The Drawing Room W1 £134 3️⃣4️⃣4️⃣
Albemarle St   020 7493 6020   3–3C
"Even better than The Ritz…", "on a par with Fortnum's…" – for many aficionados of London's top afternoon tea experiences, this wood-panelled drawing room within creaky old Brown's Hotel is the top dog. Built in 1837 (and with famous patrons including Queen Victoria and Agatha Christie) – it helps that it's "a lovely, traditional space": "delightful and just more intimate" than its main rivals. "Nothing is too much trouble (even to please a picky sub-teenager!)" and "the sandwiches and tea are just as good as elsewhere". / W1S 4BP; www.roccofortehotels.com; browns_hotel; Mon-Sun 9 pm.

Brunswick House Café SW8 £64 3️⃣2️⃣5️⃣
30 Wandsworth Rd   020 7720 2926   11–1D
"An architectural salvage display room" lit by chandeliers – in a Georgian mansion fronting the Vauxhall Cross gyratory system – provides a "lively, boho and very relaxed" backdrop for this unusual but successful venue. Amazingly, it "works so well", with "above average (if expensive) modern British fare" from highly regarded chef Jackson Boxer. ("Well worth the detour/ taking your life in your hands navigating the Vauxhall one way!"). / SW8 2LG; www.brunswickhouse.london; brunswick_house; Wed-Sat, Tue 9.45 pm, Sun 4.30 pm.

Trattoria Brutto EC1 £59 3 4 5
35-37 Greenhill Rents   no tel   10–1A

Russell Norman's skillful love letter to Florentine trattorias is "hard to fault for a classic Italian" and, in particular, its "buzzy" ("if noisy" and "crowded") "glamourous" style is a brilliant escape from the grey streets of Clerkenwell (near Smithfield Market). The "Negronis are lethal" and the "heavy-hitting, rustic fodder" is "simply done, but top quality". An archetypal 'Bistecca alla Fiorentina' (T-bone steak) is a central menu feature, as are lesser-known treats such as "the moreish coccoli (or 'cuddles') of deep-fried dough that you stuff with soft cheese and prosciutto". For all its virtues, though, Russell is a darling of the foodie media, so the place receives regular "hype", and the only weaker reviews come from those expecting more culinary fireworks, given that "the food is good, but not great". / EC1M 6BN; msha.ke/brutto; bru.tto; Tue-Sat 11 pm.

Bubala £41 4 4 3
15 Poland Street, W1   no tel   4–1C
65 Commercial Street, E1   no tel   13–2C

"Every course hits harder than the next… and you don't even realise all are vegetarian!" – this former pop-up – now with outlets in Soho (on the site of the now-transferred Vasco & Piero's) and Shoreditch – serves "stunning" Middle Eastern-style dishes from founder Marc Summers (ex-Berber & Q) and head chef Helen Graham (ex-Palomar and Barbary). "If I could eat this food every day, I could easily become meat-free". Plan ahead – "it's hard to get a table!" / bubala_london.

The Bull N6 £69 3 3 2
13 North Hill   020 8341 0510   9–1B

This old Highgate pub with a big outside terrace makes a "good local" with "hearty gastropub fare", although its 2022 acquisition by the Metropolitan Pub Company may not have contributed to the atmosphere. / N6 4AB; thebullhighgate.co.uk; bull_highgate; Mon-Thu 11 pm, Fri & Sat midnight, Sun 10.30 pm.

Bull & Last NW5 £79 4 3 3
168 Highgate Rd   020 7267 3641   9–1B

A "fabulous bistropub" – "now also a hotel with comfortable rooms" – in a "great location" near Parliament Hill and Hampstead Heath. "Giles Coren is not wrong" – the Times columnist is a local and a big fan. Any complaints? "If only they'd turn the music down…". / NW5 1QS; www.thebullandlast.co.uk; thebullandlast; Mon-Thu 11 pm, Fri & Sat midnight, Sun 10.30 pm.

Bund N2 £56 3 3 3
4-5 Cheapside, Fortis Green   020 8365 2643   1–1B

"Good all round", say local fans of this Pan-Asian fixture, which offers East-meets-West presentation of dishes drawn from a variety of cuisines. It brings some light to the thinly provided boonies between Muswell Hill and East Finchley. / N2 9HP; bundrestaurant.co.uk; bundrestaurant; Tue-Sun 10 pm.

Burger & Beyond E1 £49 3 2 2
147 Shoreditch High Street   020 3848 8860   13–1B

This former food-truck and market-stall operation now has three bricks-and-mortar bars around the capital serving US-style burgers made from dry-aged Yorkshire-bred beef – and "wow, they're really good". You can enjoy them at home, too, thanks to a trio of delivery-only kitchens. Top Menu Tip – "the Bacon Butter Burger is great". / E1 6JE; burgerandbeyond.co.uk; burgerandbeyond; Mon-Thu 10 pm, Fri & Sat 11 pm, Sun 9 pm.

Burger & Lobster £77 4️⃣3️⃣2️⃣
Harvey Nichols, 109-125 Knightsbridge, SW1   020 7235 5000   6–1D
10 Wardour Street, W1   020 3205 8963   5–4A
26 Binney Street, W1   020 3637 5972   3–2A
29 Clarges Street, W1   020 7409 1699   3–4B
36 Dean Street, W1   020 7432 4800   5–2A
6 Little Portland Street, W1   020 7907 7760   3–1C
18 Hertsmere Road, E14   020 3637 6709   12–1C
52 Threadneedle Street, EC2   020 7256 9755   10–2C
Bow Bells Hs, 1 Bread St, EC4   020 7248 1789   10–2B
"The lobster roll is just lovely" at this surf'n'turf-meets-burger chain, where you'll find "plenty of very tasty grub". "I was expecting to be disappointed, but the food was excellent". A dozen years on from its launch, the group's nine London venues tend to be "full of people done up for a big night out, taking lots of selfies for their Insta". / www.burgerandlobster.com; burgerandlobster.

Busaba £51 2️⃣2️⃣2️⃣
Branches throughout London
After 25 years, this Thai-fusion group is generally regarded as "solid but far from spectacular". Creator Alan Yau (who also has Wagamama and Hakkasan among his credits) is no longer involved and out-of-town branches in Oxford and Cardiff have closed down, leaving 10 outlets in the London area. / www.busaba.com; busabaeathai.

**Butler's Restaurant,
The Chesterfield Mayfair W1** £90 3️⃣3️⃣3️⃣
35 Charles St   020 7958 7729   3–3B
Dover sole filleted at the table, "choosing from pick'n'mix from the sweet trolley" and "cocktails in a smoking glass" typify the retro flourishes favoured by the comfy dining room and bar of this traditional Mayfair venue. Feedback isn't super-plentiful, but all upbeat – "a lovely experience at a reasonable price". / W1J 5EB; www.chesterfieldmayfair.com; chesterfieldmayfair; Mon-Sun 10 pm.

Butlers Wharf Chop House SE1 £85 2️⃣2️⃣3️⃣
36e Shad Thames   020 7403 3403   10–4D
"Handy for the location" by the Thames, with spectacular views of Tower Bridge from its terrace, this modern take on the British chop house was created by the late Sir Terence Conran as part of his 'Gastrodome' complex in the 1990s. Nowadays owned by D&D London, it is a useful spot for tourists and business diners. / SE1 2YE; www.chophouse-restaurant.co.uk; butlerswharfchophouse; Tue-Sat 9 pm, Mon 9.30 pm, Sun 6 pm; SRA-accredited.

Byron £47 2️⃣2️⃣3️⃣
Branches throughout London
Now down to a dozen outlets nationally and just four in London from its 2018 peak of 67, this early 'better burger' chain has dropped ratings across the board this year. But, compared to other chains, feedback is far from rock-bottom – indeed complaints are notably absent – so perhaps there are still some legs in the brand? / www.byron.co.uk/about-us; ByronBurgersUK.

C&R Café W1 £36 4️⃣2️⃣2️⃣
3-4 Rupert Court   020 7434 1128   4–3D
"Please don't dress up to dine in this cheap little no-frills café" on the edge of Chinatown, but prepare to eat some "truly fantastic, highly spiced Malaysian food" – "the beef rendang is absolutely the best", and "the laksa lives up to expectations". / W1D 6DY; www.cnrcaferestaurant.com; c&r; Tue-Thu, Sun 10 pm, Fri & Sat 11 pm.

Cabotte EC2 £86 343
48 Gresham St   020 7600 1616   10–2C

"One of the best options for fine dining in the City" – "if you want a good French restaurant in the Square Mile, with a great wine list, look no further" than this "slick and intimate" venue, which boasts "one of the best wine selections in London" – a particular "dream-list for lovers of Burgundy and Champagne". "Very good service is worth a shout out". / EC2V 7AY; www.cabotte.co.uk; cabotte_; Mon-Fri 10 pm.

The Cadogan Arms SW3 £75 334
298 King's Road   020 3148 2630   6–3C

"When all that wealth and beauty on the King's Road become too much", this "tastefully restored" old pub (built in 1838) is something of an antidote. It wins praise all round for its "attentive" service and "traditional British fare" that's "on the button and carefully presented". If there's any reservation, it's that it doesn't dazzle quite as much as its restaurant royalty backing might lead you to hope (the owners of JKS Restaurants, with food overseen by Kitchen Table's James Knappett). Top Menu Tip – "prawn cocktail and skinny chips with a side order of hot sauce". / SW3 5UG; thecadoganarms.london; cadoganarmspublichouse; Mon-Thu 10 pm, Fri & Sat 10.30 pm, Sun 6 pm.

Cafe Cecilia E8 £65 444
Canal Place, 32 Andrews Road   0203 478 6726   14–2B

"Cool places rarely fit the hype… but this one does!" Max Rocha's "low key and informal" Hackney two-year-old is going from strength to strength. "A light airy space by the canal, it's great for a relaxed meal", with service that – "though achingly hip – is very good". The "slightly unusual" food is all about small portions of intense flavours and "super-fresh seasonal ingredients", and results are "excellent". "Bonne chance getting a table!" Top Menu Tip – "the Guinness bread is very tasty". / E8 4RL; www.cafececilia.com; cafececilialondon; Thu-Sat 8.30 pm, Wed 3 pm, Sun 3.30 pm.

Café Deco WC1 £69 322
43 Store Street   020 8091 2108   2–1C

The "superb neighbourhood café we'd all love to have around the corner" – this upgraded greasy spoon "in a dead area of Bloomsbury" provides "particularly tasty, modern French fare" realised with a "delicious and light" touch by co-founder Anna Tobias, former head chef at Rochelle Canteen. / WC1E 7DB; www.cafe-deco.co.uk; cafe_deco_bloomsbury; Tue-Sat 9.30 pm.

Café du Marché EC1 £62 345
22 Charterhouse Sq   020 7608 1609   10–1B

"You actually feel as though you might be in a brasserie in France" at this City-fringe "favourite", tucked away in an atmospheric former warehouse, near Smithfield Market (and long predating the trendification of the area). "A great staple for both business and pleasure", it "has a lovely atmosphere with a real, vibrant buzz which should surely impress" either a client or date. The "pleasing", solid Gallic fare offers "decent value", but "it is the overall experience that makes it stand out". / EC1M 6DX; www.cafedumarche.co.uk; cafedumarche; Tue-Fri 10 pm, Sat 9.30 pm.

Café in the Crypt,
St Martin in the Fields WC2 £36 224
Duncannon St   020 7766 1158   2–2C

A "long-established cafeteria" in the beautiful, brick-vaulted crypt of St Martin-in-the-Fields that's a useful venue for daytime and pre-theatre refuelling – "cheap and tasty and near the National Gallery". In summer, they open a 'Café in the Courtyard', too. / WC2N 4JJ; stmartin-in-the-fields.org; stmartininthefields; Mon, Wed, Fri-Sun 5 pm, Tue 7.30 pm.

Café Japan NW11   £41   3 3 2
626 Finchley Rd   020 8455 6854   1–1B

Some of the "best reasonably priced sashimi and sushi" in London has long been found at this basic but "friendly" café, near Golders Green Tube. In recent years, it's fallen under the ownership of top Japanese fish and seafood wholesaler T&S Enterprises, with outlets (usually under the Atariya brand) in Finchley, Kingston, Swiss Cottage and West Acton. / NW11 7RR; atariya.co.uk; cafejapanlondon; Wed-Sun 11 pm.

Café Kitsuné at Pantechnicon SW1   £47   3 3 4
19 Motcomb Street   020 7034 5425   6–1D

"With the pâtisserie, the Japanese and Parisian influences are combined in such a wonderful way… and the coffee is sooo good", according to fans of this mezzanine and foyer café, within a beautiful Belgravia landmark. But, perhaps predictably considering the frou-frou nature of this luxe locale, it can also seem plain "overpriced". / SW1X 8LB; www.pantechnicon.com; _pantechnicon; Mon-Sun 6 pm.

**Café Lapérouse,
The OWO SW1** NEW
57 Whitehall Place   Awaiting tel   2–3C

Just the name of the Dior-affiliated designer (Cordeilia de Castellane), evokes glamour at the courtyard eatery of this mega-development scheduled to open in late 2023. It's a spin-off from the 250-year-old Parisian venture of the same name – France's first restaurant with three Michelin stars back in the day (which it held, on and off, until 1968) – and looks set to be cut from the same (chic but extremely expensive) cloth as the original on the Place de la Concorde. / SW1A 2EU; Wed-Sat 10 pm, Sun 9.30 pm.

Cafe Murano   £74   3 4 2
33 St James's St, SW1   020 3371 5559   3–3C
36 Tavistock St, WC2   020 3371 5559   5–3D
Pastificio, 34 Tavistock Street, WC2   020 3535 7884   5–3D
184 Bermondsey Street, SE1   020 3985 1545   10–4D

"Reliably good Italian food at fair prices" and particularly "switched-on service" won revitalised support this year for Angela Hartnett's "very serviceable" mini-chain, which is generally a "very safe choice", and – at its best – "memorable" in the level of "very confident" cooking it can achieve. Even fans, though, concede the "atmosphere can be a bit low key", in particular at the "rather gloomy" WC2 branch (and the best reports are at St James's). / www.cafemurano.co.uk; cafemurano.

Café Spice Namaste E16   £63   5 4 4
1-2 Lower Dock Walk, Royal Dock   020 7488 9242   12–1D

"Cyrus and Pervin Todiwala have done it again, with the new incarnation of their bastion of Indian and Parsee food", on the Royal Docks "just moments from London Excel and City Airport". "After 26 years, they moved from the fringe of the City in E1 to Royal Albert Wharf E16" and "the food and the personal service remain of the highest nature". "It's just such original and delicious cuisine", "especially on nights when Cyrus cooks Parsee (but it's always good anyway)". Unless you happen to live out that way, though, the new spot could be mistaken for "the middle of nowhere": "we travel over two hours to dine here: the new menu is delicious, the themed evenings a joy… but I wish they were back in Prescott Street!". / E16 2GT; www.cafespice.co.uk; cafespicenamasteldn; Tue-Sat 10 pm.

Caffè Caldesi W1 £86 3 3 2
118 Marylebone Ln   020 7487 0754   2–1A

"Very good Italian family food is served in a buzzy atmosphere" at chef Giancarlo Caldesi and his wife Katie's Marylebone flagship – *"all the classic dishes are available"*, accompanied by an *"interesting wine list"*. The couple also have a country restaurant in Bray and a cookery school, while Tuscany-born Giancarlo has written a healthy cookbook following his diagnosis as a diabetic. / W1U 2QF; www.caldesi.com; caldesiinmarylebone; Mon-Sat 10 pm, Sun 4.30 pm.

Cah Chi KT3
79-81 Kingston Road   020 8949 8880   1–4A

A new location for an old restaurant: this latest incarnation of a family-run business opened in New Malden – serving the sizable local Korean expat community – in spring 2023. Grace Dent of The Guardian visited in May 2023 and was a fan of its *"simple yet delicious"* cooking – *"Cah Chi isn't trying to change the world; it's just quietly representing skilful Korean cooking and creating a haven for hungry passers-by"*. / KT3 3PB; cahchi.co.uk; cahchibbq; Tue-Sat 10.30 pm, Sun 10 pm.

Caia W10 £69 4 3 3
46 Golborne Road   07927 328076   7–1A

"In a scruffy but lovely part of London, in the shadow of the Trellick Tower", this year-old, Portobello-fringe bar/restaurant is *"top notch"*. It serves *"small plates of interesting combinations charred on an open grill"* and *"bar seats offer great views of the actual cooking"*. Beyond the food, it's an *"excellent night out"* all round thanks to its *"warm ambience"*, helped along by a brilliantly curated vinyl collection. / W10 5PR; caia.london; caia.london; Tue-Thu midnight, Fri & Sat 1 am.

Cakes and Bubbles, Café Royal W1 £89 3 4 3
70 Regent Street   020 7406 3310   4–4C

"Living up to the naturally high expectations"; this prime site within the Café Royal, off Piccadilly Circus, wins praise – albeit on limited feedback this year – for the *"meticulous patisserie"* you would hope for from Albert Adrià (who, back in the day, was pastry chef at his brother Ferran's world-famous destination restaurant: El Bulli, long RIP). / W1B 4DY; www.cakesandbubbles.co.uk; cakesandbubbleslondon; Mon-Sun 9 pm.

The Camberwell Arms SE5 £67 4 4 4
65 Camberwell Church St   020 7358 4364   1–3C

The *"seasonal, generous and top-notch food"* at this *"great local"* in Camberwell is delivered via *"laid-back but professional service that exudes cool – much like the local clientele"*. Having established itself as one of the capital's best gastropubs over the past decade, there are no signs of easing off. Top Menu Tip – *"get the pork fat and Scotch bonnet toast"*. / SE5 8TR; www.thecamberwellarms.co.uk; thecamberwellarms; Wed-Sat, Tue 11 pm, Sun 5 pm.

Cambio de Tercio SW5 £87 3 3 3
161-163 Old Brompton Rd   020 7244 8970   6–2B

"You leave feeling everything is good in the world" according to fans of Abel Lusa's accomplished stalwart (est. 1995) on the borders of South Ken and Earl's Court: one of London's original Spanish restaurants of quality and still at the cutting edge, with its *"luxurious tapas"*, *"excellent Iberian wines"* and *"wonderfully fun and atmospheric"* style. A slip in ratings, though, accompanies one or two concerns that *"it should offer better value"*; or that *"it risks slipping from a smart and exciting place to being lower-energy"*. But that didn't stop Wimbledon winner Carlos Alcaraz from eating here with his family five times during the Championships this year – and on the days he

didn't go, he ordered deliveries to be sent to his accommodation. Apparently, his favourite dish is the crispy salmon nigiri (a Spanish version of sushi with sweet soy sauce, Spanish vinegar and chipotle mayonnaise). / SW5 0LJ; www.cambiodetercio.co.uk; cambiodetercio; Tue-Sat 11.30 pm, Sun & Mon 11 pm.

Camino £66 ②②②

3 Varnishers Yd, Regent Quarter, N1   020 7841 7330   9–3C
2 Curtain Road, EC2   020 3948 5003   13–2B
15 Mincing Ln, EC3   020 7841 7335   10–3D

"Reliable tapas in handy locations" is the USP of this 16-year-old trio with a flagship near King's Cross station (by far the best known) and offshoots in Shoreditch and Monument. But while they're "decent enough", they offer "standard fayre" – it's "nothing exceptional". / www.camino.uk.com; caminolondon.

The Campaner SW1

1 Garrison Close, Chelsea Barracks   020 4580 1385   6–3D

Opened shortly before the 2023 Chelsea Flower Show, this svelte looking newcomer – with coffee and light bites during the day and food from the Josper oven available at lunch and dinner – aims to be an anchor attraction of the nearby Chelsea Barracks development, and is operated by José Parrado (who runs a number of high-profile Barcelona restaurants). A glance at the menu's panic-inducing prices suggests the cost-of-living crisis is in full swing, with a tomato juice at £9, a bowl of chips at £8.50, and most mains on the lunch or dinner menu around the £40 mark. Nor is our only early feedback encouraging: "there is a lot of marketing hype on this place… do not believe it". / SW1W 8BP; thecampaner.com; thecampanerchelsea; Tue-Thu 11.30 pm, Fri & Sat midnight, Sun 5 pm.

Canto Corvino E1 £83 ②③③

21 Artillery Lane   020 7655 0390   13–2B

This modern Italian bar/restaurant by Spitalfields is consistently well-rated in all feedback. There's a continued theme from last year, however, that even fans of its antipasti, pasta and grills from the Josper oven can find it plain "overpriced". / E1 7HA; www.cantocorvino.co.uk; cantocorvino; Mon-Sat 9 pm.

Canton Arms SW8 £62 ③③④

177 South Lambeth Rd   020 7582 8710   11–1D

This "top-notch local boozer" in Stockwell offers arguably the "best pub food in South London" – "simple and hearty fare, but always served with verve and understanding" by on-the-ball service. Its slightly remoter address and a lack of theatres nearby means it is slightly less busy than its famous foodie stablemate, the Anchor & Hope in Waterloo. / SW8 1XP; www.cantonarms.com; Tue-Sat 9.45 pm, Sun 3.45 pm.

Capeesh E14 £56 ③③③

4 Pan Peninsula Square   020 7538 1111   12–2C

Dazzling views from the 48th-floor of a Canary Wharf tower help create a sense of occasion at this family-run, five-year-old Italian restaurant and 'Sky Bar'. Its long menu of pasta, pizza, grills and other fare doesn't inspire a huge volume of feedback, but the limited amount we have is all upbeat. / E14 9HN; www.capeesh.co.uk; capeeshlondon; Mon-Sun 10.30 pm.

Capri W4 NEW £52 ③③③

6 Turnham Green Terrace   020 8994 3800   8–2A

"Lovely fresh seafood" and "excellent pasta dishes" – everything "brimming with flavour" – have won an enthusiastic welcome for this "new Italian run by a very experienced team" in Turnham Green. Founders Ben and Michael have worked together for more than 20 years, running an independent restaurant in Italy and in five-star hotels. / W4 1QP; caprirestaurant.uk; caprirestaurant.uk; Tue-Thu 10 pm, Fri & Sat 11 pm, Sun 9 pm.

Caractère W11 £139 3|3|3
209 Westbourne Park Road   020 8181 3850   7–1B

"Run by Michel Roux's daughter" Emily and her husband Diego Ferrari (former head chef of Le Gavroche), this Notting Hill five-year-old "gives us the best of two culinary worlds: French and Italian". The "precise, thoughtful and delicious dishes (celeriac, crab, turbot, veal)…" are "real high-end comfort food" and the "dining room is cool and buzzy without being overly formal". "Both wine list and cheeseboard are on the conservative side, but none the worse for that"; and "the Italian sommelier has an encyclopaedic knowledge of Italian wines and will always steer us to something new and unusual". Some reports note a "post-Covid blip amidst staff changes", and a slip in ratings generally backs up those who feel the experience is "not bad, and better than average, but not quite the quality it was previously". Top Tip – "lunch is particularly good value". / W11 1EA; www.caractererestaurant.com; caractererestaurant; Tue-Sat 9 pm.

Caraffini SW1 £73 2|4|3
61-63 Lower Sloane St   020 7259 0235   6–2D

"Still as popular with its regular clientele as ever" – this "civilised old-favourite" near Sloane Square "doesn't change much", to the relief of its massive, silver-haired following ("you could do away with the menu, as all the customers know exactly what they will order before they arrive. It'll be the same as they've been ordering for the last 25 years!"). The traditional, "comfort-Italian" food is "reliable", but it's the "extremely courteous service and wonderful greeting" that really carries the day. Top Menu Tip – "best calves' liver in London". / SW1W 8DH; www.caraffini.co.uk; caraffinirestaurant; Mon-Sat 10.30 pm.

Caravaggio EC3 £66 2|3|2
107-112 Leadenhall St   020 7626 6206   10–2D

With its "classic menu" of "pricey but good-quality" food, this "friendly" Italian occupies a former banking hall in the heart of the City, where it entertains senior money men and women. Luciano Pavarotti, the late 'King of the High Cs', was a guest at its 1996 opening. / EC3A 4DP; www.caravaggiorestaurant.co.uk; caravaggio_ldn; Mon-Fri 10 pm.

Caravan £63 2|2|2
Yalding House, 152 Great Portland Street, W1   020 3963 8500   2–1B
30-35 Drury Lane, WC2   Awaiting tel   5–1D NEW
1 Granary Sq, N1   020 7101 7661   9–3C
30 Great Guildford St, SE1   020 7101 1190   10–4B
Unit 2, Reuters Plaza, E14   020 3725 7600   12–1C
11-13 Exmouth Mkt, EC1   020 7833 8115   10–1A
Queen Victoria Street, EC4   020 3957 5555   10–3C

"The most original brunches" – with "a good selection of super-tasty, tapas-style dishes" fusing eclectic flavours from the Middle East to the Pacific – are the top feature of these "nicely vibey" haunts, which also boast "great coffee and pastries, plus interesting non-alcoholic drinks (like sodas and kombuchas)". And they serve "lots for vegans and veggies too". On the downside, they become "noisy"; staff can be "overstretched" and ratings are dragged down by those who find them "a convenient option, but, in truth, a slightly disappointing one". Expansion is still on the cards, though, with 2023 seeing a big new opening in Covent Garden, in a workspace on Drury Lane, complete with outside terrace. / www.caravanonexmouth.co.uk.

Caravel N1 £49 **4 4 4**
172 Shepherdess Walk   020 7251 1155   14–2A

"So romantic!": "down a hidden waterway alley" near Angel, this debut venture from brothers Lorcan and Fin Spiteri – sons of John Spiteri (Quo Vadis, Sessions Arts Club) and Melanie Arnold (Rochelle Canteen) – is by all accounts "a little oasis of beauty". "Start the night with a cocktail on the jetty, then head down the stairs into a lovely converted barge with low-level lighting", where "very impressive Italian-leaning food is achieved in a tiny kitchen". / N1 7ED; thestudiokitchen.co.uk; caravel_restaurant; Thu-Sat, Wed 11 pm, Sun 4 pm.

Carlotta W1 **NEW**
77-78 Marylebone High Street   no tel   2–1A

"FUN FUN FUN!" – that's practically the only feedback we have so far on Big Mamma Group's fifth London opening, which threw open its doors in Marylebone in May 2023, just as our survey was concluding. Decked out in the maximalist style that characterises their approach – here it's a riff on a retro, Italian-glam theme with acres of ruched wall material, wood panelling, dark leather seating and loud carpeting. Cutting down on the calories? – don't go for the 10-tiered chocolate fudge cake... in fact, maybe avoid most of the Italian/American menu... / W1U 5JX; www.bigmammagroup.com; bigmamma.uk; Mon-Thu 9.30 pm, Fri & Sat 10, Sun 9 pm.

Carmel NW6 £68 **5 3 4**
Lonsdale Road   020 3848 2090   1–2B

"Interesting Israeli/Middle Eastern dishes" served in a "fun, vibey setting" have created a big winner for the Berber & Q team at this Queen's Park two-year-old: a "great neighbourhood addition". "There are super veg options, but also fab meat and fish ones too". "The large shared table might not be for everyone" although there is also some more conventional seating (mostly for couples). Top Tip – the small terrace in summer is particularly "nice, as there are no cars outside". / NW6 6RR; www.carmelrestaurant.co.uk; carmelrestaurantldn; Tue-Sat 11 pm.

Carousel W1 £72 **4 4 2**
19-23 Charlotte Street   020 7487 5564   2–1C

"Buy your ticket and wait and see... the chefs give their all and I've never had a disappointing evening!" – typical feedback on this Fitzrovia venue, whose "signature is a rotating selection of outstanding chefs cooking at the top of their game, for just a few weeks at a time" from the open kitchen. "It is a showroom (or perhaps a labour exchange!) for the rising stars of international dining... often the room is full of extra affection and praise as the chef's family or colleagues from past brigades offer enthusiastic support. The courses are skillful and generous, and stints reflect a wide range of global experience". "It's hard to compare the different chefs, but the standard generally is so high and service is very well done". / W1T 1RL; www.carousel-london.com; carousel_ldn; Tue-Sat midnight, Sun 6 pm.

The Carpenter's Arms W6 £62 **3 3 3**
91 Black Lion Ln   020 8741 8386   8–2B

A superior backstreet boozer in the cute enclave near Hammersmith's posh St Peter's Square – a "lovely spot" with a sweet garden serving a menu that's ambitious for pub cooking. / W6 9BG; www.carpentersarmsw6.co.uk; thecarpentersarmsw6; Mon-Sat 9 pm, Sun 6 pm.

Casa do Frango **£56** 3|3|5
Sir Simon Milton Square, SW1   no tel   2–4B NEW
31-32 Heddon Street, W1   020 3535 5900   4–3A NEW
32 Southwark Street, SE1   020 3972 2323   10–4C
3 King John Court, EC2   020 7654 3020   13–1B
"I would never have imagined chicken 'n' chips could be so delicious! It's like being on a mini holiday!" – the original, "über-busy" SE1 branch of this growing chain of "posh Nandos" is a smash hit. "The yummy food, the fabulous greenery, the buzzy atmosphere, the extensive vinho verde wine list. Who'd have thought such a gem would be found under a grubby railway arch in South London!" Expanding under owners MJMK (who also own Lisboeta and Kol), the group has a less-high-profile Shoreditch spin-off, and is also set to open in 2023 in Victoria, on the site last occupied by Hai Cenato (RIP). Top Tips – don't just stick to the peri-peri chicken – look out for the African rice, chorizo and other menu options. Also, at SE1 "there is a downstairs, but try to eat upstairs in the lovely loft-style space, with plenty of light and enough plants to require a full time gardener!"
/ www.casadofrango.co.uk; casadofrango_london.

Casa Fofó E8 **£80** 4|3|3
158 Sandringham Road   020 8062 2489   14–1B
"The depth of flavour which Adolfo brings out in his ever-changing menus means we visit at least once or sometimes twice a month: nowhere else would we ever dream of doing the same!" – Adolfo de Cecco's Hackney shop-conversion is "always a pleasure for its inventive dishes", which meld Asian influences with European ingredients into an intriguing and individual culinary mashup. At any one time, there is a single tasting option, and he "manages to maintain high standards with each iteration". "The front room is arguably more dull than the very light rear area, which is a sort of conservatory. And there are interesting choices of music at low levels".
/ E8 2HS; www.casafofolondon.co.uk; casafofolondon; Wed-Sun 9.30 pm.

Casa Pastór & Plaza Pastór N1 **£59** 2|2|2
Coal Drops Yard   020 7018 3335   9–3C
Within the arches of ever-so-hip Coal Drops Yard, this Hart Bros spin-off was one of the first tenants of the development. Surprisingly, given the trendy locale and regular queues, feedback in our annual diners' poll on its mix of tacos, tostadas and sharing plates is thin on the ground and rather lukewarm. / N1C 4AB; www.tacoselpastor.co.uk; tacos_el_pastor; Tue-Sat 11 pm, Sun 8 pm.

Casse-Croute SE1 **£69** 4|3|4
109 Bermondsey St   020 7407 2140   10–4D
"Visited with French friends. Their verdict: better than Paris! They loved it" – this "proper Gallic bistro" in Bermondsey is "very popular for good reasons", including "impeccable food" and a "delightful" atmosphere. It offers "a simple daily changing menu of three starters, three mains, and three desserts all done well, plus classic Gallic service". / SE1 3XB; www.cassecroute.co.uk; cassecroute109; Mon-Sat 10.30 pm, Sun 4.30 pm.

Cavita W1 £85 3 2 3
55 Wigmore Street 020 3928 1000 3–1B
"Confidently spiced, really excellent Mexican dishes" washed down with "brilliant cocktails" have won high acclaim from aficionados of Latino cuisine for Adriana Cavita's lively Fitzrovia yearling, which – according to the FT's Tim Hayward – "redefines the city's Mexican food scene". Not all our reporters are quite as sure though, a typical report being: "pretty good, but it needed something more to give it the wow factor". It doesn't help that the menu can strike first-timers as "incomprehensible"; and on some occasions staff can be "inarticulate" in explaining it. / W1U 1PU; www.cavitarestaurant.com; cavita.restaurante; Tue-Sun 10.15 pm.

Cay Tre £48 3 3 2
42-43 Dean St, W1 020 7317 9118 5–2A
301 Old St, EC1 020 7729 8662 13–1B
"Thoughtful" Vietnamese food is served at "fabulous prices for the generous portions" at this duo in Soho and Hoxton from Hieu Trung Bui, who has done much to popularise pho and other southeast Asian dishes in London over more than 20 years. That "plenty of Asian people eat there too" speaks for its "authentic" style. / www.caytrerestaurant.co.uk; caytrerestaurant.

Cecconi's £87 2 3 3
19-21 Old Compton Street, W1 020 7734 5656 5–2A
5a Burlington Gdns, W1 020 7434 1500 4–4A
58-60 Redchurch Street, E2 020 3841 7755 13–1C
The Ned, 27 Poultry, EC2 020 3828 2000 10–2C
Sit at the bar where there's "Prosecco on tap" and hang with the Mayfair glam crowd at this "always buzzy" and "professional" Italian brasserie in Burlington Gardens, at the back of the Royal Academy: "a favourite for some good people watching". Nowadays part of Soho House, "there's something for everyone on the menu" and it's a favoured lunch spot for local business types. On the downside, prices are high, the food is "average" and service can be so-so. (Reports on its Soho 'Pizza Bar' spin-off and City branches are few and far between). / cecconis.co.uk; cecconislondon.

Cedric Grolet at The Berkeley SW1 £97 3 4 3
Wilton Place 020 7235 1200 6–1D
Parisian über-pâtissier Cedric Grolet's first outpost outside Paris (which opened in early 2022) is to be found at this bright, chic bakery, within the swish Knightsbridge 5-star. Internationally he is renowned for his Insta-friendly, trompe l'oeil fruit and flowers – amongst London's fooderati he's famous for charging £135 per head for the chef-counter experience. We have maintained its (fairly good) rating on the basis of complimentary, if limited, feedback this year. But some other reviewers sound a warning note, including that of Tanya Gold in the March 2023 Spectator who concluded: "It's too flimsy – too credulous, too fragile – to hate, and soon, like Dorothy [in The Wizard of Oz], it will blow away". / SW1X 8RL; www.the-berkeley.co.uk; cedricgrolettheberkeley; Mon-Sun 7 pm.

Cent Anni SW19 £58 3 3 3
33 High Street 020 3971 9781 11–2B
"Standing out from the chain restaurants in the area, this vibrant Italian-inspired restaurant in the heart of Wimbledon Village" has a big fan club drawn from neighbouring postcodes. The more cautious view is that "it's nothing spectacular but the food standard is reliable with some good mid-week deals". / SW19 5BY; centanni.co.uk; centannirestaurant; Mon-Sat 11 pm, Sun 10.30 pm.

Cepages W2 £60 3 2 4
69 Westbourne Park Road   020 3602 8890   7–1B
"Great vibe", "wonderful cooking", "super wine list" and "so, so French!" – this "friendly and authentic" little wine bar/bistro in Westbourne Park celebrates its tenth anniversary this year. / W2 5QH; www.cepages.co.uk; cepages_london; Mon-Sat 11 pm, Sun 10 pm.

Ceru £43 3 2 2
7-9 Bute St, SW7   020 3195 3001   6–2C
13 Queensway, W2   020 7221 2535   7–2C
"Ever-reliable, ultra-tasty sharing plates" and "brisk but jolly service" are the order of the day at "this buzzy South Ken local" (and its Queensway offshoot) from Barry & Patricia Hamilton. The "interesting" mix of Greek and Middle Eastern cuisines is backed up by a "very different wine list – Lebanese, Macedonian, Greek, Armenian". / www.cerurestaurants.com; ceruLondon.

Ceviche Soho W1 £60 3 2 3
17 Frith St   020 7292 2040   5–2A
This fresh Peruvian small-plates specialist is "still a lovely place for lunch in Soho", with "a range of interesting small plates to share". Some long-term fans feel it "doesn't quite reach the heady heights of yesteryear" (it opened in 2012) but that's maybe more to do with the capital's increasing familiarity with this style of cooking. / W1D 4RG; cevichelondon.com; cevicheuk; Mon-Sat 11.30 pm, Sun 10.30 pm.

Chakra W8 £59 3 3 3
33c Holland Street   020 7229 2115   6–1A
"Fragrant and tasty dishes" win approval at this cute Indian hidden away in a Kensington backstreet. Its siblings in Little Venice, Barnes and Kingston get very little notice from reporters. / W8 4LX; www.chakralondon.com; chakralondon; Tue-Thu 10 pm, Fri & Sat 10.30 pm, Sun 9 pm.

Champor-Champor SE1 £65 3 2 4
62 Weston St   020 7403 4600   10–4C
Unusual, eclectically decorated venue with an interesting Thai-Malay menu, in a sidestreet near Guy's Hospital and London Bridge station – it no longer attracts the attention it did a decade ago, but its ratings remain pretty solid. / SE1 3QJ; www.champor-champor.com; champorchamporldn; Mon-Sat 10 pm, Sun 9.30 pm.

Charlie's at Brown's, Brown's Hotel W1 £118 4 5 5
Albemarle Street   020 7493 6020   3–3C
"The great Jesus Adorno and his team (aided by his no. 2 Paul Stabbins) have brought the charm and atmosphere of the hugely missed Le Caprice" to this "very smooth operation" within Rocco Forte's London flagship hotel, which fans say is "the new classiest place in town" (Adorno joined in 2021). It occupies a fine, panelled dining room that for traditionalists is "one of the loveliest in the capital", complete with "marvellous spacious tables". Since 2019, Adam Byatt (of Trinity, see also) has overseen the kitchen, which gives a modern spin to the preparation of top British ingredients: "wonderful" if not especially foodie. BREAKING NEWS: in early September 2023, it was announced that Jesus would be leaving Charlie's to re-join Jeremy King in founding a new restaurant back on the site of Le Caprice (but under a different name). These will be big shoes to fill here... / W1S 4BP; www.roccofortehotels.com; browns_hotel; Mon-Sun 10 pm.

Chateau W4 £52 3 4 2
213 Chiswick High Road 020 8742 2344 8–2A
"Cake shop by day, Lebanese by night" – this "very friendly and welcoming" spot on Chiswick High Road is an "excellent spot for lunch and a good dinner venue, too". "I've recently discovered their breakfasts – awesome!". / W4 2DW; chateau-chiswick.com; chateau_chiswick; Mon-Sun 10 pm.

The Cheese Barge W2 £56 2 3 3
Sheldon Square 07862 001418 7–1C
Mathew Carver's floating ode to the cheeses of Britain and Ireland is a 96 ft double-decker barge moored in Paddington Basin that delights turophiles with cheese-based meals accompanied by a "nice selection of wines at a reasonable price", with simpler cheese boards and toasties available in the afternoon. The group also operates a cheese conveyor belt in Seven Dials and a new cheese and natural wine bar, Funk, in Shoreditch. / W2 6HY; www.thecheesebar.com; thecheesebarldn; Tue-Sun 11 pm.

Cher Thai SW4 £47 3 4 3
22 North Street 020 3583 3702,Ää 11–1D
The "warm welcome, good food and great prices all impress" at this "simple Thai restaurant" in Clapham, from a husband-and-wife team who are "trying to elevate it above the 'standard UK Thai' menu and doing a good job". The result: "a buzzing place with happy-looking customers". / SW4 0HB; www.cherthailondon.co.uk; cherthailondon; Tue, Thu, Wed 10.30 pm, Fri & Sat 11 pm, Sun 10 pm.

Chet's,
Hoxton Hotel W12 NEW £44 3 3 3
65 Shepherd's Bush Green 020 3540 3150 8–1C
"Part of the ongoing gentrification of Shepherd's Bush" – LA chef Kris Yenbamroong has found a permanent showcase for his US-style 'nu Thai' cuisine at the new Hoxton Hotel overlooking Shepherd's Bush Green. It's "surprisingly fun"… "lively, tasty, and fairly priced". The food is brash and impactful ("I had a delish bowl of fries, deep-fried chicken wings with hot sauce and tuna melt sandwich with a refreshing lychee lemonade"), while "large rounds of beer heading to most tables often contributes to the merriment". A few reporters do have quibbles – that the "sharing plate concept doesn't really work gastronomically"; or that the "LA influence is too horribly sweet, missing out on the salty and sour components of good Thai cooking". But even some critics feel it's "finding its feet: I've been back four times since December and the menu improves each visit". / W12 8QE; www.chetsrestaurant.co.uk; chets_ldn; Fri & Sat 1 am, Sun-Thu midnight.

Chez Antoinette £47 3 3 2
The Caxton, 22 Palmer Street, SW1 020 3990 5377 2–4C
Unit 30 The Market Building, WC2 020 7240 9072 5–3D
This "bustling bistrot tucked down a side street near Victoria" feels "just like being in a small, rushed French café". Lyon-born founder Aurelia Noel-Delclos named the business after the grandmother who inspired her love of food. The 10-year-old original branch, in the tourist 'ground zero' of old Covent Garden market, is less reported-on, but said to be "decent" for "post-matinée early dinner".

Chez Bruce SW17 £110 5 5 3
2 Bellevue Rd   020 8672 0114   11–2C

"Long live Chez Bruce!". It has "a neighbourhood feel", but Bruce Poole's "jewel in south west London's crown" by Wandsworth Common is one of the capital's most revered restaurants and – for the 18th year running – is voted Londoner's No.1 favourite in our annual diners' poll. Key to its appeal is the delivery of "top quality, but without the pretensions of some places". Chef Matt Christmas has worked with Bruce for over 10 years, and the kitchen produces modern British dishes that are "very memorable", but "without being fussy or fad-ish, nor horrendously overpriced". "Doing simple food this well is the ultimate in difficulty, there is just nowhere to hide!" "Professional and friendly service continues to excel", "seemingly effortlessly delivering a superb feeling of conviviality" and enlivening a space that's "classy and understated", but not intrinsically that special. "Bruce himself frequently still wanders around the dining room greeting and chatting informally to diners" and the whole operation practically "never puts a foot wrong". That all this can be enjoyed "without breaking the bank" seals the "absolute pleasure of eating there". / SW17 7EG; www.chezbruce.co.uk; chez.bruce; Tue-Thu 9.15 pm, Fri & Sat 9.30 pm, Sun 9 pm.

Chez Elles E1 £61 3 3 3
45 Brick Ln   020 7247 9699   13–2C

"A simple menu with unexpectedly great food" is to be found at this 'bistroquet' on Brick Lane, which has flown the Tricolor in curry country for the past 11 years with a parade of Gallic classics including snails, frogs' legs and veal sweetbreads. / E1 6PU; www.chezellesbistroquet.co.uk; chezellesbistro; Tue-Sat 11.30 pm.

Chicama SW10 £91 3 3 3
383 King's Road   020 3874 2000   6–3C

"I keep coming back for all the ceviches" at this "excellent Peruvian seafood specialist" on the King's Road in Chelsea – an offshoot from Pachamama in Marylebone. The atmosphere is lively, too, although some reckon the music is just "too loud". / SW10 0LP; www.chicamalondon.com; Mon-Fri 11 pm, Sat & Sun 4 pm.

Chick 'n' Sours £43 4 3 3
1 Earlham Street, WC2   020 3198 4814   5–2B
390 Kingsland Rd, E8   020 3620 8728   14–2A

"Full marks" say fans of the fried-chicken burgers, sarnies and other crispy poultry treats at these Haggerston and Covent Garden pit-stops. Order 48 hours in advance and you can enjoy the 'Whole Fry' – at £35 it's their 'iconic whole fried chicken' with two sides and the dressing of your choice… / www.chicknsours.co.uk; chicknsours.

The Chiltern Firehouse W1 £113 2 2 4
1 Chiltern St   020 7073 7676   2–1A

"It may not be quite as high on 'places to be seen' lists as it used to be", but – "having made a name for itself as a celebrity hotspot" – this beautiful-crowd haunt in Marylebone is proving surprisingly enduring. "You're paying a pretty hefty premium for the trendy location": "the food/price ratio is off kilter, as the food really is not good and outrageously expensive". But does anyone care? For its many fans "you can't go wrong with the Firehouse – it always feels like a treat!" ("Our daughter was excited to spot one of David Beckham's sons and his girlfriend, so extra brownie points for me. LOL!") / W1U 7PA; www.chilternfirehouse.com; Mon-Sun 10 pm.

China Tang,
Dorchester Hotel W1   £112   3 3 4
53 Park Ln   020 7319 7088   3–3A

"Gorgeous" decor taking inspiration from 1930s Shanghai (particularly in the marvellous, small cocktail bar) has always won admiration for this deluxe basement (originally created by the late Sir David Tang). When it opened in 2005, it was a pioneer of serving dim sum at any time of day, but there's also a full menu offering blow-out dishes to share for £200-£300 including Peking duck with caviar, suckling pig, abalone and seafood hotpot. Complaints about pricing were absent this year, and praise for the cuisine and "romantic" atmosphere on the up. / W1K 1QA; www.chinatanglondon.co.uk; chinatanglondon; Mon-Sun 11 pm.

La Chingada SE8   £16   3 3 2
206 Lower Road   020 7237 7448   12–2B

This "surprisingly good Mexican café in the back of nowhere" – well, deepest Surrey Quays – even imports soft drinks from Mexico for added authenticity. Top Menu Tip – "the prawn tacos are great – crispy, juicy and they come with a fiery salsa". / SE8 5DJ; lachingada.co.uk; lachingadalondon; Tue-Sat 10 pm, Sun 9 pm.

Chishuru W1   £52
3 Great Titchfield St   07960 002150   3–1C

Adejoké 'Joké' Bakare moved in September 2023 to this new, 50-cover Fitzrovia location, having closed the SW9 site where she won the Brixton Kitchen competition in 2019 for her original supper club, offering the dishes of her Nigerian childhood but 'given a London sensibility'. Open-fire cooking will be a feature as well as an extended pastry selection. It has been very highly PR'd though, so let's hope it lives up to all the coverage – even in the former location there was the odd review along the lines of: "nice people, but disappointing after the hype". / W1W 8AX; www.chishuru.com; chishuru.

Chisou   £76   4 3 2
22-23 Woodstock Street, W1   020 7629 3931   4–1A
31 Beauchamp Pl, SW3   020 3155 0005   6–1D

The "absolute dogs for real Japanese dining" – this "authentic" duo in Mayfair (the original – "a welcome oasis from Oxford Street") and Knightsbridge (in posh Beauchamp Place) offer "exemplary sushi and cooked dishes" backed up by "a wide sake list". "As is always the case with this cuisine, it's never cheap, but great for a treat". / www.chisourestaurant.com; chisoulondon.

Chook Chook SW15   £46   4 3 4
137 Lower Richmond Road   020 8789 3100   11–1B

This "great little local" in Putney "bills itself as an Indian railway kitchen and leans into the theme very nicely – the decor feels like an old-school carriage, and much of the menu is based on genuine street food, taken up a notch". It's certainly "not your standard curry house", and the "fresh, flavourful dishes are full of individual tastes". "It can be tricky to get a table if you don't book ahead, but once you're in, service is attentive". / SW15 1EZ; chookchook.uk; chookchooklondon_; Mon-Thu 10.30 pm, Fri & Sat 11 pm, Sun 10 pm.

Chotto Matte   £73   4 4 4
11-13 Frith St, W1   020 7042 7171   5–2A
26 Paddington Street, W1   020 7058 4444   2–1A

Kurt Zdesar's "loud and dark" haunts promise a culinary journey from Tokyo to Lima with some "brill cocktails" thrown in. It's "great fun" and the Nikkei food is an "interesting fusion" too, if also a pricey one. Since 2022, the London presence has doubled with the addition of a Marylebone branch to join the first Soho one. It also has six siblings in North America and a couple in the Middle East. / chotto-matte.com; chottomatteldn.

Chourangi W1 £66 443
3 Old Quebec Street   020 3582 2710   2–2A
*"Craft cocktails and delicious upscale street food in a swank setting" is the
proposition at this interesting Marble Arch two-year-old named after a
historically important district of Calcutta (from chef-patron Anjan Chatterjee
and airline entrepreneur Aditya Ghosh). "Finding good Bengali food from
Calcutta has been a struggle, but not any more!" – this is "a taste of real
Indian regional food crafted using exceptional ingredients which elevate the
flavours of each dish". / W1H 7DL; chourangi.co.uk; chourangildn; Sun-Thu 10 pm,
Fri & Sat 10.30 pm.*

Christopher's WC2 £102 223
18 Wellington St   020 7240 4222   5–3D
*This stunning Covent Garden mansion (once a high-class brothel) is named
for the son of one of Thatcher's cabinet ministers, who launched it in its
current guise as a grand American restaurant; and for about a decade it was
the height of fashion. It retains a "great atmosphere" – and also, something
of a following for business, brunch and its martini bar. But, given its location
and dramatic interior, it attracts remarkably little feedback these days.
/ WC2E 7DD; www.christophersgrill.com; christopherswc2; Tue-Sat 10 pm, Sun
3.30 pm.*

Chucs £94 223
25 Eccleston Street, SW1   020 3827 3000   2–4B
65 Lower Sloane Street, SW1   020 3827 2999   6–2D
31 Dover St, W1   020 3763 2013   3–3C
97 Old Brompton Road, SW7   020 8037 4525   6–2B
*Inspired by La Dolce Vita lifestyle (indeed, there used to be an accompanying
apparel resort-wear brand), this small Italian group strives to evoke the retro
glamour of the 1960s 'jet set'. There's some enthusiasm for them amongst
reporters, but a recognition that the food is "nice but not exceptional": "I
had an excellent martini. But the dishes were either overly seasoned or (the
salad) not dressed at all". / www.chucsrestaurants.com; chucsrestaurants.*

Chuku's N15 £65 343
274 High Road   no tel   1–1D
*"Billed as the first Nigerian tapas restaurant in London – this small but
buzzy venue" in Seven Sisters "provides a modern spin on traditional
Nigerian cuisine". The "friendly" siblings behind the project, Emeka and
Ifeyinwa Frederick (motto 'chop, chat, chill'), attracted headlines in early
2023 when they were selected for an £8,000 grant by the BeyGood
Foundation during the London leg of Beyoncé's world tour. / N15 5AJ;
www.chukuslondon.co.uk; chukusldn; Tue-Sat 10.30 pm, Sun 8.30 pm.*

Chungdam W1 NEW
35-36 Greek Street   020 7287 0526   5–2A
*On the Soho-fringe site of the much-lamented YMing (RIP), this April 2023
newcomer is a Korean BBQ bringing the pyeonbaek steam box to London –
a three-tiered box made from hinoki wood, a type of cypress. It's named
after Cheongdam-dong, an affluent – and foodie – district of Gangnam in
Seoul. It opened too late to inspire survey feedback – reports please!
/ W1D 5DL; chungdam.co.uk; chungdam.london; Mon-Sat midnight.*

Church Road SW13 £74 3 4 2
94 Church Road 020 8748 0393 11–1A
Fans of Rebecca Mascarenhas's Barnes fixture (which some may still recall as Sonny's, long RIP) say it "deserves higher recognition and praise", benefitting as it does from "the Phil Howard magic" (the co-owner, who lives nearby) in delivering "excellent" food (for example, "a perfect lobster and chips lunch") and a "thoughtfully compiled wine list". But what is a "sophisticated setting" for many supporters can also appear to "lack atmosphere". / SW13 0DQ; www.churchroadsw13.co.uk; churchroadsw13; Wed, Sat 10 pm, Thu & Fri 10.30 pm, Sun 3 pm.

Churchill Arms W8 £47 3 2 4
119 Kensington Church St 020 7792 1246 7–2B
"Still a first choice for a fun, good-value Thai meal" – the "freshly cooked" scoff in the "bonkers" flower-filled dining conservatory of this quirky 1750 tavern, near Notting Hill Gate, still makes it a top destination for the budget conscious. Popularity comes at a price, though – "booking is essential after 6pm". Top Tip – the pub itself is worth a visit too – it was renamed in the statesman's honour, and his grandparents visited in the Victorian era. / W8 7LN; www.churchillarmskensington.co.uk; churchillarmsw8; Mon-Sat 9.30 pm, Sun 9 pm.

Chutney Mary SW1 £91 4 4 4
73 St James's Street 020 7629 6688 3–4D
"Always a good experience" – this "upmarket Indian" in St James's is the original venture of Ranjit & Namita Mathrani, plus the latter's sister, Camellia Panjabi (who run other top Indians and the Masala Zone chain). One of London's first 'nouvelle Indians' (when it opened, on its former site, in SW10), its "complex and well-balanced" dishes are "done well enough to let them off the high prices" and served in a great space, whose "wonderful décor gives it character". Rishi's a regular apparently. / SW1A 1PH; www.chutneymary.com; chutneymary.london; Mon-Sat 10 pm, Sun 9.15 pm.

Chutneys NW1 £25 3 3 2
124 Drummond St 020 7388 0604 9–4C
"A stalwart on London's cheap-eats itinerary for decades" – this canteen in the 'Little India' enclave behind Euston station "has moved a smidgen upmarket since the pandemic". Top Tip – the "lovely fixed-price vegetarian buffet" – a "longstanding favourite" – remains in place at lunchtime. / NW1 2PA; www.chutneyseuston.uk; chutneysnw1; Mon-Sat 11 pm, Sun 10 pm.

Ciao Bella WC1 £54 3 4 5
86-90 Lamb's Conduit St 020 7242 4119 2–1D
"You could be in Italy" at this "authentic" old-school trattoria that has provided four decades of its "great atmosphere" in Bloomsbury – "it's like being at home but with no washing up". "Everyone looks like they are enjoying themselves" – as Boris Johnson did in his days as Mayor of London, when he shared chips and house red here with his squeeze-du-jour, Jennifer Arcuri. / WC1N 3LZ; www.ciaobellarestaurant.co.uk; ciaobella_london; Mon-Sat 10.45 pm, Sun 10.30 pm.

Cibo W14 £81 4 4 4
3 Russell Gdns 020 7371 6271 8–1D
This tasteful backstreet 1980s Italian, with interesting art on the walls, sits in the no-man's-land between Kensington and Olympia; and has become less well-known since the death of Michael Winner ten years ago (who used to plug it remorselessly in The Sunday Times as his favourite restaurant). Its quiet virtues as a high quality and authentic venture have changed little over the years: "still love this venue, but best to go in the week when the kitchen isn't too busy". Top Menu Tip – go for fish and seafood here. / W14 8EZ; www.ciborestaurant.net; Mon-Sat 9.45 pm.

Cigalon WC2 £62 3 4 4
115 Chancery Lane   020 7242 8373   2–2D
A glass-ceilinged former auction house in Chancery Lane is home to this homage to Provençal cuisine from Pascal Aussignac's Club Gascon group – making it an "excellent place for a business lunch in an otherwise under-served area". Plus points include an interesting list of southern French and Corsican wines, and the downstairs cocktail bar Baranis. Top Tip – "ask for a booth to celebrate a special occasion". / WC2A 1PP; www.cigalon.co.uk; cigalon_london; Tue-Fri 9 pm.

Cilantro Putney SW15 NEW £70 4 4 2
244 Upper Richmond Road   02033439317   11–2B
'Fresh, Tasty, Healthy' is the mantra at this November 2022 newcomer on the site of Ma Goa (RIP), which aims for a "modern" variant of Indian cuisine. The first UK outpost of a family-owned group with restaurants in India itself – its "above average" standards make it a worthy successor to its long-established predecessor. / SW15 6TG; www.cilantro.london; cilantro_london; Tue-Sat 10.30 pm, Sun 9 pm.

Cinder £82 3 3 2
66 Belsize Lane, NW3   020 7435 8048   9–2A
5 St John's Wood High Street, NW8   0207 4358 048   9–3A NEW
This "superb, cosy local" in Belsize Park now also has an offshoot that's proving "a great addition to St John's Wood". The focus is on "interesting food cooked with fire" from chef-owner Jake Finn (ex-LPM and The Ritz), who takes inspiration from Mediterranean, Peru and Japan: "a sharing concept from a menu that's not huge but with good variety and lots of veggie options". Both sites provide "wonderful combinations, simply done", with meat, fish and veggies that are "both charred and succulent". "It's not inexpensive, but great value given the quality of ingredients and cleverness of the cuisine". Top Menu Tip – "whole sea bream, fennel, radish and fresh herbs is a standout". / www.cinderrestaurant.co.uk; cinder_london.

Cinnamon Bazaar WC2 £64 5 4 3
28 Maiden Lane   020 7395 1400   5–4D
"From the pricing, you'd be forgiven for expecting a 'standard' Indian restaurant", but Vivek Singh's popular café is "surprisingly good" to those who've not yet discovered it and delivers outstanding value for somewhere in Covent Garden. "The menu is anything but run-of-the-mill, with interesting and creative twists on classics and some wholly new creations". The worst gripe this year? It can get "too noisy when it's packed". / WC2E 7NA; www.cinnamon-bazaar.com; thecinnamoncollection; Mon-Sat 11 pm, Sun 10 pm.

The Cinnamon Club SW1 £82 4 4 5
Old Westminster Library, Great Smith St   020 7222 2555   2–4C
"Fantastic food in a fabulous building – what more could you ask for?" So say fans of Vivek Singh's "impressive" HQ "in the beautiful setting of Westminster's former public library", which remains the most-mentioned non-European restaurant in our annual diners' poll. The "progressive" cuisine is "perfectly spiced and brings together the best of Indian and European cooking" with "exquisite" results. The "lovely light, spacious and glamorous" setting "lends real class to the occasion", but "it isn't stuffy, and staff are very welcoming". "It's just a shame so many politicians eat here too!" Top Tip – "the lunch menu offers exceptional value for money". / SW1P 3BU; www.cinnamonclub.com; thecinnamoncollection; Mon-Sat 11 pm; SRA-2 stars.

Cinnamon Kitchen £60 **4 3 3**
4 Arches Lane, SW11   020 3955 5480   11–1C
9 Devonshire Sq, EC2   020 7626 5000   10–2D
"Attractive Indians with a good range of different dishes" – Vivek Singh's
dynamic duo of affordable spin-offs from his celebrated Cinnamon Club
inspire practically nothing but high praise. The long-established City outlet set
inside a rather 1980s atrium development is "a solid option around
Liverpool Street" (although at times "the cavernous interior can feel a bit
odd and echoey"); the newer Battersea branch occupies a railway arch near
the power station and feels "different" (in a good way).
/ www.cinnamon-kitchen.com; cinnamonrestaurants; SRA-2 stars.

Cinquecento £51 **3 3 3**
6 Greek St, W1   020 7287 7705   5–2A **NEW**
1 Cale Street, SW3   020 7351 9331   6–2C
115 Notting Hill Gate, W11   020 7792 8881   7–2B
233 Portobello Road, W11   020 3915 3797   7–1A
73 Haverstock Hill, NW3   020 7483 0113   9–2A **NEW**
"Top pizza by the boys from Napoli!" – Carmelo Meli and Emanuele
Tagliarina's "small" venues offer "great pizzas" (it's down to the San
Marzano tomatoes and EVO oil apparently) and "a good atmosphere". The
original in SW3 is the highest rated, and W11 also wins numerous
favourable reports. Also now in Hampstead (since 2022) and – new in mid-
2023 – Soho. / cinquecentopizzeria.com; cinquecentopizzeria.

Circolo Popolare W1 £64 **3 4 5**
40-41 Rathbone Square   no tel   5–1A
"Massive, Instagram-tastic and buzzy" – Paris-based Big Mamma Group's
Sicilian trattoria in Fitzrovia is "great for a night out with the kids". "If only
as much thought had been put into the food as the decor!" – although to be
fair, the simple and generous Italian dishes are served at a quality and price
that most find very acceptable. / W1T 1HX; www.bigmammagroup.com;
bigmamma.uk; Mon-Sat 10.30 pm, Sun 10 pm.

Citro N6 £62 **4 4 2**
15A Swain's Lane   07840 917586   9–1B
This "authentic Italian" in Highgate "with an ever-changing seasonal menu"
is "run by two brothers", Nunzio & Salvatore, who ensure that everything is
"freshly made by hand" – ranging from pasta and pizza to "Dad's home-
made cannolis" and "interesting small plates such as chickpea fritters with
lemon mayonnaise or grilled lamb skewers with salsa Siciliana". The
"attentive and welcoming service" makes it ideal for "casual lunch, family
dinner or romantic meal". / N6 6QX; www.eatcitro.com; citro_restaurant; Tue-Sat
10 pm.

City Barge W4 £61 **2 2 3**
27 Strand-on-the-Green   020 8994 2148   1–3A
"I can forgive any failings for the riverside location", say fans of this pub at
Strand-on-the-Green, "on the Thames near Chiswick" – a "great local" with
"reliable food… nothing challenging". / W4 3PH; www.citybargechiswick.com;
citybargew4; Mon-Fri 11 pm.

City Social EC2 £122 ③③④
Tower 42 25 Old Broad St   020 7877 7703   10–2C
"Beautiful views from the old NatWest Tower" help seal the deal at Jason Atherton's City outpost. *"It feels quite corporate but is a good place for business"*, and wins many recommendations from expense-accounters as their top venue for wining and dining. *"The food is always very good with a good seasonal choice on the menu. Staff are well trained and happy to spend time chatting to guests even when they're busy. The setting is unique overlooking the Square Mile and the ambience is special"*. / EC2N 1HQ; www.citysociallondon.com; citysocial_t42; Tue-Sat 9.30 pm.

The Clarence Tavern N16 £66 ③③③
102 Stoke Newington Church Street   020 8712 1188   1–1C
This Grade II listed Stokey boozer was taken under the wing of the gastropub magicians behind the Anchor & Hope and Canton Arms three years ago, and now boasts a *"delicious seasonal menu"* and *"very good Sunday lunch"*. The move has been such a success that the Clarence team now has a West End outpost – at no less an address than Soho's historic Kettner's (see also). Top Menu Tip – *"the pies for two: I'm still dreaming about the chicken and leek"*. / N16 0LA; www.clarencetavern.com; theclarencetavern; Tue-Sat 11 pm, Sun 6 pm.

Clarette W1 £100 ②③③
44 Blandford St   020 3019 7750   3–1A
"The wine list is pricey, even by Marylebone High Street standards" at this Tudorbethan pub, with leaded windows and inset stained glass. That's to be expected, as it's backed by Alexandra Petit-Mentzelopoulos – part of the family who own the legendary Château Margaux – and you really have to be a lover of wine (some famous names are available by the glass using the Coravin system) to get the most out of the place, which has extensive listings – amongst other areas – of bottlings from Bordeaux and Burgundy: for example, there is a 'Château Margaux Experience': a 'degustation' of 50ml glass of 4 vintages for £95. Viewed purely as a place to get fed? *"We liked it, the food is lovely, but there are options offering better value"*. / W1U 7HS; www.clarettelondon.com; clarettelondon; Tue-Sat 11 pm.

Claridges Foyer & Reading Room W1 £118 ③④④
49 Brook Street   020 7107 8886   3–2B
"Endless sandwich and tea refills and no clock ticking in the background (unlike at some other London five-star establishments)" make this *"comfortably opulent"* foyer *"a wonderful place to enjoy an immensely satisfying afternoon tea, which will obviate any need for dinner later"*. Fans also say there's *"nowhere better for breakfast"* either: *"a marvellous tranquil setting with immaculate service"* and *"highly recommended"*. / W1K 4HW; www.claridges.co.uk; claridgeshotel; Mon-Sun 11 pm.

Claridge's Restaurant, Claridge's Hotel W1 NEW
49 Brook St   020 7107 8886   3–2B
Plus ça change! After 20 years of mucking about with megastar chefs, like Gordon Ramsay, Simon Rogan and Daniel Humm – this landmark Mayfair hotel's glorious Art Deco dining room is finally going back to sailing under its 'own brand' flag: returning to an updated version of the format it abandoned two decades ago. Coalin Finn is to be at the stoves, and the food will be a bit fancier than when the space was something of an undiscovered traditional gem. Few five stars in the late '90s were serving barbequed radish skewers braised in homemade teriyaki, laced with horseradish; but grilled native lobster with crushed Jersey royals and sauce Américaine… that sounds more like it. / W1K 4HW.

Clarke's W8 £115 **4 5 3**
124 Kensington Church Street 020 7221 9225 7–2B
"Terrific ingredients, cleverly but unfussily combined" has long been the hallmark of Sally Clarke's "impeccably run restaurant" in Notting Hill, which has been at the cutting edge of promoting seasonal, Californian-inspired cuisine since 1984. "It's on the pricey side, but quality remains superb"; the setting is "romantic"; and the service, from a loyal and seemingly well-looked-after contingent of staff is "excellent, all overseen by Sally herself". The "marvellous" wine list has an "unusual emphasis on North American wines" and some "reasonably priced alternatives to famous names". Top Tip – "the good-value daily lunch set menu is a fantastic way to try this restaurant out". / W8 4BH; www.sallyclarke.com; sallyclarkeltd and sallyclarkefood; Tue-Sat 10 pm.

Clipstone W1 £86 **3 3 2**
5 Clipstone Street 020 7637 0871 2–1B
"An upmarket but wonderfully understated local without pretensions" that's "just 10 minutes' walk from Oxford Circus". Will Lander and Daniel Morgenthau's well-regarded – if "fairly cramped and noisy" – Fitzrovia corner site wins continues to win support with its "very competent, modern British cooking", "varied international wine list, with many options by the glass", and "staff who are friendly and passionate about what they serve". Is it the cost of living crisis though? – "rather small portions" is a repeat complaint this year. Top Tip – "great value lunch with an (always) interesting menu". / W1W 6BB; www.clipstonerestaurant.co.uk; clipstonerestaurant; Tue-Sat 9.45 pm, Sun 8.45.

Clos Maggiore WC2 £98 **3 4 5**
33 King St 020 7379 9696 5–3C
"On more than one occasion we have observed someone 'popping the question' here!" – the "magical" setting "never fails to impress" at this Covent Garden oasis, yet again voted London's No.1 venue for romance in our annual diners' poll. "Sitting in the conservatory is a joy, especially in good weather when the retractable roof is open" and its "most beautiful interior courtyard is tailormade for a date". "The largely Provençal and Tuscan cuisine is good but the star of this show is the magnificent wine list, with choices from around the world and prices to suit all budgets. The only recommendation is to read the wine list at home in advance, otherwise you'll spend the first hour ignoring your date!". / WC2E 8JD; www.closmaggiore.com; clos_maggiore; Mon-Sat 10.30 pm, Sun 10 pm.

The Clove Club EC1 £220 **3 3 2**
Shoreditch Town Hall, 380 Old St 020 7729 6496 13–1B
The UK's leading position on World's 50 best has helped underpin the longevity of this mould-breaking icon, which opened 10 years ago to phenomenal acclaim in the incongruous hipster surroundings of Shoreditch Town Hall. Fans "love the vibe of the room"; and say Isaac McHale's "awesome and imaginative" cuisine "just gets better and better". Even they, though, can concede that with the tasting menu now costing £195 per person it is "getting a little expensive now". And then there is a minority for whom it's not only "overpriced" but "vastly overrated and living off the PR" ("I adore fine dining and was fully prepared to spend on a fantastic meal. But the food, while technically fine, felt over-thought and overly fussy, with scant imagination or soul"). / EC1V 9LT; www.thecloveclub.com; thecloveclub; Tue-Sat 11 pm.

Club Gascon EC1   £167   4 3 3

57 West Smithfield   020 7600 6144   10–2B

"Reliably inventive Michelin-quality tasting menus with quirky-but-good wine pairings" continue to inspire joy at Pascal Aussignac and Vincent Labeyrie's long-standing foodie temple to the cuisine of southwest France, which occupies a stately former Lyons Tea House near Smithfield Market. It partly achieved its renown originally by serving everything with foie gras, but nowadays a "superb vegetarian tasting menu" is also a feature. / EC1A 9DS; www.clubgascon.com; clubgascon; Tue-Sat 9.30 pm.

The Coach EC1   £70   3 3 3

26-28 Ray Street   020 3954 1595   10–1A

"Very decent" French-influenced food helps elevate this fine old Clerkenwell pub restaurant into being a "good all-rounder", as does its attractive, glazed dining area. That said, it doesn't attract the attention it did a few years ago when Henry Harris was at the stoves. / EC1R 3DJ; www.thecoachclerkenwell.co.uk; thecoachlondon; Mon-Sat 11 pm, Sun 4 pm.

Coal Office N1   £78   4 4 4

2 Bagley Walk   020 3848 6085   9–3C

"Loud… buzzy… delicious" – this "original, exciting and cool" venue designed by the neighbouring Tom Dixon studio, by Granary Square, "is a full-on, in-your-face Tel Aviv sort of place". The "superb Israeli small plates, which you are invited to share" are overseen by executive chef, Assaf Granit: "very flavoursome food with some unusual combinations". "Tables are very close" inside, which is "noisy", with "drum and bass in the background" and lots of chatter; "so, it's best to go for lunch on a sunny day on the terrace and take in the views over the renovated King's Cross area". Top Menu Tips – "their signature polenta starter remains strong… a must. Octopus is amazing, tender and tasty. Desserts are also a high point… as is the powerful coffee!" / N1C 4PQ; coaloffice.com; coaloffice; Mon-Wed, Sat & Sun, Thu & Fri 11 pm.

Coal Rooms SE15   £75   3 3 2

11a Station Way   020 7635 6699   1–4D

This "interesting" conversion of the Victorian booking hall and goods rooms at Peckham Rye station accommodates a café/restaurant whose modern menu is "thoughtful without being too crazy". The day-time brunch offering gets a thumbs-up, too, as "many steps ahead of the typical avo on toast". (A back-handed compliment from north of the river: "As an ex-north Londoner, I was amazed to find this in central Peckham. How things have changed!") / SE15 4RX; www.coalroomspeckham.com; coalrooms; Wed-Sat 11 pm, Sun 6 pm.

The Coal Shed SE1   £84   3 2 2

One Tower Bridge   020 3384 7272   10–4D

With its "straightforward" offering including "very good fish and lamb" and its "welcome service", this offshoot of a Brighton steakhouse is "a top option in the locality of The Bridge Theatre", near City Hall – "it just works". / SE1 2SE; www.coalshed-restaurant.co.uk; thecoalshed; Tue-Sat 11 pm, Sun 6 pm.

CoCoRo W1   £38   4 3 2

31 Marylebone Lane   020 7935 2931   3–1A

They look modest, but "great value Japanese food" (for example, "delightful sushi" and "very fresh salmon and tuna") of "consistently high quality" is served by "lovely people" at this well-established Marylebone restaurant and its more deli-style offshoots in Highgate, Bloomsbury and Bayswater. / W1U 2NH; cocororestaurant.co.uk; cocorolondon; Mon-Sun 10.30 pm.

Cocotte £58 **3** **3** **2**

271 New King's Road, SW6   020 7610 9544   11–1B
11 Harrington Road, SW7   020 7589 1051   6–2C
95 Westbourne Grove, W2   020 3220 0076   7–1B
8 Hoxton Square, N1   020 7033 4277   13–1B
79 Salusbury Road, NW6   020 7625 6606   1–2B

*"Chicken with amazing sides" is the winning formula at Romain Bourrillon's rotisserie chain, which imports its chooks from France. "Nice brunch", too.
/ www.mycocotte.uk.*

Colbert SW1 £84 **2** **2** **3**

51 Sloane Sq   020 7730 2804   6–2D

"Always a good place to meet people" – this Wolseley Group operation on a corner of Sloane Square feels like "a slice of Paris in London" and its supremely "convenient location" means it "can get very busy". Somehow standards have never quite gelled here as well as at the group's better-known sites: the "predictable, ersatz French brasserie fare" is merely "fine"; the service can be "quite patchy"; and the "buzzy atmosphere" can tip into bland anonymity. Harsh criticisms were absent this year, though, and seemingly there's "been no perceptible drop in quality since C&K's departure". / SW1W 8AX; colbertrestaurant.com; colbertchelsea; Mon-Sat 10.30 pm, Sun 10 pm.

The Collins Room,
The Berkeley Hotel SW1 £131 **3** **3** **4**

Wilton Place   020 7107 8866   6–1D

*Hermès, Loewe and Zimmermann help inspire the Spring/Summer 2023 Prêt-à-Portea collection on the 'cakewalk' of this Belgravia chamber, which takes annual inspiration for its wizard patisserie selection from the catwalk of the fashion industry. If you have money to burn, it's an impressively skillful and witty twist on the afternoon tea experience – tuck into "Hermès' tasselled bucket bag, crafted out of Victoria sponge sandwiched with apricot jam, wrapped in chocolate and finished with a chocolate feather plume!"
/ SW1X 7RL; www.the-berkeley.co.uk; the_berkeley; Mon-Sun 10.30 pm.*

Le Colombier SW3 £95 **2** **4** **4**

145 Dovehouse Street   020 7351 1155   6–2C

"My refuge when feeling homesick for France" – Didier Garnier's "long standing favourite" in a quiet Chelsea backstreet is "a typical French restaurant of the kind that you might find in the Dordogne". "It can get very crowded and there's not much privacy between the tables. But it has a very loyal following" particularly amongst a well-heeled, silver-haired crowd, for whom it's a "go-to" destination thanks to its "traditional, buzzy atmosphere", "dependable French-bistro cuisine" and a "wine list which has some great bargains" ("not your usual SW3 mark up – try the wines priced £30-£60, top value"). Didier himself presides over the "discreet and effortless service" and provides "excellent professional advice on the choice of vintage". The odd naysayer finds it all "shockingly old-fashioned"… but folks have been saying that for years. / SW3 6LB; www.lecolombier.restaurant; Tue-Sat 10.30 pm.

Colonel Saab WC1 £69 **4** **3** **4**
Holborn Hall, 193-197 High Holborn 020 3004 0004 5–1D
*"Great food, attentive service, and an overall lovely experience" are winning
a small but very enthusiastic fan club for this quirky, late 2021 Indian two-
year-old. Despite the interest of a historic building – Holborn's former Town
Hall – it inhabits something of a restaurant graveyard site, which has seen
off numerous previous occupants (Shanghai Blues, Gezellig, Burger &
Lobster). And, shortly after opening, it too was written off as a 'Curry
Catastrophe' by the Evening Standard's David Ellis. So kudos to owner Roop
Partap Choudhary for persevering with his very personal vision for the
enterprise. / WC1V 7BD; www.colonelsaab.co.uk; colonelsaab; Mon-Sat 10 pm.*

**Colony Grill Room,
The Beaumont W1** £101 **3** **3** **4**
8 Balderton Street, Brown Hart Gardens 020 7499 9499 3–2A
*With its colourful murals, dark-wood features and plush leather seating, the
"lovely" dining room of this Art Deco hotel near Selfridges faithfully recreates
a rather Manhattan-esque style. The menu is likewise praised by some
reporters for its "superb American fare" (although its mix of grills with
caviar, oysters and more generic locally sourced dishes – such as Dover sole
– equally fit the image of typical British clubland venues). No longer run by
Corbin & King as once it was, it is "still consistent but now quite expensive".
/ W1K 6TF; www.colonygrillroom.com; thecolonygrillroom; Mon-Wed 9.30 pm, Thu-Sat
10 pm, Sun 3 pm.*

Compton EC1 £83 **3** **4** **2**
47-48 St Johns Square 020 4548 6939 10–1A
*"Somewhere to go that isn't fine dining but is above the ordinary" – this
Clerkenwell site became well-known under chef Anna Hansen as The
Modern Pantry (RIP), and was relaunched (under new ownership) as this all-
day restaurant and deli in 2022. It does do brunch, but that's no longer the
top feature it was in its former guise. The menu includes some "retro" dishes
such as prawn cocktail ("mains of Holstein chicken and mushroom ragu
were excellent") and has a something-for-everybody quality to it. What's
more, "service is a notch above the usual" helping to create "a relaxed feel
to the place". (In his November 2022 review, The Telegraph's William Sitwell
noted the venue's "polite" qualities and thought it a place to "take my
favourite aunt".) / EC1V 4JJ; www.compton.restaurant; compton.restaurant; Tue-Fri
11 pm, Mon 5 pm.*

The Connaught Grill W1 £161
Carlos Place 020 7107 8852 3–3B
*That there's too few reports in our annual diners' poll for a rating on this
Mayfair chamber is remarkable given the lofty heritage of its famous name
(for many decades applied to the room that's nowadays Hélène Darroze,
upstairs). After a hiatus of many years, this new space opened in 2020 and
has never inspired much press reviewer attention – perhaps due to its
'citizens of nowhere' contemporary styling and modern JG Vongerichten-
curated menu. Still, such feedback as we do receive on results from the
luxurious rotisserie and wood-burning grill is all good. / W1K 2AL;
www.the-connaught.co.uk; theconnaught; Wed-Sat 10.15 pm, Sun 4.30 pm.*

Contigo WC2 NEW
1-3 Grand Building, Strand   no tel   2–3C

Despite tons of money thrown at its numerous incarnations, the site of the former Strand Dining Rooms, just off Trafalgar Square, has never really cut through in recent years. Maybe this new Nikkei (Japanese/Peruvian) operation – a 'Coming Soon' as we go to press – will break the mould, which will feature a sushi counter and bar named Lima; a main open kitchen called Osaka; and an outdoor terrace. / WC2N 5HR; www.eatcontigo.co.uk; Tue-Sun 10 pm.

Coppa Club   £64   2 2 4
29 Brewhouse Lane, SW15   020 3937 5354   11–2B
Three Quays Walk, Lower Thames St, EC3   020 7993 3827   10–3D

"Sat in an outdoor pod with the family, drinking mimosas and with lovely views of the river" is a key feature of London's two outposts of these comfy venues (part of a national chain), both of which have riverside terraces featuring all-weather igloos for year-round fun. The Italian-ish food in the dining rooms is "unexceptional", but "their lounge areas are cosy and just the place for morning coffee or afternoon tea". / www.coppaclub.co.uk; coppaclub.

Copper & Ink SE3   £74   3 3 3
5 Lee Road   020 3941 9337   1–4D

"A jewel in Blackheath's crown" – extravagantly moustachioed (and inked) chef Tony Rodd's "stunning monthly changing menu, using seasonal and mostly local ingredients, is worthy of a central London establishment". Partner Becky Cummings runs the FOH at this distinctive and distinguished neighbourhood spot. / SE3 9RQ; www.copperandink.com; copperandink; Wed-Sat 11.30 pm.

Copper Chimney W12   £54   3 3 3
Westfield London, Ariel Way   020 8059 4439   1–3B

Near the main entrance to Westfield, this Indian venue will celebrate its fifth year in 2024, but is easily lost amongst the glossy anonymity of the surrounding units. It's the London outpost of a 45-year-old chain that's 15-strong in India itself. Although it doesn't inspire a huge volume of feedback, reports are consistently upbeat: "good value, freshly cooked dishes, lovely ambience". / W12 7GA; www.copperchimney.uk; copperchimney_uk; Sun-Thu 9.30 pm, Fri & Sat 10.30 pm.

Coq d'Argent EC2   £99   2 2 2
1 Poultry   020 7395 5000   10–2C

"Signs of returning normality with a full Coq!". This "purring" D&D London operation sits on the top floor of No 1 Poultry – with leafy roof terraces in sight of the Bank of England – and is a well-established linchpin of the Square Mile lunching scene. For foodies, it can seem a disappointing experience, but for those packing corporate plastic it's valued as a "great location in the heart of the City for a pricey-but-decent business lunch serving upmarket staples with a French twist". Top Tip – "good for breakfast in the summer on the outside terrace". / EC2R 8EJ; www.coqdargent.co.uk; coqdargent; Mon-Sat midnight; SRA-accredited.

Coqfighter W1   £37   3 2 2
75 Beak Street   020 7734 4001   4–2C

The "divine chicken" at these funky East-meets-West outlets – founded by three mates who missed the Korean fried chicken they ate in Melbourne's Chinatown – is "worth the pain of the uncomfortable seating and queue". The business has graduated from home cooking and pub pop-ups to five permanent sites with a Soho flagship and a thriving delivery arm. / W1F 9SS; www.coqfighter.com; coqfighteruk; Mon-Sun 11 pm.

Cora Pearl WC2 £86 3 4 4
30 Henrietta Street   020 7324 7722   5–3C

*With its "good short menu" of "delicious" (if sometimes "very rich") dishes;
"very friendly service and great atmosphere", this is a "cosy, charming little
restaurant in Covent Garden". It's a sibling to Kitty Fisher's in Shepherd
Market, Mayfair – both named after historical local ladies of the night – and
ideal for a "relaxed" occasion. / WC2E 8NA; www.corapearl.co.uk; corapearlcg;
Mon-Sat 9.30 pm, Sun 3.30 pm.*

CORD EC4 £89 4 3 4
85 Fleet Street   020 3143 6365   10–2A

*"Doing a grand job of showcasing the school" – "seemingly simple small
dishes done with exemplary refinement" ("perfect pork belly and a delicate
citrus tart slice") impress diners at this year-old restaurant, where you can
sample the work of the august Le Cordon Bleu culinary institute (founded in
Paris in 1895). Set in an "well-spaced, light-filled" dining room in Fleet
Street's Grade II listed former Reuters building (designed by Lutyens), it also
has a "clean lined and attractive" adjoining daytime café worth visiting for its
"accurately toasted" sandwiches and cakes. / EC4Y 1AE;
www.cordrestaurant.co.uk; cordrestaurant; Mon-Fri 10 pm.*

Core by Clare Smyth W11 £231 5 5 4
92 Kensington Park Rd   020 3937 5086   7–2B

*"World-class cooking from the best female chef in the country" inspires
nothing but reams of rapturous reports on Clare Smyth's "seemingly
effortless and very special" Notting Hill HQ – again the No. 1 gastronomic
choice in our annual diners' poll and "well deserving its three Michelin stars"
(the same of which could not be said for most of London's other holders of
these laurels). The "virtuoso" cuisine is "simply exquisite" yet "without
seeming pretentious": it says something that one of this Northern Irish
farmer's daughter's key signature dishes is made out of potato! "Everything
from the welcome, the theatre of the kitchen, the execution of the cooking,
the comprehensive wine list, the crisp, airy and bright dining room and the
enthusiastic and delightful service" provides a "profoundly good experience
with incredible attention to detail". "Clare is in the kitchen each time" and
regularly greets guests personally, and "although the bill is high, it is not
outlandish for the culinary performance that is delivered". "Always at the top
of its game" – ratings here have held very steady in a year that has seen
wobbles at many of its rivals. / W11 2PN; www.corebyclaresmyth.com;
corebyclaresmyth; Thu-Sat, Tue, Wed 9.45 pm.*

Cork & Bottle WC2 £69 2 3 4
44-46 Cranbourn St   020 7734 7807   5–3B

*"A secret, below-ground escape from the mayhem of Leicester Square" for
more than half a century – this "well-hidden", "old-school" wine bar has
"only got better" over the years, first under founder Don Hewitson and
latterly under Will Clayton. Top Menu Tip – "share the ham and cheese pie
(it is absolutely enormous)", and has sold around a million portions since
1971. / WC2H 7AN; www.thecorkandbottle.co.uk; thecorkandbottle; Mon-Sun
10.30 pm.*

Cornerstone E9 £97 5 5 4
3 Prince Edward Road   020 8986 3922   14–1C
"Tom Brown's single-minded passion for fish and seafood shines through" at his "mecca of fine dining" – a post-industrial space "tucked away not far from the canal" in "wondrously trendy Hackney Wick". "We love its informality and the friendliness of the staff" who give "detailed descriptions explaining the provenance of each dish" from "a stunning menu". "So, get your skinny jeans on, tousle that beard (man bun optional) and go!" Top Menu Tip – "fabulous crab bun with pear hoisin"; "shrimps in a sort of panna cotta, decorated with sprouting herbs and vegetables… inspired". / E9 5LX; cornerstonehackney.com; cornerstonehackney; Wed-Sat, Tue 9 pm.

Corrigan's Mayfair W1 £139 3 4 4
28 Upper Grosvenor St   020 7499 9943   3–3A
"Excellent traditional British cuisine with an Irish accent" helped win very consistent praise this year for Richard Corrigan's comfortable Mayfair bastion of 'all that is coastal, wild, furred and feathered'. It's a "classic dining experience" but service is "wonderfully welcoming" and is "pitch perfect" for business entertaining in particular. Top Tip – "the set lunch menu cushions the blow to the wallet". / W1K 7EH; www.corrigansmayfair.com; corrigans bar & restaurant; Tue-Sat midnight.

Côte £59 1 2 3
Branches throughout London
"OK its a chain", but these faux French brasseries are one of the most talked-about brands in our annual diners' poll, due to their huge army of fans who see them as a "not-brilliant but consistent" standby for a "cheap 'n' cheerful meal disguised as something more upmarket" thanks to their "reasonable prices" and "very pleasant" ambience. For an easygoing breakfast, "family-friendly" meal or pre-theatre pit stop, they are particularly nominated. But while standards of service have held up relatively well here post-Covid, there was a strong feeling this year that the food is "on the wane" with lots of reports of "boring" or even "bad and unappealing" meals ("What has happened to Côte? It used to be so reliable, but we have had several experiences recently when we had to send dishes back because they'd been poorly cooked"). / www.cote.co.uk; coteuk.

Counter 71 N1
71 Nile St   no tel   13–1A
Opened in summer 2023, former Fenn head chef Joe Laker's debut project is a 16-seater chef's table with a focus on less familiar British produce, presented in a minimalist style. There's a touch of the TARDIS to it – on the outside, it looks like a bog-standard old corner pub; on the inside, it transforms into an open kitchen surrounded by a slick dining counter made from green marble. The venue has its own separate cocktail bar, Lowcountry, featuring whiskeys from the Georgia to North Carolina coast under Savannah-born mixologist Ryan Sheehan. Lowcountry also has a menu of southern US small plates such as shrimps and grits prawn toast. Top Menu Tip – "the custard tarts with fennel seeds are a real show-stopper". / N1 7RD; Mon-Sat 11 pm.

The Cow W2 £80 3 2 4
89 Westbourne Park Rd   020 7221 0021   7–1B
One of London's original gastropubs, Tom Conran's Irish-themed "neighbourhood joint" in Bayswater still hits the spot after nearly 30 years. "Whoever is in the kitchen does a terrific job, as the food is delicious". It "can be noisy with bigger parties" and "the upstairs dining room is only small" – but you can always eat in the main bar. / W2 5QH; thecowlondon.com; thecowlondon; Mon-Sat 11 pm, Sun 10 pm.

Coya £116 ②②③
118 Piccadilly, W1   020 7042 7118   3–4B
Angel Court, 31-33 Throgmorton St, EC2   020 7042 7118   10–2C
"Absolutely delicious" Peruvian food ("we took our foodie friends, who loved it too!") features in practically all reports on Arjun Waney's glossy haunts in Mayfair and near Bank (as well as Paris, Dubai, Mykonos…). There's a lot of feeling even amongst fans, though, that they're just "not worth the money any more" ("yes it's good, but at these prices it should be. Perhaps it's just their rents but spending just short of £200/head and being rushed off the table left me underwhelmed. I could rave about the wondrous dishes, but not sure it's worth it…") / www.coyarestaurant.com; coyamayfair.

The Crabtree W6 £57 ②②④
Rainville Road   020 7385 3929   11–1A
Making the most of its "brilliant setting" – on the pedestrian path along the Fulham shore of the Thames, midway between Craven Cottage and The River Café, and with a big garden and small waterside terrace – this well-known and popular old tavern has a decent pub-grub offering, and gets rammed on summer weekends and Fulham match days. / W6 9HA; www.thecrabtreew6.co.uk; thecrabtreew6; Mon-Sat 11 pm, Sun 10.30 pm.

Crate Brewery and Pizzeria E9 £35 ③②③
7, The White Building, Queens Yard   020 8533 3331   14–1C
Hang with the hip crowd at this groovy Hackney Wick haunt – a canal-side warehouse ('The White Building') just across the water from the Olympic Park, with a big outside terrace. On the menu: affordable and yummy pizza, washed down with quality brews from the in-house microbrewery. Downside? At busy times it's a bit of a zoo. / E9 5EN; www.cratebrewery.com; cratebrewery; Sun-Thu 11 pm, Fri & Sat 1 am.

Crisp Pizza,
The Chancellors W6 NEW £59 ⑤②②
25 Crisp Road   020 8748 2600   8–2C
"Believe the hype… these pizzas are remarkable!" – there's nothing gastro in appearance when it comes to this mock Tudor pub: "a proper old man's boozer" behind Hammersmith's Riverside Studios. But self-taught pizzaiolo Carl McCluskey has set social media ablaze with folks travelling from far and wide and queuing round the block for his NYC-inspired creations. Even Harry Kane's a fan! It's a homespun and quirky set-up, which can struggle under weight of numbers. In particular, "be sure to book your dough before you go!" – you can reserve your pizza (to ensure you don't go hungry and can take out if needs be), even if tables are reserved for walk-ins only. Is it the capital's best? Jimi Famurewa in his March 2023 Evening Standard review neatly captured the nigh-impossibility of living up to such legendary billing. "The fact that McCluskey's slices may not instantly supersede all the other half-remembered London pizzas you have eaten – and they didn't quite, for me – does not make them any less exceptional, rare or worth crossing town for". (Apparently, McCluskey is now on the hunt for a more conventional central London site). / W6 9RL; crisppizzaw6.

Crocker's Folly NW8 £58 ③③③
23-24 Aberdeen Place   020 7289 9898   9–4A
"Outstanding, really tasty Lebanese food" can be a surprise find at this "very ornate pub" – a beautifully restored, late-Victorian, Renaissance-style gin palace in St John's Wood, whose dazzling interior was originally supposed to act as that of a major railway hotel (due to the 'folly' of the owner, as the tracks ultimately ended up terminating in Marylebone). In its current guise, it's "one of the few Maroush group restaurants that survived post-Covid". / NW8 8JR; www.maroush.com; maroush; Mon-Sun midnight.

The Crystal Moon Lounge, Corinthia Hotel London SW1 £105 3 4 4
Whitehall Place 020 7321 3150 2–3C
The "gorgeous setting" of a lounge with a 1,001-crystal chandelier at this luxury hotel off Trafalgar Square is ideal for a "wonderful afternoon tea, especially after spending time in the spa". "The delightful little sweet creations will be topped up if required" to provide "a miracle! – tea for elderly mother's birthday done to her full satisfaction". / SW1A 2BD; www.corinthia.com; corinthialondon; Mon-Sun midnight.

The Culpeper E1 £61 3 3 3
40 Commercial Street 020 7247 5371 13–2C
"Buzzing" old boozer on a Spitalfields corner site, which was very stylishly upgraded nine years ago and nowadays boasts an airy upstairs dining room with an "always interesting, always reliable" British bistro menu. "The roof terrace is a great bonus", too. / E1 6LP; www.theculpeper.com; theculpeper; Mon-Thu midnight, Fri & Sat 1 am, Sun 9 pm.

Cut, 45 Park Lane W1 £188 2 3 2
45 Park Ln 020 7493 4545 3–4A
If it wasn't for the celebrity of chef Wolfgang Puck and its prime Park Lane location – across the door from the main entrance of The Dorchester – we would be tempted to skip an entry for this swanky Mayfair steakhouse. If you're not paying, you're likely to enjoy picking from its British-farmed steaks, USDA meat, Australian or Japanese wagyu. But it inspires very little feedback in our annual diners' poll, and even those who say it's "good all-round" feel it's "only for expense-accounters". / W1K 1PN; www.dorchestercollection.com; 45parklane; Mon-Sun 10 pm.

Cycene E2 £218 5 4 4
9 Chance Street 020 7033 6788 13–1C
"Akoko's chef and staff uprooted to here, this time without African-inflected cuisine… it's awesome!" – Theo Clench is now installed in the happening hipster venue in Shoreditch that was previously Mãos (part of the 'Blue Mountain School'). You start in the bar, in the lower portion of this two-floor space, which begins "an incredible evening from start to finish". Clench and his team serve a 10-course menu which promises to marry classic techniques with influences from Eastern Asia and Australasia. The result is "high-end dining, with amazing attention to detail but which feels very relaxed at the same time". The intimate and "stylish room" contributes to a "great experience all round". / E2 7JB; www.bluemountain.school; bluemountain.school.

Cyprus Mangal SW1 £48 3 3 2
45 Warwick Way 020 7828 5940 2–4B
"Delicious chops piled high, good gluggable house red – what's not to like?" at this long-running and "extremely good-value" Turkish-Cypriot grill near Victoria station in Pimlico. It's "not a place for a romantic tête-à-tête, but great fun – you'll leave very well fed and watered, and with a smile on your face". / SW1V 1QS; www.cyprusmangal.co.uk; cyprusmangal; Mon-Sun 11 pm.

Da Mario SW7 £54 3 2 3
15 Gloucester Rd 020 7584 9078 6–1B
This "long-established" family-owned Italian in a Venetian Gothic building near the Albert Hall is "set up as a sort of homage to Princess Diana", who used to bring Princes Wills and Harry for pizza and pasta. / SW7 4PP; www.damario.co.uk; da-mario-kensington; Mon-Sun 11.30 pm.

Da Mario WC2   £73   2️⃣3️⃣3️⃣
63 Endell Street   020 7240 3632   5–1C

"Very friendly" and "authentic" – this "family-run traditional Italian trattoria" is a "dependable and good-value" option in Covent Garden, "with outside tables in decent weather". The food is "good but not exceptional". Top Menu Tip – "try the calves' liver and tiramisu". / WC2H 9AJ; www.da-mario.co.uk; da_mario_covent_garden; Tue-Sat 11 pm, Sun 9 pm.

Da Terra, Town Hall Hotel E2   £293   5️⃣4️⃣5️⃣
8 Patriot Square   020 7062 2052   14–2B

Rafael Cagali provides "precise, innovative and fully-flavoured" Brazilian-influenced cuisine that's "some of the best food in London" at his acclaimed Bethnal Green venture – a site in the area's former town hall which has housed a number of the capital's most notable restaurants (The Typing Room, Viajante) over the last fifteen years. "The lovely setting is very good as it is intimate but still allows you to see the kitchen and how they prepare your food". / E2 9NF; www.daterra.co.uk; daterrarestaurant; Wed-Sat 8 pm.

Daddy Bao SW17   £34   4️⃣3️⃣3️⃣
113 Mitcham Road   020 3601 3232   11–2C

"Our teen kids love this place and we do too!" – so say fans of Frank Leung's Tooting venue, which provides steamed Taiwanese buns, washed down with decent cocktails, in an atmospheric neighbourhood setting. See also 'Mr Bao' in Peckham. / SW17 9PE; www.daddybao.com; daddybao; Tue, Wed, Sun 9.45 pm, Sat, Fri 10.45 pm, Thu 9.45 pm.

Daddy Donkey EC1   £18   4️⃣3️⃣2️⃣
50b Leather Lane   020 7404 4173   10–2A

"Reliable, generously proportioned burritos with a great range of extra fillings" keeps 'em coming to this fast-food café/takeaway, on a corner amidst Leather Lane Market. / EC1N 7TP; www.daddydonkey.co.uk; daddydonkeyburritos; Mon-Thu 7 pm, Fri 3 pm.

Daffodil Mulligan EC1   £72   4️⃣4️⃣3️⃣
70-74 City Road   020 7404 3000   13–1A

Richard Corrigan's "unassuming but amazing" bar/restaurant, just south of Silicon Roundabout, has – perhaps due to its pre-pandemic debut – never quite capitalised on his renown and its high quality. An "imaginative menu" of Irish-inflected dishes are "all matched by the superb, friendly, welcoming service" led by his son Richie. "Not cheap but equally not too expensive and certainly worth the visit". / EC1Y 2BJ; www.daffodilmulligan.com; daffodilmulligan; Wed-Fri 10 pm, Sun 8 pm.

La Dame de Pic London EC3   £179   4️⃣3️⃣3️⃣
10 Trinity Square   020 7297 3799   10–3D

"A perfect marriage of traditional and modern culinary approaches" is to be found in the "impeccably-run" dining room of this impressive five-star hotel near the Tower of London. The Pic in question is Anne-Sophie, owner of Maison Pic near Lyon and Michelin's most decorated female chef. Fans say her team's contemporary French cuisine, led by head chef Evens López, is "on a different level from almost every other restaurant in the capital – presented like modern art and with each dish a lovely surprise". In fact, given its consistent quality (as recognised by two of the tyre men's stars) it's surprising that – perhaps due to its Square Mile location – it still maintains a relatively low profile in the capital's food scene. / EC3N 4AJ; ladamedepiclondon.co.uk; ladamedepiclondon; Tue-Sat 9 pm.

Daphne's SW3 £96 3 3 5
112 Draycott Ave   020 7589 4257   6–2C

"A terrific Italian with super service… that's amore!", declare fans of this smart Chelsea haunt, founded in 1964 by Richard Burton's agent, Daphne Rye, and frequented in the 1990s by Princess Di. Now part of Richard Caring's Caprice group, it seems to be defying the ravages of time and remains a "favourite, if expensive" rendezvous near Brompton Cross. Top Menu Tip – "the crab and chilli linguine is to die for". / SW3 3AE; www.daphnes-restaurant.co.uk; daphneslondon; Mon-Sat 10.45 pm, Sun 10.15 pm.

Daquise SW7 £67 2 3 4
20 Thurloe St   020 7589 6117   6–2C

"A wonderful survivor", this old-world "gem" by South Ken tube has served "solid, Polish food" ("all the old hits: duck, goose, herring…") at "sensible prices" since 1947, and its devotees love its "real sense of authenticity" ("I feel happy when I walk in the door: the menu never changes and I hope it never will!"). It may be "a level down from Ognisko" culinary-wise, but "you're coming here for the charm, not the workmanlike fare". Top Tip – "it's well situated close to the South Kensington museums and a good alternative to the numerous expensive and unexciting chains!" / SW7 2LT; www.daquise.co.uk; daquise_london; Tue-Sun 11 pm.

Darby's SW11 £81 3 3 4
3 Viaduct Gardens Road, Embassy Gardens   020 7537 3111   11–1D

In a style not dissimilar to an NYC steakhouse, Irish chef Robin Gill's "lovely" venue is an "excellent addition" to the new Nine Elms development – and should make staff at the US Embassy next door feel right at home with its "solid" menu of seafood and steaks and "nice cocktail bar vibe". "Oysters are good value in happy hour", accompanied by "spot-on martinis" or draught Guinness. Other highlights include breakfast, Sunday lunch with live music, and Southeast Asian BBQ treats from 'The Hatch' in the beer garden. / SW11 7AY; www.darbys-london.com; darbyslondon; Wed-Sat 10 pm.

Daroco Soho W1
Manette St   Awaiting tel   5–2A

With siblings in the 2nd and 16th arrondissements of Paris, this October 2023 newcomer aims to import its brand of 'offbeat Parisian chic and sunny Italian generosity' to Soho (on an intriguing cut-through between Greek Street and Charing Cross Road). It's a large spot – with 100 covers and a 50-seater terrace – where the focus will be on pasta and pizza. / W1D 4AL; Mon-Sat 10.30 pm.

The Dartmouth Castle W6 £58 3 2 3
26 Glenthorne Rd   020 8748 3614   8–2C

"This unassuming pub tucked around the back of Hammersmith's one-way system serves good and hearty Mediterranean food", in particular some "lovely pasta dishes" – "don't miss the penne with Italian sausage ragu". It's also a "top sun trap for early-evening drinks on the patio". / W6 0LS; www.thedartmouthcastle.co.uk; thedartmouthcastle; Mon, Sat, Tue-Fri 9.30 pm, Sun 8.30 pm.

Darwin Brasserie EC3 £88 2 2 4
1 Sky Garden Walk   033 3772 0020   10–3D

"The view from the gallery over the city is great" at this sky-high brasserie, on the 36th floor of the 'Walkie Talkie'. Reports this year were limited and rather uneven, so we've taken ratings down a peg. It won particular praise, though, as a glam breakfasting destination. / EC3M 8AF; skygarden.london; sg_darwin; Tue-Sun 10.30 pm, Mon 10 pm.

Dastaan KT19 £49 5️⃣4️⃣3️⃣
447 Kingston Rd   020 8786 8999   1–4A
"Well worth a detour by car, bus and/or train to eat in this small restaurant near Tolworth" – "looking just like your typical, noisy curry house on a dual carriageway… except that it is fully booked every night". "From pani puri to chicken Chettinad, the flavours are exquisite" with "a lasting intensity that can leave you punchdrunk". It's not utterly ridiculous to hail it as "the very best Indian food in the UK at any price point, and yet it's still very reasonably priced compared with the Indian palaces of Marylebone and Knightsbridge". Top Menu Tip – "the lamb chops are an absolute must". / KT19 0DB; dastaan.co.uk; dastaan447; Tue-Sun 10.30 pm.

Daylesford Organic £73 1️⃣2️⃣2️⃣
44b Pimlico Rd, SW1   020 7881 8060   6–2D
6-8 Blandford St, W1   020 3696 6500   2–1A
76-82 Sloane Avenue, SW3   020 3848 7100   6–2C
208-212 Westbourne Grove, W11   020 7313 8050   7–1B
Lady Bamford's quartet of London 'rus in urbe' cafés should have caught the zeitgeist, with their focus on home-produced organic ingredients from her estate. But the offering is variable, with food that's too often slated as "poor"; or incidents of "staff hanging around not knowing what to do". The Pimlico branch scores the best of the bunch, but it's worthy of note that visitors to the Daylesford farm mothership in the Cotswolds report an altogether different and "delightful" experience. / www.daylesfordorganic.com; daylesfordfarm; SRA-3 stars.

Dean Street Townhouse W1 £78 2️⃣4️⃣4️⃣
69-71 Dean St   020 7434 1775   4–1D
"The warm and welcoming ambience is hard to beat" at this all-day brasserie, from the Soho House group – part of a hotel, which enjoys a "brilliant central location". The food? "Uncomplicated, nothing special, but very acceptable" (especially for brunch), if "expensive for what you get". But it's the "lovely" atmosphere that carries the day here. / W1D 3SE; www.deanstreettownhouse.com; deanstreettownhouse; Mon-Thu midnight, Fri & Sat 1 am, Sun 11 am.

Decimo WC1 £97 3️⃣2️⃣4️⃣
The Standard, 10 Argyle St   020 3981 8888   9–3C
"A spectacular room with spectacular views (including from the loos!)" sets a high-octane scene at Peter Sanchez-Iglesias's dramatic Mexican venue: a high-ceilinged space on the top of King's Cross's über-hip Standard Hotel, with a breathtaking outlook over St Pancras station next door, and accessed via an exterior, red, glass-walled lift. "It seems less busy at lunch – it looks more like one for the cool kids after dark". Most reporters are "pleasantly surprised by the food" which majors in ribs, steaks and seafood from the grill "(I thought it was going to be yet another celebrity rip-off)". It's far from a cheap experience, though, and one or two dud meals were also reported. / WC1H 9JE; www.decimo.london; decimo.london; Tue, Wed midnight, Fri & Sat 2 am, Thu 1 am.

Dehesa W1 £60 2️⃣2️⃣2️⃣
25 Ganton Street   020 7494 4170   4–2B
We're in two minds about the inclusion of this former star of London's tapas scene, which generates very little feedback nowadays despite a prime mid-Soho site. Fans do still laud its "well-crafted dishes and Spanish wines", but others say "the food has that 'here's one I made earlier' quality. OK, but not very exciting". / W1F 9BP; www.saltyardgroup.co.uk; dehesarestaurant; Mon-Sat 11 pm, Sun 9 pm.

Delamina £53 333
56-58 Marylebone Lane, W1   020 3026 6810   3–1A
151 Commercial Street, E1   020 7078 0770   13–2B
"Consistently very good food" results from the menu of small sharing plates at this modern Levantine duo in Marylebone and Shoreditch, created by Israeli-born cook Limor Chen and her husband Amir. There's a "buzzy atmosphere without being too noisy" and a playlist that channels the Tel Aviv vibe. / www.delaminaeast.co.uk; delaminakitchen.

The Delaunay WC2 £72 244
55 Aldwych   020 7499 8558   2–2D
"Viennese in style" – this "elegantly understated" sibling to The Wolseley sits on the easterly fringe of the West End, and is "very much a power location": "the ambience is perfect for business meals – bustling but not too noisy – with well-spaced tables and comfortable seating"; and "obliging" service that's "efficient and warm". Its "Mittel European brasserie menu with schnitzel/goulash/wurst etc" is "nothing special, but it is consistent and very acceptable" and "with something amongst the selection of dishes that anyone and everyone can eat". "Despite the loss of founders Corbin and King, it is mercifully unaltered under its new ownership" with ratings practically identical to last year's. Top Tip – "fabulous for breakfast", whether you are dealmaking or not. / WC2B 4BB; www.thedelaunay.com; thedelaunay; Mon-Sat 10.30 pm, Sun 5 pm.

Delfino W1 £80 332
121a Mount St   020 7499 1256   3–3B
This family-owned Italian wins consistently good ratings for the straightforward menu of "authentic" pasta, pizza and more it has served – at a prominent corner site in Mayfair – for half a century now. Despite a recent refurb, prices remain exceptionally reasonable for this part of town. / W1K 3NW; www.delfinomayfair.com; delfinomayfair; Mon-Sat 10.30 pm.

Delhi Grill N1 £40 423
21 Chapel Mkt   020 7278 8100   9–3D
"Value for money! Truly punchy curries that sing on the tongue" continue to win fans for this street-food inspired cheap eat, on Islington's Chapel Market. / N1 9EZ; www.delhigrill.com; delhi_grill; Mon-Thu, Sat, Fri 10.30 pm, Sun 10 pm.

Les 2 Garcons N8 £79 553
14 Middle Lane   020 8347 9834   9–1C
"Jean-Christophe's Slowik's affability and lovely front-of-house wisdom and Robert Reid's fine cheffing remain delightful as ever" at this "happily old-school bistro in Crouch End, located firmly in the great late 80s dining scene"; and its February 2023 crowdfunded "move to (slightly) larger, nearby premises has made eating here a more comfortable experience". "If every neighbourhood had a restaurant as good as this", the world would be a better place. "Traditional, un-fancy French food is simply and lovingly prepared and served" – "… wish they had restaurants like this in France!". Top Menu Tip – "tarte Tatin is not to be missed; and if they are doing the pig's trotter Pierre Koffman, which chef Robert used to cook for MPW, then don't hesitate". / N8 8PL; www.les2garconsbistro.com; les2garconsbistro; Tue-Sat 9.30 pm.

The Devonshire W1 NEW
17 Denman St   020 7437 2445   4–3C
Fooderati favourite, Oisín Rogers – previously of The Guinea Grill – and Flat Iron founder Charlie Carroll created their dream pub in the heart of the West End at this refurbished boozer, just north of Piccadilly Circus (opposite Brasserie Zédel). Opened in Autumn 2023, it's no surprise given their joint heritage that prime steak – dry aged and butchered on the premises – is intrinsic to the formula. But so, too, is just dropping in for a pint. / W1D 7HW; Mon-Sat 11 pm.

Diba   £54
386 King's Road, SW3   020 7349 9499   6–3B NEW
87 The Broadway, SW19   020 8545 0207   11–2B
"Big portions of tasty Persian food" make this "friendly" duo in Chelsea and Wimbledon "great value for money". Top Menu Tip – "you must have the bread fresh out of the clay oven". / dibarestaurant.co.uk; diba_restaurant_.

Dim Sum Duck WC1   £43   522
124 King's Cross Road   020 7278 6018   9–3D
This tiny café whose menu is summed up in its name is one of the capital's champion cheap eats, with "stunning" Cantonese cuisine. "Just a shame it's not bigger as the queuing time and outdoor seating on the grimy King's Cross Road isn't ideal". The only solution is to go early or in the afternoon. / WC1X 9DS; dimsum-duck.business.site; dimsumandduck; Mon-Sun 10 pm.

Din Tai Fung   £61   222
5-6 Henrietta Street, WC2   020 3034 3888   5–3D
Centre Point, Tottenham Court Road, WC2   awaiting tel   5–1A
An international Taiwanese-based chain with a trio of UK outlets in Covent Garden, Selfridges and most recently Centre Point ("with a great view"). To well-travelled connoisseurs of the original, they are "more upmarket here and more expensive too" ("I lived in Asia for several years and ate at a DTF at least weekly, but here they've jacked the prices up to a level that is taking the p***"). But to the uninitiated, they can seem like "the best ever dumplings", and – Top Menu Tip – even their sternest critics say "don't ignore the Xian Long Bao" (soup dumplings). / www.dintaifung-uk.com; dintaifunguk.

The Dining Room, The Goring Hotel SW1   £124   223
15 Beeston Pl   020 7396 9000   2–4B
Very often recommended as an "expensive but reliable" venue for a "perfect business lunch", this "decorous", family-run hotel near Buck House (where the Middletons stayed before Kate & Will's big day) has won renown as a "very classy", traditionally British affair, where "everything is done perfectly". Post-Covid, however, its dining room's performance seems to have been on the slide and the downward trend noted last year continued in this year's poll amidst gripes that it was "not as good as previously", serving "bland food" and with "too many high expectations dashed". Top Tip – "a quintessential English afternoon tea" in the lounges here is still a popular event. / SW1W 0JW; www.thegoring.com; thegoring; Mon-Sun 9.45 pm.

Dinings £101 5 3 2
22 Harcourt St, W1   020 7723 0666   9–4A
Walton House, Walton St, SW3   020 7723 0666   6–2C
Such is their similarity, that we continue to write up this Japanese duo in a single entry, even though the chefs who own them split the business a few years ago and now run each independently. Both provide "dishes to wow the palate" – and "a feast for the eyes" too: "each beautiful, tiny dish tastes as good as it looks". If you're looking for differences, SW3 receives more attention nowadays, but fractionally lower ratings and can seem "crowded". / dinings.co.uk; dinings_sw3.

Dinner by Heston Blumenthal,
Mandarin Oriental SW1 £156 2 2 2
66 Knightsbridge   020 7201 3833   6–1D
"A menu of deep historical appreciation and stimulating intellectual connections adds up to a total experience that's much more than great fine dining", according to fans of Heston Blumenthal's Knightsbridge venue, whose "original takes on classic English cuisine" are, apparently, inspired by Heston's love of historic British gastronomy and research into cookbooks from the 14th century onwards. Supporters say "the signature meat fruit and tipsy cake are so good, you can just have them every time" and that his other more recent (re)creations can also be "magnificent". But that it's a case of "Emperor's new clothes" is another commonly held belief about this hotel dining room, which – in 1 in 3 reports – is said by diners to be their most "overpriced" meal of the year; and which, despite Hyde Park views from some tables, struggles to generate much in the way of atmosphere. "Seriously, a disappointment after The Fat Duck. Just not value for money!" / SW1X 7LA; www.dinnerbyheston.com; dinnerbyhb; Mon-Sun 9.30 pm.

Dipna Anand Restaurant & Bar WC2 £51
South Wing, Somerset House, Strand   020 7845 4646   2–2D
Within glorious Somerset House, Dipna Anand (part of the family who founded the famous Brilliant Restaurant in Southall) took over this stately, traditional chamber last year, and mostly earned recommendations for its Indian cuisine. Not all reports were 100% positive, though, and in summer 2023 it underwent a temporary closure (with re-opening slated for early September 2023). / WC2R 1LA; dipnasomersethouse.co.uk; dipnaatsomersethouse; Wed-Sat 10 pm, Sun 4 pm.

Dishoom £52 3 4 5
22 Kingly St, W1   020 7420 9322   4–2B
12 Upper St Martins Ln, WC2   020 7420 9320   5–3B
The Barkers Building, Derry Street, W8   020 7420 9325   6–1A
Stable St, Granary Sq, N1   020 7420 9321   9–3C
Wood Wharf, 15 Water Street, E14   020 7420 9326   12–1C
7 Boundary St, E2   020 7420 9324   13–1B
"You really can't go wrong with Dishoom". Shamil and Kavi Thakrar's phenomenal chain remains the most commented-on in our annual diners' poll and its "bustling and loud, throwback, Bombay-colonial-era atmosphere" and "distinctively superior" menu – such a "novel variation from what you get in a typical curry house" – have given UK diners a welcome jolt as to what can be expected from an Indian meal. This includes their "Asian-inspired alternative to the usual 'Full English' breakfast", which has revolutionised the start of the day for many folks. "Super-friendly staff do all they can to create a great experience", which – along with the "delectable cocktails" – helps to underpin the "good vibes" that makes their ambience so buoyant. Perhaps inevitably, ratings for its food have slipped a tad in recent times from being exceptional to merely good, but the overall verdict remains that the overall package is "relatively cheap and always really tasty". The ability to book is restricted at certain times and at certain

branches, but "the queue is worth it!" Top Menu Tips – "stupendous black dahl"; "you could have their okra fries by the bucket"; "ruby murray is a must try"; "that bacon naan… with unlimited chai latte = heaven!". / www.dishoom.com; dishoom; SRA-2 stars.

Diwana Bhel-Poori House NW1   £33   3 2 1
121-123 Drummond St   020 7387 5556   9–4C
"Terrific dosas" and other South Indian vegetarian fare have been on the menu for 60-odd years at this stalwart of the 'Little India' array of cheap 'n' cheerful canteens near Euston station. / NW1 2HL; www.diwanabph.com; diwanabhelpoorihouse; Mon-Sat 10.30 pm, Sun 9.30 pm.

Donostia W1   £93   3 2 2
10 Seymour Pl   020 3620 1845   2–2A
"Delicious baby-brother alternative to Lurra" (the more formal restaurant across the road) – this "rather crowded" bar/restaurant provides a "superb Basque tapas" plus a "small but select wine list". "It's especially good sitting at the bar" – less so in the somewhat stranded rear tables. / W1H 7ND; www.donostia.co.uk; donostiaw1; Mon-Sat 10.30 pm, Sun 9 pm.

Doppo W1 NEW
33 Dean Street   020 7183 2100   5–2A
On a Soho corner, this straightforward but stylish independent opened in early 2023. No survey feedback as yet, but The Standard's David Ellis was impressed on his February 2023 visit, hailing the "quiet elegance" of its interior and light, well-realised Tuscan-influenced cuisine to match, plus a strong wine list. / W1D 4PW; dopposoho; Wed & Thu, Tue 10 pm, Fri & Sat 11 pm.

Dorian W11 NEW   £51   4 4 5
105-107 Talbot Road   020 3089 9556   7–1B
With Chris D'Sylva's background (Notting Hill Fish Shop and Supermarket of Dreams) "the ingredient quality was always going to be superb" at this "constantly buzzing" new 'bistro for locals', which has instantly become something of a "modern classic" for the Notting Hillbilly in-crowd. Chef Max Coen "manages to make decadent dishes seem simple" ("steak is to die for"; or "feast on the most melting buttery liver pâté") and "counter seats are excellent for kitchen watching" – "you get the cooking show and a fantastic atmosphere with lots of interesting fellow diners". / W11 2AT; dorianrestaurant.com; thedoriansf; Tue-Sat 9.30 pm, Sun 4.15 pm.

Dorothy & Marshall BR1 NEW   £59   2 3 3
Bromley Old Town Hall, 4 Court Street   020 3989 9092   1–4D
"A super addition to Bromley" – the borough's old Town Hall has had £20m spent on a refit as a boutique hotel, complete with this new landmark dining room which launched in late 2022: an imposing chamber, with a soaring vaulted ceiling, wood-panelled walls and clerestory windows. It serves a menu of British classics, and is aiming to be a linchpin of the area. Our early feedback (and press reports) are up-and-down: one reporter liked the "very friendly staff and great building", but thought "the menu needs to be a little more adventurous". Another was "slightly disappointed all round, but went shortly after it opened and they were obviously still ironing out stuff". (Both comments have echoes of Grace Dent's review in The Guardian: "a gorgeous space…with a brief menu… service is delightful… prompt and friendly, but it's hard to regard the place as much more than a cafe"). / BR1 1AN; www.dorothyandmarshall.co.uk; dorothyandmarshall; Tue-Thu 10 pm, Fri & Sat 10.30 pm, Sun 7 pm.

Double Standard WC1 £68 **3 5 5**
The Standard, 10 Argyle St 020 3981 8888 9–3C
Conveniently sited bang opposite St Pancras, the authentically 1970s backdrop of the former Camden Town Hall Annexe provides the stylishly time-warped (and convenient) home for this hip haunt: the vibey ground-floor bar of Standard Hotels' London outpost. An ideal rendezvous – especially for creative types – the simple brasserie fare is reliable and staff are particularly professional and welcoming. Don't go if you don't like it loud though: expect the sounds of the seventies at 80-90dB with powerful bass. / WC1H 8EG; www.standardhotels.com; isla.london; Mon-Sun 11 pm.

The Dove W6 £50 **3 4 5**
19 Upper Mall 020 8748 9474 8–2B
This "historic" venue on Hammersmith's Upper Mall (owned by local brewer Fuller's since 1798) is unquestionably "one of the nicest pubs in London": with its "delicious" pub grub, "cosy log fire in the winter, a terrace overlooking the river in the summer – what else would you want?". Top Menu Tip – yummy burgers. / W6 9TA; www.dovehammersmith.co.uk; the_dove_hammersmith; Mon-Sat 11 pm, Sun 10.30 pm.

**Dovetale by Tom Sellers,
1 Hotel Mayfair W1** **NEW**
3 Berkeley Street 020 3137 4983 3–3C
Part of a swanky nine-story hotel that opened in summer 2023, primely located opposite The Ritz (on the junction of Piccadilly and Berkeley Street), this Mayfair newcomer is another recent initiative of Tom Sellers (who also opened Story Cellar in Covent Garden in April 2023). The launch is the UK's first from a luxury international chain whose styling includes lots of plant-filled spaces. According to the website, the dining room features an 'abundant raw bar' and is 'grounded in a deep respect for seasonal, organic, and locally sourced ingredients'. One heavily trailed feature: two dessert trolleys dispensing customisable, 'curated' knickerbocker glories, named 'Apollo One' and 'Apollo Two'. / W1J 8DJ; www.1hotels.com; dovetalelondon; Mon-Fri 2.30 pm.

Dragon Castle SE17 £61 **3 2 2**
100 Walworth Road 020 7277 3388 1–3C
"You could be in Hong Kong" at this "barn-like" Chinese venue near Elephant & Castle, where you'll find "truly authentic", "super-fresh dim sum, alongside old-school Cantonese favourites". "So pleased it has found its mojo again" after a long post-pandemic closure. / SE17 1JL; www.dragoncastlelondon.com; dragoncastle100; Mon-Sat 11 pm, Sun 5 am.

The Drapers Arms N1 £67 **3 3 3**
44 Barnsbury Street 020 7619 0348 9–3D
This "very popular gastropub" in Islington has been transformed from an early Victorian boozer by Nick Gibson, and now "does so well you really need to book". The "consistently good food and great wine list" show a strong French influence, and it's "lovely outside at the back in summer". / N1 1ER; www.thedrapersarms.com; thedrapersarms; Mon-Sat 10.30 pm, Sun 8.30 pm.

The Drawing Room at The Dukes Hotel SW1 £70 **3 4 4**
35 Saint James's Place 020 7318 6574 3–4C
"Ignore The Ritz around the corner, for afternoon tea this is the place to go" according to fans of this St James's bastion: "the scones are soft and freshly baked", "the sandwiches and cakes are divine", and the "famous Dukes 'James Bond' martini is an optional extra". / SW1A 1NY; www.dukeshotel.com; afternoonteauk; Mon-Sun 6 pm.

Dropshot Coffee SW19 £23 ③④④
281 Wimbledon Park Road   07445 673405   11–2B
Don't be fooled by the tennis theme – this indie haunt a strong serve away from the All England Club is absolutely serious about its "delicious brews from different roast houses" and "tasty made-to-order toasties" – in fact, fans claim it's "without a doubt the BEST coffee shop in SW London", and "so friendly: only problem is it's too popular and the queues can be sooooo long". / SW19 6NW; dropshotcoffee.co.uk; dropshotcoffeeldn; Mon-Sun 5 pm.

The Duck & Rice W1 £76 ③②③
90 Berwick St   020 3327 7888   4–2C
This "pub with an Oriental twist" on Soho's Berwick Street is a concept that "works well", with "lovely, tasty food"; even if – eight years after its launch by ace restaurateur Alan Yau – it has never matched the success of his hit concepts Wagamama, Hakkasan or Yauatcha. Top Menu Tip – "the pork scratchings are amazing". / W1F 0QB; www.theduckandrice.com; theduckandrice; Tue-Sat 11 pm, Sun 9 pm.

Duck & Waffle EC2 £99 ②②③
110 Bishopsgate, Heron Tower   020 3640 7310   10–2D
Open 24/7 on top of the City's 40-storey Heron Tower, this elevated posh diner comes particularly recommended for a "great breakfast" or a chilled date ("when you get tired of looking into each other's eyes, the views over London are pretty impressive"). The food, including the signature duck, is mostly up to scratch, but "you just feel it could be better". / EC2N 4AY; www.duckandwaffle.com; duckandwaffle; Mon-Sun 11.30 pm.

The Duck Truck E1 £18 ④③②
Bishops Square   07919 160271   13–2B
"This truck at Spitalfields continues to be a favourite of everyone I take there" – parked just outside the market, it delivers generous filled buns of the eponymous roasted bird, or boxes with meat, chips and salad. / E1 6AN; www.theducktruck.com; theducktruck; Mon-Fri 4 pm.

Ducksoup W1 £79 ④④③
41 Dean St   020 7287 4599   5–2A
This "cool spot" with a "tight menu that changes daily" is "a Soho go-to, even if you get turned away at the door because it's too damned successful!" Now in its second decade, it was way ahead of the curve with its modern Mediterranean/North African menu and biodynamic wine list ("tried orange and natural wines here before they became popular categories elsewhere"). / W1D 4PY; www.ducksoupsoho.co.uk; ducksoupsoho; Wed-Sat, Mon & Tue 10 pm, Sun 5 pm.

The Duke of Richmond E8 £60 ③③③
316 Queensbridge Road   020 7923 3990   14–1A
"Delicious food" and "attentive service" are the order of the day at this ambitious gastropub on the Dalston-Haggerston border, where the kitchen is headed by chef Tom Oldroyd, whose self-named restaurant in Islington closed down during the pandemic. / E8 3NH; www.thedukeofrichmond.com; thedukeofrichmond; Mon, Wed 9 pm, Fri & Sat, Thu 9.30 pm, Sun 8 pm.

The Duke of Sussex W4 £67   2️⃣2️⃣3️⃣
75 South Pde   020 8742 8801   8–1A
"Avoiding a typical pub-forgettable menu" – this Victorian tavern on a
prominent corner overlooking Acton Green Common "offers a tapas
selection of real quality and a lovely interior to boot". That's it on a good day,
though – it's not consistent and some "unexceptional" results dragged on
the rating a little this year. You can eat anywhere in the pub, although the
grand dining room at the rear is the most comfy location, and "the garden is
very pleasant on a fine day". / W4 5LF; www.thedukeofsussex.co.uk; thedukew4;
Mon-Wed 11 pm, Fri & Sat midnight, Thu 11 am, Sun 10 pm.

Dumplings' Legend W1 £41   3️⃣2️⃣1️⃣
16 Gerrard St   020 7494 1200   5–3A
"It's all about the dumplings" at this "efficient" and "good-value" Chinatown
dim sum specialist – "and luckily they're worth it". "The best time to go is a
Sunday just before the lunch rush". / W1D 6JE; www.dumplingslegend.com;
dumplingslegend; Mon-Thu 11 pm, Fri & Sat 3 am, Sun 10 pm.

Durbar W2 £43   3️⃣3️⃣2️⃣
24 Hereford Rd   020 7727 1947   7–1B
This "brilliant local curry house" off Westbourne Grove has "been there
forever (since 1956, in fact) for good reason" – "we've been going for over
40 years and it's always delicious and great value" and there's "always a
friendly welcome". Top Tip – "it no longer has an alcohol licence and is now
BYOB, so is even better value". / W2 4AA; www.durbartandoori.co.uk;
durbarrestaurant; Mon-Sat 11.30 pm.

The Dusty Knuckle £39   5️⃣2️⃣3️⃣
429 Green Lanes, N4   no tel   9–1D
Abbot Street, E8   020 3903 7598   14–1A
"Down a classic dodgy Dalston alleyway, this beautiful place awaits!" (there's
also an offshoot in Green Lanes, Haringey). "I love the good old Dusty
Knuckle", which inspires affection not just for its "absolutely top bread,
pastries and sarnies" plus "excellent coffee"; but also for its social enterprise
role supporting at-risk young East Londoners. / www.thedustyknuckle.com;
thedustyknuckle.

The Dysart Petersham TW10 £94   5️⃣4️⃣4️⃣
135 Petersham Road   020 8940 8005   1–4A
Kenneth Culhane's "superb cooking – inventive within the boundaries of
modern British cuisine" – has generated a groundswell of interest in this
"unique" venue: an Arts & Crafts home bordering leafy Richmond Park and
near the Thames. "The building itself is absolutely stunning and, like the
menu, feels both progressive and traditional"; the atmosphere of civilised
luxury extends to monthly dinners featuring a classical recital on an antique
rosewood Bechstein grand piano. / TW10 7AA; www.thedysartpetersham.co.uk;
thedysartpetersham; Wed & Thu, Sun, Fri & Sat 8.30 pm.

E&O W11 £77   3️⃣3️⃣3️⃣
14 Blenheim Crescent   020 7229 5454   7–1A
Over more than 20 years, Will Ricker's Notting Hill stalwart – fuelled by
cocktails, sushi, and other pan-Asian bites – has proved incredibly enduring. It
still has a few big fans, particularly local ones, but one or two reporters feel
it's now "lost its charm". / W11 1NN; www.eandolondon.com; eandonotthill;
Mon-Sat midnight, Sun 10 pm.

The Eagle EC1 £45 ③③④

159 Farringdon Rd 020 7837 1353 10–1A

"Gastropub heaven!" – this basic boozer on the busy Farringdon Road is where the gastropub revolution started in 1991, and it's *"still fabulous after all these years"* – *"no fuss, no pretence, just wholehearted focus, as ever, on simple yet perfect flavour combinations. Unbeatable!"*. Head chef Edward Mottershaw celebrates two decades as head chef this year, and still chalks up the daily changing menu of Mediterranean-influenced dishes a matter of minutes before service, ensuring *"simplicity and perfection without scary prices"*. / EC1R 3AL; www.theeaglefarringdon.co.uk; eaglefarringdon; Mon-Sat 11 pm, Sun 5 pm.

Eat Tokyo £40 ③②②

16 Old Compton St, W1 020 7439 9887 5–2A
50 Red Lion St, WC1 020 7242 3490 2–1D
27 Catherine St, WC2 020 3489 1700 5–3D
17 Notting Hill Gate, W11 020 7792 9313 7–2B
169 King St, W6 020 8741 7916 8–2B
14 North End Rd, NW11 020 8209 0079 1–1B
628 Finchley Rd, NW11 020 3609 8886 1–1B

"Proper" Japanese food at a *"very affordable price"* (*"the sushi is seemingly no more expensive than Yo! Sushi, but so much better quality"*) ensures that these Tokyo-inspired pitstops are *"always busy"* and there are *"often queues"*. *"The canteen atmosphere and sometimes inflexible service doesn't make you want to linger"* but no-one cares given the *"extensive menu – made with fresh ingredients and served up super quick – that's good overall value"*. Top Tip – *"the bento boxes are tasty and authentic"*. / www.eattokyo.co.uk; eattokyoldn.

Eataly EC2 £58 ②②③

135 Bishopsgate 07966 544965 10–2D

"A great place for anything Italian" – Oscar Farinetti's *"huge"* food mall concept has swept the world and its London outpost near Liverpool Street station (a relatively late arrival in 2021) boasts no fewer than 11 restaurants, bars and counters to feed you, alongside shops and stalls where you can pick up goodies to take home. Gastronomically, the sheer scale works against it, so even the flagship Terra elicits comparatively little praise, but the whole enterprise has a pleasant buzz; *"staff work hard to please"*; and simpler items in particular *"benefit from the ready supply of super ingredients"*. / EC2M 3YD; www.eataly.co.uk; eatalylondon; Mon-Sat 11 pm, Sun 10 pm.

Edera W11 £63 ③④③

148 Holland Park Ave 020 7221 6090 7–2A

"Roberto, Francesco and Alberto are finally back" (after a prolonged closure during Covid) and *"really go out of their way to make you feel welcome"* at their *"wonderful neighbourhood Italian"* in posh Holland Park. Its large local fanclub sometimes acknowledge that *"prices are too high"*, but don't mind because the food (including a number of Sardinian specialities) is *"tasty and well presented"* and the overall performance makes it *"dependable for any occasion"*. / W11 4UE; www.edera.co.uk; Mon-Sun 11 pm.

EDIT E8 NEW
217 Mare Street   no tel   14–1B
Near London Fields, this 'hyper-seasonal' spot in Hackney (from Elly Ward and the team behind plant-based pioneer Super Nature) opened in spring 2023 and focuses on a low-waste philosophy. There's a short array of meat-free, modern British dishes, accompanied by a selection of low-intervention wines, beers and ciders. Or, in the evenings, you can go for an eight-course tasting menu with the option of a drinks pairing. No survey feedback as yet, but if you are avoiding meat, this is one of the more interesting-looking openings this year. / E8 3QE; www.edit.london; edit.restaurant; Mon & Tue, Sun 3 pm, Wed-Sat 9 pm.

**081 Pizzeria,
Peckham Levels SE15** NEW   **£37**   5 2 2
95a Rye Lane   020 3795 8576   1–4D
"Best pizza for miles…" Andrea Asciuti's mega-popular pizza powerhouse has found its first permanent home in Peckham, opening in Feb' 2023 at this small, 20-cover unit. "Frantic service from Italians, but that doesn't matter because the pizza's so good!". (It also serves Napoli-inspired street food such as frittatina, arancina, crocche…. He also operates within pubs at the Smugglers Tavern in Fitzrovia and at Camden Town's Colonel Fawcett). / SE15 4ST; www.081pizzeria.com; 081pizzerialdn; Mon-Sun 11 pm.

The eight Restaurant W1 NEW   **£38**   3 2 2
68-70 Shaftesbury Avenue   020 3332 2313   4–3D
"A top choice for a Hong-Kong-style café menu" – this "rushed" tearoom on the edge of Chinatown opened in 2022 and serves everything from light bites to full meals from its huge selection of dishes. The food is consistently well rated. / W1D 6LZ; www.theeightrestaurant.co.uk; theeightlondon; Mon-Sun 10.30 pm.

**Ekstedt at The Yard,
Great Scotland Yard Hotel SW1**   **£118**   3 4 3
Great Scotland Yard   020 7925 4700   2–3C
"Niklas Ekstedt's trademark open-fire cuisine" has its first outpost (beyond Stockholm) in Westminster's Hyatt hotel, where the "relaxed and peaceful ambience, theatrical open kitchen and flames" and "unexpectedly delicate flavours" win over most reporters. Its ratings would be even higher, were it not for the occasional sceptic who feels the performance "relies on the drama of the grill rather than the quality of cooking". / SW1A 2HN; www.ekstedtattheyard.com; ekstedtldn; Tue-Sat 9 pm.

Ekte Nordic Kitchen EC4   **£64**   3 2 2
2-8 Bloomberg Arcade   020 3814 8330   10–3C
Soren Jessen's "slick, Nordic cafe in the City of London" occupies part of the Bloomberg Arcade and contributes to the development's renown for offering "good food in the dry desert of the Square Mile". It majors in Danish smørrebrød (rye bread with toppings): "nice for a change", but "you can rack up a fair bill eating these delicate one-bite-and-they-are-gone appetisers" (though "there there are decent main courses such as fish, schnitzel and venison fillet"). On the downside, results can end up seeming "not as Scandi and varied as expected" – "I prefer IKEA meatballs, even if they are not as prettily presented!" / EC4N 8AR; www.ektelondon.co.uk; ektelondon; Mon-Sat 10 pm.

El Pastor £56 3️⃣3️⃣4️⃣

Brewer Street, W1   020 3092 4553   4–3C
7a Stoney Street, SE1   no tel   10–4C

"Properly authentic tortillas and tacos transport you to Mexico City" with their *"spicy but very delicious"* flavours, at this Mexican duo from the Hart Brothers, whose original venue in a *"great location"* on the edge of Borough Market is deservedly *"very busy"*. The Soho branch has a late-night basement bar, 'Mezcaleria Colmillo', while 'big sister' Casa Pastor at Coal Drops Yard in King's Cross (see also) features live music. / www.tacoselpastor.co.uk; tacos_el_pastor.

El Ta'koy WC2

3 Henrietta Street   07377 220955   5–3D

Hawaiian street food marrying Latino and Asian cuisines is the promise at this small cellar and tiki bar, in a Covent Garden basement below three other restaurants. Open in 2021, it has yet to generate much in the way of survey feedback, but The Independent's Kate Ng describes a "fun, flirty little spot" with "generous plates" that are "middling to pretty damn good", plus "dangerously delicious" cocktails. / WC2E 8LU; el-takoy.com; el_takoy_london; Mon-Sun 11 pm.

Ela & Dhani SW13 £36 3️⃣4️⃣2️⃣

127 Church Road   020 8741 9583   11–1A

"Surprisingly and deliciously different" Indian cooking can be found at this *"smart little"* two-year-old on the main drag in Barnes – a debut restaurant from three friends who grew up together in the Punjab, one of whom runs the upmarket Barnes Pantry just up the road. Local regulars say they *"love this place and the staff"*. / SW13 9HR; www.eladhani.co.uk; ela_and_dhani; Tue-Thu 10 pm, Fri & Sat 10.30 pm, Sun 9 pm.

The Elder Press Café W6 £25 3️⃣3️⃣4️⃣

3 South Black Lion Lane   020 3887 4258   8–2B

Very *'zen'* for somewhere barely 100m from the A4 – this *"delightful"* Hammersmith café serves an *"original and interesting"* menu of light bites and luscious cakes and makes a handy stop-off from a riverside stroll. It was beautifully converted from a builders' merchants four years ago by chef Lindsay Elder; and its calm interior is a good match for the yoga and pilates sessions in the upstairs room. / W6 9TJ; www.theelderpress.co.uk; theelderpress; Mon-Sun 5 pm.

Eline E2 🆕 £73 4️⃣5️⃣3️⃣

1c Rosewood Building, Cremer Street   020 4547 2702   14–2A

"So special" and *"clearly the product of two people who absolutely love what they do and want to share it with as many other people as possible"* – Maria Viviani and chef Alex Reynolds' September 2022 newcomer *"hasn't been open that long but has made such an impact"* in Hoxton: It provides *"really welcoming, accessible fine dining"*. *"Alex showcases his exemplary skills in the kitchen"* delivering *"precise imaginative cooking"* in the *"cool dining room"* (although *"it can feel like a goldfish bowl on a quiet winter night"*). *"Meanwhile the lovely Maria is on hand to find you some of the most exciting and approachable low-intervention, natural wines around"*. Top Tip – *"their bottle shop is an absolute bonus for those passing by and needing to pick up something spectacular for dinner at home!"* / E2 8GX; www.restauranteline.co.uk; elinelondon; Wed-Sun 9.30 pm.

Elis,
Town Hall Hotel E2 £69 **4**|**4**|2

Patriot Square   020 7871 0460   14–2B

"I'm pleased they kept the hanging lights of the former Corner Room" – the previous occupant of this restaurant space within the monumental, erstwhile Bethnal Green Town Hall (nowadays a hotel). Chef Rafael Cagali runs the much-fêted Da Terra next door, and this October 2022 newcomer provides "a simplified version of the Michelin two-star cuisine" at its neighbour. Reports included plus points: "the quality combinations are full of flavour" and service is "decent", while on the debit side, ambience has sometimes proved elusive and sentiments seem a tad muted: there are no full-on raves at how marvellous and incredible it all is. Top Menu Tip – dulce de leite doughnuts. / E2 9NF; www.restaurantelis.co.uk; elis.ldn.

Elliot's £79 **3**|**3**|2

12 Stoney St, SE1   020 7403 7436   10–4C

121-123 Mare Street, E8   020 3302 5252   14–2B

"Excellent modern cooking with Med influences" and a "good natural wine list" are the strengths of this Borough Market staple that has championed organic and biodynamic wine for more than a decade; and which was joined two years ago by a spin-off near London Fields. The cuisine is "down to earth, with some stonking small plates" and matched with "efficient service and a relaxed atmosphere" to provide a "very enjoyable meal". / www.elliots.london; elliotslondon.

Elystan Street SW3 £105 **4**|**3**|3

43 Elystan Street   020 7628 5005   6–2C

Former Square chef, "Philip Howard's magical touch" is evident in much of the "very well-realised, modern and light" 'flexitarian' cuisine at his grown-up HQ, in one of the posh side streets surrounding Brompton Cross. Ambience-wise, it's not a riot, but "unustuffy", "very civilised and not noisy". Incidents of "inept performance" post-Covid continue to drag on its rating for service, but most reporters are "very well looked after" and a typical report is of a "truly delightful" meal. / SW3 3NT; www.elystanstreet.com; elystanstreet; Mon-Thu 2145 pm, Fri & Sat 10.30 pm, Sun 4 pm.

Emilia's Crafted Pasta £56 **3**|**3**|3

12 George Street, Wood Wharf, E14   020 8176 1100   12–1C

77 Alie Street, E1   020 3358 0317   10–2D

Unit C3 Ivory House, St Katharine Docks, E1   020 7481 2004   10–3D

"Excellent pasta" is the straightforward proposition at this Italian trio, with a flagship in Canary Wharf, which takes its name and inspiration from Italy's Emilia-Romagna region. / www.emiliaspasta.com; emiliaspasta.

Emmanuelle EC1 **NEW**

5a Rosebery Avenue   no tel   10–1A

Yuma Hashmi's latest venture is a seventies-styled wine bar (complete with a peacock rattan chair, famous from 1974's X-rated film Emmanuelle) directly opposite Tehran-Berlin (fka The Drunken Butler), his Persian restaurant in Clerkenwell. The wine list is modern, with natural and biodynamic options, and is backed up by French and Iranian snacks and small plates. / EC1R 4SP; emmanuellewinebar.com; Mon, Fri-Sun 10.30 pm.

Empire Empire W11 NEW
16 All Saints Road   020 3930 3658   7–1B

Aiming to 'epitomise India's groovy seventies scene', this disco-themed dive in Notting Hill features drinking, dancing and dining and is the brainchild of Harneet Baweja, the owner of Gunpowder. It launched too late for survey feedback, but early online buzz from fans of Gunpowder suggest it's worth a whirl. The menu – with dishes incorporating goat, duck and guinea fowl – reads well; while on the drinks list, 'sharing cider' is a feature, alongside a short wine selection and non-Indian beers. / W11 1HH;
www.empire-empire.restaurant; empirempire_london; Mon-Sat 10 pm, Sun 4 pm.

The Empress E9 £58 334
130 Lauriston Rd   020 8533 5123   14–2B

Consistently one of London's better-performing gastroboozers, this substantial Victorian tavern near Victoria Park in Hackney was iconic in the area's gentrification over twenty years ago, and "just keeps delivering as a local pub and place to eat". It does a "perfect Sunday roast" while also catering well for non-meat-eaters. / E9 7LH; www.empresse9.co.uk; the_empress_e9; Mon-Sun 10 pm.

Endo at The Rotunda,
TV Centre W12 £280 545
101 Wood Lane   020 3972 9000   1–2B

"A total one off" – Endo Kazutoshi's "zen-like" venue occupies a unique site, on the top of the old BBC Television Centre, and is "spectacular in all respects". "Chef Endo has ruined all other sushi restaurants for me… watching Endo and his team preparing individual pieces of sushi… the rice perfect and still slightly warm, the seafood surely all the best money can buy and prepared with utmost respect. It could be pretentious, but Chef Endo is such a warm and welcoming presence that it never feels like it". Despite the ruinous expense, all reports say it's "worth every penny": "The best meal ever… until you go back!" / W12 7FR; www.endoatrotunda.com; kazutoshi.endo; Tue-Sat 9 pm.

Endo Kazutoshi,
The OWO SW1 NEW
57 Whitehall Place   Awaiting tel   2–3C

From the all-star team behind Endo at the Rotunda – another Japanese-influenced rooftop venture: this time a 60-seater on top of London's splashiest hotel opening in decades, complete with outside terrace. Kazutoshi is backed by Misha Zelman, the man who created the likes of Burger & Lobster and the Goodman steakhouse chain. / SW1A 2EU; Tue-Sat 10.30 pm.

Enoteca Turi SW1 343
87 Pimlico Road   020 7730 3663   6–2D

"The personal touch is invaluable" at Giuseppe & Pamela Turi's "thriving" and "very confident" Italian stalwart, which "has gone from strength to strength since moving from Putney to Pimlico in 2015, and is always full" (often of long-term customers, who "happily make the trek" into the centre of town). "If Italian wine is your thing, this is the place to go": Giuseppe's all-Italian list is a "masterpiece in its own right" and even if "a ton of money is sometimes required, the vintages are not expensive for what they are". To match it: "refined cooking, with classics, specials, and seasonal variations, reflecting the team's heritage". It's a "grown-up" and "very confident experience, without bowing to fashion" – "the Turis be found at the restaurant every day, and there is always a smile to welcome you". BREAKING NEWS – In August 2023, the Turis announced their retirement, thus rendering the above entry otiose. A month later, just before we went to press, experienced restaurateur, Dominic Ford, and Liberty Wines owner, David Gleave, were announced as the new patrons. Much of the team

remains in place, as does the cellar. But – as our read feedback clearly demonstrates – this whole enterprise has always been a supremely personal one and the Turis will be a hard act to follow. We've maintained its rating (but taking service down a notch, reflecting the very personal style of the founders). / SW1W 8PH; www.enotecaturi.com; enotecaturi; closed Sun.

The Enterprise SW3 £72 ②③④
35 Walton St   020 7584 3148   6–2C
"Amusing locals and colourful regulars liven up the atmosphere" at this smart watering hole for the Chelsea set, where guests enjoy immaculate white tablecloths, "excellent, often entertaining service" and "perfectly fine gastropub food". / SW3 2HU; www.theenterprise.co.uk; theenterprise35; Mon-Sat 10.30 pm, Sun 10 pm.

Epicurus NW1 NEW
The North Yard, Camden Stables Market   07843 199560   9–2B
The latest venture from a pair of ex-Palomar chefs, in Camden Market's expansion into North Yard, marries North American diner food with Middle Eastern flair and flavours. Shiri Kraus and Amir Batito already run the Black Cow steakhouse nearby and the result here is an interesting twist on a seemingly familiar (fairly meaty) formula. It opened in late April 2023, too late to generate feedback in our annual diners' poll. / NW1 8AH; www.epicuruscamden.co.uk; epicuruscamden; Tue-Sun 11 pm.

L'Escargot W1 £100 ③③③
48 Greek Street   020 7439 7474   5–2A
This Gallic treasure (est. 1927, but ultimately dating back to 1896) is London's oldest French restaurant and – complete with its snail carpet – remains a Soho landmark. Its standards under owner Brian Clivaz have held up well over the years, and its ratings continued to be solid in this slightly turbulent year (which saw the establishment close from February to May 2023 to allow for a financial restructuring). The fairly classic menu is appealing and mixes affordable entry-level dishes (croque monsieur at £12) with more luxurious options (such as baked lobster with garlic butter, or fillet of beef 'Rossini', both at £54). Top Tip – superb-value prix fixe at lunch and early evening: two courses £19, three courses £24. / W1D 4EF; www.lescargot.co.uk; lescargotsoho.

Escocesa N16 £71 ③③②
67 Stoke Newington Church Street   020 7812 9189   1–1C
An "excellent Stokey local", "deservedly very popular" for its Spanish tapas, in particular its "absolutely wonderful fish": its Glasgow-born founder, former record producer Stephen Lironi, has made it his mission to intercept some of the top-quality Scottish fish usually exported to Spain. One quibble this year: "surely it's time to upgrade the school chairs". Top Tip – "half-price oysters before 7pm". / N16 0AR; www.escocesa.co.uk; escocesa_n16; Mon-Thu 10 pm, Fri & Sat 11 pm, Sun 9.30 pm.

Estiatorio Milos SW1 £140 ②②④
1 Regent Street   020 7839 2080   4–4D
"One of the best fish restaurants anywhere" – Costas Spiladis's London outpost of his luxurious international chain channels the brilliance of the Mediterranean, with its bright, white walls and high ceiling. "The fish is displayed beautifully on ice at one end of the venue and hosed down every 20 mins or so" – "a fantastic selection that always delivers a fabulous meal". Sadly, though, you have to be a Greek shipping magnate to afford it nowadays ("just reading the menu is a shock"), and even those who think it's "worth the hype" can find it "so eye-wateringly expensive, I think it might be

one visit per year from now on". Those less well disposed to it, say "if you like being served a smidgen of food and being charged a fortune, this restaurant is for you!" / SW1Y 4NR; www.estiatoriomilos.com; estiatoriomilos; Mon-Sat 11 pm, Sun 10 pm.

Evelyn's Table at The Blue Posts W1 £161 543
28 Rupert Street 07921 336010 4–3D
"This intimate little counter-dining venue" in an ancient pub that nowadays finds itself part of Chinatown "shows levels of skill and technique to compete with much better-known places that leave you with a far higher bill". James Goodyear has taken over from Luke Selby (the latter departing to be head chef at Le Manoir), but all reports swoon over "a truly special experience" and a multi-course tasting menu that's "absolutely exceptional". "Love the counter-top layout of the restaurant and the chefs are very happy to talk, explaining in detail how things are made (important to me because I am a very keen cook!)". "It has a buzzy vibe and is a bit of a squeeze (in both space and time), making it a very different formula than nearby Aulis. Having said that, the cooking is consistently delightful, imaginative and bold. The menu feels well thought-through, building and balancing as it progresses". "File it under 'one to watch' as they plan to build out the ambition even further": from mid-2023 they are opening on Monday nights and also incorporating their wine bar, The Mulwray, and the pub, The Blue Posts, into the overall offering at Evelyn's Table. / W1D 6DJ; www.theblueposts.co.uk; evelynstable; Tue-Sat 11 pm.

Everest Curry King SE13 £32 332
24 Loampit Hill 020 8691 2233 1–4D
"A staple fixture for the local Sri Lankan community, serving good portions of tasty grub for very reasonable prices", this Lewisham shopfront outfit (with a geographically misleading name) is "now slightly smartened-up, with a new glass frontage". Recent convert Jay Rayner of The Observer swooned at a beetroot curry of "all-engrossing, soothing power". / SE13 7SW; Mon-Sun 11 pm.

Everest Inn SE3 £56 322
41 Montpelier Vale 020 8852 7872 1–4D
This Nepalese venue in Blackheath Village is popular with locals, who rate it "a cut above" standard curry-house fare. Ideal after a stroll on the common it overlooks. / SE3 0TJ; www.everestinn.co.uk; everestinn; Tue-Sat 11 pm, Sun 10 pm.

Evernight SW11 NEW £64 333
3 Ravine Way 020 4547 6390 11–1D
Near the new American Embassy in Nine Elms, this modern izakaya opened in September 2022 and is the creation of Singapore-born Lynus Lim (ex-The Laughing Heart) and Chase Lovecky (formerly of The Clove Club). Foodwise, it's a bit of a mashup, aiming to 'highlight Japanese cookery techniques whilst engaging the micro-seasonality of produce from the British Isles'. Most reports say the result is "a super newcomer with really enjoyable food showing great balance of flavours and representing value for money". On the downside, there's the occasional view that "though good it's been very hyped up and some dishes work better than others (a bit overcomplicated)". / SW11 7BH; evernightlondon.co.uk; Tue-Sat 11 pm.

Fadiga W1 £38 453
71 Berwick Street 020 3609 5536 4–1C
"My own family comes from the Emilia Romagna and I can vouch for the authenticity of the delicious (and also generously proportioned!) dishes", says one fan of this "tiny, restaurant, run by a family from Bologna" in Soho. "Dad cooks, Mum is the sommelier, daughter serves tables. Excellent!" / W1F 8TB; www.fadiga.uk; fadiga_ristorantebolognese; Tue-Sat 11 pm.

Fair Shot Café W1
17 South Molton Street   020 7499 9007   3–2B

Bianca Tavella's ground-breaking non-profit moved from Mayfair to splendid new Covent Garden premises in early 2023, bringing tasty treats, light lunches and a proper caffeine hit to guests, while its workforce of young people with learning difficulties get their first proper shot at a job. This social enterprise is a winner, too: 100% of its graduates move on to paid employment, against the UK's 95% unemployment rate among adults with learning difficulties. / W1K 5QT; fairshot.co.uk; fairshotcafe; Sun-Fri 6 pm, Sat 7 pm.

Fallow St James's SW1   £101   3 3 3
2 St James's Market   07785 937900   4–4D

To instant acclaim two years ago, Jack Croft and Will Murray transplanted their renowned Heddon Street residency, known for its "interesting" small plates, to this large (150-cover) site, with open kitchen, chef's counter and bar, at the southern end of Haymarket. All accounts this year continue to vaunt its cooking and "fun" style, but ratings weakened across the board amidst a general feeling it risks becoming a victim of its own success: "it felt a bit rushed…"; "the food was good, but prices were crazy…" Top Tips – "smoked cod's head? Yes please!"; and breakfast is now available here both weekends and weekdays, and is highly recommended. / SW1Y 4RP; www.fallowrestaurant.com; fallowrestaurant; Mon-Sun 10.30 pm.

La Famiglia SW10   £85   2 3 4
7 Langton Street   020 7351 0761   6–3B

Fans of this "old-fashioned" and datedly glam trattoria near World's End in Chelsea (est. 1966, and the haunt, in its heyday, of folks like Jack Nicholson) say it may "not be tops for food, but the atmosphere and ambience are addictive"(especially in its adorable garden in summer). Fears that it's becoming too long in the tooth have been around for years, with sceptics suggesting "they're just painting by numbers nowadays"; but true believers insist this view is "just snotty – the food is delicious and the service charming". Top Tip – for a blast from the past, "the dessert trolley is an attractive feature". / SW10 0JL; www.lafamiglia.co.uk; lafamiglia.sw10; Tue-Sat 9.45 pm, Sun 9.15 pm.

Farang N5   £53   4 4 3
72 Highbury Park   020 7226 1609   9–1D

"Super spicy (in a good way) cooking", "really interesting dishes" and "roti to die for" keep aficionados of new-wave Thai cuisine coming back to Sebby Holmes's Highbury venue – originally a pop-up, but now firmly established after eight years on the scene. / N5 2XE; www.faranglondon.co.uk; farangldn; Wed-Sat 9 pm.

Farmacy W2   £76   4 3 4
74 Westbourne Grove   020 7221 0705   7–1B

Camilla Fayed's "wonderful" plant-based project in Bayswater, supplied by her biodynamic farm in Kent, offers "a wide range of options to keep you returning", with veggie versions of fashionable global dishes – ramen, tacos, pad thai and "juicy and delicious burgers, absolutely to die for". "You can certainly tell she's sunk millions into this place – it's really rather pretty, and the enormous central bar is impressive". / W2 5SH; www.farmacylondon.com; farmacy kitchen; Mon-Thu 9 pm, Fri & Sat 10 pm, Sun 8 pm.

The Fat Badger TW10 £69 3 2 2
15-17 Hill Rise   020 3743 0853   1–4A
Like its other five London ventures, the Gladwin family's Richmond bar/restaurant supplies modern (rather eclectic) British plates and wines sourced from its farm and vineyard in Sussex. Reports are relatively limited, mixing all-round good feedback with sentiment such as: "an average meal from a chain from which I would expect slightly more". / TW10 6UQ; www.thefatbadger-restaurant.com; thefatbadger_resto; Tue-Sat 10 pm, Sun 8 pm.

Fatt Pundit £59 3 2 3
77 Berwick Street, W1   020 7287 7900   4–1C
6 Maiden Lane, WC2   020 7836 8883   5–3D
"Delicious small plates that are unusual, interesting and at times rather spicy" distinguish this Soho and Covent Garden duo presenting the Indo-Chinese cuisine developed by Kolkata's historic Hakka community. / www.facebook.com/fattpundit; fattpundit.

Fatto A Mano N1
3 Pancras Sq   020 3148 4900   9–3C
One minute's walk from Google HQ, amidst the clean-lined new canyons north of King's Cross, this is the year-old London outpost of Brighton & Hove's well-regarded chain (whose unit in Shoreditch's Boxpark is no longer in operation). Reports on the Brighton operations are all very upbeat, but this one has yet to spark much in the way of interest. / N1C 4AG; www.fattoamanopizza.com; fattoamanopizza; Sun-Thu 10 pm, Fri & Sat 10.30 pm.

Feels Like June E14
15 Water Street   02035307700   12–1C
LA came to Canary Wharf at this California-inspired venue, which opened in summer 2022, and whose all-day menu (also with brunch and dinner alternatives) aims to reflect the west coast's debt to the cuisines of Latin America and Italy. The sunny styling of the interior is a winner – regarding the grub we have limited (but upbeat) feedback. / E14 9SB; www.feelslikejune.com; feels_like_june; Mon-Sun 1 am.

Fenchurch Restaurant,
Sky Garden EC3 £110 3 3 4
20 Fenchurch St   033 3772 0020   10–3D
Limited feedback in this year's annual diners' poll on the 37th floor of the City's 'Walkie Talkie' – perhaps many Londoners regard it as touristy. Such accounts as we have, though, on the cooking under chef Kerth Gumbs is upbeat: you can have an eight-course tasting menu for £115 or eat à la carte (although the latter is not much less inexpensive with main dishes circa £50). Incredible views, of course. / EC3M 3BY; skygarden.london; sg_skygarden; Tue, Sun 9 pm, Wed & Thu 9.30 pm, Fri & Sat 8.30 pm.

Fez Mangal W11 £50 3 2 1
104 Ladbroke Grove   020 7229 3010   7–1A
"Still one of the best Turkish grills in town" – this Ladbroke Grove fixture might be "a bit spartan", but "speedy service and BYO" make it a "cost-effective alternative to eating at home". Top Tip – there's "slightly less-packed seating in the extension next door". / W11 1PY; www.fezmangal.com; fezmangal; Mon-Sun 11.30 pm.

50 Kalò di Ciro Salvo WC2 £49 🄸🄸🄸
7 Northumberland Avenue 020 7930 9955 2–3C
"Not quite as good as the original in Naples, but still a safe bet if you want a traditional Neapolitan pizza in the heart of the capital" – Ciro Salvo's offshoot of his award-winning chain (which is indeed headquartered in Napoli) serves "seriously great" pizza "as Naples intended" (using his special long fermentation dough); and its "busy and vibrant" quarters are "an excellent find so close to Trafalgar Square!". A few pizza anoraks say "it's fine, just not London's best". / WC2N 5BY; www.xn–50kal-yta.it; 50kalolondon; Mon-Sun 11 pm.

Firebird W1 £80 🄸🄸🄸
29 Poland Street 020 3813 1430 3–1D
"They like grilling!" – in fact pretty well every dish at this "thoroughly enjoyable" Soho yearling, from St Petersburg restaurateurs Madina Kazhimova and Anna Dolgushina, has been 'touched by flames', resulting in some really "lovely food". It's served in a very contemporary interior, alongside a list of natural wines. / W1F 8QR; firebirdlondon.co.uk; firebird.london; Mon-Sat 11 pm.

Fischer's W1 £69 🄶🄶🄸
50 Marylebone High Street 020 7466 5501 2–1A
"The Wolseley's popular little brother provides a setting somewhere between a Munich beer cellar and a Viennese Cafe" in fashionable Marylebone. You don't come here for the food – a "pretty underwhelming pastiche" of Austrian/German cuisine with schnitzel a menu mainstay – and the feeling is widespread that "they should do better". But even the many who feel it's becoming ever-more "disappointing" given the "steep" prices often acknowledge that "it's a useful spot and usually busy". / W1U 5HN; www.fischers.co.uk; fischerslondon; Sun & Mon 9.30 pm, Tue-Sat 10 pm.

Fish Central EC1 £43 🄸🄸🄶
149-155 Central St 020 7253 4970 13–1A
This "authentic chippy" in Clerkenwell – a Greek-Cypriot family-run veteran of more than 50 years' standing – scores well for its "excellent fish" and "warm, humorous service". / EC1V 8AP; www.fishcentral.co.uk; fishcentralrestaurant; Mon-Thu, Sat 10 pm, Fri 10.30 pm.

fish! SE1 £78 🄸🄶🄸
Cathedral St 020 7407 3803 10–4C
This "great fish restaurant offering a range of seafood (and other) dishes" has been a fixture for more than 20 years, behind a glass frontage "in the middle of buzzing Borough Market". The fish is "the freshest" and there are "usually some unusual specials" – although many would argue that "the most appealing thing is its location". / SE1 9AL; www.fishkitchen.co.uk; fishboroughmarket; Sun-Wed 10 pm, Thu-Sat 11 pm.

Fishers SW6 £46 🄸🄸🄶
19 Fulham High Street 02073715555 11–1B
"The fish is consistently very good (whether battered, grilled or steamed)" at this "perennial favourite" chippy near Putney Bridge in Fulham, which offers "takeaway and a small dine-in area with a half-dozen tables". "The chips are not bad and the price is reasonable". / SW6 3JH; www.fishersfishandchips.co.uk; fisherslondon; Mon-Sun 10 pm.

F S A

Fishworks £82 3 3 2
7-9 Swallow St, W1   020 7734 5813   4–2B
89 Marylebone High St, W1   020 7935 9796   2–1A
2-4 Catherine Street, WC2   020 7240 4999   5–3D
The "super-fresh fish" – "simply prepared" and "never overcooked" – "never disappoints" at this "good value" trio of West End seafood brasseries, in Covent Garden, Marylebone and Swallow Street, off Piccadilly. / www.fishworks.co.uk; FishworksUK.

Fiume SW8 £76 2 2 2
Circus West Village, Sopwith Way   020 3904 9010   11–1C
This "elegantly decorated, modern Italian" with a terrace overlooking the river near the redeveloped Battersea Power Station is "useful in the neighbourhood" – a "safe bet", albeit "expensive for what it is". High-profile chef Francesco Mazzei parted company with the owners, D&D London, in early 2023, boosting the sentiment that this potentially spectacular venue has never fully realised its potential. / SW8 5BN; fiume-restaurant.co.uk; fiume.london; Mon-Sat 10 pm, Sun 8.30 pm; SRA-accredited.

The Five Fields SW3 £201 4 4 3
8-9 Blacklands Ter   020 7838 1082   6–2D
"For a very civilised meal", Taylor Bonnyman's "refined" and "romantic" venue – in a Chelsea townhouse, hidden way near Peter Jones – has become a huge hit: out of the PR limelight, but in the Top 40 most-mentioned restaurants in our annual diners' poll and "well worthy of its Michelin star" thanks to its "immaculate but unobtrusive" service and Marguerite Keogh's "superb and assured cooking": "wonderfully light, creative, beautiful and flavoursome food" from "their own kitchen garden in Sussex" (which the most ardent fans feel is "at a level above their tyre-company rating"). Its ratings slipped a little this year amidst cost of living concerns (and a number of reporters noting that "it's a pity that they only do a tasting menu"). As a result, its style can appear more "hushed" and "formal" and "very expensive" ("we find it just too costly to visit anymore, although we love this place as one of the most amazing providers of interesting and totally divine food"). That's still a minority view, though – for most diners it's just "just a brilliant experience". Top Tip – "stellar wine selection". / SW3 2SP; www.fivefieldsrestaurant.com; the5fields; Tue-Sat 10 pm.

500 N19 £58 3 4 2
782 Holloway Rd   020 7272 3406   9–1C
Near Archway, this "great little local" (named after the diminutive Fiat Cinquecento) is both "reliable and good value". It may "feel a tad old school", but chef-patron Mario Magli and his team serve up "wonderful food with love and enthusiasm". ("I have had many meals here with friends and it has always been delightful and an example of how delicious Italian cooking can be".) / N19 3JH; www.500restaurant.co.uk; 500restaurant; Wed-Sat 10 pm, Sun 9 pm.

500 Degrees SE24 £46 3 2 3
153a Dulwich Road   020 7274 8200   11–2D
"Great pizza that's very good value" is the USP of this Neapolitan-style shopfront outfit by Brockwell Park. It used to have three offshoots across South London, but now only the Herne Hill branch is ongoing. / SE24 0NG; www.500degrees.co; 500degreeshernehill; Mon-Sat 11 pm, Sun 10 pm.

FKABAM (Black Axe Mangal) N1 £56 4 2 3
156 Canonbury Road   no tel   9–2D
"Nothing else quite like this in London!" – Lee Tiernan's renowned heavy-metal BBQ (renamed with a nod to Prince a couple of years ago) "may look closed from the outside, but inside, this tiny venue (30 seats) is jumping". It's known for its kick-ass flatbreads: "flavours pack a punch, the decor's wild and the music loud. We love it!" / N1 2UP; www.blackaxemangal.com; blackaxemangal; Wed-Sat 10.30 pm.

The Flask N6 £54 2 3 4
77 Highgate West Hill   020 8348 7346   9–1B
Not to be confused with its namesake near Hampstead tube on the other side of the Heath – this classic, traditional pub (which boasts Dickens as a former patron) sits in a beautiful slice of period Highgate, and benefits from a large outside terrace, a characterful interior and dependable grub. / N6 6BU; www.theflaskhighgate.com; theflaskhighgate; Mon-Sat 10 pm, Sun 9 pm.

Flat Iron £39 3 3 3
17 Beak St, W1   020 3019 2353   4–2B
42-44 James Street, W1   no tel   3–1A
17 Henrietta St, WC2   020 3019 4212   5–3C
9 Denmark St, WC2   no tel   5–1A
9 Young Street, W8   no tel   6–1A **NEW**
47-51 Caledonian Rd, N1   no tel   9–3D
112-116 Tooley Street, SE1   no tel   10–4D
41-45 The Cut, SE1   no tel   10–4A
Soho Wharf, Clink Street, SE1   no tel   10–3C
88-90 Commercial Street, E1   no tel   13–2C
77 Curtain Road, EC2   no tel   13–1B
"One of the best bangs for your buck in town" – this "well-priced" steak chain has a "sensible formula" and has "managed to keep standards up despite constant expansion" (its latest, 11th London site, opened in March 2023 in Kensington). "Surroundings are basic" and "their menu is very simplistic: you choose a cut of meat, sauce and sides – the cuts are cooked to perfection", "chips are hot, the service is punctual" and "free ice cream at the end ensures happy faces when people leave". / www.flatironsteak.co.uk; flatironsteak.

Flat White W1 £13 3 3 2
17 Berwick St   020 7734 0370   4–2D
This "small, often crowded" independent coffee shop by Soho's Berwick Street market is a pilgrimage site for caffeine junkies, as the source of Antipodean 'third wave' coffee culture in Britain since its 2005 opening. And yes, "the coffee's very good". / W1F 0PT; www.flatwhitesoho.co.uk; flat white; Mon-Fri 5 pm, Sat 6 pm, Sun 6.30pm.

Flesh and Buns £68 4 4 3
32 Berners Street, W1   020 3019 3492   3–1D
Bone Daddies, 41 Earlham Street, WC2   020 7632 9500   5–2C
"A taste-tingling sensation of Japanese and other Asian delights" – the "most amazing bao buns", plus "Korean wings, poke bowls and sushi that are all so good" – win a big thumbs up for this duo of "great Asian-fusion restaurants" (under the same ownership as Bone Daddies). If anything, their star has risen since they cut back to just two branches in Fitzrovia and Covent Garden. / www.fleshandbuns.com; fleshandbuns.

Flora Indica SW5　　　　**£60**　　3|3|3
242 Old Brompton Road　020 7370 4450　6–2A
"A quirky steampunk theme combined with an emphasis on cocktails and craft beers accompanies very sound modern Indian cooking" at this Earl's Court venture, whose name pays tribute to the 19th-century Scottish botanists who classified the subcontinent's plants. "After a few false starts on the site, this restaurant has found its forte under the same ownership as its predecessor Mr Wing (RIP)". / SW5 0DE; www.flora-indica.com; flora_indica; Tue-Sun 11 pm.

Flour & Grape SE1　　　　**£51**　　3|3|4
214 Bermondsey St　020 7407 4682　10–4D
This new-wave Italian in Bermondsey is "deservedly packed at all times" with fans of its "very moreish" pasta-only dishes in "generous servings". "Not being able to book is a bit of a gamble", but you can queue in the downstairs cocktail bar, 'Two One Four'. / SE1 3TQ; www.flourandgrape.com; flourandgrape; Mon-Sun 10 pm.

Foley's W1　　　　**£56**　　3|3|3
23 Foley Street　020 3137 1302　2–1B
High ratings express continued satisfaction with this 70-seater in Fitzrovia, where an outside bar is something of a feature. The website promises 'Asian-inspired food, cocktails and sake' and steady feedback confirms that's what it consistently delivers. / W1W 6DU; www.foleysrestaurant.co.uk; foleysrestaurant; Mon-Thu 10 pm, Fri & Sat 10.30 pm, Sun 9 pm.

Fortnum & Mason,
The Diamond Jubilee Tea Salon W1　**£90**　　3|3|4
181 Piccadilly　020 7734 8040　3–3D
"Delicious sarnies and pastries keep on coming" at this elegant chamber, just down the road from its rival The Ritz, to which it is a close second in votes as offering London's top afternoon tea. There is a huge selection of brews, plus "excellent homemade ice creams and sorbets" and "yummy savoury snacks as well". "Take a friend from overseas and pretend you come here all the time!" / W1A 1ER; www.fortnumandmason.com; fortnums; Mon-Sat 8 pm, Sun 6 pm.

45 Jermyn St. SW1　　　　**£85**　　2|3|3
45 Jermyn Street　020 7205 4545　3–3D
With its many booths, Fortnum & Mason's "comfortable" bar/restaurant (with its own, independent street entrance) provides a "discreet" and "decently located" venue that's ideal for a St James's light bite, meal, tea, coffee or cocktail; and is most often tipped as a handy option for a business get-together. Since its very promising launch in 2015, its ratings have waned, with its cooking increasingly judged "reliable but not spectacular". Top Menu Tip – "breakfast is always a pleasure; go for the Welsh rarebit". / SW1Y 6DN; www.45jermynst.com; 45jermynst; Mon-Sat 10.15 pm, Sun 4.45 pm.

40 Maltby Street SE1　　　　**£58**　　3|3|3
40 Maltby St　020 7237 9247　10–4D
Firmly established after more than a decade, highly rated chef Steve Williams's no-frills canteen is attached to a biodynamic wine warehouse in a railway arch behind London Bridge station. It's "always busy, but the trek is worth it for the food" – seasonal ingredients transformed in a basic-looking open kitchen and served "with a smile and a laugh". / SE1 3PA; www.40maltbystreet.com; 40maltbystreet; Wed-Sat 10 pm.

Forza Win SE5 333
29-33 Camberwell Church Street   07454 898693   1–3C
"Inventive and delicious Italian cooking in a cheerful trattoria" is the
straightforward but engaging offer at Bash Redford and Michael Lavery's
Camberwell newcomer, relocated from its former well-known Peckham
location in late 2022. Top Menu Tips – *"the homemade focaccia is the best,
either plain or with a dipping sauce such as nduja, wild garlic pesto or crab
and lemon; the antipasti are so varied and good and – if you have room –
the signature dessert, custardo, is terrific"*. / SE5 8TR; www.forzawin.com;
forzawin; Mon-Sun 10.30 pm.

Forza Wine SE15 £61 343
Floor 5, Rye Lane   020 7732 7500   1–4D
"Find of the year and worth the trek to Peckham" (although the foodie in-
crowd have known about it and its sibling Forza Win, newly transferred to
Camberwell, for several years now) – this rooftop wine bar with a *"buzzing
ambience, perched above Peckham Rye station"*, offers *"a great selection of
small plates"* to nibble on while sipping *"natural wine only, but a fair few
easy-drinking bottles"* (or cocktails if you prefer). In September 2023, they
opened a large new offshoot on the terrace at the National Theatre: there
are 100 covers inside with an open kitchen, and a sheltered outside area
with seating for 70 drinkers and diners. / SE15 4ST; www.forzawine.com;
forzawine; Sun-Thu 11.30 pm, Fri & Sat 12.30 am.

Four Regions TW9 £59 333
102-104 Kew Rd   020 8940 9044   1–4A
This *"stalwart neighbourhood Chinese restaurant"* on the fringes of
Richmond (as you head to Kew) is well known after more than 30 years for
the *"consistently good food"* that means it's *"usually busy"*. / TW9 2PQ;
www.fourregions.co.uk; four regions; Mon-Sat 11 pm, Sun 10.30 pm.

Four Seasons £68 411
11 Gerrard Street, W1   020 7287 0900   5–3A
12 Gerrard St, W1   020 7494 0870   5–3A
23 Wardour St, W1   020 7287 9995   5–3A
84 Queensway, W2   020 7229 4320   7–2C
*"It's worth the spartan interior and mixed service to eat the roast duck
and/or char siu pork"* at these Cantonese canteens, where *"the best roast
duck in the world is the claim"* – from no less an authority than The FT –
"and it must be up there" with *"meat and crispy skin so well done (no pun
intended)"*; and don't forget *"the crispy pork belly – an especial fat-lover's
treat!"*. Launched in Queensway 34 years ago, the group now has three
venues around Chinatown plus the new Chop Chop nearby in the
Hippodrome Casino. Further afield there are outlets in Colindale's Bang Bang
Oriental food hall, Oxford and Leicester. / www.fs-restaurants.co.uk;
fourseasons_uk.

14 Hills EC3 £96 224
120 Fenchurch Street   020 3981 5222   10–3D
"Great decor" in the shape of 2,500 living evergreen plants vie with the
"stunning 14th-floor views" over the City for top billing at this D&D London
venue in 120 Fenchurch Street. By comparison, the *"expensive but good
food"* from an Anglo-French menu is somewhat in the shade. / EC3M 5BA;
www.danddlondon.com; danddlondon; Mon-Sun 10.30 pm; SRA-accredited.

Fox & Grapes SW19 £63 343
9 Camp Rd 020 8619 1300 11–2A

"You feel miles away from London" at this Georgian gastroboozer on the edge of Wimbledon Common, which provides "a great atmosphere in very cosy surroundings". "There's a more relaxed vibe than when it originally emerged from its old 'boozer' days. The staff are lovely, attentive, fun but not over the top, and the food is perfect". / SW19 4UN; www.foxandgrapeswimbledon.co.uk; foxandgrapeswimbledon; Wed-Sat 9.15 pm, Sun 8 pm.

The Fox & Hounds SW11 £70 343
66-68 Latchmere Road 020 7924 5483 11–1C

"Super-charming service" and a "great hidden garden" that feels "secluded and away from London life" are key ingredients behind the success of this "jolly pub-restaurant" on a prominent corner in Battersea; very "decent" Mediterranean-inspired food too. / SW11 2JU; www.thefoxandhoundspub.co.uk; thefoxbattersea; Mon-Sat 10 pm, Sun 9 pm.

The Fox and Pheasant SW10 £61 334
1 Billing Road 020 7352 2943 6–3B

A "charming 'country-pub-style' local, cutely hidden away in west Chelsea" in 'The Billings' close to Stamford Bridge; and which nowadays is "celeb-owned" (by singer James Blunt and his wife Sofia). "The food has always been of great quality and the fact that you can relax in the pub bit afterwards makes for a lovely lazy afternoon and evening". / SW10 9UJ; www.thefoxandpheasant.com; thefoxandpheasantpub; Mon-Sat 10 pm, Sun 9 pm.

Franco Manca £39 222
Branches throughout London

With its "delicious sourdough bases", and its "excellent choice of toppings with regularly changing specials" from "well-sourced ingredients", these "buzzing" cafés are still seen as "a refreshing angle on the pizza theme" and – if "nothing special" – "pretty decent and fairly priced". Those questioning "what the fuss is about" are growing in number though, as its ratings head south into PizzaExpress territory. (In April 2023, the Fulham Shore owners of the group were sold to Japanese investors, Toridoll Holdings, making its future direction hard to call.) / www.francomanca.co.uk; francomancapizza.

Franco's SW1 £90 344
61 Jermyn St 020 7499 2211 3–3C

"A great all-rounder in St James's", particularly popular amongst a well-heeled SW1 business clientele – this "reassuring" veteran provides the "careful service" of "no frills", "traditional" dishes and "has been going for years" – since 1945 in fact – "and long may it last". But even those for whom it's a favourite note that "you pay the price when the bill comes". / SW1Y 6LX; www.francoslondon.com; francoslondon; Mon-Sat 11 pm.

Frank's Canteen N5 £45 332
86 Highbury Park 020 7354 4830 9–1D

This "great local" on Highbury Corner has developed from a catering company and supper club into a fully fledged "neighbourhood restaurant, serving proper food at reasonable prices", with separate all-day brunch/lunch and evening menus featuring modern European dishes. / N5 2XE; www.frankscanteen.com; frankscanteen; Mon & Tue, Sun 4 pm, Thu-Sat, Wed 9.30 pm.

Franklins SE22   **£65**   **3** **4** **3**

157 Lordship Ln   020 8299 9598   1–4D

"Lunching here is like a warm hug with a dear friend", say fans of Rod Franklin and Tim Sheehan's "perfect local restaurant" in East Dulwich – a "good balance of the classic and quirky" that celebrates its quarter century this year. Top Tip – "Sunday lunches are a particular local legend with extra Yorkshire puds on the side for the really hungry"; and "lots for vegans/veggies". / SE22 8HX; www.franklinsrestaurant.com; franklinsse22; Mon-Sat midnight, Sun 10.30 pm.

Frantoio SW10   **£68**   **3** **2** **4**

397 King's Rd   020 7352 4146   6–3B

A meal is "always fun" at this long-running Chelsea trattoria near World's End, where host Bucci looks after his guests well. The service may "lack finesse", but the food is "fine" and comes in "massive portions". / SW10 0LR; frantoio.co.uk; frantonio_london; Mon-Sun 11 pm.

Freak Scene SW6 **NEW**   **£44**   **4** **4** **3**

28 Parsons Green Lane   020 7610 9863   11–1B

Ace Aussie chef, Scott Hallsworth has revived his raved-about Freak Scene pan-Asian restaurant once again – this time off Parsons Green in Fulham in spring 2023. Based on a small number of initial ratings, his amped-up fusion fare (sushi plus wackier creations such as miso-yaki foie gras croissant with star anise jus) is in fine form. / SW6 4HS; www.freakscenerestaurants.com; freakscenedn; Wed-Sat 10.30 pm, Sun 9.30 pm.

Frederick's N1   **£71**   **3** **4** **4**

106 Camden Passage   020 7359 2888   9–3D

Set among the antiques shops of Camden Passage, this "comfortable" Islington institution has been superbly run by two generations of the Segal family for 55 years. The "simple but very good quality food is served in a bright and well-spaced conservatory dining room at the back", at tables that are "nicely spaced", with "just the right amount of buzz to have a conversation". Top Tip – huge garden area for summer dining. / N1 8EG; www.fredericks.co.uk; fredericks_n1; Tue-Sat 10 pm.

The French House W1   **£72**   **4** **4** **5**

49 Dean Street   020 7437 2477   5–3A

"The lovely Soho institution above this legendary pub" (where de Gaulle is said to have composed some of his speeches during WWII) is currently "in the very safe hands of Neil Borthwick" (Angela Hartnett's hubbie). There's "wizardry afoot" here but "no faff or fancy" – by "doing simple but really excellent things to top produce but not doing much to it" he creates "a tight menu of absolute bangers", with "big flavours singing out" ("a plate of greens can be as full of oomph as a tartare or a chop"). "Staff are tremendous" and for many reporters this is "a go-to destination in the West End". / W1D 5BG; www.frenchhousesoho.com; frenchhousesoho; Mon-Sat 11 pm, Sun 10.30 pm.

Frenchie WC2   **£92**   **3** **3** **3**

18 Henrietta Street   020 7836 4422   5–3C

We have Jamie Oliver to thank for the name of this "quintessential modern French bistro" in Covent Garden, who gave the nickname to owner Gregory Merchand when he worked for him many years ago at Fifteen (long RIP). It's the spin-off to Marchand's (and wife Marie's) Parisian venue of the same name, "featuring the speed, simplicity, flavour and lightness, essential for a satisfying pre-theatre experience". "This is honest Gallic fare which does not disappoint": "dishes made with good ingredients, treated respectfully". "The

*counter is always a good area to sit if just two are dining. There's the chance
to engage with bar staff and have a good view of the comings and goings".
/ WC2E 8QH; www.frenchiecoventgarden.com; frenchiecoventgarden; Mon-Sat 10 pm,
Sun 8 pm.*

Frog by Adam Handling WC2   £241   443
35 Southampton Street   020 7199 8370   5–3D
*Many "magical and simply sublime" meals were reported this year at Adam
Handling's "exceptional" Covent Garden HQ, whose open kitchen delivers
"creative, passionate and sustainably resourced modern British cooking"
("intricate beyond belief in presentation; and a delightful explosion of taste
and texture"). The "buzzing" setting is kept in "relaxed" mood by the "fun",
"slightly irreverent" service. The catch? "You get an incredible meal, but it
comes with an incredible price tag!" / WC2E 7HG; www.frogbyadamhandling.com;
frogbyah; Wed-Sat, Mon & Tue 11 pm.*

La Fromagerie   £56   333
2-6 Moxon St, W1   020 7935 0341   3–1A
52 Lamb's Conduit St, WC1   020 7242 1044   2–1D
30 Highbury Park, N5   020 7359 7440   9–2D
*"Simple food done well...and the cheese!!" – this small group has basic
eateries attached to their stores as well as "an enormous selection of cheese
to buy at retail". WC1 is by far the most popular outlet – "like wandering
into a village restaurant in the heart of Bloomsbury". "If you like cheese and
wine, what's not to love about this place?" / www.lafromagerie.co.uk;
lafromagerieuk.*

Fumo WC2   £55   234
37 St Martin's Lane   020 3778 0430   5–4C
*The "beautiful setting" and "elegant small sharing plates of tapas-like
cicchetti" make this "great spot" from the San Carlo group "perfect for pre-
or post-Coliseum dining" and it inspires uniformly positive feedback from a
big and diverse fan base. / WC2N 4JS; sancarlofumo.co.uk; sancarlorestaurants;
Sun-Fri 11 pm, Sat midnight.*

Gallipoli Again N1   £50   324
119 Upper Street   020 7226 8099   9–3D
*This "cheap 'n' cheerful Turkish operation" has been an atmospheric fixture
on Upper Street for more than 25 years, offering "well cooked and
presented dishes in generous portions". "The smaller Gallipoli has gone, so
all efforts have been put into this larger branch", which has "a relaxed style,
with different areas to sit in depending on the occasion". / N1 1QP;
gallipolicafe.co.uk; Sun-Thu 11 pm, Fri & Sat midnight.*

Galvin at Windows,
Park Lane London Hilton Hotel W1   £111   334
22 Park Ln   020 7208 4021   3–4A
*"What a view you get over London" from the 28th floor of Hilton Hotel on
Park Lane (when it opened in 1963, the capital's first skyscraper hotel). Run
since 2006 by the Galvin Bros, there is the odd grumble that the fare is
"pedestrian and overpriced", but most diners feel you get "wonderful service
and food to match the vista", with head chef Marc Hardiman providing a
variety of à la carte and tasting options. Top Tip – good-value set lunch.
/ W1K 1BE; www.galvinatwindows.com; galvinatwindows; Mon-Sun 9.30 pm.*

Galvin Bistrot & Bar E1   £68   **3** **4** **2**
35 Bishops Square   020 7299 0404   13–2B
Occupying "an excellent spot in the City, overlooking a pedestrian square behind Bishopsgate" – this is, say fans, a "reliable" bistro, whose "great French food and friendly service" delivers "the Galvin experience, but at approachable prices", right next door to the brothers' high-end La Chapelle (see also). More critical reporters, though, diagnose price creep here, which they feel is starting to erode the level of value, especially given the relatively humble interior. Top Tip – "sit outside on the terrace". / E1 6DY; galvinrestaurants.com; galvinbistrot; Mon-Sat 9.30 pm.

Galvin La Chapelle E1   £121   **4** **4** **5**
35 Spital Sq   020 7299 0400   13–2B
"One of the best dining rooms in London", the Galvin Bros' "impressive" Spitalfields venue occupies a "spectacular" space that looks like a church, but which was actually part of a late-Victorian girls' school – a "real special occasion place" both for romantics or for an "unbeatable, proper business lunch in the City". It won improved ratings this year for its "fabulous", "classic" cuisine, its "professional" service and its "refined" wines from a "huge book of vintages". / E1 6DY; www.galvinlachapelle.com; galvinrestaurants; Mon & Tue 9.15 pm, Wed-Sat 9.15 pm, Sun 9 pm.

La Gamba SE1 NEW   £59   **3** **4** **2**
Unit 3, Royal Festival Hall,   020 7183 0094   2–3D
Need a bite near the Southbank Centre? This new Galician-inspired tapas spot at the foot of the centre itself, complete with outside terrace, opened in February 2023. It is run by Jack, Harry and Matthew Applebee, who run the Applebee's at Borough Market (see also). Stylewise, the appeal is far from cutting edge, with almost-retro decor and with Spanish cuisine that's not designed to wow the fooderati. But amidst the anonymity of the area, our early reports say it creates good vibes: "very new...very good... family welcome absolutely perfect... tapas are fresh and plentiful... a great addition to the South Bank!" (And The Observer's Jay Rayner is a fan too. In a June 2023 review he blessed its "extremely solid and pleasing take on the Spanish repertoire" and he too notes its "personal" style: "You do not sense the dead hand of head office, as you might in the surrounding places"). / SE1 8XX; www.lagambalondon.com; lagamba.london; Mon-Sun 11 pm.

The Game Bird SW1   £124   **3** **3** **4**
16-18 St James's Place   020 7518 1234   3–4C
'Hoof, feather and field' is the billing given to the meaty options (which are the top choices) at this traditional dining room – a peaceful space, discreetly hidden away in St James's and overseen from afar by its 'food director', star-chef Lisa Goodwin-Allen of The Stafford's sister property, Northcote (in Lancs). Practically all reports applaud its all-round professional performance and also its "extensive" cellar. Top Tip – a shout out to the "sumptuous and plentiful" afternoon tea served on the "wonderful comfortable sofas" nearby complete with "free refills for the sandwiches!" / SW1A 1NJ; thestaffordlondon.com; thestaffordlondon; Mon-Fri 9 pm, Sun 9 pm, Sat 9 pm.

Ganapati SE15   £45   **4** **4** **3**
38 Holly Grove   020 7277 2928   1–4D
"A true neighbourhood go-to" – in her 20th anniversary year, Peckham food pioneer Clare Fisher is "still doing things with South Indian flavours that make the heart sing". Top Tip – "don't forget to buy a jar of homemade garlic or beetroot pickle to take home". / SE15 5DF; www.ganapatirestaurant.com; ganapati.peckham; Tue-Sat 10.30 pm, Sun 10 pm.

Ganymede SW1 £88 3️⃣3️⃣3️⃣
139 Ebury Street   020 3971 0761   2–4A

"More gastro French than pub, but delicious" – the successor to much-missed Belgravia institution the Ebury Street Wine Bar (long RIP) has got off to a strong start, helped by a "very high standard of food and service" from "welcoming, friendly and courteous staff". / SW1W 9QU; ganymedelondon.co.uk; ganymedesw1; Mon-Sat 10 pm, Sun 6 pm.

The Garden Cafe
at the Garden Museum SE1 £62 3️⃣3️⃣4️⃣
5 Lambeth Palace Rd   020 7401 8865   2–4D

"Excellent food in a leafy setting, especially on a warm and bright day" makes the elevated café at Lambeth's Garden Museum "a complete go-to" for foodies in the know. George Ryle, the chef who co-founded it to great acclaim in 2017, left after five years to return to his native Yorkshire, but the kitchen has barely missed a beat under his successor Myles Donaldson (ex-Noble Rot and Anchor & Hope among others). / SE1 7LB; www.gardenmuseum.org.uk; gardenmuseum; Mon, Wed & Thu, Sat & Sun 3 pm, Tue, Fri 9 pm.

Le Garrick WC2 £63 3️⃣3️⃣3️⃣
10-12 Garrick Street   020 7240 7649   5–3C

"Candlelit booths, rustic French food and wine, and discreet service" make this "little slice of France in Covent Garden" "perfect for a date or anniversary". If possible, "go downstairs and experience the brick arched cellar dining area, which is full of character and charm". The "classic bistro fare" is "adequately prepared and comes at very reasonable prices considering the location". / WC2E 9BH; www.legarrick.co.uk; le_garrick; Mon-Sat 11 pm.

The Garrison SE1 £84 3️⃣3️⃣3️⃣
99 Bermondsey Street   020 7089 9355   10–4D

"Still a very good gastropub", this green-tiled ex-boozer was a leading light in Bermondsey's emergence as a foodie destination when it opened 21 years ago, and remains in the gastronomic high ground with its commitment to ethically sourced ingredients. / SE1 3XB; www.thegarrison.co.uk; thegarrisonse1; Mon-Thu 11 pm, Fri & Sat midnight, Sun 10.30 pm.

The Gate £62 3️⃣3️⃣3️⃣
22-24 Seymour Place, W1   020 7724 6656   2–2A
51 Queen Caroline St, W6   020 8748 6932   8–2C
370 St John St, EC1   020 7278 5483   9–3D

"A go-to favourite vegetarian… they have been going for 30 years" – this small group "still maintains high standards" with "very imaginative dishes that will even please your meat-eating friends". The W6 original – a characterful space, above a church behind Hammersmith's Eventim Apollo – is the most popular, but its spin-offs near Sadlers Wells and in Seymour Village are also well-regarded. / thegaterestaurants.com; gaterestaurant.

The Gatehouse N6 £66 3️⃣3️⃣2️⃣
1 North Road   020 8340 8054   9–1B

"A perfect rabbit stew" was one of the options given the thumbs up this year at this black-and-white gabled, 1930s pub in central Highgate, where many of the dishes have a Spanish spin. Notable features include a large garden area and even its own theatre upstairs. / N6 4BD; www.thegatehousen6.com; thegatehousen6; Mon-Wed 10 pm, Thu-Sat 10.30 pm, Sun 9 pm.

Gaucho £87 ②②②
Branches throughout London
This Argentinian-inspired group celebrates its 30th anniversary this year, now with a dozen branches in London and another seven in provincial cities. In its heyday, it "used to be the best place for a steak", backed up by a "well-compiled list" of South American wines. But while fans still applaud it for "reliably good" meals (albeit acknowledging it "could do with a few more non-meat options"), critics – and its competition – have multiplied over the years, and there's a feeling "you can now find better elsewhere".
/ www.gauchorestaurants.co.uk; gauchogroup; SRA-1 star.

Gauthier Soho W1 £120 ③④④
21 Romilly St 020 7494 3111 5–3A
"Alexis is now 100% vegan and the result is outstanding", say disciples of his quirky Soho venture – a "beautiful townhouse with a series of intimate, romantic rooms", which he's run since 2010, and which went fully meat-free in 2021. Vegetarians of course worship it, but so do many meat-eaters too ("I am an avowed carnivore and my mind was blown by this restaurant – how anyone can create something so superb from the humble vegetable is beyond my comprehension"). But that's not to say it's all plain sailing as many diners are in two minds about the switch and "still not completely convinced that the vegan offering is as good as the old omnivorous one". One or two are just outright disappointed; but for most there's a feeling that "some menu items are trying too hard and miss the mark". A recurrent gripe is that "it seems odd that so much of his vegan menu imitates meat forms" ("I have no problems with a vegan establishment; my only annoyance is the tendency to imitate non-vegan dishes. I just wish they would stick to their guns and stop impersonating non-vegan cuisine because there is no question that Alexis and the team are very talented chefs"). The "slick service" and "fabulously atmospheric" space are the same as they ever were. / W1D 5AF; www.gauthiersoho.co.uk; gauthierinsoho; Tue-Sat 9.30 pm.

Le Gavroche W1 £160 ③③④
43 Upper Brook St 020 7408 0881 3–2A
"Perfect in so many ways" – Michel Albert Roux's Mayfair legend is part of the nation's gastronomic history. It was the first UK restaurant to win three Michelin stars in 1982 after his father Albert moved it to this basement near the former US embassy from its original Chelsea site. And it has been ably run by MasterChef judge Michel since 1992, when père moved over for fils (since which time it has held two stars). "The entrance leads to a small bar for pre-dinner drinks (arrive early), with a staircase down to the main restaurant": an old-fashioned space – all "soft furnishings and discreet dividers" – whose 1980s decor has a certain retro charm. Old traditions are maintained – for example, "some diners are surprised that only the person named in the reservation has prices shown on their menu". "Classic French cuisine is served with style and reverence: dishes are very much 'old-school'" and prepared with "flair and skill". "The wine list is to drool over", "if you have time to read it (it's so long!)". "Michel himself works the room, which adds to the experience", greeting guests in his whites, and with a longstanding team, including twins Sylvia & Ursula Perbersschlager managing the show. Post-Covid, the restaurant significantly cut its opening times, and – perhaps due to the pressures of soaring costs – concerns over value since the pandemic have taken ratings from being outstanding to merely good. Many guests still say "prices are reasonable given the excellent cooking and unique sense of occasion"; but there is a growing minority of regretful regulars for whom the experience is just "not as good as on previous visits", with some meals plain "disappointing". The lack of lunchtime service is a particular issue ("this was my favourite restaurant and lunch was a treat, but unfortunately it's no longer offered and we simply can't afford to eat there anytime. The prices are horrendous"). For the majority, though, it's still "worth

it for a special blow out" and "there is a long waiting list so you need to book well in advance". Top Menu Tip – "the double cooked cheese souffle is incredible". BREAKING NEWS: in mid-August 2023, Michel announced that Le Gavroche will close in January 2024. Up till that point there will be a series of special dinners… but good luck getting a booking! In fact, given the fact that all available seats at the restaurant are pretty much now taken, we've listed it as closed. / WIK 7QR; www.le-gavroche.co.uk; le_gavroche_restauraunt; Tue-Sat 10 pm.

Gazette £65 222**3**
79 Sherwood Ct, Chatfield Rd, SW11   020 7223 0999   11–1C
147 Upper Richmond Rd, SW15   020 8789 6996   11–2B
218 Trinity Road, SW17   020 8767 5810   11–2C
17-18 Took's Court, EC4   020 7831 6664   10–2A
This popular small bistro group is "so very French", especially when eating at the original "buzzy" Battersea branch, which opened in 2007 "at an attractive location near the river". The other branches – in Putney, Wandsworth Common and the City (plus one inside the Institut Français in South Kensington) – are also applauded as "good value" options, but results can also seem a little "unadventurous". / www.gazettebrasserie.co.uk.

GBR (The Great British Restaurant)
at The Dukes Hotel SW1 £90 **3**2**3**
35 St James's Pl   020 7491 4840   3–4C
Traditional, peaceful hotel brasserie, hidden away in a cute warren of St James's streets, which has successfully upped its profile in recent years. It provides a "very good standard of food and wine that's not expensive for the quality". The only recurrent gripe is service that can be a tad "erratic". Top Tip – "reasonably priced set menu". / SW1A 1NY; www.dukeshotel.com; dukeslondon; Sun & Mon 11 am, Tue-Sat 9.30 pm.

Gem N1 £48 **333**
265 Upper Street   020 7359 0405   9–2D
This "small and crowded" grill on Islington's main drag serves "reasonably priced Turkish, Kurdish and Greek-style food" and is "clearly a local crowd-pleaser". The 'Hidden Gem' basement is available for private parties. / N1 2UQ; www.gemrestaurant.org.uk; gemrestaurantuk; Mon-Sat 11 pm.

German Gymnasium N1 £76 **11**3
1 King's Boulevard   020 7287 8000   9–3C
"It occupies an amazing, high-ceilinged space" (built in 1865 for the German Gymnastics Society – and venue for London's first indoor Olympic games), but "it's a shame other aspects of the offering are so weak" at this D&D London property, immediately behind King's Cross station. Fans do claim "all German food boxes are firmly ticked, with tasty and well-presented schnitzel and weißwurst", but even they admit "the building is the star of the show". And far too many reporters "expected much better than the very poor quality for the prices" – which are "on the high side" – "terrible service that doesn't seem to care" and cuisine that's somewhere between "pretty standard" and "below average". Top Menu Tip – breakfast with "pretzel to die for" is its most recommended feature. / N1C 4BU; www.germangymnasium.com; thegermangym; Mon-Sat 10 pm; SRA-accredited.

Giacco's N5 NEW
176 Blackstock Road   020 3649 4601   9–1D
This micro Italian wine bar in Highbury's Blackstock Road (formerly the Light Eye Mind arts space) opened in March 2023 and operates as a bottle shop and café by day and a 20-cover wine bar by night, serving low-intervention Italian wines along with cheese and salumi from small producers and pasta. The cakes are from Forno in Hackney, and they produce their own small-batch gelato. Co-owner Leonardo Leoncini ran Highbury's Farewell Cafe, which closed in 2021. / N5 1HA; www.giaccos.bar; giaccos_ldn; Wed-Sat 11 pm, Sun 10 pm.

Giacomo's NW2   £52   3 3 2
428 Finchley Rd   020 7794 3603   1–1B
Home-made pasta and other Italian classics hit the spot at this "enjoyable local restaurant" in Child's Hill, a family-run business for more than four decades which moved to its present address 22 years ago. / NW2 2HY; www.giacomos.co.uk; Tue-Sun 10.30 pm.

Ginger & White Hampstead NW3   £15   3 3 3
4a-5a Perrins Court   020 7431 9098   9–2A
Loyal locals endure the (sometimes lengthy) queue for this favourite Hampstead hang-out, thanks to its "very good coffee" and "top breakfast" (shakshuka something of a speciality). / NW3 1QS; www.gingerandwhite.com; gingerandwhitelondon; Mon-Fri 5.30 pm, Sat & Sun 6 pm.

Ginza SW1   £101   3 3 3
15 Bury St   020 7839 1101   3–3D
With its counters for teppanyaki and sushi, this sizable St James's basement (with 70 covers) offers a high-quality, traditional Japanese dining experience. All reports on the food say it can be of an exceptional standard, but even ardent fans can also find it "overpriced". / SW1Y 6AL; www.ginza-stjames.com; ginzastjames; Mon-Sun 10.30 pm.

Giulia W12   £61   4 3 2
77 Askew Rd   020 8743 0572   8–1B
On the site that was for aeons the locally loved Adam's Café (RIP), this "relative newcomer" in 'Askew Village' "hits the right notes" as a replacement. It "still feels a bit like a café inside", but is warmed up by the personable service, who provide a "short but interesting menu of Italian dishes" including "delicious homemade pasta"; and other "well cooked, prettily presented food". / W12 9AH; www.giuliarestaurant.co.uk; giulia.restaurant; Tue-Sat 10.30 pm, Sun 4.30 pm.

Gloria EC2   £66   2 3 5
54-56 Great Eastern Street   no tel   13–1B
"Great for a fun dinner out with friends or family, thanks to the lovely cocktails and amazing decor!" – Big Mamma Group's happening Shoreditch Italian is a happy, overblown pastiche of retro Amalfi-coast style. Results are "inconsistent in quality, but some dishes are mind blowing" (if only in terms of their heart-attack-threatening creaminess). Top Menu Tip – yummo pizza. / EC2A 3QR; www.bigmammagroup.com; bigmamma.uk; Mon-Wed 10.45 pm, Thu-Sat 11 pm, Sun 10.30 pm.

Go-Viet SW7   £56   3 4 2
53 Old Brompton Rd   020 7589 6432   6–2C
South Kensington Vietnamese from former Hakkasan chef Jeff Tan, whose "incredibly consistent" food is "always prepared with the lightest of touches"; and where lunches are notably "good value". A warehouse-style older sibling, Viet Food, is often packed out in Chinatown. / SW7 3JS; vietnamfood.co.uk; govietnamese; Sun-Thu 10.30 pm, Fri & Sat 11 pm.

La Goccia WC2 £64 3 3 3
Floral Court, off Floral Street   020 7305 7676   5–3C
"It's lovely to sit at the outside tables in the summer" in the *"beautiful courtyard"* of Covent Garden's Floral Court, dining on *"interesting small plates"* of Italian food – *"albeit on the expensive side"* – at the central London offshoot from the well-known Petersham Nurseries in Richmond. It's just *"great for a girls' day lunch or dinner".* / WC2E 9DJ; petershamnurseries.com; petershamnurseries; Mon-Wed 10 pm, Thu-Sat 11 pm, Sun 6 pm.

Goddards At Greenwich SE10 £27 3 4 3
22 King William Walk   020 8305 9612   1–3D
One of the vanishingly few traditional pie 'n' mash dynasties left in London, four generations of Goddards have run the family business since 1890. *"Always friendly to regulars and tourists alike",* they offer a *"good choice of pies",* from the standard beef mince to a vegan option. / SE10 9HU; www.goddardsatgreenwich.co.uk; Sun-Thu 7.30 pm, Fri & Sat 8 pm.

Gold W11 £72 2 4 5
95-97 Portobello Road   020 3146 0747   7–2B
This "cool vibes" Portobello Road hang-out with a "let-your-hair-down ambience" was carved out of an old Notting Hill boozer by nightclub entrepreneur Nick House (Mahiki and Whisky Mist). The tapas-y food, by former River Café chef Theo Hill, divides opinion: it's either *"exemplary"* and *"delicious",* or *"sloppy", "heavy-handed and over-priced".* Top Tip – *"if you don't like noise, ask for a table upstairs".* / W11 2QB; goldnottinghill.com; goldnottinghill; Mon-Thu 12.30 am, Fri & Sat 1 am, Sun 11.30 pm.

Gold Mine W2 £45 3 2 2
102 Queensway   020 7792 8331   7–2C
This classic Cantonese in Queensway specialises in "delicious dim sum" and roast meats; and though *"there are better venues in the area"* you may still face a long queue at busy times. It also has a Chinatown sibling at 45 Wardour Street, London W1D 6PZ. / W2 3RR; goldmine.bayswater; Sun-Thu 11 pm, Fri & Sat 11.15 pm.

Golden Dragon W1 £53 3 2 2
28-29 Gerrard St   020 7734 1073   5–3A
This "very busy" Cantonese stalwart is "a cut above its rivals" on the Chinatown main drag. There's *"nothing special about the environment, but it serves some of the best and best-value dim sum available in London".* / W1 6JW; www.gdlondon.co.uk; goldendragon_uk; Mon-Sun 10 pm.

Golden Hind W1 £52 3 3 2
73 Marylebone Ln   020 7486 3644   2–1A
"Going strong" since 1914, this Marylebone veteran is one of the oldest in central London, serving *"reliable and authentic fish 'n' chips in a part of town where no-nonsense dining is not so easy to find".* Unusually for a chippy there's *"outdoor seating in warmer months",* and when it's cold you can finish your meal with a traditional sponge pudding. / W1U 2PN; www.goldenhindrestaurant.com; Mon-Fri 10 pm.

Good Earth £75 3 3 2
233 Brompton Rd, SW3 020 7584 3658 6–2C
143-145 The Broadway, NW7 020 8959 7011 1–1B
11 Bellevue Rd, SW17 020 8682 9230 11–2C
*This well-known family-owned quartet of "upmarket Chinese" operations –
in Knightsbridge, Mill Hill, Wandsworth Common and Esher – are
"longstanding favourites" for many reporters. "The menus may not excite
any true aficionados of Asian cuisine, but its consistency excites us!" And
even if it's "never cheap, it's always worth the price".*
/ www.goodearthgroup.co.uk.

Goodman £89 3 4 3
24-26 Maddox St, W1 020 7499 3776 3–2C
3 South Quay, E14 020 7531 0300 12–1C
11 Old Jewry, EC2 020 7600 8220 10–2C
*"Steak, steak, and steak are all brilliant" at Misha Zelman's NYC-style grill-
houses also praised for their "great wine pairings" and "knowledgeable
staff". With branches in Mayfair, the City and Canary Wharf, they are a
particular business favourite, and had the edge on their arch-rival
Hawksmoor in survey results this year. Meat is sourced from Scotland, the
US, Australia and Japan, dry-aged on site and cooked over charcoal.*
/ www.goodmanrestaurants.com; goodman_london.

Gordon Ramsay SW3 £231 2 2 2
68-69 Royal Hospital Rd 020 7352 4441 6–3D
*The Hell's Kitchen chef's original Chelsea HQ is increasingly "trading on its
reputation", attracting more criticism than it does praise nowadays. Even
fans sometimes acknowledge this "rather beige" room has a "stilted"
ambience, and opinions on the service vary widely: from "impeccable" to
"overwhelming" or even "robotic". When it comes to the fairly classical
cuisine, there's also a pick 'n' mix of views: from "unbeatable" to "overly
fussy" or "safe". What both sides do often agree on is that the experience
comes "at the most ridiculous second mortgage prices", with almost two in
five of diners' voting it their most overpriced meal of the year. A fair middle
view is that: "as you should expect from a three Michelin star restaurant, the
food is lovely; but it's a struggle to work out in what way it is better than
many other two-star or even one-star restaurants. It's good, but not that
good".* / SW3 4HP; www.gordonramsayrestaurants.com; restaurantgordonramsay;
Tue-Sat 11 pm.

Gouqi SW1 NEW £120 2 3 2
25-34 Cockspur Street 020 3771 8886 2–3C
*Fans hail an "excellent addition to the Asian fine dining scene" at this West
End spring 2023 newcomer – the first solo restaurant from Tong Chee
Hwee, the masterchef behind Hakkasan's rise to global fame over the past
two decades, and focused on Chinese cuisine. Our few early reports
unanimously applaud the high quality of its dishes, although one does gripe
about it being too pricey or with a poor ambience. (Both of these negative
sentiments are echoed by Times critic Giles Coren in his May 2023 review:
while acknowledging the food "is in general fine", Giles really gives it both
barrels for its "unforgivable" prices; what he considers a "horrid, horrid"
location on the fringes of Trafalgar Square; and his suspicions that social
media agencies have been used to paint it in an overly favourable light
online).* / SW1Y 5BN; Wed-Sat 10.30 pm, Sun 9.30 pm.

Gourmet Burger Kitchen £41 3 3 2
Branches throughout London

"Still my favourite burger", proclaim loyalists of the brand that launched the contemporary vogue for upmarket burgers – although the original 2001 branch in Battersea's Nappy Valley is now gone, a victim of cost-cutting in recent years. Birmingham's 'chicken king' Ranjit Boparan bought the chain out of administration in 2020, with the closure of almost half its 60-odd outlets. Judging by the limited but positive feedback this year, he appears to have brought an upward trend to the surviving 35 branches plus eight delivery-only kitchens. / www.gbk.co.uk; gbkburgers.

Goya SW1 £92 3 3 2
34 Lupus St 020 7976 5309 2–4C

This Pimlico veteran has served "tasty, reliable and good-value tapas" including "particularly enjoyable seafood" for more than 30 years – putting it well ahead of the more recent vogue for Hispanic cuisine. "The menu is always the same and always very good", which suits local regulars well. / SW1V 3EB; www.goyarestaurant.co.uk; Mon-Sat midnight.

Granary Square Brasserie N1 £52 2 3 4
1 Granary Square 020 3940 1000 9–3C

"Eating outside overlooking the square is extremely pleasant" at this "large brasserie", which is particularly well-located in the new developments north of King's Cross; and wins praise for its "great buzzy atmosphere". But it suffers from the Ivy Collection's habitual weakness of "disappointing and unimaginative food – all the classics not done that well". / N1C 4AB; www.granarysquarebrasserie.com; granarysquarebrasserie; Mon-Sun midnight.

Granger & Co £64 2 2 3
237-239 Pavilion Rd, SW1 020 3848 1060 6–2D
105 Marylebone High Street, W1 020 8079 7120 2–1A
175 Westbourne Grove, W11 020 7229 9111 7–1B
Stanley Building, St Pancras Sq, N1 020 3058 2567 9–3C
The Buckley Building, 50 Sekforde St, EC1 020 7251 9032 10–1A

"Excellent breakfasts… you just need to be patient" – "after all these years, the queue outside is there for a reason" according to fans of this Aussie-inspired chain, owned by celeb chef Bill Granger. There are five nowadays, but it's still the OG Notting Hill branch – cited by fans as "the best brunch spot in West London!" – which receives the most attention. But whereas all feedback acknowledges the "nice buzz" they create, ratings are capped by reports of food that's merely "meh". / grangerandco.com; grangerandco.

Great Nepalese NW1 £45 3 2 3
48 Eversholt St 020 7388 6737 9–3C

Fay Maschler's review from the 1980s is blown up for all to see as you enter this "old stalwart that's had a brush-up" in recent years: a low-key curry house (est. 1982) long known as one of the few bright culinary sparks near Euston station. Go for the smattering of Nepalese specials amidst the "simple and unchanging" selection of subcontinental dishes. Bills can end up higher, though, than its "basic" style might suggest. / NW1 1DA; www.great-nepalese.co.uk; Mon-Sat 10.30 pm.

Green Cottage NW3 £56 3 2 2
9 New College Parade 020 7722 5305 9–2A

This "typical local Chinese" amidst a parade of shops in Swiss Cottage has put in more than 50 years' service. Why? "The food is relatively good and prices reasonable". / NW3 5EP; www.greencottage22.com; Mon-Sun 10.30 pm.

Greenberry Café NW1 £63 2|3|3
101 Regents Park Road 020 7483 3765 9–2B
This "fun and buzzy local restaurant" in Primrose Hill is especially a brunch favourite. The food menu is a bit "hit/miss", but it wins particular shout-outs for its "good coffee" and "hard to beat salads". / NW1 8UR; greenberrycafe.co.uk; greenberrycafe; Sun & Mon 3 pm, Tue-Sat 10 pm.

The Grill by Tom Booton (fka The Dorchester Grill) W1 £145
53 Park Lane 020 7629 8888 3–3A
This illustrious chamber was closed during our annual diners' poll, awaiting a May 2023 relaunch under the brand of talented whippersnapper, Tom Booton (who has only just hit 30). It is the first time the grill has had a chef's name over the door in its 92-year history, and heralds a major change of gear for the space – no longer is it to be a hallowed foodie temple, but now more of a luxe brasserie with 'Tom's cheeky personality shining through' (at least that's what the press release says). In comes breakfast for the first time (with truffled egg and soldiers and omelette Arnold Benedict); Sunday lunch; a chef's counter; sharing dishes; and a general culinary 'tie loosening' moment with 'twists on British classics'. As part of this cuddlier style we are also promised 'playlists hand selected by Tom'; and 'playful cocktails and artisan English beer'. / W1K 1QA; www.dorchestercollection.com; thedorchester; Mon-Sat 10 pm, Sun 4 pm.

Grumbles SW1 £66 3|4|2
35 Churton St 020 7834 0149 2–4B
Little has changed at this "unstuffy" Pimlico bistro since it opened 60 years ago (except that, back then, a couple could eat here for under £3!). The original wooden panelling and furniture are still in place, the fish pie is still topped with piped potato, and pricing is still "cheap 'n' cheerful". It also does a "great Sunday lunch for the kids". / SW1V 2LT; www.grumblesrestaurant.co.uk; grumblesrestaurant; Mon-Sun 10 pm.

The Guildford Arms SE10 £60 3|3|3
55 Guildford Grove 020 8691 6293 1–3D
Co-owner Guy Awford's "brilliantly executed, classically inspired" cooking is well above "pub grub" standard, and has established this "well-maintained, upmarket" Georgian tavern as a leading option in Greenwich. / SE10 8JY; www.theguildfordarms.co.uk; guildfordarms_; Tue-Sat 11 pm, Sun 8 pm.

The Guinea Grill W1 £111 2|1|3
30 Bruton Pl 020 7409 1728 3–3B
"Yes, it is expensive (if not by Mayfair standards) but it is a meat-lover's nirvana in a great setting" – that's long been the accepted view on this quirky, grill room (est. 1952) behind a Young's pub, tucked away in a scenic central mews. "Old fashioned pies, mixed grills and excellent steaks" are washed down with an "impressive, if over-priced, wine list" and served in a quaint, period setting, whose "overcrowded tables are part of the experience". In the last couple of years, though (even prior to the departure last year of well-known manager Oisín Rogers), ratings have been on the slide. Some "shockingly bad" cooking has been reported, alongside service that's "so indifferent"; and the current impression is that they are relying ever more heavily on their "captive market" of local business-lunchers. / W1J 6NL; www.theguinea.co.uk; guineagrill; Mon-Sun 10 pm.

The Gun E14 £78 **3 2 4**

27 Coldharbour 020 7515 5222 12–1C

A spectacular riverside setting, directly opposite The O2, sets the scene at this Grade II-listed Docklands tavern, ten minutes' walk from Canary Wharf. Run by Fuller's, its "enjoyable food and lovely cocktails" are best enjoyed from the large modern terrace in summer. / E14 9NS; www.thegundocklands.com; thegundocklands; Mon & Tue, Sun 10 pm, Wed-Sat midnight.

Gunpowder £63 **4 3 3**

20 Greek Street, W1 020 3813 7796 5–2A

One Tower Bridge, 4 Crown Square, SE1 awaiting tel 10–4D

11 Whites Row, E1 020 7426 0542 13–2C

"Innovative small plates pack a flavour punch" ("the lamb chops are some of the most glorious things ever") at this "buzzy if rather cramped" Indian street-food trio, with operations near Tower Bridge, and in Spitalfields and Soho. Top Tip – "good, if limited, pre-theatre menu. Virtually no choice but, with tasty and large portions costing £22 for two courses or £25 for three, excellent value". / www.gunpowderlondon.com; gunpowder_london.

Gura Gura WC2 £52 **3 4 4**

19 Slingsby Place 07918 352879 5–3B

Festooned with foliage and feathers, this late 2022 newcomer is set in Covent Garden's 'The Yards' development. It's not made huge waves, but early reports on its cocktails and pan-Asian sushi and other fare are uniformly upbeat: "excellent and inexpensive pan-Asian tapas", "great choice" and "delicious dim sum". / WC2H 9DL; www.guragura.co.uk; guraguralondon; Mon-Thu 10 pm, Fri & Sat 11.30 pm, Sun 9.30 pm.

The Gurkhas W1 NEW £54 **3 4 3**

110 Great Portland Street 020 7637 4198 2–1B

From the Nepalese team behind Hot Stone in Islington, this upmarket new venue in Great Portland Street, Fitzrovia aims to showcase an 'elevated' take on classic Nepalese cuisine. Head chef Joe Allen has a Nepalese wife and Gurkha father-in-law, and has travelled extensively in Nepal to study some of its culinary secrets. An early visit backed up the initial positive feedback we have on the place, finding precisely prepared, slightly unusual dishes; and early days service that was at pains to get everything right. / W1W 6PQ; www.thegurkhasrestaurant.com; thegurkhas_restaurant; Tue-Thu 9 pm, Fri & Sat 9.30 pm.

Gustoso Ristorante & Enoteca SW1 £69 **3 2 2**

35 Willow Pl 020 7834 5778 2–4B

This "good-value" Italian "with excellent-quality cooking" and "always-welcoming staff" near Westminster Cathedral in Pimlico "stands out in an area with not much else". / SW1P 1JH; www.ristorantegustoso.co.uk; gustoso_ristorante; Mon-Sat 9.30 pm.

Gymkhana W1 £98 **5 4 3**

42 Albemarle St 020 3011 5900 3–3C

"Setting the benchmark for high-end Indian gastronomy in London" – "the capital may have a lot of hot new Indian destinations, but this Sethi family property in Mayfair is still at the top thanks to dazzling cuisine" – "interesting twists on the classics" with "exceptional spicing", all served by "thoroughly welcoming" staff in a "richly decorated and buzzy environment". / W1S 4JH; www.gymkhanalondon.com; gymkhanalondon; Mon-Sun 10.45 pm.

Haché £61 332
95-97 High Holborn, WC1   020 7242 4580   2–1D
329-331 Fulham Rd, SW10   020 7823 3515   6–3B
24 Inverness St, NW1   020 7485 9100   9–3B
37 Bedford Hill, SW12   020 8772 9772   11–2C
153 Clapham High St, SW4   020 7738 8760   11–2D
147-149 Curtain Rd, EC2   020 7739 8396   13–1B

"Fab burgers with a posh turn" – including "awesome sweet potato fries" – still lead the charge at these Frenchified fast-food outfits, but they are transitioning into a brasserie group under the ownership of Hush Mayfair's Jamie Barber. The 20-year-old original – a "great, cosy little spot in Camden" – and its Balham offshoot are all that remain as pure burger bars, while Kingston, High Holborn and Chelsea are now branded as brasseries with an extended menu to match. / www.hacheburgers.com.

Hagen Chelsea SW3 £15 342
151 Kings Road   07958 060036   6–3C
With nine branches scattered across the capital's wealthier neighbourhoods, this "popular" Copenhagen-inspired coffee-shop group offers the "best coffee" from hip Danish roasters Prolog, plenty of "hygge" (if "limited seating" in some venues), and cinnamon buns commissioned from Blake's Kitchen in the Cotswolds. / SW3 5TX; www.thehagenproject.com; thehagenproject; Wed-Sat 9 pm, Sun 5.30 pm.

Hakkasan £123 423
17 Bruton St, W1   020 7907 1888   3–2C
8 Hanway Pl, W1   020 7927 7000   5–1A
"Best Asian restaurant I've eaten in!" – these "beautiful" nightclubby haunts ("quite why they keep them so dark is beyond me") have maintained an impressive standard for over 20 years, and the Tottenham Court original has since been replicated not just in Mayfair but in numerous cities around the globe. Their ratings have fluctuated over many years, always around the same concerns – "success has got the better of them…"; "chaotic" and/or "attitude-y" service; punishing prices. The believers still carry the day, though, saying they are "always a special experience" with a "delectable" mix of dim sum, Peking duck (with or without caviar) and other classic Chinese dishes – "definitely take a big wallet, but I love it!" / www.hakkasan.com; hakkasanlondon.

Ham Yard Restaurant, Ham Yard Hotel W1 £71 234
1 Ham Yd   020 3642 1007   4–3D
"A quiet oasis on the fringe of messy Soho" – this hotel comes complete with a cute and rather unexpected courtyard and makes a "great setting" for a "comfortable and reasonably priced afternoon tea". The food at other times is "comforting but not exciting", although the set menu offers "good value for pre-theatre dining". / W1D 7DT; www.firmdalehotels.com; firmdale_hotels; Mon-Sun 10.30 pm.

The Hampshire W6 £51 333
227 King Street   020 8748 3391   8–2B
A short step from Hammersmith Town Hall and its ongoing surrounding property developments – this "spacious" and stylish pub was taken over by an Indian restaurant during the pandemic (although you can still just drop in for a pint). The food is fair value and "very good" from "an extensive menu with some unusual dishes"; and the owners have invested heavily in the large and comfortable garden. / W6 9JT; www.the-hampshire.com; thehampshire; Tue-Sun midnight.

Hankies W1 £47 3 3 2
67 Shaftesbury Avenue   020 7871 6021   5–3A
In the heart of Theatreland, this Indian street-food operation is focused on dishes served with 'hankies' – hand-spun roti folded around the dish – and still receives good marks (if from a limited number of reports). There used to be offshoots in Marble Arch and Paddington, but both have closed over the last couple of years. / W1D 6LL; hankies.london; hankies_shaftesbury; Wed-Sat 8.30 pm.

Hannah SE1 £138 3 3 2
Southbank Riverside, Belvedere Road   020 3802 0402   2–3D
This top-class Japanese dining room in the monolithic former County Hall near the London Eye is "a surprising delight in an area largely devoid of good eating options". Daisuke Shimoyama, previously head chef at Umu in Mayfair who began his career at 15 washing pots in Kanagawa, serves everything from "good-value lunch bentos to enticing main menus", including a 13-course omakase with the chef's sake pairing. / SE1 7PB; www.hannahrestaurant.london; hannah_japanese_restaurant; Wed-Sun 10 pm.

Hans' Bar & Grill SW1 £87 3 3 3
164 Pavilion Road   020 7730 7000   6–2D
A very appealing looking spot, in one of Chelsea's more chichi little enclaves – this café bar is part of nearby boutique hotel, 100 Cadogan Gardens. It's not the cheapest venue, and service can lag, but for a breakfast or light shopping lunch it's praised (albeit in limited feedback) as "a good all-rounder". / SW1X 0AW; www.hansbarandgrill.com; hansbarandgrill; Mon-Sat 10 pm, Sun 7 pm.

Hare & Tortoise £44 2 3 2
11-13 The Brunswick, WC1   020 7278 9799   2–1D
373 Kensington High St, W14   020 7603 8887   8–1D
156 Chiswick High Rd, W4   020 8747 5966   8–2A
38 Haven Grn, W5   020 8810 7066   1–2A
296-298 Upper Richmond Rd, SW15   020 8394 7666   11–2B
90 New Bridge St, EC4   020 7651 0266   10–2A
"Where else can you get ramen and laksa in the same place?", ask fans of this "efficient and friendly" pan-Asian chain founded almost 30 years ago in Bloomsbury's Brunswick Centre and now with branches in Ealing, Putney, Kensington and Chiswick plus two delivery-only kitchens. / www.hareandtortoise.co.uk; hare_tortoise.

Harrods Dining Hall SW1X £90
Harrods, 87-135 Brompton Road   6–1D
From October 2023, this golden-hued space, with its stunning Edwardian tiling – originally built to house the Harrods Food Hall's meat and fishmongers counters, and converted into a dining hall four years ago – will be re-launched with four new outlets in addition to the existing Kerridge's Fish 'n' Chips (see also): Sushi by Masa (from NYC celeb chef Masayoshi ('Masa') Takayama); Kinoya Ramen Bar – an import from Dubai; Assembly Mezze & Skewers, from vaunted Lebanese chef Athanasios Kargatzidis ('Chef Tommy'); and an upgrade of the existing Pasta Evangelists outlet, in partnership with top Veronese chef Giancarlo Perbellini (which becomes 'Pasta Evangelists by Perbellini'). / SW1X 7XL; www.harrods.com/en-gb/restaurants; https://www.instagram.com/harrods/.

Harvest NW10 NEW
68 Chamberlayne Road   020 3848 8111   1–2B

In Kensal Green – just down the road from his well-established neighbourhood operation, Parlour – chef Jesse Dunwood Green launched this small, casual all-day haunt in June 2023, with green leather seating for about 40. It opened after our survey had concluded, but looks like a useful addition to the area, with service from breakfast onwards, and an array of cocktails. Steak is a feature and some main dishes – say, a whole sea bass or chicken – are available to share. / NW10 3JJ; www.harvestrestaurantuk.com; harvestrestaurantuk; Mon-Sun 10 pm.

Harwood Arms SW6   £89   4 3 3
Walham Grove   020 7386 1847   6–3A

London's best pub (yet again No.1 in our annual diners' poll) "truly deserves its Michelin star and the old feel of creaky wood chairs and tables is what makes it a pub that still feels like a pub" (though space for drinkers is actually very limited). Lost deep in the backstreets near Fulham Broadway, it delivers "sublime British food at its best", in particular "good game, especially deer". Top Menu Tips – "amazing Sunday lunch" and "you must try the Scotch egg". / SW6 1QP; www.harwoodarms.com; theharwoodarms; Mon-Thu 9.15pm, Fri & Sat 9.15 pm, Sun 8.15 pm.

Hatched SW11   £86   4 4 3
189 Saint John's Hill   020 7738 0735   11–2C

Between Clapham Junction and Wandsworth Town, this grey-walled fixture (also with counter dining) puts the focus on the cooking from Shane Marshall's open kitchen. Choose from an à la carte menu of modern bistro fare, with a roast on Sunday – its small fan club from the SW postcodes rate it very highly. / SW11 1TH; www.hatchedsw11.com; hatchedsw11; Wed-Sat 11 pm, Sun 1.30 pm.

Haugen E20   £75
9 Endeavour Square   020 4568 1444   14–1D

You can't miss this remarkable, oversized swiss-chalet-inspired structure run by D&D London, which sits on the fringes of the Olympic Park, a short walk from Westfield Stratford. Its roof terrace is a prime spot for drinks on a sunny day. When it comes to eating, the Alpine-inspired fodder (fondue, rösti, schnitzel…) inspires remarkably little feedback: such as we have is positive, but insufficient to safely repudiate some of the brickbats thrown at the place online. BREAKING NEWS. In September 2023, it was announced that Haugen will soon close, although a new occupant is being sought for this impressive site. / E20 1JN; www.haugen-restaurant.com; haugenldn; Mon-Thu 11 pm, Fri-Sun 11.30 pm; SRA-accredited.

The Havelock Tavern W14   £65   3 3 3
57 Masbro Rd   020 7603 5374   8–1C

This "lovely local pub with decent food" behind Olympia has been a significant presence on the West London gastropub scene for almost 30 years, with its distinctive blue-tiled facade and elevated menu. Long-time regulars feel "it's not like it was in the old days" (when folks flocked from miles around), but they still feel it's "good all round". / W14 0LS; www.havelocktavern.com; havelocktavern; Mon-Sat 11 pm, Sun 10 pm.

Hawksmoor £95 3|3|2

5a Air St, W1   020 7406 3980   4–4C
11 Langley St, WC2   020 7420 9390   5–2C
3 Yeoman's Row, SW3   020 7590 9290   6–2C
16 Winchester Walk, SE1   020 7234 9940   10–4C
Wood Wharf, 1 Water Street, E14   020 3988 0510   12–1C
157 Commercial St, E1   020 7426 4850   13–2B
10-12 Basinghall St, EC2   020 7397 8120   10–2C

"Still one of the steak stalwarts of London…"; "still our go-to place for a relaxed night out…"; "still the place for a discreet business meeting in the City…". Few brands inspire as much long-term adulation as Huw Gott and Will Beckett's steakhouse chain, which has ridden the zeitgeist since its founding in 2006; and which is now (with the help of Graphite Capital, who own most of it nowadays) to be found in NYC and Dublin, as well as Manchester, Edinburgh and Liverpool. A "terrific" cocktail in the bar, precedes "awesome steaks with fantastic side dishes, all in a cool setting". At least, that's long been the accepted wisdom anyway, although there's a widespread feeling that quality "has dropped off a bit in recent years". In this year's annual diners' poll, ratings improved in some respects and declined in others, with historical concerns over stratospheric prices supplanted by niggles that maybe the formula is just "starting to look a tad tired" and that service – though often "excellent" – can also sometimes seem increasingly "impersonal" ("you are just a number!"). The majority verdict for the time being, though? Still "always hits the spot". / www.thehawksmoor.com; hawksmoorrestaurants; SRA-3 stars.

Hawthorn TW9 NEW £65 3|5|3

14 Station Parade   020 8940 6777   1–3A

"A very worthy successor to the beloved Glasshouse (RIP)" – this new Kew favourite is co-owned by its predecessor's former manager, Patra Panas. Service is particularly "well-drilled and friendly"; and regulars are "delighted to find that little has changed" after a "seamless" changeover, with "many of the furnishings still in place" in the agreeable (a few feel, "slightly uninspiring") dining room. Diners dispute whether the "intelligent and carefully crafted" cuisine, from chef and co-owner Josh Hunter, is a step up or down from before, but practically all agree it's "very competent", and say "we shall definitely return and recommend it highly!" / TW9 3PZ; www.hawthornrestaurant.co.uk; hawthorn_kew; Tue-Sat 10 pm.

Haya W11 £57 3|4|3

184a Kensington Park Road   0203 995 4777   7–1B

This appealing café/restaurant in Notting Hill is "just a gentle place to be", with a modern eastern Mediterranean menu inspired by founder Victoria Paltina's visits to Tel Aviv. / W11 2ES; haya.london; haya.ldn; Mon-Sun 11.30 pm.

Haz £63 3|2|2

9 Cutler St, E1   020 7929 7923   10–2D
14 Finsbury Square, EC2   020 7920 9944   13–2A
34 Foster Ln, EC2   020 7600 4172   10–2B
64 Bishopsgate, EC2   020 7628 4522   10–2D
6 Mincing Ln, EC3   020 7929 3173   10–3D

"Good mezze and grilled meat" help tick the boxes for "delicious food that is not expensive" at this Turkish business with five branches in the City – making them suitable "for business or social occasions" (although they can be "noisy"). In summer 2023, the group made its West End debut with the opening of Olea Social in Covent Garden, with a more general Mediterranean focus. / www.hazrestaurant.co.uk; hazrestaurantofficia.

Hélène Darroze,
The Connaught Hotel W1 £175 3 3 2
Carlos Pl   020 3147 7200   3–3B

"Yes, the food is very, very good" – the tasting menu is "absolutely incredible (every dish a piece of art and served on stunning crockery)" – according to fans of this superstar French chef, who has presided over the main dining room of this most blue-blooded of Mayfair hotels since 2008. Her reign has always been a little controversial here – for example, no-one is wild about the uneventful recent makeover of this fine, period chamber. But since its elevation to three Michelin stars, prices have become "extortionate (and with numerous supplements on the menu!)" and those diners who feel "this all-round exceptional experience is worth every penny" vie with the 2 in 5 who feel "the wallet-destroying prices are beyond extravagant" – "if I have to sell a kidney to eat here, I expect the food to win my heart… I'm not sure it did!" / W1K 2AL; www.the-connaught.co.uk; theconnaught; Tue-Sat 9 pm.

Heliot Steak House WC2 £78 3 2 2
Cranbourn Street   020 7769 8844   5–3B

"A go-to place for top USDA steaks" – this unusual space, hewn out of the old circle of the former Hippodrome Theatre, is worth a trip, with food that's much better than you might expect. It's great value too (perhaps as a loss leader to get you into the casino?), making it ideal as a pre-theatre option; and on Monday you can BYO wine. NB. Under 25s must have ID. / WC2H 7AJ; www.hippodromecasino.com; hippodromecasino; Sun-Thu 10 pm, Fri & Sat 11 pm.

Helix (Searcy's at The Gherkin) EC3 £91 3 3 5
30 St Mary Axe   0330 1070816   10–2D

Originally closed to the public when it opened 20 years ago, Norman Foster's 'Gherkin' – arguably the most iconic of the City's modern towers – now has a dining room run by catering company Searcy's on its 40th floor, which is "just so wonderful, with a glass-roofed bar and wall-to-wall windows in both bar and restaurant" – "it's my 'go-to' when I visit London for an excellent meal, first-class presentation, attentive staff, and all at a reasonable price. Win, win, win all round". / EC3A 8EP; searcysatthegherkin.co.uk; searcysgherkin.

Hereford Road W2 £60 4 4 3
3 Hereford Rd   020 7727 1144   7–1B

"Interesting and reasonably priced seasonal British food, expertly cooked and full of flavour" has underpinned the winning formula for 15 years at this old butcher's shop in Bayswater from ex-St John chef Tom Pemberton. "This is farm-to-table, but done properly", "letting the ingredients speak for themselves with flawless cooking that you can watch in the open kitchen" – made to look "deceptively simple" and served in an appropriate "slightly spartan ambience". / W2 4AB; www.herefordroad.org; Fri & Sat, Tue-Thu 10 pm, Sun 3.30 pm.

Heritage SE21 £55 4 4 3
101 Rosendale Road   020 8761 4665   1–4D

"Just amazing food bursting with flavour… and in generous portions" inspires very enthusiastic reports for Dayashakar Sharmar's ambitious Dulwich Indian – "it's so good for a local!" – and its small-but-dedicated fan club travel from across south east London. / SE21 8EZ; www.heritagedulwich.co.uk; heritageindiandulwich; Tue-Sat 10.30 pm, Sun 9 pm.

Hicce N1 £73 ②②③
Coal Drops Yard   020 3869 8200   9–3C

It has a "good location and a buzzy atmosphere too", but this early linchpin of the Coal Drops Yard development continues to produce mixed reports. Most feedback does acclaim Pip Lacey's "interesting menu" of "lovely sharing plates". But "tiny portions at sky-high prices" remains something of a theme ("I was shocked by the bill, especially as we'd eaten so little!)". Top Tip – "a particularly nice spot on a summer's evening". / N1C 4AB; www.hicce.co.uk; hiccelondon; Wed & Thu, Tue 11 pm, Fri & Sat midnight, Sun 5 pm.

Hicce Hart N1 NEW
58 Penton Street   020 3848 8168   9–3D

A corner-pub (formerly the Day & Night), on Islington's Chapel Market, provides the site for high-profile chef Pip Lacey's late 2022 newcomer. It's a spin-off from her first opening in Coal Drops Yard, with a focus on cooking over wood fire. No survey feedback yet, although social posts support the view that the value provided here is similar to the good-but-pricey reports we receive on the original. / N1 9PZ; www.hiccehart.co.uk; hiccehart; Mon-Wed 11 pm, Thu-Sat midnight, Sun 10 pm.

Hide W1 £177 ③②③
85 Piccadilly   020 3146 8666   3–4C

"The views over the park make for a magical setting" at this luxurious venue near Green Park station, where the kitchen is overseen by star chef Ollie Dabbous. Under the same ownership as famous merchants, Hedonism Wines, it shares their "spectacular list" ("by obsessives for obsessives"… and "with some surprising pockets of value nestling in its more obscure reaches" if you look hard enough). Hitherto, it traded as two distinct entities with 'Hide Below' a place for a "high level breakfast" or informal luxe-brasserie meal any time of day; and 'Hide Above' reserved for Ollie's "innovative" tasting menus – "terrific" but "don't mention the price… they're definitely not for everyday dining!" In mid-2023, though, they announced a change of direction – the same combined offering with the main features from both spaces will now be available on either floor: so you can now have breakfast with the same leafy vistas previously reserved for diners in 'Above' (or, tuck into the full, blow-out luxury menu while seated 'Below'. / W1J 8JB; www.hide.co.uk; hide_restaurant; Tue-Sun 9.30 pm.

High Road Brasserie W4 £72 ③②④
162-166 Chiswick High Road   020 8742 7474   8–2A

For the Chiswick fast-set (if there is such a thing?), this prominently sited outpost of the Soho House empire (from the early days, before it went global) is "THE best place for brunch", and at weekends in summer it's all designer sunnies and expensive casualwear out on the deck. It doesn't generate a huge volume of feedback, but was well-rated this year. / W4 1PR; highroadbrasserie.co.uk; highroadbrasserie; Sun-Thu 11 pm, Fri & Sat midnight.

High Timber EC4 £70 ③③②
8 High Timber Street   020 7248 1777   10–3B

"Hidden away on the north bank of the Thames" by the 'Wobbly Bridge', directly opposite Tate Modern, you'll find Neleen Strauss's "well-executed Western Cape restaurant", which is "big on steaks" but arguably most notable for its "very good and well structured" South African wine list. Top Tip – "I bring all my City contacts here". / EC4V 3PA; www.hightimber.com; hightimberrestaurant; Mon-Fri 10 pm.

Hispania EC3 £86 3 3 4
72-74 Lombard Street   020 7621 0338   10–2C
Set over two spacious floors in the grand Victorian former HQ of Lloyds Bank, this "classy Spanish restaurant is a great place to eat and drink" – with food and atmosphere that are more than a match for most of its City rivals. / EC3V 9AY; www.hispanialondon.com; hispanialondon; Mon-Fri 10 pm.

Holborn Dining Room WC1 £89 2 1 3
252 High Holborn   020 3747 8633   2–1D
For a "good solid business lunch" it remains recommendable, but otherwise reports are uneven regarding this grand hotel's 'British brasserie', where traditional pies are a big menu feature: the least enthusiastic diners feel it's "disappointing, since it is supposed to be a five star". / WC1V 7EN; www.holborndiningroom.com; holborndiningroom; Mon-Sat 10 pm, Sun 9.45 pm.

The Holland W8 £50 4 3 3
25 Earls Court Road   020 4599 1369   8–1D
"A fantastic new gastropub near Holland Park", in the no-man's-land location just south of Kensington High Street as you head down to Earl's Court. It was converted in September 2022 (from The Princess Victoria, RIP) with an upstairs dining room serving a modern British menu from chef Max de Nahlik, whose pop-up Oxalis was highly regarded. Initial high ratings and reports – "lovely Sunday roast…", "good and attentive service…", "deserves to be fuller than the night we went there…" – suggest it's worth discovering. / W8 6EB; www.thehollandkensington.co.uk; thehollandkensington; Wed-Sat 11 pm, Sun 6 pm.

Holly Bush NW3 £79 3 2 3
22 Holly Mount   020 7435 2892   9–1A
This "hidden gem" – a picture-book Grade II-listed Georgian tavern down a Hampstead side street – is "a great place to take the day off work", particularly "now the food has been improved". / NW3 6SG; www.hollybushhampstead.co.uk; thehollybushpubhampstead; Mon-Thu, Sat 11 pm, Fri 10 pm, Sun 8 pm.

Holy Carrot SW1 £59 4 4 4
Urban Retreat, 2-4 Hans Crescent   020 3897 0404   6–1D
"My find of the year… and I'm not vegetarian/vegan!" – former fashion model and producer Irina Linovich's two-year-old plant-based debut venture was scheduled to move into new Notting Hill premises in late 2023 from its original perch in a wellness salon near Harrods (and a vintage Airstream caravan by Battersea Power Station). There's a "really wide choice of imaginative food", with dishes such as 'Sexy Tofu' (eat your heart out, Richard Caring) that "certainly change your perception of vegan living". / SW1X 0LH; www.holycarrot.co.uk; holycarrotrestaurant; Mon-Sat 10 pm, Sun 5 pm.

Holy Cow SW11 £35 3 3 2
166 Battersea Pk Rd   020 7498 2000   11–1C
"A cut above when it comes to delivered Indian food" – most reporters know this brand through its 'at home' business, with 15 sites delivering "a wide selection of always hot and very tasty dishes on time to your door". They do also have two restaurants though in Putney and – since January 2023 – in Canary Wharf. The few reports we have on them say they are "a bit better than your typical curry house". / SW11 4ND; www.holycowfineindianfood.com; Sat & Sun, Mon-Fri 9 pm.

Homeslice £63 | 3 | 2 | 3 |
50 James Street, W1   020 3034 0621   3–1A
13 Neal's Yd, WC2   020 7836 4604   5–2C
101 Wood Lane White City, W12   020 3034 0381   1–2B
374-378 Old Street, EC1   020 3151 1121   13–1B
69-71 Queen Street, EC4   020 3034 0381   10–3C
This "hectic but enjoyable" trio of pizzerias from Alan & Mark Wogan (the late Sir Terry's sons) – in "lovely Neal's Yard", Marylebone and the City – specialises in large 20-inch pizzas (enough for 2 or 3), with "not the usual toppings" – air-dried wagyu beef with truffle creme fraiche, curried minced lamb with smoked burrata – "served alongside the usual ones". Top Tip – "you can have a half-and-half if you can't decide". / www.homeslicepizza.co.uk; homesliceldn.

Homies on Donkeys E11 NEW £15 | 4 | 4 | 4 |
686 High Road Leytonstone   07729 368896   14–1D
"Delicious tacos in a lovely new location" are to be found at this hip-hop-blasting, graffiti-walled taqueria, which has taken over the old Spicebox site on Leytonstone High Road. Arriving with a strong reputation from a five-year stint in a smaller Walthamstow location, the selection mixes classic Mexican flavours with more local ingredients. In a June 2023 review, The Guardian's Grace Dent thought its "astonishingly good" food to be "one of the more exciting things to have happened in this distant area of east London for a while… This is not Claridge's – in fact, I've had a comfier seat at Costa Coffee – but they play Kool G Rap while you eat, you leave very full and the bill is utterly reasonable". / E11 3AA; www.homiesondonkeys.com; homiesondonkeys; Tue, Thu 10 pm, Fri & Sat 11 pm, Sun 2.30 pm.

Honest Burgers £51 | 3 | 2 | 2 |
Branches throughout London
"Nearly but not quite the last man standing after the burger wars" – this "busy" chain offers "a limited menu" that's generally credited with being a "reliable" way to "hit the spot" when craving a "decent" burger with "fragrant rosemary fries". Ratings, though, do support those who say they are "not as good as they used to be" and risk becoming "nothing special" if the trend continues. / www.honestburgers.co.uk; honestburgers.

Honey & Co WC1 £71 | 3 | 2 | 2 |
54 Lamb's Conduit Street   020 7388 6175   2–1D
"Warren Street's loss is Bloomsbury's gain as Honey & Co sets up in Lamb's Conduit St on the former site of Cigala (RIP)", bringing with it the "interesting" middle Eastern cuisine ("lots of choice for vegetarians") that has won TV appearances and recipe-book deals for husband and wife, Sarit Packer and Itamar Srulovich. But while this 2022 newcomer is "a good addition to WC1", it "is now a proper and comparatively large restaurant compared to its former location and has lost its 'special' ambience". And for a few regulars, this disappointment extends to the food too ("not a patch on the original… it was packed solid so others may disagree, but we felt they're now just cashing in on their previous good name"). / WC1N 3LW; www.honeyandco.co.uk; honeyandcobloomsbury; Mon-Sat 10.30 pm.

Honey & Smoke W1 £72 | 3 | 2 | 2 |
216 Great Portland Street   020 7388 6175   2–1B
"Different" and "interesting" Middle Eastern cooking wins praise for this grillhouse near Great Portland Street from influential husband-and-wife team Sarit Packer and Itamar Srulovich. It also attracts some criticism, though – the setting is "quite loud", service can be "amateurish" and some diners "were not blown away by the meal: it was good, but not amazing". / W1W 5QW; honeyandco.co.uk; honeyandsmokerestaurant; Tue-Sat 10.30 pm.

Hoppers   **£49**   3 3 3
49 Frith St, W1   no tel   5–2A
77 Wigmore Street, W1   020 3319 8110   3–1A
Unit 3, Building 4, Pancras Square, N1   020 3319 8125   9–3C
"A fantastic menu of unusual Sri Lankan street food" with "lots of
interesting ingredients (breadfruit, squid, dal, etc) in a mix-and-match format"
has won a huge fan club for JKS Restaurants three-strong chain (with a
fourth branch planned to open late in 2023 in Shoreditch). Ratings slipped
across the board, though, this year – incidents of "hit 'n' miss service" and
"packed and noisy" conditions can make them appear "a bit pricey".
/ www.hopperslondon.com; hopperslondon.

Hoshi SW20   **£44**   3 3 2
54 Durham Road   020 8944 1888   11–2A
This "relaxed local Japanese" in Raynes Park "opened recently on the site of
(confusingly similarly named) Hashi". Reports suggest "the quality of the
food is better", with "authentic, skillfully prepared dishes" including "good
fresh sushi". / SW20 0TW; hoshirestaurant.co.uk; Tue-Sat 10.30 pm, Sun 10 pm.

Hot Stone N1   **£91**   2 2 2
9 Chapel Market   020 3302 8226   9–3D
Many diners do applaud "wonderful ingredients, impeccably presented" at
this ambitious Japanese venue on Islington's Chapel Market, and say that the
"signature sashimi, maki rolls and different types of wagyu that you cook on
a hot stone are all spectacular". But a slew of critical reports – in particular
regarding voucher promotions – has dented ratings; and such feedback is
peppered with a variety of critiques and disappointments, including some
"fairly average dishes" and some items charged at "outrageous prices".
/ N1 9EZ; www.hotstonelondon.com; hotstonelondon; Mon & Tue 9 pm, Wed & Thu,
Sun 8.45 pm, Fri & Sat 9.30 pm.

**House of Ming,
St James's Court SW1**
54 Buckingham Gate   020 7963 8330   2–4C
India's famous Taj group brought their take on the cuisines of Sichuan and
Canton to their St James's Court hotel (near Buck House) in May 2021. It's
stablemate to the establishment's Keralan superstar Quilon, and reflects the
popularity of Chinese cuisine in India itself. As it launched after our annual
diners' poll we have no direct user feedback, but early online reviews are
upbeat. / SW1E 6AF; www.houseofming.co.uk; homlondon; Mon-Sun 11 pm.

Humble Chicken W1   **£38**   4 3 4
54 Frith Street   020 7434 2782   5–2A
"One of the most exciting options in Soho nowadays": Angelo Sato's
ambitious and "really rather good multi-course omakase" – in the premises
of the original Barrafina – features "really innovative dishes, executed to
perfection in a casual, buzzing atmosphere". The Tokyo-born chef, who
trained under Clare Smyth and headed the kitchen at Restaurant Story,
originally opened the venue as a yakitori, specialising in chicken skewers,
before upgrading in early 2023 to its present, rather less humble
incarnation. Diners sit at the counter to enjoy the theatrical preparation.
/ W1D 4SJ; www.humblechickenuk.com; humblechicken_uk; Tue-Thu 10 pm, Fri & Sat
11 pm.

Humble Grape £67 2|3|3
11-13 Theberton Street, N1   020 3887 9287   9–3D
2 Battersea Rise, SW11   020 3620 2202   11–2C
18-20 Mackenzie Walk, E14   020 3985 1330   12–1C
8 Devonshire Row, EC2   020 3887 9287   10–2D
1 Saint Bride's Passage, EC4   020 7583 0688   10–2A
James Dawson's wine shops/clubs/bars are "great places to catch up with friends over a bottle you might not ordinarily have tried". "The staff are super-helpful, with lots of suggestions" of bottles from independent and sustainable producers. The food is "OK if a little uninspiring", but "who cares when there's one evening a week when you can drink wine at retail prices". / www.humblegrape.co.uk; humblegrape.

Humo W1 NEW £91 5|5|4
12 St George Street   020 3327 3690   3–2C
An "amazing newcomer" on the former Mayfair site of Wild Honey (RIP), where chef Miller Prada (who worked with Endo Kazutoshi at Endo at The Rotunda) infuses Japanese flavours into his dishes at a four-metre wood grill (using no electricity or gas in the cooking process). It's "a very cool setting" with "notably good" service and the culinary invention of the technique means "every dish has a wow factor". (However, both Giles Coren of The Times and William Sitwell of The Telegraph have found the experience "great… but pretentious"; "sublime… [but] somewhat self-satisfied"). / W1S 2FB; humolondon.com; humolondon; Tue-Sat 10.15 pm.

Hunan SW1 £120 4|2|1
51 Pimlico Road   020 7730 5712   6–2D
"Course after course of utter deliciousness!" – comprised of "Chinese tapas that never ceases to impress" – has won renown for this Pimlico veteran, whose "very different 18-course tasting menu is tailored in terms of spiciness and dietary preferences" in discussion with the staff. It's a formula that's served the Peng family well for over 40 years (although their personal service is not quite as intrinsic to a visit as once it was). "As other authentic Chinese cuisine has become available across London", it is perhaps no longer the leading destination it once was, although all diners feel "the food deserves its excellent reputation". "The venue does not create much in the way of ambience" however and it is often noted in feedback that a meal here has become "very expensive now". Top Tip – "don't eat all day before you go". / SW1W 8NE; www.hunanlondon.com; hunanlondon; Mon-Sat 11 pm.

Huo SW10 £72 3|3|3
9 Park Walk   020 3696 9090   6–3B
This "always enjoyable" two-year-old on 'Chelsea Beach' entices a stylish local crowd with its fresh-tasting take on the cuisines of China and Southeast Asia, and bleached-pastel contemporary decor. Regulars tip its "best curries". It's a sibling to Uli in Notting Hill and Marylebone, from restaurateur Michael Lim. / SW10 0AJ; huo.london; huo.london; Mon-Sat midnight, Sun 11 pm.

Hush W1 £99 2|3|4
8 Lancashire Ct   020 7659 1500   3–2B
"Perfectly located just away from the hubbub of Bond Street/Oxford Street/Regent Street but easy to get to", this slick Mayfair venue with a "great outdoor courtyard" for summer dining makes "an excellent place to talk business over a meal and wine". The pleasure "comes at a price", though – "one the food struggles to justify". Fun fact: the founding investors include Evgeny Lebedev, the son of a Soviet spy who now sits in the House of Lords. / W1S 1EY; www.hush.co.uk; hushmayfair; Mon-Sat 10 pm.

Hutong,
The Shard SE1   £125   3 4 4

31 St Thomas St   020 3011 1257   10–4C

"You pay for the view… it stings the wallet…", but they seem to have pulled their socks up at this well-known Asian venue on the 33rd floor of the famous London landmark. True, "large numbers of diners seem more interested in taking photos of themselves and their food rather than eating it… it's definitely an Insta trophy". But it avoided the usual harsh critiques this year and practically all reports acknowledged the "surprisingly good Chinese cooking AND nighttime vistas over London". / SE1 9RY; www.hutong.co.uk; hutongshard; Mon-Sun 10.30 pm.

Ibérica   £67   2 2 2

Zig Zag Building, 70 Victoria St, SW1   020 7636 8650   2–4B
195 Great Portland St, W1   020 7636 8650   2–1B
12 Cabot Sq, E14   020 7636 8650   12–1C
89 Turnmill St, EC1   020 7636 8650   10–1A

This "buzzy but very noisy" Hispanic quartet (in Marylebone, Farringdon, Victoria and Canary Wharf) offers a "good range of tapas" and "interesting wines by the glass and the bottle". They still have plenty of admirers as a "reliable" option, even if they "no longer provide the novelty or the high standards they once did". / www.ibericarestaurants.com; ibericarestaurants.

Icco Pizza   £19   3 3 2

46 Goodge St, W1   020 7580 9688   2–1C
21a Camden High Street, NW1   020 7380 0020   9–3B

"Awesome, thin and crispy pizza" has built quite a following for this "fast, simple, really cheap and really cheerful" Goodge Street spot – where, "unless strip lighting, functional metal tables and chairs are your thing, the ambience is forgettable". Celebrating its quarter-centenary this year as 'The People's Pizzeria', it now has a branch in Camden and 'click & collect' kitchens in Wood Green, Colindale and Croydon. / www.icco.co.uk; icco_pizza.

Ikeda W1   £94   4 3 2

30 Brook St   020 7629 2730   3–2B

After half a century, this high-quality Mayfair veteran is "still one of the best Japanese restaurants in London", with particularly "good fish" – although it has a lower profile than many newer and more flashy rivals. "Having the kitchen open to the dining area adds some theatre to aid the digestion". / W1K 5DJ; www.ikedarestaurant.com; Tue-Fri 9 pm, Mon 9.15 pm.

Ikoyi WC2   £345   2 3 2

180 The Strand   020 3583 4660   4–4D

Iré Hassan-Odukale and Jeremy Chan have won huge renown for their 'haute' interpretation of West African culinary themes, but this year saw very unsettled reports. Perhaps, in part, this owes to the disruption of a move to 180 The Strand, although the copper-hued, minimalist design there isn't wholly at odds with the look and feel of the former location in St James's Market. But to a large extent, this year's themes are a continuation of last year's; and complaints that seemed to set in after they jacked up their prices following all the Michelin and 'World's 50 Best' accolades. True, some reports do acknowledge an "outstanding gastronomic experience" from the blind tasting menu which sees jollof rice and plantain jostling with luxury ingredients, foams and emulsions. But too many are mixed: "we had a couple of stunners, but a dish that was so bitter it was unpleasant. So expensive and given the unpredictability it makes Core look like a bargain…"; "really did not enjoy this. Dull atmosphere, combinations of food which just did not work and service not firing on all cylinders. First time I've ever not enjoyed a two-star restaurant…"; "was expecting something so special: it wasn't!" / WC2C 1EA; www.ikoyilondon.com; ikoyi_london; Thu-Sat, Mon-Wed 8.45 pm.

Imad's Syrian Kitchen W1 £28 **3** **4** **4**
Kingly Court, Kingly Street 07473 333631 4–2B
"The poignant history" of Syrian chef Imad Alarnab (who fled Damascus in 2015) helps inspire excellent reviews for his "convivial" venue: a "gem in Kingly Court". Our feedback – citing "delicious" Syrian cooking and "thoughtful service" – came just before his May 2023 move to a bigger unit in the same development (where breakfast is a new feature): "the fact that you have to book with plenty of notice says it all… I'm not surprised to hear they're expanding". / W1B 5PW; imadssyriankitchen.co.uk; imadssyriankitchen; Tue-Sat 10 pm, Mon 9 pm.

Imperial China WC2 £59 **3** **2** **2**
25a Lisle St 020 7734 3388 5–3A
"Fresh and very tasty dim sum" ensures that this 30-year-old Cantonese over three storeys on the edge of Chinatown "soon fills up with regulars". "It may be a blessing that the ambience is not exactly chic – it keeps the tourists away". / WC2H 7BA; www.imperialchinalondon.com; imperialchinalondon; Mon-Thu 11 pm, Fri & Sat 11.30 pm, Sun 10.30 pm.

Imperial Treasure SW1 £147 **4** **3** **2**
9-10 Waterloo Place 020 3011 1328 4–4D
"Expensive, but worth it for a treat!" is the positive view on this West End fixture – part of a Singapore-based group, whose London outpost occupies an expensively converted former banking hall in the West End, whose atmosphere has ended up somewhere between impressive and stilted. "Very good, classic Chinese cuisine is reverently served by a stream of waiters… but the prices!… £200 for Peking duck with caviar anyone?" Indeed, such is the size of the bill that there is a school of thought that the level of value doesn't stack up and that – irrespective of its many qualities – the overall experience is overpriced and/or disappointing. / SW1Y 4BE; www.imperialtreasure.com; imperialtreasureuk; Mon-Sun 11 pm.

Inamo £65 **3** **2** **4**
134-136 Wardour Street, W1 020 7851 7051 4–1D
11-14 Hanover Place, WC2 020 7484 0500 5–2D
"Launched in 2008 as the world's first interactive restaurant", these Soho and Covent Garden venues are "great for an alternative afternoon tea" and attract a "young, tech-savvy crowd". A meal here is "certainly an experience – you have to see it to believe it", and the pan-Asian "unlimited lunch" is "of a high standard". / www.inamo-restaurant.com; inamorestaurant.

Indian Ocean SW17 £31 **3** **3** **3**
214 Trinity Rd 020 8672 7740 11–2C
This "fabulous, family-run" curry house near Wandsworth Common has built a loyal local following over the years for its "delicious food" and "always charming" welcome. / SW17 7HP; www.indianoceanrestaurant.com; Sun-Thu 11 pm, Fri & Sat 11.45 pm.

Indian Zing W6 £61 **4** **3** **3**
236 King St 020 8748 5959 8–2B
Reaching "classic" status after almost two decades of "outstanding food and great service", this Ravenscourt Park venue is a haven of "superb Indian cuisine", thanks to chef-patron Manoj Vasaikar's "well-spiced" cooking and "quality ingredients". The late Michael Winner was an early fan. / W6 0RS; www.indian-zing.co.uk; indianzinguk; Mon-Sun 10 pm.

Indigo,
One Aldwych WC2 £71 **3** **3** **4**
1 Aldwych   020 7300 0400   2–2D
This conveniently situated mezzanine venue in a luxury hotel near Covent Garden is a real treat thanks to its "lovely setting" and "high standard" of cooking. The kitchen is "particularly accommodating for those with dietary restrictions" – "the wheat and dairy-free afternoon tea is joyous, with wonderful flavours and ingenious combinations, plus a wide selection of unusual teas". / WC2B 4BZ; www.onealdwych.com; onealdwychhotel; Mon-Sat 9.30 pm, Sun 11.

INO W1 £58 **3** **4** **4**
4 Newburgh Street   020 3701 6618   4–2B
One or two "outstanding" reports inspire interest in this modern Greek off Soho's Carnaby Street, whose name means 'wine' in ancient Greek (there's an all-Hellenic list), and where the menu focus is on plates from the charcoal grill. (It's from the team behind Opso, who also run the two-Michelin-star Funky Gourmet in Athens).Our rating errs on the conservative side, but we still don't get as many reports on the place as we would like. Top Tip – very good value set lunch. / W1F 7RF; www.inogastrobar.com; ino.restaurant; Mon-Sat 11 pm, Sun 10 pm.

Ishtar W1 £71 **3** **3** **2**
10-12 Crawford St   020 7224 2446   2–1A
Celebrating its 20th anniversary this year, this smart Turkish operation in Marylebone wins consistently solid marks for the "excellent quality and taste" of its dishes – in particular the grilled meat and mezzes. / W1U 6AZ; www.ishtarrestaurant.com; ishtarlondon; Sun-Thu 11 pm, Fri & Sat midnight.

Isla WC1 £66 **3** **5** **4**
The Standard, 10 Argyle St   020 3981 8888   9–3C
The gorgeous, glazed summer terrace adjoining the main lounges is a highpoint at this bar/restaurant opposite St Pancras. Its other features include the superb 1970s decor and shelves lined with books inherited from the hotel's former life as the Camden Council Library. Extra convenient if you need a meeting place near King's Cross – it serves a dependable all-day modern European menu and service is particularly friendly and efficient. / WC1H 8EG; www.islalondon.com; isla.london; Mon-Sun 11 pm.

Issho-Ni E2 £43 **4** **4** **2**
185 Bethnal Green Road   020 7366 0314   13–1D
"Top-end sushi for a fair price" is the deal at this Bethnal Green izakaya from Claire Su, who delights her guests with "the freshest sushi and some great hot dishes too". The weekday bento-box lunches are extremely good value, and the "unlimited brunch (starters, sashimi and maki rolls) on Saturdays is fantastic". Top Menu Tip – "don't get me started on the butter fish". / E2 6AB; issho-ni.com; isshoniuk; Tue-Thu 10.30 pm, Fri & Sat 11 pm.

Italian Greyhound W1 £61 **3** **3** **3**
62 Seymour Street   020 3826 7940   7–1D
Attractive casual two-year-old not far from Marble Arch, whose mid-pandemic opening perhaps robbed it of PR it might otherwise have generated. Feedback remains limited, but the response is all very good when it comes to the stylish interior; 20-seat outside terrace; and Italian cuisine (from pizza and pasta to some more 'serious' dishes). / W1H 5BN; theitaliangreyhound.co.uk; greyhoundmarylebone; Mon-Sat 11 pm, Sun 10.30 pm.

The Ivy WC2 £97 ②②③
1-5 West Street   020 7836 4751   5–3B
The eclipse of this former icon of Theatreland by the nationwide chain it spawned (and its adjoining club) is continuing, and the volume of feedback it inspired sank significantly this year. A fair amount of glam still remains, but the A-listers are long gone, and standards are "hit and miss nowadays" to the extent that it too often delivers an experience that's "overpriced, formulaic and mediocre". / WC2H 9NQ; www.the-ivy.co.uk; theivyweststt; Mon-Sat 11 pm, Sun 10.30 pm.

The Ivy Asia £84 ③②④
8-10 North Audley Street, W1   020 3751 4990   3–2A
201-203a King's Road, SW3   020 7486 6154   6–3C
20 New Change Passage, EC4   020 3971 2600   10–2B
"Wanted to hate this chain but it's actually really good" – Despite being totally un-PC in its level of cultural appropriation, it looks like Richard Caring's is going to make a go of this "extraordinary" new sub-branch of the Ivy brand (which has opened five further branches around the UK). True, "it's part of a big corporate machine with little intrinsic character"; the über-"kitsch" styling is "love-it-or-hate-it"; and some diners feel "these places are ghastly and overpriced". But even if "the jewelled floor is more interesting than the food", most folks feel that the "OTT decor" "justifies the trip in itself" and that the long, pan-Asian menu is "so much better than expected". / www.theivyasia.com; theivyasia.

The Ivy Café £88 ①①②
96 Marylebone Ln, W1   020 3301 0400   2–1A
120 St John's Wood High St, NW8   020 3096 9444   9–3A
75 High St, SW19   020 3096 9333   11–2B
9 Hill Street, TW9   020 3146 7733   1–4A
"Trading on a once-great name but disappointing in every category (except perhaps breakfasts)" – this brasserie brand themed around the Theatreland classic feels "very 'chain restaurant' now". Some reporters do suggest their "comfort food staples" and "buzzy interiors" make them useful destinations, but too many suggest they are "haphazard" and "not a place to return to". / ivycollection.com/our-restaurants.

The Ivy Grills & Brasseries £87 ②②③
66 Victoria Street, SW1   020 3971 2404   2–4B
26-28 Broadwick St, W1   020 3301 1166   4–1C
1 Henrietta St, WC2   020 3301 0200   5–3D
197 King's Rd, SW3   020 3301 0300   6–3C
96 Kensington High St, W8   020 3301 0500   6–1A
One Tower Bridge, 1 Tower Bridge, SE1   020 3146 7722   10–4D
50 Canada Square, E14   020 3971 7111   12–1C
Dashwood House, 69 Old Broad St, EC2   020 3146 7744   10–2D
With the "lovely decor" replicated from the Theatreland icon for which they are branded, Richard Caring's "always buzzy" spin-offs have found a gigantic audience nationally. But "these places live off the name for sure" and "it's the ambience that keeps them going" – while fans say the food is "reliable", more sceptical types dismiss it as "conveyor-belt cooking"; and say service is merely so-so. Some branches are better than others: best in London is 'Chelsea Garden', which has the same "distinctly average" standards as the others, but reliably offers an "uplifting" atmosphere and "great people watching" (and "on a sunny afternoon there is literally NO WHERE ELSE TO BE but its large garden. HEAVEN!!"). Also worth mentioning is the outlet by The Thames in SE1: "excellent views of Tower Bridge", "even better if outside in summer and convenient for The Bridge Theatre". / theivymarketgrill.com.

Izakaya Nights W11 NEW

Supermarket of Dreams, 126 Holland Park Ave   01904 610370   7–2A

After shopping hours, the Supermarket of Dreams in Holland Park Avenue morphs into an upscale Japanese restaurant, with guests seated at a long central table. It started as a pop-up, and announced it was to become a permanent feature in March 2023. Dishes are created by Juan Cardona (formerly of Endo at The Rotunda), and Jaime Finol (formerly of Sumi) and sushi is the mainstay of the menu (as you'd hope, given the stellar renown of both those places in that respect). Reports please! / W11 4UE; www.izakaya-york.co.uk; izakaya.york; Wed-Sat midnight.

Jacuzzi W8   £72   ①②④

94 Kensington High Street   no tel   6–1A

"A fun place for the Insta crowd…" – "the setting is absolute bling (but enjoyable for that)" at this mammoth Kensington newcomer from the Big Mamma group (Gloria, Circolo Popolare, etc), complete with a Sicilian-styled mezzanine with retractable roof and glitter-ball disco toilet. But too often it's "all about the vibe and location" – the humongous portions of Italian fare can be tolerable, but strike unlucky and "OMG the food is bad"; and service "needs focus" not "annoying loud Italian-style showmanship". Top Menu Tip – "the pizza is pretty decent". / W8 4SH; www.bigmammagroup.com; bigmamma.uk; Mon-Sat 10.15 pm, Sun 9.45 pm.

Jam Delish N1   £52   ⑤④③

1 Tolpuddle Street   07957 439777   9–3D

"Deserving all the plaudits and great value too" – siblings Jordan & Chyna Johnson graduated from residencies and pop-ups to this bricks-and-mortar perma-home in 2022: a hard-to-define, good-times restaurant and cocktail bar in Islington, with a "super soundtrack and slightly bonkers decor". What makes it particularly of interest is the "quirky-in-a-good-way" Caribbean cuisine that's not only hearty for meat-free cooking – and with "an unexpected range of flavours" – but also absolutely bangin'. Add in "lovely staff" and it's "a real find". / N1 0XT; www.jamdelish.co.uk; jam.delish; Tue-Sat 10.30 pm, Sun 7 pm.

Jamavar W1   £83   ③③③

8 Mount Street   020 7499 1800   3–3B

"A beautiful restaurant interior, plus warm, professional and attentive staff" have helped Samyutka Nair and family's "posh Indian" near Mayfair's Berkeley Square acquire a reputation as "one of the best subcontinental restaurants in London". Its ratings sank this year, though amidst a number of experiences of cooking that was "solid, but not as refined as expected" – "It was very nice… but is it so different to many others that have sprung up to justify the high price here?" Top Tip – "set lunch is a steal!" / W1K 3NF; www.jamavarrestaurants.com; jamavarlondon; Mon-Sat 10.30 pm, Sun 9.30 pm.

Jashan N8   £42   ③③②

19 Turnpike Ln   020 8340 9880   1–1C

Nobody is entirely happy about the change of style at this "wonderful curry house" of more than three decades' standing in Turnpike Lane, following a recent "facelift", although "if that's what they had to do to survive the pandemic, then fair enough I suppose – but we really miss the old place". Some feel it's now "essentially a large takeaway counter with the restaurant area tucked behind under glaringly bright lights", while more positive types feel that overall it's "still recommended for a quick casual eating experience, but not for a relaxed evening out as in the past". / N8 0EP; www.jashan.co.uk; Mon-Sun 11 pm.

Jean-Georges at The Connaught W1 £132 2 3 3
Carlos Place   020 7107 8861   3–3B
Other than for a deeply cosseting afternoon tea, it's hard to be too thrilled by this blue-blooded hotel's luxurious conservatory dining room. Although it's branded with the name of the famous NYC chef, it's difficult to discern any trace of JGV's fingerprints in the design of the ubiquitous, international-luxe menu of caviar, fish, posh pizza, burgers, salads and so forth. Of course, if you find yourself in Mayfair, and are sanguine about spending £30+ for a bowl of mushroom bolognese or shrimp salad, it's a jolly pleasant experience. Viewed through a more demanding lens, though, it can seem "overpriced" for something with little in the way of distinctive culinary personality. / W1K 2AL; www.the-connaught.co.uk; theconnaught; Mon-Sun midnight.

Jeru W1 £106 3 3 4
11 Berkeley Street   020 3988 0054   3–3C
"Two atmospheric dining rooms" make a "beautiful setting" for Aussie celeb chef Roy Ner to showcase his "pan-Middle Eastern" cuisine, featuring his signature chocolate-aged beef among other creations. But even some who feel the food is "perfectly acceptable" can quibble at the Mayfair prices. / W1J 8DS; jeru.co.uk; jerulondon; Mon-Thu 10.15 pm, Fri & Sat 11.15 pm.

Jiji N1 £70 3 3 3
6g Esther Anne Place   020 7486 3929   9–3D
"An amazing variety of small, tasty and unusual combination dishes served in a very cool environment" continues to win a thumbs up – if from a tiny fan club – for this Israeli-Japanese one-year-old in the shiny new Islington Square development. / N1 1WL; jijirestaurants.com; jijirestaurant; Tue-Sun 11 pm.

Jikoni W1 £83 4 3 4
21 Blandford Street   020 7034 1988   2–1A
This "beautiful little restaurant with a neighbourhood feel" in Marylebone, from chef and food writer Ravinder Bhogal, offers a "wide-ranging and ever-changing selection of consistently good dishes" inspired by her 'no borders kitchen' philosophy. "It's a melange of Middle Eastern, African and Indian influences" that results in "very creative flavours – not just in the cooking but also outstanding cocktails such as a Negroni with pomegranate and rose". / W1U 3DJ; www.jikonilondon.com; jikonilondon; Tue, Sat 10 pm, Wed-Fri 11 pm, Sun 9 pm.

Jin Kichi NW3 £62 5 4 3
73 Heath St   020 7794 6158   9–1A
"Now happily doubled in size" – this favourite stalwart near Hampstead tube "hasn't been spoilt by its recent expansion" and remains "an atmospheric local gem", much to the relief of its large following. "You feel like you might be in Tokyo here", such is its unpretentious yet "elegantly bustling" nature; and "wonderful sushi and yakitori" (especially the latter) gives it a justifiable claim to offering "the best value Japanese food of its quality in London". / NW3 6UG; www.jinkichi.com; jinkichi_restaurant; Tue-Sun 10 pm.

Jinjuu W1 £73 3 2 2
16 Kingly St   020 8181 8887   4–2B
The "small plates of big Korean taste bombs never disappoint" in this basement dining room (with a ground-level bar) off Carnaby Street, where traditional cuisine meets contemporary K-pop youth culture. Top Menu Tip – "prawn tacos and spicy cauliflower". / W1B 5PS; www.jinjuu.com; jinjuusoho; Mon & Tue 10 pm, Wed & Thu 11 pm, Fri & Sat midnight, Sun 9.30 pm.

Joe Allen WC2 £62 2️⃣3️⃣4️⃣
2 Burleigh St 020 7836 0651 5–3D
The "Manhattan-esque atmosphere" is the perennial attraction of this
Theatreland favourite (sibling to a famous NYC brasserie near Times
Square), which retains the retro charm of a 1970s period piece, even though
it was completely rebuilt on a new site just around the corner from the
original one just four years ago. "Despite the luvvie buzz, the American food
is decidedly second rate (though the off-menu burger is fine)". "Prices are
not unreasonable for the location", however, and "the youthful staff do their
best". / WC2E 7PX; www.joeallen.co.uk; joeallenlondon; Mon-Thu 9.45 pm, Fri & Sat
10.30 pm, Sun 4.30 pm.

JOIA SW11 £114 3️⃣3️⃣4️⃣
Battersea Power Station, Circus Road West 020 3833 8333 11–1C
"You feel like you're on the set of Blade Runner next to the floor-to-ceiling
windows" of this striking newcomer on the 16th floor of the new Battersea
art'otel, with gobsmacking sightlines over the top of the power station and of
the London skyline. Fêted Portuguese chef, Henrique Sá Pessoa, provides a
not-unaffordable selection of tapas, petiscos, tortilla, grills (from the Josper)
and a few large plates. Our reporters were generally more enthusiastic than
The Standard's Jimi Famurewa (whose food "lurched, haphazardly, from
forgettably luxe to clumsily experimental"), referencing "classic Portuguese
dishes, all executed with impeccable attention to detail". But one reporter did
feel their meal was only "fine… like JimFam we were thinking of the much
more interesting and better value menu at Lisboeta". Top Tip – dip your toe
in the water by "heading to the rooftop bar next door which has stunning
views: order some drinks and nibble on small plates". / SW11 8BJ;
www.joiabattersea.co.uk; joiabattersea; Tue, Wed midnight, Thu-Sat 1 am.

Jones & Sons N16 £67 3️⃣3️⃣4️⃣
Stamford Works, 3 Gillett Street 020 7241 1211 14–1A
"Deservedly something of a local institution" – this industrial-style restaurant
and grill "manages to provide a cut-above dining experience while retaining
a low-key Hackney vibe" – making it the perfect location for the 2021 film
Boiling Point, which was spun out into a BBC TV series in 2023. / N16 8JH;
www.jonesandsonsdalston.com; jones.and.sons; Wed-Sat 10 pm, Sun 6 pm.

The Jones Family Kitchen SW1 £85 3️⃣3️⃣4️⃣
7-8 Eccleston Yard 020 3929 6000 2–4B
"A great option near Victoria" – this indie venue in the stylish Eccleston
Yards project provides a comfy spot for its Josper-grilled steaks, other grills
from 'sea, land and field' and fish tartares. It's "relatively simple fare" but
well-realised from a wide variety of menus, including Sunday roasts. And the
venue "makes a virtue of its converted warehouse space" with "very
friendly" service that helps it win votes both for business and as a good spot
to spend "a lovely lazy afternoon". Top Tip – wonderful outside dining in
summer. / SW1W 9AZ; www.jonesfamilykitchen.co.uk; jonesfamilyrestaurants; Mon-Sat
11.30 pm, Sun 9 pm.

José SE1 £62 5️⃣3️⃣4️⃣
104 Bermondsey St 020 7403 4902 10–4D
"For maybe a decade now, José has been London's most reliable and
enjoyable restaurant", assert fans of the tiny tapas bar José Pizarro opened
on Bermondsey Street in 2011, now the spiritual home of a growing culinary
empire. "Whether it's a quick lunch or hours spent at the bar, it simply never
misses". "Always incredibly fun, always worth the queue, always get the
croquetas". / SE1 3UB; www.josepizarro.com; jose_pizarro; Mon-Sat 10.30 pm, Sun
10 pm.

José Pizarro EC2 £68 **3**22
Broadgate Circle 020 7256 5333 13–2B
The Broadgate Circle tapas bar from the trailblazer of contemporary Hispanic cooking in London provides "excellent food in a modern environment" – even if aficionados of the more atmospheric original insist it "doesn't replicate the better José across the river" in Bermondsey.
/ EC2M 2QS; www.josepizarro.com; josepizarrorestaurants; Mon-Fri 10.30 pm, Sat 9.45 pm.

**José Pizarro at the RA,
Royal Academhy W1** £60 **3**3**4**
Burlington Gardens, Piccadilly 020 7300 5912 3–3D
"Talk about high ceilings and light" – this "really lovely addition to the RA" is "worth a trip just for the beautiful dining room". According to supporters, "it's a clear exception to the rule that restaurants in art galleries never live up to their surroundings, with imaginative tapas in good-sized portions and at very reasonable prices for the area". That said, its ratings have slipped since it first opened and there are one or two critics who say "we've always been fans of José, but the RA offering isn't as good as the other JPs".
/ W1J 0BD; josepizarro.com; jose_pizarro; Tue-Thu, Sat & Sun 6 pm, Fri 9 pm.

Jugemu W1 £40 **5**22
3 Winnett St 020 7734 0518 4–2D
Yuya Kikuchi's no-frills, very personal, small Soho six-year-old inspired little feedback this year, although we have received rave reviews in the past, particularly about the sushi. You can eat quite cheaply here, but aficionados of Japanese cuisine regularly go nuts for his £120, 18-course omakase. The FT's Tim Hayward was one such in February 2023, declaring it "the best Japanese food in London" where "the chef's attention to his ingredients is quite staggering… his craft skills second-to-none". We have never had any complaints, but read Tripadvisor reviews if you are at all sensitive to poor service… / W1D 6JY; jugemu.uk; Mon-Sat 10.30 pm.

The Jugged Hare EC1 £75 **3**2**4**
49 Chiswell Street 020 7614 0134 13–2A
The "excellent meat-driven menu" at this "busy bar opposite the Barbican" is led by British game in season, backed up by prime cuts of beef and such treats as Herefordshire snails. "It's not simple pub grub, and you do pay for it, but it's worth it", say fans. It's also "particularly useful pre- or post-events in the nearby arts centre". / EC1Y 4SA; www.thejuggedhare.com; thejuggedhare; Mon-Sun 11 pm.

Junsei W1 £74 **3**4**2**
132 Seymour Place 020 7723 4058 7–1D
"Top-notch cooking that uses every bit of the chicken and won't cost a wing and a leg" draws an appreciative Marylebone crowd to this Japanese two-year-old which "specialises in yakitori skewers with some very interesting options (gizzard anyone?)". "Go sit at the counter to see the open kitchen at work" and "revel in the omakase menu". / W1H 1NS; junsei.co.uk; junsei_uk; Wed-Sat 10 pm, Sun 9 pm.

Kaffeine £17 2**5**3
15 Eastcastle St, W1 020 7580 6755 3–1D
66 Great Titchfield St, W1 020 7580 6755 3–1C
"One of the original Aussie coffee shops", founded in 2009 by Melburnian Peter Dore-Smith and now with two branches in Fitzrovia serving "fabulous artisanal brews". They make a "perfect escape from the chain experience of nearby Oxford Street" with their "great service and vibe", "fresh sandwiches" and "very good lunchtime salads". / kaffeine.co.uk; kaffeinelondon.

Kahani SW1 £80 [4][4][3]
I Wilbraham Place   020 7730 7634   6–2D

Peter Joseph (raised in Chennai) "has maintained high standards and always delivers value for money" at his culinarily "interesting" Indian venture near Sloane Square (behind Cadogan Hall), where he uses a robata grill and tandoor to "delicious" effect. "Initially, we thought it was an unpromising basement, but it was one of our best meals of the year". / SW1X 9AE; www.kahanilondon.com; kahani_london; Mon-Sat 10.30 pm, Sun 8 pm.

Kai Mayfair W1 £133 [4][4][3]
65 South Audley St   020 7493 8988   3–3A

"Chinese cuisine at its finest, with service to match" helps inspire high ratings this year for Bernard Yeoh's luxurious Mayfair fixture – now of two decades' standing – which describes its culinary focus as 'Liberated Nanyang Cooking'. Part of this freewheeling approach is the curation of a very comprehensive cellar: perhaps wash down your roasted Peking duck with a 1990 Château Pétrus at over £9,000 per bottle… / W1K 2QU; www.kaimayfair.co.uk; kaimayfair; Mon-Sun 11 pm.

Kaifeng NW4 £79 [4][4][3]
51 Church Road   020 8203 7888   1–1B

One of North London's more consistent and interesting culinary success stories: Hendon's kosher Chinese restaurant "continues to operate at a very high standard", with "tasty and authentic cooking" and "a great ambience". It takes its name from a Chinese city with an ancient Jewish community. / NW4 4DU; www.kaifeng.co.uk; Sun-Thu, Sat 10.30 pm.

Kaki N1 £53 [3][3][2]
125 Caledonian Road   020 7278 6848   9–3D

"Authentic, mostly fiery, Sichuan cooking" is showcased at this modern pub-conversion, "conveniently a few minutes' walk along the canal from King's Cross". The menu includes plenty of items that in Britain used to be hidden away behind untranslated Chinese characters – chicken feet, frog legs, pig intestines – and "given the large plates, you need a big group to do it justice". / N1 9RG; www.thekaki.co.uk; kaki_london; Sun-Thu 10 pm, Fri & Sat 11 pm.

Kalimera N8 £53 [4][3][3]
43 Topsfield Road   07446 981139   1–1C

It's "definitely worth a trip to Crouch End" to sample the "lovely Greek mezze, stews and fish dishes from a short and well-chosen menu" at Télémaque Argyriou's two-year-old venture, where the olives and oil are sourced directly from his family's farm in Laconia, close to Sparta. Now with spin-offs in Paris and Lille, it's pitched as a showcase for modern ("not tourist-oriented") Greek cuisine, with some "interesting Hellenic wines". / N8 8PT; kalimera.london; eatkalimera; Tue-Sat 11 pm.

Kanada-Ya £42 [4][2][2]
3 Panton St, SW1   020 7930 3511   5–4A
28 Foubert's Place, W1   020 3435 8155   4–1B
64 St Giles High St, WC2   020 7240 0232   5–1B
3B Filmworks Walk, W5   020 3375 2340   1–3A **NEW**
35 Upper Street, N1   020 7288 2787   9–3D

"The best ramen in London, IMO – the rich, porky broth is perfect", say fans of former pro-cyclist Kazuhiro Kanada's five noodle bars – in Angel, Piccadilly, Covent Garden, Carnaby and Ealing. "If you're going to do one thing, do it well, and they do" – so they "deserve the frequent queues". / www.kanada-ya.com; kanada_ya_ldn.

Kanishka W1 £103 **3**22
17-19 Maddox Street 020 3978 0978 4–2A
"Delicious and quite unusual dishes" help win praise for Atul Kocchar's Mayfair five-year-old, which is "handy to know about just off the West End's main shopping streets". Even fans, though, feel that the prices for some items are a bit "ridiculous". / W1S 2QH; kanishkarestaurant.co.uk; kanishkamayfair; Mon-Sat 10.30 pm, Sun 9.30 pm.

Kaosarn £42 **3**4**3**
110 St Johns Hill, SW11 020 7223 7888 11–2C
181 Tooting High Street, SW17 020 8672 8811 11–2C
Brixton Village, Coldharbour Ln, SW9 020 7095 8922 11–2D
This family-owned traditional Thai trio – in Brixton, Battersea and Tooting – is "always packed" – a tribute to the high levels of hospitality they have maintained over the years. The BYO policy means they are good value, too. / www.kaosarnlondon.co.uk; kaosarntooting.

Kapara by Bala Baya W1 NEW
James Court, Manette Street 020 8079 7467 5–2A
Inspired by Israeli home cooking as well as the Tel Aviv party scene (Kapara is Hebrew slang for 'darling'), this all-day-and-late-night, Soho-fringe newcomer is from Eran Tibi (the chef behind Bala Baya in Southwark). It opened shortly prior to our survey in Spring 2023, and didn't generate much in the way of reports. Early online buzz suggests that even if there's the odd wrinkle to iron out, it has potential. / W1D 4AL; www.kapara.co.uk; kapara; Mon-Sat 1 am, Sun 11.30 pm.

Kappacasein SE1 £11 **5**3**2**
1 Stoney Street no tel 10–4C
"Quite simply the best cheese and onion toastie ever" – and equally yummy raclette – is found at Bermondsey raw cheesemaker Bill Oglethorpe's Borough Market stall, named after one of the proteins in milk. / SE1 9AA; www.kappacasein.com; kappacasein; Thu-Sat 5 pm.

Kasa & Kin W1 £50 **3**4**3**
52-53 Poland Street 020 7287 5400 4–1C
"Worth a visit for the mural alone!" – this brightly decorated two-year-old, just off Regent Street, has "raised the bar for consistently good Filipino food in the West End". Admittedly that's not from a high base, but all reports on its BBQ-focused menu are enthusiastic: "you get little fuss, no hype, just great nosh and cocktails too". / W1F 7NQ; kasaandkin.co.uk; kasaandkin; Tue, Wed 9 pm, Thu-Sat 10 pm, Sun 6 pm.

Kashmir SW15 £53 **3**4**2**
18-20 Lacy Road 07477 533888 11–2B
"Very good food", "charming service" and what they claim is the 'only authentic Kashmiri cuisine in England' are the distinguishing features of this Putney venture from Rohit & Shweta Razdan, whose culinary journey took them to New Delhi and Singapore before settling here eight years ago. / SW15 1NL; www.kashmirrestaurants.co.uk; kashmirrestuk; Sun-Thu 10.30 pm, Fri & Sat 11 pm.

The Kati Roll Company W1 £28 **3**22
24 Poland Street 020 7287 4787 4–1C
A kati roll is made of skewer-roasted fillings wrapped in a paratha – tasty Indian street food that hits the spot for a small but enthusiastic fan club amongst our reporters. With branches in Soho and Bethnal Green, they are imports from a four-strong Manhattan-based chain. / W1F 8QL; www.thekatirollcompany.com; thekatirollcompany; Mon-Sun 11 pm.

Kazan SW1 £64 **3** **3** **2**
93-94 Wilton Rd 020 7233 7100 2–4B
"Honest Turkish food and very good value" continue to inspire enthusiasm for this Pimlico local of over two decades' standing: "meat is grilled to perfection" and there's "a high standard of service". / SW1V 1DW; www.kazan-restaurant.com; kazan_restaurant_london; Mon-Sat 10 pm, Sun 9.30 pm.

Kebab Queen WC2 £125 **4** **4** **3**
4 Mercer Walk 020 7439 9222 5–2C
"I know that I am not the first person to have been blown away by the imagination displayed in this deconstruction of the kebab!" – this no-longer-secret 10-seater counter in the basement of Kingly Court's Le Bab aims to rocket-propel the kebab taste-palate to new heights, with a multi-course tasting menu served (smeared?) onto a special heated countertop (you scoop with your fingers). "Tasty... good patter from the chefs... engaging... quite the experience". In August 2023, it relaunched with Pamir Zeydan as the new head chef (although he had already been working here with departing Manu Canales). The sort of dishes to expect? 'Dover sole kebab delivered on an ironed hispi cabbage taco with roasted red pepper purée'. / WC2H 9FA; www.eatlebab.com; eatlebab; Sun & Mon 9.30 pm, Wed-Sat 10.30 pm, Tue 10 pm.

Ken Lo's Memories SW1 £73 **3** **3** **2**
65-69 Ebury St 020 7730 7734 2–4B
Now in its fifth decade and almost 30 years after Ken Lo's death, the Victoria venture he founded to showcase his brand of Chinese cuisine continues to feed a loyal (if now, perhaps somewhat ageing) band of regulars. All rate it well, although it can seem "pricey even for somewhere on the edge of Belgravia". / SW1W 0NZ; www.memoriesofchina.co.uk; kenlosmemoriesofchina; Wed-Sat, Tue, Sun 10.30 pm.

Kennington Tandoori SE11 £57 **3** **4** **3**
313 Kennington Rd 020 7735 9247 1–3C
"Kowsar Hoque's stylish Indian emporium" in Kennington, opened by his father almost 40 years ago, "continues to deliver excellent dishes which are reasonably priced for the high quality and make you feel you're in the company of experts"... actually you are likely in the company of our less-than-expert ruling class, given that the venue has long been a favourite of MPs from nearby Westminster, including David Cameron and BoJo. / SE11 4QE; www.kenningtontandoori.com; kennington tandoori; Mon-Sun 10.30 pm.

Kerridge's Bar & Grill WC2 £118 **3** **3** **4**
10 Northumberland Avenue 020 7321 3244 2–3C
Within a "luxurious and pampering" five star, the "unpretentious but stylish setting" of TV-star Tom Kerridge's high-ceilinged chamber provides a "wonderful" yet relaxed atmosphere to suit most types of occasion and the place is "always busy". However, the bill for the posh brasserie fare is "eye-watering" – to fans "pricey but terrific", but critics opine that "some gastropubs do this better for half the cost... but then again you are in The Corinthia". Top Tip – unbelievably good-value set lunch, for £15 per person. / WC2N 5AE; www.kerridgesbarandgrill.co.uk; kerridgesbandg; Mon-Sat 10.30 pm, Sun 9 pm.

Kerridge's Fish & Chips, Harrods SW1 £105 2 3 4

87-135 Brompton Road   020 7225 6800   6–1D

Within the gorgeous tiled space of Harrods Dining Hall, TV Tom's seafood counter (as well as the National Dish, menu options include caviar, whole lobster, and seafood curry) is a favourite for the odd reporter, and no-one rates its food less than good. Even so it is sometimes rated as disappointing, due in large part to the Knightsbridge prices. / SW1X 7XL; www.harrods.com; harrods; Tue-Sat 10.30 pm, Mon 9 pm, Sun 6 pm.

Kettners W1 NEW

29 Romilly St   020 7734 6112   5–2A

Dating from 1867, this fine Soho landmark should be famous, but has slipped off the restaurant map in recent years: initially due to its indifferent standards; and then due to Soho House's purchase of the building, and its closure to non-members since 2019. In July 2023, the club once again threw open its doors to the hoi polloi, with a food operation now run by the team behind the Stoke Newington pub The Clarence Tavern. Fingers crossed, this promising partnership helps it recoup some of its old mojo, rather than descending once again into the Theatreland tourist trap mode that's dogged it since PizzaExpress founder, the late Peter Boizot, sold it on in 2002. / W1D 5HP; www.kettners.com; kettnerssoho; Mon-Fri 1 am, Sat 2 am, Sun midnight.

Kibako W1 NEW

3 Windmill Street   020 7419 0305   2–1C

From the team behind Islington's Hot Stone, this February 2023 newcomer is a re-imagining of their Fitzrovia site, which previously traded as Rai and with a not-completely-dissimilar format. The cuisine is 'contemporary Japanese' in style, with sushi, sashimi and Kagoshima wagyu beef, chosen omakase-style for each diner and served in a presentation box. / W1T 2HY; www.kibakolondon.com; kibakolondon; Tue-Thu, Sun 9 pm, Fri & Sat 9.30 pm.

Kibou London SW11 £62 2 2 3

175-177 Northcote Road   020 7223 8551   11–2C

Strikingly decorated with murals, this three-year-old modern Japanese from a Cheltenham-based group has proved a "great addition" to Battersea's 'Nappy Valley', and wins praise for "exceptional signature sushi rolls", "very good cocktails" and its lively style. Ratings are limited by those who find the success of the cooking to be a case of hit and miss. / SW11 6QF; kibou.co.uk; kiboucheltenham; Tue-Sat 11 pm, Sun 10 pm.

Kiku W1 £70 4 4 2

17 Half Moon St   020 7499 4208   3–4B

A short walk from the Japanese Embassy, this veteran family-run operation in a Mayfair backstreet offers "immaculately prepared food" and "superb service" in a "calm and grown-up atmosphere". It opened in 1978, well before Japanese cuisine became fashionable. / W1J 7BE; www.kikurestaurant.co.uk; kikumayfair; Mon-Sat 10.15 pm.

Kiln W1 £54 5 4 4

58 Brewer Street   no tel   4–3C

"So cool, but with amazing food!" – Ben Chapman's "bustling" Thai BBQ in Soho continues to deliver exceptional value. With a "cramped but lovely vibe", "the best seats in the house are at the back where you can sit and watch the chefs cook over charcoal" (although "your clothes may be smelly afterwards due to the smoke from the open kitchen"). "Knowledgeable staff" provide a "menu full of things you never see at your average Thai restaurant, with stunning flavours" (and with "spice levels just on the right side of incendiary"). / W1F 9TL; www.kilnsoho.com; Mon-Sat 11 pm, Sun 9 pm.

Kima W1 NEW
57 Paddington Street   07745 205136   2–1A
Opened in June 2023, from the team behind nearby Opso, this contemporary Greek seafood specialist in Marylebone follows a zeitgeisty, no-waste 'fin-to-gill' philosophy, with fish off-cuts, tails and bones either grilled or used to make stock. Expect some meat choices, and plenty of Hellenic wines. / W1U 4JA; www.kimarestaurant.com; kima.restaurant.london; Wed-Sun 11.30 pm.

Kin and Deum SE1   **£49**   3 2 3
2 Crucifix Lane   020 7357 7995   10–4D
"Great, modern Thai food" is to be had at this stylish (although "rather cramped and noisy") pub conversion a short walk from the Shard by London Bridge station – "the kind of Thai you wish was just around the corner". It's run by siblings Roselyn, Shakris & Bank Inngern, the new generation of the family that operated Thai restaurant Suchard on nearby Tooley Street for more than 20 years, which has recently been re-opened as veggie specialist Plants of Roselyn. / SE1 3JW; www.kindeum.com; kindeum; Mon-Sun 10.30 pm.

Kindred W6   **£45**   3 3 3
Bradmore House, Queen Caroline Street   020 3146 1370   8–2C
Need somewhere civilised to meet for an informal business lunch or catch-up with a pal in Hammersmith? Then it's well worth remembering this convivial haunt, improbably located in the cellars of a large Grade II mansion (Bradmore House – nowadays a coworking space) marooned in the middle of trafficky Hammersmith Broadway, right by the tube. A short menu of simple fare is well-prepared and service is friendly. Top Tip – nice terrace on a sunny day too. / W6 9YE; www.wearekindred.com; londonkindred; Tue, Wed 11 pm, Thu-Sat midnight, Mon 6 pm.

Kipferl N1   **£55**   4 3 3
20 Camden Passage   020 77041 555   9–3D
"Lovely Austrian spot in the middle of Islington" – a fixture of cute Camden Passage for more than a decade – that's perfect "when you fancy something a bit different": "think good coffee and amazing cakes by day and gorgeous goulash and schnitzel by night". "Interesting Austrian wine list, too". / N1 8ED; www.kipferl.co.uk; kipferl_london; Mon-Thu 10 pm, Fri & Sat 11 pm, Sun 7 pm.

Kiss the Hippo   **£19**   3 4 3
51 Margaret Street, W1   020 3887 2028   3–1C
50 George Street, TW9   020 3887 2028   1–4A
"Great coffee and extremely moreish light snacks" is the simple-but-winning formula at this ethical and sustainable Scandi-style roastery that started life in Richmond six years ago and now has outlets scattered across some of central London's foodie enclaves. / kissthehippo.com; kissthehippo.

Kitchen Table W1   **£253**   4 4 4
70 Charlotte Street   020 7637 7770   2–1C
James Knappett and Sandia Chang 18-seat, chef's-table experience is "an exceptional restaurant that never ceases to amaze and delight" and some would say it's "London's best Michelin two-star by far" ("I've had four visits in the last year, and this is the most imaginative cooking in the capital!"). Even fans, though, had come to see it as "ridiculously overpriced" – "I love Kitchen Table, I really do. I've dined there quite regularly since it first opened and the food is exquisite. However, the price per person of £300 is a step too far: it's a great establishment, but that feels extortionate". The penny has dropped however, and in late May 2023 – after our survey concluded – they slashed

the price here by one third, to £200 per person for their 20-course experience. On that basis, we've rated it a little more optimistically than this year's feedback in our annual diners' poll would have suggested. / W1T 4QG; www.kitchentablelondon.co.uk; kitchentable1; Wed-Sat 11 pm.

Kitchen W8 W8 £95 443
11-13 Abingdon Road   020 7937 0120   6–1A
"I've had dinner here at least 20 times over the last 10 years and have never had a bad meal. I'm a fan!" – this smart and *"very comfortable"* (*"slightly dull?"*) fixture sits in a side road off Kensington High Street and is very accomplished by the reckoning of neighbourhood venues (and is nowadays in the top-100 most mentioned London restaurants in our annual diners' poll). Star chef Phil Howard is a partner in its management, and standards are *"very good all round"*, including the *"really creative and delicious"* modern European cuisine. / W8 6AH; www.kitchenw8.com; kitchenw8; Sun-Thu 9.30 pm, Fri & Sat 10 pm.

Kitty Fisher's W1 £82 343
10 Shepherd's Market   020 3302 1661   3–4B
"Consistent, tasty, dependable" food at a *"price-point that's pretty competitive given its Mayfair location"* is the deal at this Shepherd Market outfit named after an 18th-century courtesan. At almost 10 years old, the excitement it generated at launch has diminished, although fans reckon it *"continues to excel"* as both *"a business destination with character"* and *"a romantic and atmospheric"* spot. / W1J 7QF; www.kittyfishers.com; kittyfishers; Tue-Sat 9.30 pm.

Knife SW4 £79 443
160 Clapham Park Road   020 7627 6505   11–2D
This indie steakhouse on the Clapham-Brixton border *"does that one thing very well, then adds a big helping of friendly service"*. A former Top Steakhouse winner in the Harden's London Restaurant Awards, it is a local favourite for Sunday roasts. / SW4 7DE; kniferestaurant.co.uk; kniferestaurant; Wed-Sat 9.30 pm, Sun 4.30 pm.

Koji SW6 £86 444
58 New King's Rd   020 7731 2520   11–1B
"You could be in the West End" at this *"exceptional local restaurant"* by Parsons Green, *"serving contemporary Japanese cuisine"* – *"the ambience is glamorous and cool, the service friendly and efficient, and the food excellent, fresh and tasty"*. It also has an *"elegant and classic cocktail bar"*. / SW6 4LS; www.koji.restaurant; kojirestaurant; Tue, Wed 10.30 pm, Thu-Sat 11 pm.

Kol W1 £124 444
9 Seymour Street   020 3829 6888   2–2A
"A revelation: I don't think I really understood the beauty of chillies until I went to Kol, where they complement different ingredients in each dish… a gentle burn… never overpowering but genius!" – Santiago Lastra's smart and well-spaced dining room, just off Portman Square, is justifiably hailed by its fans as *"one of the more interesting restaurants in the capital"*. *"Top-quality, seasonal British produce is turned into amazing, refined Mexican food"* and it *"constantly surprises with its journey around Mexican spicing and cuisine, with many wonderful twists on traditional Latin flavours"*. To accompany the menu there is a list of mezcals (and indeed an adjoining 'mezcaleria' and cocktail bar) and *"many unusual wines which explore the less well known parts of the globe"*. *"Some of the cooking is clever, some beautifully presented, and it's all excellent"*. / W1H 7BA; kolrestaurant.com; kol.restaurant; Tue-Sat midnight, Sun 4.30 pm.

Kolamba W1 £39 4 3 2
21 Kingly Street   020 3815 4201   4–2B
"Interesting and original spicing" makes the "Sri Lanka-inspired small
plates" and "amazing curries" at this "rather cramped" Soho four-year-old a
"good choice if you like really spicy food". Top Menu Tip – "superb hot
butter cuttlefish". / W1B 5QA; kolamba.co.uk; kolamba.ldn; Mon-Sat 10 pm, Sun
9 pm.

Koya £46 4 4 3
50 Frith St, W1   020 7434 4463   5–2A
10-12 Broadway Market Mews, E8   07342 236933   14–2B
Queen Victoria Street, EC2   no tel   10–3C
"Love the original Koya, sitting at the long counter with a bowl of udon –
even if you do have to queue", say fans of this Soho noodle bar. Top Tip – the
"definitive zen breakfast" is well liked, too, both here and also at the
Bloomberg Arcade and Hackney spin-offs. / www.koya.co.uk; koyalondon.

Koyn W1 £103 3 4 4
38 Grosvenor Street   020 3376 0000   3–2B
Samyukta Nair and family's 'contemporary izakaya' in Mayfair provides an
evolved menu of sushi, tempura and robata dishes in a westernised style not
dissimilar to that of Nobu or Roka, overseen by NZ-born chef Rhys
Cattermoul. No-one has a bad word to say about the cooking, but there is
the odd gripe about the size of the bill… / W1K 4QA; www.koynrestaurants.com;
koynlondon; Mon-Sat 10.45 pm, Sun 10.30 pm.

Kricket £56 5 4 4
12 Denman Street, W1   020 7734 5612   4–3C
2 Television Centre, 101 Wood Lane, W12   –2B
41-43 Atlantic Road, SW9   11–1D
"Clever, subtly infused curries a wonderful step up from your local Indian"
("the flavours of every option are incredible with each dish spiced to
perfection") have catapulted this project by university friends Will Bowlby
and Rik Campbell from a Brixton pop-up to three thriving tapas-style
restaurants, including a Soho flagship with cocktail bar, in less than 10 years.
/ closed Sun, SW9 Tue-Thu closed L.

Kudu SE15 £60 4 4 3
119 Queen's Rd   020 3950 0226   1–4D
Patrick Williams and Amy Corbin's original Peckham opening (it now has
siblings like Little Kudu, and has become a well-known pin on southeast
London's restaurant map (owing only partly to the celebrity of Amy's father,
Chris Corbin, among the capital's foodie commentariat). Amidst the menu
choices, there is the occasional nod to Patrick's heritage (South African), but
the inspiration for the "tasty, small plates" magpies from all over the globe.
Brunch is a big occasion here for which there's a dedicated menu; and
"friendly" service is also a feature. Top Tip – eat in the back garden on
warmer days. / SE15 2EZ; www.kuducollective.com; kudu_restaurant; Thu-Sun
10 pm.

Kudu Grill SE15 £53 4 4 3
57 Nunhead Lane   020 3172 2450   1–4D
High ratings all-round again this year for Amy Corbin and Patrick Williams's
spin-off venture – an open-fire restaurant, which takes the South African
braai for part of its inspiration. It occupies an attractively converted former
Truman's pub in Nunhead. / SE15 3TR; www.kuducollective.com; kudugrill; Wed-Sat
10 pm, Sun 2.30 pm.

Kuro Eatery W8 NEW £73 443
5 Hillgate Street 020 7221 4854 7–2B

"A super little spot in the 'hood" – Hillgate Village now boasts another reason to travel to this cute enclave, off Notting Hill Gate: an offshoot of the coffee shop across the road. With its sparse, pale-wood interior, it has "Nordic" looks, although the menu claims to be 'broadly Mediterranean inspired'. Whatever you call it, there's "great innovation" from Andrianos Poulis's "interesting, exciting and tasty" "fusion" cuisine. A downside? – "it's so noisy!" / W8 7SP; www.kuro-london.com; kuro__london; Tue-Sat 11 pm, Sun 4 pm.

Kutir SW3 £70 444
10 Lincoln Street 020 7581 1144 6–2D

"A surprise hidden treat just off the King's Road" – Rohit Ghai's Chelse townhouse is set in a series of "several small and intimate" chambers, and there's even a first-floor lounge bar with a "nice little roof terrace". His "deeply spiced", "non-generic" Indian cuisine is in the capital's premier league: "very original and authentic" and contributing to an overall experience that's "refined, without being splashily luxurious". Gripes? – "wish the menu was slightly longer". / SW3 2TS; kutir.co.uk; kutirchelsea; Tue-Sun 10 pm.

The Ladbroke Arms W11 £71 324
54 Ladbroke Road 020 7727 6648 7–2B

With its "perfect pub atmosphere", "pretty front garden" and "excellent, interesting food that never disappoints", this unusually gracious Ladbroke Grove local is "a real contender" as one the capital's better hostelries. On the debit side, service was often said to be "up and down" this year ("smiling and helpful, but run off their feet"). / W11 3NW; www.ladbrokearms.com; ladbrokearms; Mon-Sat 11 pm, Sun 10 pm.

Lahore Kebab House E1 £37 422
2-10 Umberston St 020 7481 9737 12–1A

"The original Pakistani joint" – this "perfect" East End pitstop of over half a century's standing is as "cheap and consistent as ever" (and as grotty…). For "legendary" lamb chops, "the best ever dry lamb curry" and "amazing chicken tikka", it can't be beat. / E1 1PY; www.lahore-kebabhouse.com; Tue-Sat 10 pm, Sun 9 pm.

Lahpet £60 432
21 Slingsby Place, WC2 020 3883 5629 5–3C
58 Bethnal Green Road, E1 020 3883 5629 13–1C

"A revelation!" this "unpretentious" yet "awesome" outfit offers "a wonderful introduction to Burmese cuisine" – "intense, fragrant and refreshing", but "not as fierce as Thai" – at its new venue in Covent Garden's The Yards development. Founders Dan Anton and chef Zaw Mahesh started out in a Hackney warehouse, and still have a restaurant in Shoreditch. It's named after the "unique and superb tea leaf salad" on its menu. / lahpet.co.uk; lahpet.

Laksamania W1 £49 322
92 Newman Street 020 7637 9888 3–1D

"A great selection of different laksa and very tasty too!" – a key appeal of this street-food destination off Oxford Street, which is named for its Malaysian noodle soups (though other dishes are also served). / W1T 3EZ; www.laksamania.co.uk; laksamania; Mon, Wed & Thu 9 pm, Fri & Sat 9.30 pm, Sun 8 pm.

The Landmark, Winter Garden NW1 £85 3 3 5

222 Marylebone Rd   020 7631 8000   9–4A

"*Wonderful afternoon tea in a huge glass-roof covered area with palm trees*" is the big hit at "*beautiful*" Palm Court: a hotel atrium, eight storeys tall near Marylebone station (and one of London's more Instagrammed spaces). Not a bad spot for a business (or romantic) meal: the food – served from breakfast through to dinner – is uniformly well rated, and even those who feel it's "*absurdly expensive*" say "*it was worth it to see the atrium!*" / NW1 6JQ; www.landmarklondon.co.uk; the_landmark_london; Mon-Sun 10 pm.

The Lanesborough Grill SW1 NEW £93 2 2 4

Hyde Park Corner   020 7259 5599   2–3A

"*The room is the star*" at this swish hotel restaurant on Hyde Park Corner, with its gorgeous domed glass ceilings (providing natural light by day) and huge chandeliers. Formerly known as Celeste (RIP), it has now adopted a less fancy, more fashionably straightforward menu under chef Shay Cooper. The overall experience is much more consistently well-rated in this new guise, although there are still some quibbles over "*so-so*" results and "*patchy*" service. Most consistent is support for the "*sublimely elegant*", "*reassuringly traditional, tasty and well-presented afternoon tea*". / SW1X 7TA; www.oetkercollection.com; the_lanesborough; Mon-Sun 10 pm.

Langan's Brasserie W1 £76 2 2 3

Stratton Street   020 7491 8822   3–3C

Were it not still considered "*outrageously expensive*" in over 40% of reports, it might be easier to recommend this "*well-located*", old-faithful brasserie (est. 1976). When it was relaunched under new ownership in late 2021, it was widely derided for its poor standards. But even though its cooking is still too often dismissed as "*standard fodder*", overall feedback on its food improved this year, with fans praising its "*menu to suit all tastes, including many traditional and down-to-earth dishes*". And anyway, cost-be-damned, it's "*still the haunt of the business lunch crowd*" thanks to its "*long-established, buzzy ambience*" and handy location near The Ritz. / W1J 8LB; www.langansrestaurants.co.uk; langansbrasserie; Mon-Sat 10.30 pm, Sun 9.30 pm.

Palm Court, The Langham W1 £100 2 3 3

1c Portland Place   020 7636 1000   2–1B

"*Always a treat*" – this luxurious lounge in a swanky five-star opposite the Beeb makes a "*beautiful setting for a classic afternoon tea*": indeed the hotel claims the ceremony started here! (The venue spent the latter half of 2023 hosting evening meals as 'The Good Front Room': south London chef Dom Taylor's celebration of his Caribbean heritage, with elevated versions of dishes including curry goat and rice and peas. The residency was his prize for winning Channel 4 show 'Five Star Kitchen', hosted by chef Michel Roux Jr, the Langham's culinary director.) / W1B 1JA; www.palm-court.co.uk; langham_london; Mon-Sun 11 pm.

Langosteria, The OWO SW1 NEW

57 Whitehall Place   Awaiting tel   2–3C

With branches in Paris, near Portofino, St Moritz and – now here at this mega new five-star on Whitehall – Enrico Buonocore's Italian newcomer originates (like Paper Moon) from Milan. Seafood is the big deal here, and if it follows the template of the original no meat or veggie options will be served. / SW1A 2EU; Tue-Sat 10.30 pm.

Lasdun,
National Theatre SE1 NEW
Upper Ground   no tel   2–3D
Named for National Theatre architect Sir Denys Lasdun, the latest incarnation of this South Bank landmark's flagship eatery is an all-day brasserie, run by the team behind The Marksman. It opened in late May 2023 (after our annual diners' poll had closed) but the press immediately rushed in and drooled. It helps if you like the Brutalist design of the space: nearly all restaurant critics, it seems, get off on that kind of thing. One such is the FT's Tim Hayward, who in early June 2023 declared – "Go for the soul-nourishing architecture" and "pointedly British" fare that "operates in tune with the [surroundings]… austere but elegant… it honours its materials rather than obscuring them with decoration". The cynical would also say, go ASAP, before – like its predecessors – it is tempted to coast on the captive market its pre-theatre trade provides. / SE1 9PP; www.lasdunrestaurant.com; lasdunrestaurant; Mon-Sat 11 pm.

Launceston Place W8   **£102**   **4 4 4**
1a Launceston Place   020 7937 6912   6–1B
"Tucked away from the hustle and bustle", in the kind of ultra-picturesque Kensington backwater where one imagines Mary Poppins floating about on her umbrella – this "quirky" converted town-house provides a "special", "understated but comfortable setting" and "always impeccable personal service with attention to detail": it's "ideal for a romantic evening". "You might not expect much of the cooking as it's part of the D&D London Group – but you'd be wrong!" – Ben Murphy has been at the stoves since 2017 and his "refined and interesting" cuisine goes from strength to strength: "food that just makes you smile about how it looks and how it tastes". Top Tip – "good value at lunch". / W8 5RL; www.launcestonplace-restaurant.co.uk; launcestonplace; Wed-Sat 10 pm, Sun 9 pm.

The Laundry SW9   **£66**   **3 4 4**
374 Coldharbour Lane   020 8103 9384   11–2D
"A great place to have in the neighbourhood" – this "lovely" Antipodean-run fixture is set – with its own sizable outside terrace – in a large and characterful Victorian laundry; and "sitting next to Brixton Market means it always has a lively vibe with some added street theatre". "Lots of cocktails are enjoyed at the weekends here", when it's a favourite destination. But "it works for brunch, lunch or dinner" with an all-day menu incorporating a good selection of modern bistro dishes alongside more breakfast-ish staples. / SW9 8PL; thelaundrybrixton.com; brixtonlaundry; Mon-Thu 11 pm, Fri & Sat 11.30 pm, Sun 8 pm.

Lavo,
The BoTree W1 NEW
30 Marylebone Ln   020 7309 9700   3–1B
An Italian September 2023 newcomer, from Tao Group Hospitality: the business which owns the (nowadays international) Hakkasan and Yauatcha chains. Within a swish new boutique hotel in Marylebone, the press release promises 'a vibrant space illuminated by a colour-changing light feature that expands across the ceiling', where you can enjoy pastas, pizzas, 'a showstopper Wagyu meatball topped with whipped ricotta' (wow!) and 'an indulgent 20-layer chocolate cake'. / W1U 2DR; Tue-Sat 10.30 pm.

Laxeiro E2 £19 ❸❸❸
95 Columbia Road   020 7729 1147   14–2B
Well predating the gentrification of Columbia Road, this "small, local Spanish restaurant" (est 1982) is worth remembering when browsing for blooms and designer flower pots. It probably won't re-frame your understanding of Hispanic cuisine, but "prices are reasonable" and the "team are friendly and fun" (albeit sometimes under pressure at busy times). / E2 7RG; www.laxeiro.co.uk; laxeiro_restaurant; Tue-Sat 11 pm, Sun 4 pm.

Layla W10 £15 ❸❸❸
332 Portobello Road   no tel   7–1A
"Go for the cinnamon buns, top-quality coffee and croissants and amazing sarnies too", say fans of this superb "artisanal bakery", towards the very northern end of the Portobello Road. / W10 5PQ; www.laylabakery.com; layla_w10; Mon-Sun 4 pm.

The Ledbury W11 £236 ❹❹❹
127 Ledbury Rd   020 7792 9090   7–1B
"Back with a bang!" – Brett Graham's "superlative" Notting Hill HQ 'pressed pause' during Covid, but re-opened in 2022 to near-universal acclaim. "Technically exquisite, with delicate preparation and flavour combinations" – "his cuisine was straight back in with two Michelin stars – zero surprise there!". (But there are also widespread misgivings about prices that risk becoming "just too expensive"). "Many of the old staff remain and balance efficiency and familiarity with aplomb" and "Brett is very visible to chat with". "To top it off, with the new interior it has such a relaxed vibe now". Top Menu Tip – "unbelievably brilliant mushrooms". / W11 2AQ; www.theledbury.com; Tue-Sat 9.15 pm.

Legare SE1 £52 ❹❹❸
Cardamom Building, 31g Shad Thames   020 8063 7667   10–4D
"The tiny kitchen in this intimate restaurant" in Shad Thames, near Tower Bridge, "produces the most imaginative and delicious Italian food". "It's run by a talented chef who will go places", Matt Beardmore, previously of Trullo, alongside founder Jay Patel, a former Barrafina manager. / SE1 2YB; legarelondon.com; legarelondon; Wed-Sat, Tue 10 pm.

Lemonia NW1 £66 ❷❸❸
89 Regent's Park Rd   020 7586 7454   9–3B
"Everyone seems to be a regular" at this "old and long-established Greek restaurant" – a large Primrose Hill landmark which is still "buzzing from morning till night", as it has been for over three decades now. "The longstanding staff are very friendly" (but "service is not too good at busy times"). "You can always find something to eat on this long menu, but – though filling – it is very basic". / NW1 8UY; www.lemonia.co.uk; Mon-Thu 10 pm, Fri & Sat 10.30 pm, Sun 4 pm.

Leo's E5 🆕
59 Chatsworth Road   020 4559 8598   14–1B
Ex P Franco and Brawn chef Giuseppe Belvedere (backed by the team behind Milk Café and Juliet's Quality Food) is inspired by his Sardinian heritage at this skillful revamp of the former Jim's Cafe on Clapton's Chatsworth Road. Serving café staples during the day, in the evening and at Sunday lunch he provides more ambitious Italian dishes cooked over a wood fire and served alongside low-intervention Italian wines. It opened in May 2023 after our survey had concluded, but in an early June write-up, The Standard's Jimi Famurewa lauded its evocative interior as an "Italian beauty". But, where the scoff was concerned, he was left with an "abiding feeling … of a short menu eliciting lots of intrigue but, also, a nagging urge for an actual dinner". / E5 0LH; leos.london.

Leroy EC2 £96 4 4 3
18 Phipp Street   020 7739 4443   13–1B

On a quirky Shoreditch corner-site, this "relaxed" haunt offers affordable and interesting small plates, "good wine" and just the kind of "buzzy" ambience you'd hope for in these hipster environs. But for slaves to 'Le Guide Rouge' and their grading system there's a problem. "It's a really good restaurant. It's just not a Michelin star place – its star is a distraction". ("If this was a Michelin 'bib gourmand' it would be spot-on, and it absolutely deserves that sort of grade. But the star creates an expectation of something more special than this place delivers. That's the only criticism. It is a cracking spot, but someone at the tyre place got a bit carried away".) / EC2A 4NP; www.leroyshoreditch.com; leroyshoreditch; Mon-Sat 9.30 pm.

Levan SE15 £63 3 2 2
3-4 Blenheim Grove   020 7732 2256   1–4D

An "interesting and very good menu" – "prefer the à la carte to the set" – with natural wines to match draws an appreciative crowd to this open-kitchen outfit, behind Peckham overground station. Inspired by the 'bistronomy' of Paris or Copenhagen, it no longer generates the volume of feedback or stellar ratings of a couple of years ago. / SE15 4QL; levanlondon.co.uk; levanlondon; Tue-Sat 11.30 pm, Sun 3 pm.

The Light House SW19 £65 3 3 3
75-77 Ridgway   020 8944 6338   11–2B

"Almost part of Wimbledon's heritage nowadays!": after a quarter of a century's service, this local indie is a local contemporary classic, known for its "very good" Mediterranean-style food and "personable staff". Fans say it's "upped its game over the last year" too, although it "can struggle to cope when crowded". / SW19 4ST; www.lighthousewimbledon.com; lighthousewimbledon; Mon-Sat 10 pm, Sun 3 pm.

The Lighterman N1 £59 2 2 2
3 Granary Square   020 3846 3400   9–3C

Overlooking the canal at Granary Square behind King's Cross station, this striking modern gastropub certainly looks the part and packs in the crowds. It avoids harsh critiques, but feedback generally makes it clear that "the location is better than the dining experience". / N1C 4BH; www.thelighterman.co.uk; thelightermankx; Mon-Thu 11.30 pm, Fri & Sat midnight, Sun 10.30 pm.

Lilienblum EC1 NEW
80 City Road   020 8138 2847   13–1A

Israeli chef-restaurateur Eyal Shani has followed up pitta specialist Miznon, in Soho and Notting Hill, with this very different, more formal concept off the Old Street roundabout on the edge of the City. Opened (after our survey concluded) in late May 2023, it serves sharing plates from a menu divided by ingredients rather than courses. A very early June 2023 verdict from The Standard's Jimi Famurewa was mixed: "Shani's undeniable genius" is still present, "dishes were still cooked with unexpected flair, potency and restraint" but the "vast, echoing barn of a new-build space" does Lilienblum no favours, nor does the "menu construction" (split by ingredients with "wearying zaniness of… descriptions"). / EC1Y 2BJ; www.lilienblum.co.uk; lilienblumlondon; Tue, Wed 11.45 pm, Thu-Sat 11 pm.

Lina Stores   **£50**   2️⃣2️⃣3️⃣
13 Marylebone Lane, W1   020 3148 7503   3–1A
51 Greek Street, W1   020 3929 0068   5–2A
20 Stable Street, N1   awaiting tel   9–3C
22 The Pavement, SW4   020 3838 1343   11–2D NEW
19 Bloomberg Arcade, EC4   020 3002 6034   10–3C
"A nice pit-stop for pasta lovers" – this expanding chain is now up to its fifth
restaurant spin-off from the original Soho deli (with the June 2023 opening
of a new 80-seater, overlooking Clapham Common), and fans say it provides
an *"attractive", "buzzing"* setting for *"simple dishes, well cooked"*. A meal is
"unlikely to live long in the memory though", and there's a growing fear that
"as they have expanded the quality has dropped". Top Tip – at the W1
original (est. 1944 originally as a deli) *"sitting upstairs or by the bar is lovely,
the windowless basement is not particularly comfortable"*.
/ www.linastores.co.uk; linastores.

Lisboeta WC1   **£78**   4️⃣3️⃣2️⃣
30 Charlotte Street   020 3830 9888   2–1C
"Portuguese cooking at its addictive best" has delivered *"yet another hit for
Nuno Mendes"* (in partnership with MJMK Restaurants) at this *"really
enjoyable"* three-floor yearling in Fitzrovia, where *"distinctive", "top-quality"*
dishes are *"made from the best produce"*; (*"it already feels like a fixture on
the dining scene – the sort of place you want to go to again and again, and
to tell people about"*). Fans also celebrate the *"cool vibes"* of its *"buzzy (if
slightly boomy)"* café-style setting, although the interior can also seem
"cramped" and not everyone's wild about the music (*"I complained to Nuno,
but he likes it loud!"*). Success has also brought concern about *"hype"*, or
that *"some prices risk becoming a joke"* – *"it tasted good, but the price
stuck in the throat"*. Top Menu Tip – *"love the pork fat dessert"*. / WC1B 4AF;
lisboeta.co.uk; lisboeta.london; Mon-Sat 11 pm, Sun 5 pm.

Little Kudu SE15 NEW
133 Queen's Road   020 7252 8287   1–4D
*Open in June 2023 from Peckham's Kudu Collective, Little Kudu replaces the
Smokey Kudu cocktail bar in Queen's Road (which has shifted to the RIXO
fashion emporium on Chelsea's King's Road). There's a strong focus on South
African wine here, with simple, tapas-y/small plates food to soak it up (eg
Braaibroodjie: a Saffa cheese toastie). / SE15 2ND; www.kuducollective.com;
littlekudu; Wed-Sun 10 pm.*

Little Pizza Hicce N1 NEW
99 Chapel Market   020 3062 5690   9–3D
*Opposite their pub Hicce Hart in Islington's Chapel Market, chef Pip Lacey
and business partner Gordy McIntyre have launched their first permanent
pizzeria, with lots of stripped wood and a blackboard menu. Both are
offshoots from Hicce, their fashionable flagship at Coal Drops Yard behind
King's Cross station. / N1 9EY; www.littlepizzahicce.co.uk; littlepizzahicce; Tue-Sat
10 pm, Sun 9 pm.*

Little Social W1   **£80**   4️⃣4️⃣3️⃣
5 Pollen Street   020 7870 3730   3–2C
*Jason Atherton's elegant, "professional" wine bar and bistro is decked out in
an understated, classic style that's a little more retro than at his main gaff
(Pollen Street), which is across the street. Here, chef Frankie van Loo offers
less 'foodie' "bistro-style" dishes raised to a "superb" standard. The bar area
is tiny, but "you can always have a pre-dinner drink at its big brother
opposite, which has a great cocktail bar". Top Tip – visit in summer, when
you can eat outside on the pedestrianised street. / W1S 1NE;
www.littlesocial.co.uk; _littlesocial; Tue-Sat 9pm.*

Little Taperia SW17 £54 [3][4][4]
143 Tooting High St   020 8682 3303   11–2C

"A local delight" near Tooting Broadway tube station – this "fantastic tapas restaurant brings together some wonderful Iberian tastes with brilliant service"; and "the lighting is great for an intimate meal out" (the "buzzy and upbeat atmosphere adds to the feeling that you're anywhere but on Tooting High Street!"). The founders, former food journalist Madeleine Lim and Hikmat Antippa, owner of nearby Meza, are two of the prime movers behind Tooting's growing food scene. / SW17 0SY; www.thelittletaperia.co.uk; littletaperiatooting; Sun-Thu 10 pm, Fri & Sat 11 pm.

Llama Inn,
The Hoxton EC2 [NEW]
81 Great Eastern St   020 7550 1000   13–1B

Hot in NYC, this late summer 2023 newcomer is the latest incumbent on the rooftop of Shoreditch's 'The Hoxton' hotel, with its city-fringe vistas of The Barbican and the Square Mile. On offer – Americanised Peruvian fare – let's hope it's a better recipe for success than the previous occupant, Maya (RIP), which also had a US/Latino theme (then it was Baja-Mexican). / EC2A 3HU; Tue-Sun 11.30 pm.

Llewelyn's SE24 £75 [3][3][3]
293-295 Railton Rd   020 7733 6676   11–2D

This "high-level local bistro" opposite Herne Hill station is "great for date night", and its kitchen team is "very accomplished at composing dishes that bring together familiar ingredients in unfamiliar combinations to good effect, rather than for curiosity value". The latest addition is a wine bar and shop next door, called Lulu's. / SE24 0JP; www.llewelyns-restaurant.co.uk; llewelynslondon; Tue-Thu 9 pm, Fri & Sat 9.30 pm, Sun 3.15 pm.

La Lluna N10 £59 [3][3][2]
462 Muswell Hill Broadway   020 8442 2662   1–1B

"A great find" on Muswell Hill Broadway, this "buzzy, lively restaurant with very efficient service and great Spanish food" ticks all the boxes for a "super local" – serving Iberian breakfasts, a good-value set lunch, plus a full menu of tapas and classic main dishes. / N10 1BS; www.lalluna.co.uk; lallunalondon; Sun-Thu 11 pm, Fri & Sat midnight.

Locanda Locatelli W1 £104 [3][3][2]
Hyatt Regency, 8 Seymour St   020 7935 9088   2–2A

"Memorable food in a lively, buzzy but not hectic environment" maintains the appeal for fans of Giorgio Locatelli's "classic Italian", which he has run with wife Plaxy for over 20 years, in a "discreet" and stylish hotel dining room off Portman Square (and with its own entrance). There is a harsh view that "there's nothing special about it other than the outrageous prices". But that's a minority opinion, and for its majority of fans it remains an "exceptional all-rounder", as recommended for business as it is for being a "fantastic place to take the family". / W1H 7JZ; www.locandalocatelli.com; locandalocatelli; Wed-Sat, Tue 11 pm, Sun 10.30 pm.

London Shell Co. W2 £105 [3][4][5]
The Prince Regent, Sheldon Square   07553 033636   7–1C

"Stunningly fresh fish, brilliant service and a jolly super wine list" ensure that a dining cruise along the Grand Union canal aboard the barge Prince Regent is "a fabulous part of the London restaurant scene" – while "tucking into a lobster roll with a beer on the Grand Duchess, permanently docked in Paddington basin, is just as good". The company's third venue – its first on dry land – is a combined fishmonger and seafood bar in Swains Lane, near Parliament Hill Fields in Highgate, where late-afternoon oyster-and-wine deals are a special draw. / W2 6EP; londonshellco.com; londonshellco; Wed-Sat 9.30 pm, Sun 3 pm.

London Stock SW18 £56 3 3 3
2 Bubbling Well Square, Ram Quarter   020 8075 3877   11–2B
In the centre of trafficky downtown Wandsworth, this "very plain room in the brewery development" is a somewhat unsung hero of the area. The young team is headed by Le Cordon Bleu alumni Assem Abdel Hady and Andres Bernal and brings genuine gastronomic ambition to the 'Ram Quarter' with an "eight-course tasting menu at a reasonable price" – "every course is tasty" and some nothing less than "superb". / SW18 1UQ; londonstockrestaurant.co.uk; ldnstockrestaurant; Wed-Sat 8 pm.

The Lore of the Land W1 £79 3 4 4
4 Conway Street   020 3927 4480   2–1B
Perhaps our user-base isn't impressed by the c'leb ownership of Guy Ritchie's rustic Fitzrovia pub, where pal Becks has been seen pulling a pint, as we receive few reports. But such as we do get praise "fantastic food, attentive service and good value". / W1T 6BB; gritchiepubs.com; loreofthelandpub; Tue, Wed 11 pm, Thu-Sat 11.30 pm, Sun 9 pm.

Lorne SW1 £77 5 5 3
76 Wilton Road   020 3327 0210   2–4B
"Going from strength to strength... surviving a flood in its first year... then Covid… it shines triumphant!" – owner Katie Exton "has dedication in abundance" and her "superb and fairly priced" Pimlico favourite is the result. That the "lovely and intimate" room can also appear "a little understated" is the nearest any report gets to a criticism; and most are a full-on hymn of praise to its "stunning, clean-flavoured seasonal food" served with "enthusiasm and knowledge". La patronne is a top sommelier and "pound for pound her brilliant, eclectic and accessible wine list is one of the best in London; punching well above its weight for a restaurant of its size and price-point". / SW1V 1DE; www.lornerestaurant.co.uk; lorne_restaurant.

LPM (fka La Petite Maison) W1 £127 3 3 3
54 Brook's Mews   020 7495 4774   3–2B
A "gorgeous homage to the Côte d'Azur" – this "exciting" operation, just around the corner from Claridges, serves beautiful, fresh-tasting Med-inspired sharing plates to an "urbane and international" crowd, who like its informal, somewhat "cramped" style. But while the prices here have always been eye-catching, its (previously stellar) ratings slumped this year amidst a feeling that you increasingly need more "money than sense" to pay them. ("There is no doubting the cooking skill and the careful sourcing of produce. But the dishes are so simple that it feels eye-watering to pay so much for a lentil salad… that is literally just a lentil salad"). / W1K 4EG; www.lpmlondon.co.uk; lpmlondon; Mon-Sat 10.30 pm, Sun 9.30 pm.

Luca EC1 £99 4 4 4
88 St John St   020 3859 3000   10–1A
"An oasis of calm just outside the hustle of the City" (north of Smithfield Market): this "beautiful" bar and restaurant (linked – but you'd never know it – to The Clove Club) is increasingly recognised as "one of the top Italians in London", and a "special" overall experience ("everyone seems so happy just to be there!"). Even fans acknowledge it as being "on the expensive side", but there are no quibbles about its "elegant and refined" cuisine which "never fails to hit the spot". And it's "also a good place for business". Top Tips – "the Parmesan fries are dreamy"; and "the bar has a great set lunch menu and wonderful booths". / EC1M 4EH; luca.restaurant; luca.restaurant; Wed-Sat, Tue 10 pm.

Luce e Limoni WC1 £64 3 3 2
91-93 Gray's Inn Rd   020 7242 3382   10–1A
"Family-run Italian" that helps add life to a dull stretch of the Gray's Inn Road. It specialises in Sicilian cuisine presented by Fabrizio Zafarana, an engagingly "well-informed and enthusiastic" host. / WC1X 8TX;
www.luceelimoni.com; restaurant_luce_e_limoni; Mon-Thu 10 pm, Fri & Sat 11 pm.

Luciano's SE12 £60 3 4 3
131 Burnt Ash Road   020 8852 3186   1–4D
"So lucky to have this as our local in Lee" – this "perfect neighbourhood Italian" sparks joy with its home-made pasta and wood-fired pizzas. Owner Enzo Masiello named it after his father Luciano, who played football for Charlton Athletic. / SE12 8RA; lucianoslondon.co.uk; lucianoslondon; Tue-Thu 10.30 pm, Fri & Sat 11.30 pm, Mon 10 pm, Sun 9.15 pm.

Lucio SW3 £98 3 2 2
257 Fulham Rd   020 7823 3007   6–3B
"Charming old-style service and delicious food" "still packs the locals in" at this "popular family-run Italian" in Chelsea from Lucio Altana and his sons Dario and Mirko, now in its twenty-first year. / SW3 6HY;
www.luciorestaurant.com; luciorestaurant; Tue-Sat 10.30 pm, Sun 3 pm.

Lucky & Joy E5 £48 4 3 3
95 Lower Clapton Road   07488 965966   14–1B
This "fun local for Clapton hipsters" offers "exceptional" Chinese cooking from two well-travelled Western chefs, Ellen Parr (ex-Rochelle Canteen and Moro) and Peter Kelly (ex-Morito), who knock out "the freshest flavours at incredible value" – "what a great neighbourhood place!" But "expect to mime: the rendered walls and low ceiling amplify the bonhomie, so the volume is turned up to 11". / E5 0NP; luckyandjoy.co.uk; luckyandjoyldn; Tue-Sat 10.30 pm.

Lucky Cat W1 £85 1 2 2
10-13 Grosvenor Square   020 7107 0000   3–2A
The "buzzing vibe", DJs and "showmanship of dishes being completed at the table" tends to "overshadow the food and service" at Gordon Ramsay's "Pan-Asian" joint on the former site of Maze in Mayfair. The "play-safe, please-all Asian menu" runs the gamut from sushi and bao to Korean-spiced black cod and Thai green curry stone bass – "but it lacks real flavour". "If it's trying to compete with the likes of Roka and Nobu, it doesn't… apart from on prices". / W1K 6JP; www.gordonramsayrestaurants.com;
luckycatbygordonramsay; Mon-Wed midnight, Thu-Sat 2 am, Sun 11 pm.

Lume NW3 £88 3 2 2
38 Primrose Hill Road   020 7449 9556   9–2A
"Owner/front-of-house Giuseppe is Sicilian, chef Antonio is Sardinian, and the cuisine is a mix of the two" at this cute Primrose Hill corner-site, praised for its "fabulous cooking and charming service". An impressive wine list explores biodynamic bottles from the two islands. / NW3 3AD; www.lume.london; lumelondon; Tue-Sun 10 pm.

Lupins SE1 £55 4 4 4
66 Union St   020 3908 5888   10–4B
"It's amazing what they can achieve with simple ingredients", and there's "always cheerful and efficient service" at this "little sharing-plates restaurant" close to Tate Modern, which has won a solid reputation for its "very talented" founders Lucy Pedder and Natasha Cooke over the past six years. / SE1 1TD; www.lupinslondon.com; lupinslondon; Tue-Sat 9.30 pm.

Lure NW5 £52 3 2 3
56 Chetwynd Rd   020 7267 0163   9–1B
This modern fish 'n' chip shop in Dartmouth Park is "a nice, healthy (and non-smelly) alternative" to the classic old-school chippy, with "good-quality" fresh fish. / NW5 1DJ; www.lurefishkitchen.co.uk; Wed-Sat 10 pm, Sun 9.30 pm.

Lurra W1 £73 4 3 3
9 Seymour Place   020 7724 4545   2–2A
"Totally amazing in every way" – this Basque specialist in Seymour Village has a very short menu focusing on aged dairy beef ribs or whole turbot grilled over a wood fire, and is both "extraordinary, and eye-wateringly expensive" – "we spent well north of £1,000 for four, but it was worth it". "The morel and black garlic croquetas are sublime", too. Its sibling tapas bar Donostia is close by (see also). / W1H 5BA; www.lurra.co.uk; Mon-Sat 10.30 pm, Sun 3.30 pm.

Lusin W1 NEW
16 Hay Hill   07768 447398   3–3C
Just around the corner from Berkeley Square, this 100-seater Mayfair newcomer opened in late 2022; and is part of a small international chain originating in Armenia and with outlets in Saudi Arabia. It offers a menu created by Armenian cookbook author Mme Anahid Doniguian and Monaco chef Marcel Ravin. We've not had a huge number of reports to-date for a rating: early feedback suggests it has potential but you suffer a typical Mayfair trade-off: "food not bad to very good… but expensive". / W1J 8NY; lusinrestaurant.com; lusinmayfair; Mon-Sun midnight.

Lusitania SW8 £61 3 3 3
353 Wandsworth Road   020 7787 0600   11–1D
"Great fun on a Friday night, when there's music and dancing" – this large Stockwell venue opened three years ago, near the new Thames-side developments surrounding Vauxhall and Battersea; and comes complete with an 'Olive Tree Garden' for the summer months. "The food is typically Portuguese – ample and fulfilling!" / SW8 2JH; www.restaurantelusitania.co.uk; lusitania_restaurant; Tue-Thu 10 pm, Fri & Sat 2 am, Sun 9 pm.

**Lutyens Grill,
The Ned EC2** £109 3 3 4
27 Poultry   020 3828 2000   10–2C
"Is this what business lunching was like 50 year ago?" – this "elegant and wood-panelled" steakhouse, "hidden away in the vast opulence of the Ned" (itself the former Midland Bank HQ) "always impresses a client" with its "wonderful club-like atmosphere", "the smell of leather and the feeling of luxury" (it's where "old-school stockbroker dining meets Wolf of Wall Street"). "Power lunches abound within a serene ambience" – "the food leans heavily towards meat with beef Wellington a highlight". / EC2R 8AJ; www.thened.com; thenedlondon; Tue-Sat midnight.

Lyle's E1 £105 5 3 2
The Tea Building, 56 Shoreditch High Street   020 3011 5911   13–1B
"Never wavering in its excellence" – James Lowe's acclaimed canteen sits at the foot of Shoreditch's 'Tea Building' and his seasonal modern British cooking is nowadays something of a benchmark (having achieved a listing for numerous years on the World's 50 Best). At lunch, small plates can be ordered tapas-style, whereas in the evenings there's just a single tasting option. "Individual dishes look simple: actually this belies a great deal of underlying complexity, and fantastic tastes". Service is informed and passionate too: "you do not think they are temps!" The post-industrial space

it inhabits is "hard-surfaced, buzzy, and hence can be very noisy" (and there were a few more reservations this year that the overall effect can end up "slightly cold and soulless"). / E1 6JJ; www.lyleslondon.com; lyleslondon; Tue-Sat 9 pm.

Lyon's N8 £60 4 4 3
1 Park Road   020 8350 8983   1–1C
This "brilliant, buzzy local seafood restaurant" is much-loved in Crouch End and beyond for its "exciting, high-quality dishes from a short menu" and "exceptionally friendly, knowledgeable and enthusiastic staff". It works equally well for a meal with a large group or a "snack at the bar". / N8 8TE; lyons-restaurant.com; lyonsseafood; Tue-Sat 10 pm.

M Restaurants £99 2 2 2
Newfoundland, E14   020 3327 7771   12–1C
60 Threadneedle Street, EC2   020 3327 7770   10–2C
Fans and foes alike agree on the essential value trade-off at Martin (the "M" in question) Williams's large 'Gastro Playgrounds' in the City, and Canary Wharf (Victoria and Twickenham branches having fallen by the wayside). To fans, they are "a bit expensive for what they are, but you can't fault the food or wine": to foes, they are "good but not worth the money". Japan and Provence provide the culinary inspiration for the steak-focused menu (Williams is also the CEO of the Gaucho group); and the menu is backed up by a very wide-ranging wine list, with a broad range of options (including some trophy vintages for over £7,000 per bottle). The least popular part of the formula is the atmosphere created by their ultra-glossy, London via Miami interiors: "chic but soulless". / www.mrestaurants.co.uk; mrestaurants; SRA-accredited.

Ma La Sichuan SW1 £50 4 3 2
37 Monck Street   020 7222 2218   2–4C
Though "well patronised by suited government types and Sky News executives", it's easy to overlook this "unassuming restaurant in an otherwise soulless building on a Westminster corner-site". "It's a pleasure to find" though, especially if you like "classic Sichuan cooking". Chef Zhang Xiaozhong provides "thoughtfully presented and delightful dishes, with punchy flavours and consistent quality" and "the menu indicates degrees of spice / heat for each item". "Always busy – it's best to reserve" and – though very "efficient" – service can also be seen as "brusque" or "rushed". Top Menu Tip – "some dishes you don't get in most Chinese restaurants, such as delicious preserved egg". / SW1P 2BL; malasichuan.co.uk; malasichuan; Mon-Sat 10.30 pm, Sun 10 pm.

Macellaio RC £73 2 2 3
39-45 Shaftesbury Avenue, W1   020 3727 6161   5–3A
6 Store Street, WC1   020 3848 7230   2–1C
84 Old Brompton Rd, SW7   020 7589 5834   6–2B
Arch 24, 229 Union St, SE1   07467 307682   10–4B
124 Northcote Rd, SW11   020 3848 4800   11–2C
38-40 Exmouth Market, EC1   020 3696 8220   10–1A
Fans do still hail the "fabulous meat" at Roberto Costa's quirky Italian steakhouse group, but it has lost some of its red-blooded allure in recent years. "The restaurants look appealing and the menu looks promising", but lower ratings bolster those who feel "the quality has dropped with expansion", as it has grown to six venues across London (and a sister concept, Fish Game, opened in Canary Wharf in mid-2023); and at its worst, it can deliver "distinctly average steaks" at "steep prices". / www.macellaiorc.com.

Maddox Tavern W1 £79 2 2 **3**
47 Maddox Street   020 3376 9922   3–2C
"These very big premises were once a prestigious tailor's" – then more recently a branch of the Browns brasserie chain – and are now "a pub-like restaurant in the middle of Mayfair". Fans are impressed by "its competent realisation of a standard menu" of British classics. But service can be "somewhat patchy" and food can be "fairly average" as a result. / W1S 2PG; www.maddoxtavern.com; maddoxtavern; Tue-Sat midnight.

Made in Italy £57 **3** 2 2
249 King's Rd, SW3   020 7352 1880   6–3C
59 Northcote Rd, SW11   020 7978 7711   11–2C
"The sourdough base is slow-fermented for 48 hours", and there's "a great selection of toppings (but you can't beat any with the burrata heart – so creamy, so addictive!") at these rustic venues in Chelsea and Battersea. / www.madeinitalygroup.co.uk; madeinitalylondon.

Maene E1 NEW £37 **4 3 3**
7-9 Fashion Street   020 3011 1081   13–2C
"A new spin-off from Whitechapel Gallery's Townsend that's just opened": former Anglo chef Nick Gilkinson launched this hard-to-find all-day bistro, at the top of a four-storey Victorian warehouse in Spitalfields, in early April 2023. The choice of an Olde English name – meaning a sense of community, apparently – chimes with its short menu of determinedly seasonal British cuisine and we've optimistically rated it on initial reports describing "an awesome new opening, with fantastic, flavoursome food, locally sourced and provided by personable and knowledgeable staff". It is by all accounts a "lovely dining room too", with a roof terrace an expected addition. / E1 6PX; www.maenerestaurant.co.uk; maene_restaurant; Mon-Sat 9.30 pm, Sun 4.15 pm.

Magenta NW1 £83 **3 4 3**
23 Euston Road   0203 146 0222   9–3C
A trafficky location – right on Euston Road, opposite King's Cross station – doesn't augur well for this ambitious Italian bar/restaurant, within the recently revamped Megaro hotel. But, since it opened in November 2021, the limited feedback we receive suggests it can surprise with its quality and good value: "Four of us, all locals, dined here. We were delighted by everything and couldn't find anything to fault. A particular shout-out to the service!" / NW1 2SD; www.magentarestaurant.co.uk; magenta_kx; Tue-Sat 9.30 pm.

Maggie Jones's W8 £69 **3 4 4**
6 Old Court Pl   020 7937 6462   6–1A
This vintage Kensington haunt – named after the pseudonym used by the late Princess Margaret when wining and dining as a commoner – delights its guests with its gorgeous and romantic, rustic decor. Never a foodie fave rave: expect the kind of "delicious" 1970s brasserie-style comfort food which will not distract from a "lovely family meal", or more intimate tête-à-tête. / W8 4PL; www.maggie-jones.co.uk; maggiejonesrestaurant; Mon-Sun 9.30 pm.

The Maine Mayfair W1 £106 2 2 **3**
6 Medici Court, 20 Hanover Square   020 3432 2192   3–2C
"Taking you back to a different era", this glitzy American brasserie is spread over three floors of an extravagantly refurbed Georgian townhouse in Mayfair, where the entertainment runs to live jazz and burlesque shows. It's the creation of Montreal-born, Middle East-based 'tastemaker' Joey Ghazal. Naturally it does a "nice brunch", and the rather obvious menu – New England-style seafood plus some steaks and American-Italian favourites – is consistently well-rated. / W1S 1JY; www.themainemayfair.com; themainemayfair; Mon-Sun 11 pm.

Maison Bertaux W1 — £16 — 3 3 5
28 Greek St   020 7437 6007   5–2A
"One of the few remaining eccentric Soho sites left" – this *"long-established fixture"* was founded in 1871 by an exile from Paris. *"Individual, exceptional and entertaining"*, *"the food still makes it a destination"* – *"including wonderful cakes better than any chain"*. It is, though, *"very busy, clearly on the 'to-do' list of many tourists"*. / W1D 5DQ; www.maisonbertaux.com; maison_bertaux; Mon-Sun 6 pm.

Maison François SW1 — £89 — 3 3 4
34 Duke Street St James's   020 3988 5777   3–3D
This *"smart bit of France in swanky St James's"* is becoming an established favourite in the West End thanks in large part to its elegant and *"buzzy"* setting and the fact that it is *"well organised"*. The classic menu of *"French brasserie classics"* has *"lots of crowd-pleasers"*, but opinions divide on the results – to critics it is *"a little expensive for what it is"*, but fans feel *"the food is top-notch"* and ratings tend to support those who say this is *"a place for serious cooking, not just a big café"*. Top Tip – *"the dessert trolley is an utter treat"*. / SW1Y 6DF; maisonfrancois.london; maisonfrancoislondon; Thu-Sat 1 am, Mon-Wed midnight, Sun 4 pm.

Mallow SE1 — £59 — 3 3 4
1 Cathedral Street   020 7846 8785   10–4C
"As non-vegans this was a revelation!" This *"grown-up vegan restaurant"* – a spin-off from the well-established Mildreds Group – has an excellent view of Borough Market and has won a strong reputation in its two years of operation. There's *"no sense of a second-rate eating experience for lack of meat / fish etc"* and its *"inventive"* cooking provides *"really interesting flavours and combinations"*. On the downside, *"the menu doesn't change that often"*; and ratings weakened this year due to a few disappointed reporters who found it *"overrated"* due to lacklustre dishes and *"intermittent"* service. In June 2023, after our annual diners' poll had concluded, a new branch opened in Canary Wharf. / SE1 1TL; www.mallowlondon.com; mallowlondon; Mon-Sat 11 pm, Sun 10 pm.

Mambow SE15 — £37 — 4 2 1
Market, 133a Rye Lane   no tel   1–4D
"This Malaysian place at Market Peckham has wonderful food" – *"the chicken satay is as good as I've had in the UK"* and *"the Hainanese chicken sando is delectable"*. It's *"highly regarded, with fans including reviewers (Marina O'L)"*, but popularity has brought problems with *"scaling up"* – *"they need more space, staff and flexible portions"*. BREAKING NEWS – in September 2023, they announced they have found their first 'forever home' at 78 Lower Clapton Road, Lower Clapton, London E5 0RN. The bigger space, with open kitchen, will have 40 covers, with 20 seats inside and 20 seats on a 'garden' terrace. / SE15 4BQ; www.wearemambow.com; mambow_ldn; Thu-Sat 11 pm, Wed 10 pm, Sun 5 pm.

Mandarin Kitchen W2 — £71 — 4 4 2
14-16 Queensway   020 7727 9012   7–2C
"The lobster noodles are as legendary as ever" – *"best in the world!"* – chorus a legion of fans for this 45-year-old Queensway institution that's *"tops for Chinese seafood in London"*. It's a *"buzzy family restaurant"* too, with *"really lovely friendly staff"*, even if it's *"a bit too brightly lit"*. / W2 3RX; www.mandarin.kitchen; mandarinkitchenlondon; Mon-Sat 11.15 pm, Sun 23.

Mangal 1 E8 £37 5 3 2
10 Arcola St 020 7275 8981 14–1A
"One of the OGs and still one of the very best!" – this renowned Turkish dive in Dalston gets some diners' votes as *"the best-value restaurant in London"*. *"The smell of grilled meats entices you into the deservedly bustling interior"*, where it *"delivers amazing food every time"*: *"wonderful BBQ, lovely warm bread and generous salad"*. One of owner Ali Dirik's sons runs nearby Mangal 2, putting a more modern slant on grill cooking. / E8 2DJ; www.mangal1.com; mangal_ocakbasi; Sun-Thu midnight, Fri & Sat 1 am.

Manicomio £86 2 2 3
85 Duke of York Square, SW3 020 7730 3366 6–2D
6 Gutter Lane, EC2 020 7726 5010 10–2B
"Smart and buzzy", *"reliable but expensive"* – the underlying themes in reports over the years on this duo in Chelsea and the City, where *"fresh Italian food is generally well done, if a little safe and uninspired"*. Top Tip – the Duke of York Square branch benefits from a heated terrace as well as conservatory and garden, making it a *"happening place when the sun shines"*. / www.manicomio.co.uk; manicomiorestaurant.

Manteca EC2 £52 5 4 4
49-51 Curtain Road 020 7033 6642 13–1B
"Packed fuller than a tube train, but the blinding food makes it all worth it!" – Chris Leach and David Carter's *"bustling"* two-year-old *"in the heart of hipster Shoreditch"* has *"made huge waves and deservedly so"* thanks to its *"punchy, honest, original and surprisingly good-value"* Italian cooking which includes some notable pasta dishes (e.g. *"shout out for the duck fazzoletti – homemade, with a perfectly balanced sauce"*); and whose meaty options *"make full use of lesser cuts (the pig's head croquette is a special treat)"*. *"Always a good night out"*... *"superb!"* / EC2A 3PT; mantecarestaurant.co.uk; manteca_london; Mon-Thu, Sat & Sun, Fri 10.45pm.

Manthan W1 £64 3 3 2
49 Maddox Street 020 7491 9191 3–2C
Rohit Ghai's Mayfair two-year-old offers a *"glam Indian street-food experience"* – inspired by the home cooking of his childhood in Madhya Pradesh – from a *"short but always very good menu"*. / W1S 2PQ; manthanmayfair.co.uk; manthanmayfair; Tue-Sun 10 pm.

Manuel's SE19 £65 4 4 4
129 Gipsy Hill 020 8670 1843 1–4D
"A high-quality Italian, with an ever-changing menu and wide range of specials depending on market availability" – this Gipsy Hill Sicilian is well worth discovering deep in the SE postcodes. In summer the terrace comes into its own, but fans say it's *"always a pleasure to dine there"*. / SE19 1QS; www.manuelsrestaurantandbar.com; manuelsrestaurantgipsyhill; Tue-Sat 10.30 pm, Sun 9 pm.

Manuka Kitchen SW6 £61 3 3 3
510 Fulham Rd 020 7731 0864 6–4A
"Very popular at weekends with a good breakfast menu" – this NZ-inspired bistro near Parsons Green particularly comes into its own for brunches and light lunches. / SW6 5NJ; manukakitchen.co.uk; manukakitchen; Tue-Sat 11 pm, Mon 10 pm, Sun 4 pm.

Manzi's W1

1 Bateman's Buildings   020 3540 4546   5–2A

Few openings are as long anticipated as this resurrection of a long-defunct, once-famous seafood destination. Conceived when its owning company was still run by Jeremy King and Christopher Corbin, the final debut is the first major test of the ability of its successor, The Wolseley Group, to launch a new site. The business that forms the inspiration for this debut was in Chinatown, just off Leicester Square, and shuttered in the early 1990s. This revivified version is in 'Bateman's Buildings', tucked between Soho's Greek and Frith Streets. Set over two floors, it's an all-day operation with a large outdoor terrace. Dishes encompass everything from moules marinière to a wide range of crustacea, a 'catch of the day' and a classic Dover sole. / W1D 3EN; www.manzis.co.uk; manzissoho; Mon-Sat 11 pm.

Mar I Terra SE1   £56   🖪🖪🖪

14 Gambia St   020 7928 7628   10–4A

Long-standing tapas bar in a tiny converted pub near Southwark tube that's "great fun and like being in Spain" – tucked away in a backstreet, it is handily close to the South Bank's arts venues, including Tate Modern, the Old Vic and the National Theatre. / SE1 0XH; www.mariterra.net; Tue, Thu, Wed, Fri & Sat midnight.

Marcella SE8   £48   🖪🖪🖪

165a Deptford High Street   020 3903 6561   1–3D

Bright, white-walled local Italian on the high street in Deptford (sibling to Peckham's Artusi) named for food writer Marcella Hazan; according to locals the scran's "always reliable, delicious and great value". / SE8 3NU; www.marcella.london; marcelladeptford; Wed & Thu 9.30 pm, Fri & Sat, Tue 10 pm, Sun 4 pm.

Marcus,
The Berkeley SW1   £176   🖪🖪🖪

Wilton Pl   020 7235 1200   6–1D

Opinions divided this year on Marcus Wareing's august Belgravia HQ, where the day-to-day is overseen by head chef, Craig Johnston. Most reports acclaim modern European cuisine that's "very, very, very good… amazing!" and applaud the flexibility of the kitchen to particular requests ("our food intolerances were brilliantly catered for and we felt our meal was just as special as other diners"). On the downside, though, ratings were capped by a growing number of disappointments citing hefty prices, and in one or two cases "poor execution". BREAKING NEWS – in September 2023, Marcus announced it is to close on Boxing Day 2023 and Wareing is now a TV-chef without a restaurant attached. But he says he is not retiring yet, and that announcements will follow… / SW1X 7RL; www.marcusrestaurant.com; marcusbelgravia; Tue-Sat 10 pm.

Mare Street Market E8   £57   🖪🖪🖪

117 Mare Street   020 3745 2470   14–2B

This "cool hangar of a restaurant in Hackney" (part of the design-conscious Barworks group) sits in a repurposed and eclectically decorated 1960s office block and also incorporates a coffee shop, deli, barber and tattoo parlour. "Recommended for large groups – the food is very good for the price" and includes a range of global favourites plus sourdough pizza, to be eaten in the spacious 'Open Kitchen' or the cosier 'Dining Room'. / E8 4RU; www.marestreetmarket.com; marestreetmarket; Mon-Sun 10 pm.

Maremma SW2 £65 3️⃣3️⃣3️⃣
36 Brixton Water Lane   020 3186 4011   11–2D
This "cute little restaurant" near Brockwell Park in Brixton "really ticks all the boxes", with a "short selection of interesting Italian food" inspired by Tuscany's Maremma marshes – "you wouldn't expect an establishment of this quality to be hidden away here". Marks for food slipped a notch this year, although it's still "exciting and seasonal" at its best. / SW2 1PE; www.maremmarestaurant.com; maremma_restaurant; Wed-Sat 10 pm, Sun 3 pm.

Maresco W1 NEW £81 3️⃣3️⃣3️⃣
45 Berwick Street   020 7439 8483   4–1C
"Not a place for a quiet tête-à-tête: instead climb up to the bar and dig into a mixture of fine Scottish fish and seafood, prepared as Spanish-style tapas". That's the culinary mashup at Stephen Lironi's new "Soho seafood heaven" – a "lively, albeit slightly cramped" space with "lovely and engaging service and a fun atmosphere" ("as long as you are sitting upstairs" – downstairs is "a bit small and dingy"). On the downside, it can seem a bit "hyped" – "they need to smarten up if they are going to charge such high prices when you are perched on a bar stool". / W1F 8SF; www.maresco.co.uk; maresco_soho; Mon-Fri 11 pm, Sat & Sun 11.30 pm.

Margaux SW5 £76 3️⃣4️⃣3️⃣
152 Old Brompton Rd   020 7373 5753   6–2B
"Always reliable and first-class French cooking" is complemented by a serious wine list, including nine from Margaux, at this upmarket neighbourhood spot over two storeys at the Earl's Court end of South Kensington. / SW5 0BE; www.barmargaux.co.uk; barmargaux.

Margot WC2 £91 3️⃣4️⃣4️⃣
45 Great Queen Street   020 3409 4777   5–2D
"A very sophisticated Italian restaurant" in Covent Garden that combines "gorgeous" cooking and "excellent wines" with "superb" service and an "elegant" interior. Just one catch, and you can probably guess what it is… it's no bargain ("the crab ravioli at £31 had only 6 ravioli on the plate…"). Top Top – "good value for the pre-theatre menu". / WC2B 5AA; www.margotrestaurant.com; margotldn_; Tue-Sat 9.30 pm.

Maria G's £59 3️⃣3️⃣3️⃣
20 Central Avenue, SW6   020 3479 3867   11–1B NEW
Coe House, 1-4 Warwick Lane, W14   020 3479 3772   8–2D
An "attractive riverside setting" (incorporating a 45-cover outdoor terrace, complete with retractable roof) is a major selling point at star chef Robin Gill's second opening under the 'Maria G' banner, on the ground floor of a shiny new residential development, in the deepest, darkest Fulham no-man's-land near Imperial Wharf (by the big Sainsburys). Despite its out-of-the-way situation, it's already attracting more feedback than the first Maria G, which opened two years ago. That's also hard to find, and also in a glossy new block – this time part of a retirement village on the Kensington/Olympia borders. At both outlets, the culinary theme is Italian although SW6 concentrates more on its raw bar and pasta, with reports praising "some innovative dishes" (The Telegraph's William Sitwell was also a fan, proclaiming it a "chic oasis" with "delicate and authentic Italian food"). Reports in our annual diners' poll on W8 were scant (but the Daily Mail's Tom Parker Bowles found it a "lush, lovely Italian oasis… [in] the sterile, anodyne surroundings of those deluxe flats").

Maroush £67 **4** 2 1
5 McNicol Drive, NW10   020 3941 3221   1–2A
II) 38 Beauchamp Pl, SW3   020 7581 5434   6–1C
VI) 68 Edgware Rd, W2   020 7224 9339   7–1D
"Consistently delicious Lebanese food" remains a hallmark of Marouf and Houda Abouzaki's well-established restaurant group after more than 40 years. Even experienced Beirut hands report "very authentic" cooking, although service can be "inconsistent". The group shrank during the pandemic, but has bounced back with a large new restaurant/bar/emporium further west, in Park Royal. A sandwich wrap in the busy café on the ground floor of the Beauchamp Place branch is one of the top cheap eats in the Knightsbridge area. / www.maroush.com; maroush.

Maru W1 £266 **5** 4 3
18 Shepherd Market   020 3637 7677   3–4B
Taiji Maruyama – a third-generation sushi chef, who arrived in London via stints in Barcelona and Norway – delivers a 20-course omakase menu at this tiny Shepherd Market venue. All the fair number of reporters this year who made the £210 per person investment say it was money well spent: "a minute spot but with no skimping on flavour – top class dishes centred around aged fish put this straight into the top tier of London's Japanese restaurants". / W1J 7QH; www.marulondon.com; maru__london; Tue-Sat 11 pm.

Marugame Udon £18 **3** 3 2
St Christopher's Place, W1   no tel   3–1B
Unit 2.03 Entertainment Avenue, The O2, SE10   no tel   12–1D
Upper Floor, The Atrium Kitchen, Cabot Place, E14   no tel   12–1C
114 Middlesex Street, E1   020 3148 2780   13–2B
These "functional Japanese canteen-style restaurants" serve "lovely udon noodles at cheap prices" – "possibly the most reasonable in London" – along with tempura, rice bowls and "fabulous chicken katsu curry". The Kobe-based chain has more than 1,000 branches around the world, with a dozen across the capital since arriving in 2021. / marugame.co.uk; marugameuk.

Masala Zone £65 **4** 4 4
244 Piccadilly, W1   020 7930 6622   4–4D **NEW**
9 Marshall St, W1   020 7287 9966   4–2B
48 Floral St, WC2   020 7379 0101   5–2D
147 Earl's Court Rd, SW5   020 7373 0220   6–2A
"There's a reason this chain has endured for so long" – its street food and curries are "so authentic", "imaginative" and "such good value for money": "you still have to go a long way to beat their thali deals". Owned by MW Eats (who own the posh Chutney Mary, Amaya, etc), they sold off their Camden Town and Bayswater sites in the last 12 months; and in mid 2023 launched a stunning new landmark branch on Piccadilly Circus, in one of London's most historic, but (in recent times) most-under-achieving restaurant sites: the magnificent, Neo-Byzantine, mosaicked chamber dating from 1873 that for many years was The Criterion (RIP). Innovations on the new site include breakfast, 'Indian High Tea' and late opening. / www.masalazone.com; masalazone.

Master Wei WC1 £34 **4** 2 2
13 Cosmo Place   020 7209 6888   2–1D
"Hand-made and pulled noodles are the stars of the show" at this "authentic" canteen in a side-street near Russell Square, offering "fantastic Xi'an cooking" from chef-proprietor Wei Guirong. It attracts an "odd but pleasing mix of mainland Chinese businessmen & students, with tourists and the odd culinary adventurer" – and is much easier for most to visit than its sibling, Xi'an Impression near Arsenal's Emirates Stadium. / WC1N 3AP; master-wei.com; master.wei.3150; Mon-Thu 10 pm, Fri & Sat 10.30 pm, Sun 9 pm.

Mauro Colagreco, The OWO SW1 NEW

57 Whitehall Place   Awaiting tel   2–3C

A past winner of the World's 50-best – chef Mauro Colagreco of Mirazur is to run three of the dining spaces at this new Raffles hotel in Whitehall's former Old War Office building. As well as his flagship dining room – which is to showcase 'hyper-local, hyper-seasonal ingredients for a culinary experience of discovery', there will be Mauro's Table (a private room with space for 10); and 'Saison', a brasserie in a fine high-ceilinged room. / SW1A 2EU; theowo.london; theowo.london; Wed-Sat 10 pm, Sun 9.30 pm.

Mayha W1 NEW   £242   4 4 4

43 Chiltern Street   020 3161 9493   2–1A

"Not quite the best sushi omakase in the now very competitive London market but nevertheless very good" – this "beautiful and serene" Japanese venture arrived in Marylebone in early 2023 and early reporters are uniformly impressed. "Service is attentive but not overwhelming and the delicious food is prepared with a lot of care". It's an offshoot of a Beirut original from the Nothing But Love Group. (Lucy Thackray in The Independent was also a fan: "…confident and unshowy. This isn't theatrical "pan-Asian" dining made for Instagram… it's understated Japanese fine dining which takes its heritage seriously, but isn't afraid to add a twist here and there"). / W1U 6LS; www.mayhalondon.com; mayhalondon; Mon-Sat 7 pm.

Mazi W8   £78   4 4 3

12-14 Hillgate St   020 7229 3794   7–2B

"Very noisy" rustic-chic taverna tucked away near Notting Hill Gate station, which has won a sizable fan club thanks to its "delicious and inventive modern rendition" of the Greek classics. / W8 7SR; www.mazi.co.uk; mazilondon; Mon-Sun midnight.

The Meat & Wine Co Mayfair W1

17c Curzon Street   0203 988 6888   3–4B

Limited but promising feedback so far on this August 2022, Mayfair newcomer – the first UK outpost of an Aussie-based chain – which aims to deliver 'what it says on the tin', with USDA steaks and Wagyu MB5 from Australian farms, as well as Prussian Black cuts from Finland. Early reports say "if steak is your thing then you will not do much better", and speak of "very friendly staff" and an "enjoyable" overall experience. / W1J 5HU; www.themeatandwineco.co.uk; themeatandwinecouk; Mon-Thu 9.30 pm, Fri & Sat 10.30 pm.

MEATliquor   £50   3 2 2

37-38 Margaret Street, W1   020 7224 4239   3–1C
15-17 Brunswick Centre, WC1   020 3026 8168   2–1D
17 Queensway, W2   020 7229 0172   7–2C
133b Upper St, N1   020 3711 0104   9–3D
14-15 Hoxton Market, N1   020 7739 8212   13–1B
37 Lordship Lane, SE22   020 3066 0008   1–4D
7 Dartmouth Rd, SE23   020 3026 1331   1–4D
74 Northcote Road, SW11   020 7228 4777   11–2C

"The Dead Hippy burger is a dirty, dirty legend" – the best-named burger on British menus and "if not the easiest burger to eat definitely the tastiest" (especially when chased down by a boozy "hard shake") – at the "cool" chain founded 15 years ago by Scott Collins and Yianni Papoutsis. The expansion of recent years seems to have ground to a halt with the closure of branches in Boxpark Croydon and Clapham Old Town, with a new strategy based around boosting sales via a national network of delivery kitchens launched in 2023. Top Tip – "root beer is available if you want a bit of real Americana!" / meatliquor.com; meatgram.

Mediterraneo W11 £70 3 2 3
37 Kensington Park Rd   020 7792 3131   7–1A
This "decent Notting Hill Italian" is "always mobbed (and the back area is particularly noisy), but the basic fare is great quality and the service is smiley". It has notched up a quarter of a century, and spawned two offshoots in the same street – Essenza and Osteria Basilico. / W11 2EU; www.mediterraneo-restaurant.co.uk; mediterraneo_nottinghill; Mon-Sun 10.30 pm.

Medlar SW10 £115 4 4 3
438 King's Rd   020 7349 1900   6–3B
"It may not have the best location in an obscure end of the King's Road", but this "low-key" Chelsea operation (est. 2011) "continues to quietly excel" and is one of the most popular in our annual diners' poll. "Imaginative" modern British cuisine "with a good range of ingredients" is "expertly cooked by co-owner and chef Joe Mercer Nairne, and with excellent but unobtrusive service overseen by co-owner David O'Connor", including "well-targeted wine advice" on the "terrific list". Another "star of the show is the cheeseboard" ("I am still talking about it months later!"). "Much better than many one-starred Michelin restaurants in London", "it is incomprehensible that this restaurant has been passed over for regaining its star for so long". Top Tips – "the three-course lunch for £45 and lunchtime corkage of only £15 are some of the capital's great culinary bargains". "Old favourites on the menu include the Crab Raviolo." / SW10 0LJ; www.medlarrestaurant.co.uk; medlarchelsea; Mon-Sat 10.30 pm, Sun 9.30 pm.

Meet Bros W2 NEW
29-31 Craven Road   020 7723 7101   7–1C
No less a figure than Queen Azizah of Malaysia (while she was over for Charles's coronation) cut the ribbon for the May 2023 opening of this first European venture from one of Malaysia's leading restaurant groups – a steakhouse in Craven Road, Paddington, that takes its name from the meeting of Eastern and Western food cultures. No alcohol is served and the meat is fully halal, with cuts flavoured by infusion in Asian marinades. Reports please! / W2 3BX; www.meetbros.co.uk; meetbros.uk; Mon-Sun 11 pm.

Megan's £50 1 1 3
Branches throughout London
"Fairy lights, greenery and charming decor create a warm and cosy atmosphere" at this still-expanding group, which is most popular as a "reliable and friendly brunch option". Its Med-inspired tapas is typically rated somewhere between "tasty" and "nothing special" and scores overall are dragged well down by those experiencing "chaotic service" and "food that doesn't live up to the pretty dining room". / megans.co.uk; megansrestaurants.

Meiwei SW15 £17 3 3 2
315 Putney Bridge Road   020 8789 3165   11–2B
This "surprisingly good Chinese" in Putney specialises in the cuisines of Shanghai and Sichuan, and the "flavours and produce" are by all accounts "excellent" (even better if you "ask for the Chinese menu"). Top Menu Tip – "particularly fine duck". / SW15 2PP; www.meiweilondon.co.uk; Mon-Sun 11 pm.

Mele e Pere W1 £54 3 3 3
46 Brewer Street   020 7096 2096   4–3C
This "authentic Italian vermuteria" (they make their own vermouths) in the heart of Soho was founded 12 years ago by three brothers from northern Italy, and offers enjoyable cooking from their homeland, including "a great choice of pasta" and "the crispiest pizza ever – delicious!" / W1F 9TF; www.meleepere.co.uk; meleeperesoho; Mon & Tue, Sun 10 pm, Wed-Sat 11 pm.

The Melusine E1 £71 444
Unit K, Ivory House, St Katherine Dock   02077022976   10–3D
"Consistently delicious seafood" and a "lovely location" by St Katharine Dock
have put this three-year-old securely on the map. The interesting wine list is
strong on "Greek offerings" – thanks no doubt to co-founder Theodore
Kyriakou, a veteran of Livebait and The Real Greek in the '90s. Top Tip – "go
on Wednesdays for the half-price wine". / E1W 1AT; www.themelusine.co.uk;
themelusine_skd; Mon-Sat 10.30 pm, Sun 9.30 pm.

Meraki W1 £85 434
80-82 Gt Titchfield St   020 7305 7686   3–1C
London… Mykonos… er, Riyadh… – that's the lineup for this small
international group of luxe Greek restaurants owned by Peter Waney (who,
with brother Arjun, has created hits such as Zuma and Roka). It flies slightly
under the radar compared with its more famous stablemates, but shares the
same virtues: the vibe is buoyant and the food (a Greek-inflected mix of the
raw seafood, fish, grills and pasta popular with globetrotting types) "is
great… so fresh!" / W1W 7QT; www.meraki-restaurant.com; merakilondon; Tue,
Wed 10.15 pm, Thu-Sat 10.45 pm, Sun 8.30 pm.

Mercato Metropolitano SE1 £46 224
42 Newington Causeway   020 7403 0930   1–3C
Hosting a range of pop-up kitchens and bars, these "lively and fun"
sustainable markets have sprung up across the capital since opening in an
ex-paper factory near Elephant & Castle in 2016, a year after the concept
was launched at Milan's World Expo. They make a flexible and affordable
option that particularly comes into its own in summer – the Canary Wharf
branch on Wood Wharf is "brilliant for sitting outside overlooking the dock";
and SE1 boasts London's biggest beer garden. / SE1 6DR;
www.mercatometropolitano.com; mercatometropolitano; Mon-Wed 11 pm, Fri & Sat
1 am, Thu midnight, Sun 10 pm.

The Mercer EC2 £82 332
34 Threadneedle St   020 7628 0001   10–2C
This solid English brasserie in a converted banking hall not far from the
Bank of England continues to win a general thumbs-up as an "excellent
business lunch venue" – although "it could do with tables further apart".
/ EC2R 8AY; www.themercer.co.uk; themercerrestaurant; Mon-Fri 9.30 pm.

Le Mercury N1 £40 222
140a Upper St   020 7354 4088   9–2D
It's "not haute cuisine", but you'll find "reasonably well-cooked bistro fare
that's very well-priced for the location" at this old-school haunt that has done
sterling service for almost 40 years on the Islington main drag, opposite the
Almeida Theatre. "The two-tier Parisian theatre boxes are a bit of a mad
addition to the interior design", but they make "a great spot for a family
meal before a show". / N1 1QY; www.lemercury.co.uk; lemercury; Mon-Sat midnight,
Sun 11 pm.

Mere W1 £123 343
74 Charlotte Street   020 7268 6565   2–1B
TV star chef Monica Galetti often "hits the heights" at the Fitzrovia
basement she runs with her husband David – an "unfailingly delightful"
place, sometimes tipped for "romance", but mostly nominated by its large
fanclub for its "exquisite cooking" ("superbly prepared fish" in particular)
and "pampering" service. But ratings here are limited by a few more
nuanced experiences: "I kept hoping some culinary magic would happen, but
it never quite made it". / W1T 4QH; www.mere-restaurant.com; mererestaurant;
Wed & Thu, Tue 9 pm, Fri & Sat 9.30 pm.

Meson don Felipe SE1   £52   2️⃣2️⃣4️⃣
53 The Cut   020 7928 3237   10–4A

Many older Londoners tasted their first tapas at this "fun and reliable" Hispanic spot on a prominent corner of the Cut, near Waterloo – back in the days when you "had to queue (now you can book)" for a place in the "cramped interior". It's still "excellent before and after visiting the Old Vic" across the road. / SE1 8LF; www.mesondonfelipe.com; mesondonfelipe; Mon-Sat 11 pm.

Meza Trinity Road SW17   £45   3️⃣3️⃣3️⃣
34 Trinity Rd   07722 111299   11–2C

"A great neighbourhood place" – this Tooting café maintains its reputation with "reliably fresh and tasty" Lebanese cooking. / SW17 7RE; www.mezarestaurant.com; meza_res; Sun-Thu 11 pm, Fri & Sat 11.30 pm.

Michael Nadra NW1   £78   3️⃣3️⃣2️⃣
42 Gloucester Ave   020 7722 2800   9–3B

Michael Nadra's "reliable" cuisine from an eclectic modern menu has created a high-quality neighbourhood destination for the last 12 years in this corner of Primrose Hill: quirkily laid-out premises, with a cute courtyard, just off the Regent's Canal. His original restaurant in Chiswick closed down during the pandemic. / NW1 8JD; www.restaurant-michaelnadra.co.uk.

Midland Grand Dining Room NW1 🆕
Euston Road   020 7341 3000   9–3C

Set in the stunning Gothic Revival St Pancras Renaissance Hotel – and using the establishment's original name – this 'elevated brasserie' opened in May 2023 to replace The Gilbert Scott (RIP) just as our survey was concluding. Consequently even though we did have one (upbeat) initial report, there's too little feedback for a rating. But The Standard's Jimi Famurewa was also a fan, admiring the amazing "double-height main room… gilded cornice work… vast textured mirrors" (but also noting a "slight stiltedness of atmosphere"). Its modern interpretation of classic French cuisine is under ex-Chiltern Fire House chef Patrick Powell: JF notes "light kitsch… impeccable details… intricate presentation" but "a potentially ruinous bill" ("prices… can take you whistling past the £100 a head mark without even really trying"). / NW1 2AR; www.midlandgranddiningroom.com; midlandgrand; Tue-Sat 9.45 pm, Sun 4 pm.

Mildreds   £57   3️⃣3️⃣3️⃣
45 Lexington St, W1   020 7494 1634   4–2C
79 St Martin's Lane, WC2   020 8066 8393   5–3B
200 Pentonville Rd, N1   020 7278 9422   9–3D
9 Jamestown Rd, NW1   020 7482 4200   9–3B
1 Dalston Square, E8   020 8017 1815   14–1A

"So much better now it is fully vegan and more adventurous with its food" ("a wonderful range of plant-based dishes from around the world including Central America and the Middle East") – this long-established meat-free chain started with its "old favourite" Soho branch (est 1988) and has mushroomed in recent years to include five locations in all. "Tables are crammed in" and the sites can get "extremely busy", but its offering is reliably "tasty and interesting". / www.mildreds.co.uk; mildredsrestaurants.

Milk SW12   £25   3️⃣2️⃣3️⃣
20 Bedford Hill   020 8772 9085   11–2C

"The fish sando of dreams" is one item that comes highly recommended at this "über trendy" Antipodean-inspired café in Balham, known in particular as a key brunch venue. "The menu items regularly contain ingredients you've never heard of… doesn't matter, all of them are delicious!" / SW12 9RG; milklondonshop.uk; milkcoffeeldn; Mon-Fri 3.30 pm, Sat & Sun 4 pm.

Milk Beach Soho W1   £48   3 4 3

Ilona Rose House, Manette Street   020 4599 4271   5–2A

"A fairly recent addition to Soho" – sibling to an older venture in Queen's Park – this "interestingly-styled", "Aussie-themed" yearling is a handy option for "meeting up with friends". "Über-cool", "very amiable" staff provide "a great selection of unusual menu offerings to tempt the slightly adventurous or those jaded with standard fare". A disgruntled minority dismiss "average food in a cavernous space", but the main impression is of something "genuinely different from most West End options". Top Tip – dedicated menus for breakfast and pre-theatre. / W1D 4AL; www.milkbeach.com; milkbeachlondon; Tue, Wed 11 pm, Thu-Sat midnight, Sun 4 pm.

MiMi Mei Fair W1   £97   3 4 4

55 Curzon Street   020 3989 7777   3–3B

"We went there a mite apprehensive that we would be overwhelmed by pretension… but the dining rooms are beautiful!" – Samyukta Nair's Shanghai-inspired two-year-old occupies a three-story Mayfair townhouse decorated in an elegant, classic style based on a fictional 'Empress Mimi'. The chicness of the surroundings helps compensate for some "slightly overpriced" dishes, as does the generally excellent level of service. Top Menu Tip – "the fabled Peking duck is one of the best in town". / W1J 8PG; mimimeifair.com; mimimeifair; Mon-Sat 10.30 pm, Sun 10 pm.

**Min Jiang,
The Royal Garden Hotel W8**   £105   4 4 5

2-24 Kensington High St   020 7361 1988   6–1A

"Fabulous Peking Duck and dim sum comes with one of the best views of any restaurant in London" at this luxurious Chinese venue, which continues to break the normal rules applying to anywhere with a decent outlook. On the top of a five-star hotel overlooking Kensington Gardens and Palace, it's "very popular and deservedly so": service is "spot-on" and it's "just lovely". / W8 4PT; www.minjiang.co.uk; minjianglondon; Mon-Sun 10.30 pm.

Mirch Masala SW17   £26   4 2 2

213 Upper Tooting Rd   020 8767 8638   11–2D

"Always delicious", this well-known Pakistani canteen on Tooting's 'curry corridor' offers the "same fun and good-value food as it has for years". A favourite of local boy-made-mayor Sadiq Khan (so come on foot or by public transport), it has an offshoot in Coulsdon, on London's southern fringe. / SW17 7TG; mirchmasala-takeaway.co.uk; mirch masala; Mon-Sun 23.59 pm.

Miznon   £58   3 2 3

8-12 Broadwick Street, W1   no tel   4–1C

14 Elgin Cr, W11   no tel   7–1B NEW

"Get a pitta the action!" say fans of these "fast, fun, loud and daft" outlets in Soho and now also Notting Hill – part of Eyal Shani's international chain, based out of Tel Aviv. Flatbreads filled with falafel, burgers, English breakfast – you name it – exemplify the "playful" Middle Eastern menu, which everyone agrees is a "great concept" ("different and certainly worth experiencing for its unique take on pitta fillings"). But dishes that are "well-priced, fresh and tasty" in most accounts can – to a few critics – seem "bland and sloppily served". Top Menu Tip – "outstanding roasted cauliflower".

Los Mochis £56 3|3|3
2 Farmer St, W8   020 7727 7528   7–2B
100 Liverpool Street, EC2   Awaiting tel   10–2D NEW

"Fun and interesting" (if sometimes "very noisy and exhausting"), is the verdict on this "buzzy" Notting Hill Gate hang out, complete with bold Mexican-inspired wall hangings (and soon to acquire a rooftop offshoot at 100 Liverpool Street in the City, scheduled to open in autumn 2023). "The menu is less fusion, more Mexican with a nod to Japan": "flavour-packed mouthfuls" dubbed 'Baja-Nihon cuisine' by founder Markus Thesleff.

Mon Plaisir Restaurant WC2 £71 2|3|4
19-21 Monmouth Street   020 7836 7243   5–2B

"The charming warren of rooms helps make for a happy experience" at this "nostalgic", and "immensely charming" Gallic super-bistro, near Covent Garden, which opened just after WWII and which has rambled over the years into neighbouring buildings. "For many decades the menu has hardly changed and continues to reflect Parisian bistros with confit de canard, steak grillé and a fine chariot de fromages... warming in winter and equally welcoming the rest of the year". New owners, Fabio Lauro and Family took over in 2022 from Alain Lhermitte (who owned it since 1972) "leaving some people worried this place has gone off". But "the food was not what it was" before Alain retired, and ratings improved here somewhat this year – hopefully the start of a positive new chapter for this old veteran.
/ WC2H 9DD; www.monplaisir.co.uk; monplaisiragram; Mon-Sat 9.30 pm.

Monmouth Coffee Company £7 3|4|3
27 Monmouth St, WC2   020 7232 3010   5–2B
Spa Terminus, Unit 4 Discovery Estate, SE16   020 7232 3010   12–2A
2 Park St, SE1   020 7232 3010   10–4C

"Decent croissants and the best brews", delivered by "unfailingly lovely service, however long the queues", still win legions of fans for London's original cool coffee shop group, even if it has real competition these days from more Antipodean-style challengers. "They've been my top choice for over 35 years, but I can no longer cope with the uncomfortable seating at the OG Covent Garden outlet, so SE1 it is", which is "perfect to combine with a Borough Market visit". There's also a third branch at Bermondsey's Spa Terminus. / www.monmouthcoffee.co.uk; monmouthcoffee.

Monmouth Kitchen WC2 £69 3|4|3
20 Mercer St   020 7845 8607   5–2B

"A good find for a pre-theatre meal" – this "efficient and friendly" Covent Garden dining room is quite stylish for somewhere inside a modern chain hotel, and serves an offbeat mix of Peruvian and Italian dishes: "a great selection", with "lots of small-plate choices and interesting combinations" – "just enough to choose easily and all delicious". / WC2H 9HD;
monmouthkitchen.co.uk; monmouthkitchen; Mon & Tue 11.30 pm, Wed-Fri 10 pm, Sat 10.30 pm, Sun 7 pm.

Morito £59 4|3|2
195 Hackney Road, E2   020 7613 0754   14–2A
32 Exmouth Mkt, EC1   020 7278 7007   10–1A

The "lovely Moorish/Spanish sharing food" at the little sister of Sam & Sam Clark's Moro next door in Exmouth Market – and also its spin-off in Hackney Road – makes them "a go-to place when you don't know where to go": "an all-round crowd-pleaser, good for meat and non-meat- eaters alike". / www.morito.co.uk; moritotapas.

Moro EC1 £79 **4 4 3**
34-36 Exmouth Mkt 020 7833 8336 10–1A
"Have loved it forever!" – "After all these years Sam and Sam Clark's vanguard player in the 1990s British restaurant revolution still punches well up to its weight" (and scored much more consistently again this year, with one or two diners noting a "marked improvement" after a soggy couple of years). "Still packed, still pushing out creative Spanish/Moorish food, still surprisingly good value, and still in a minimalist space that's fundamentally 1990s"; it's a "heartwarming delight" for its big and ultra-loyal fan club. Other plusses include "excellent Spanish wine list and relaxed-but-efficient service". The "only issue is the noise level, which can make it difficult to hear your companion, even on a small table". / EC1R 4QE; www.moro.co.uk; restaurantmoro; Mon-Sat 10.30 pm, Sun 3 pm.

Morso NW8 £79 **3 2 2**
130 Boundary Road 020 7624 7412 9–3A
A modern Italian on Abbey Road, whose menu is "not the biggest", majoring in pasta and light 'bites'. Feedback this year was a little up-and-down: "always enjoyable" to fans, but, to other regulars "less good and more pricey than it used to be". / NW8 0RH; www.morsolondon.co.uk; morsolondon.

Motcombs SW1 £69 **2 2 4**
26 Motcomb St 020 7235 6382 6–1D
Occupying a prime site with a large pavement terrace in an ever-plusher corner of Belgravia, this old-fashioned stalwart (est 1982) had its heyday in the era of 'The Sloane Ranger Handbook' (published in the same year). Even if some reports consider the experience "overpriced" and say "and service would be easy to improve" – our poll still rates its international assortment of dishes decently (although, there are some less favourable experiences reported elsewhere online). / SW1X 8JU; motcombsbelgravia.com; motcombsofbelgravia; Mon-Sun 1 am.

Mount Street Restaurant, The Audley W1 NEW £116 **3 3 4**
41-43 Mount Street 020 3840 9860 3–3A
"Sitting next to a £1,000,000 painting does add a frisson" at this "gorgeous" autumn 2022 newcomer in the blue-blooded heart of Mayfair. An arm of international art promoters, Hauser & Wirth, it sits on the first floor of the newly refurbished Audley Pub and counted King Charles & Queen Camilla amongst its earlier customers. It's undoubtedly a "fabulous" space (hung with works by Matisse and Freud) that makes a very "interesting new addition to the Mayfair restaurant scene", but the menu is priced for plutocrats, and results are a little mixed. Most reporters do applaud "elegant surroundings with food to match". But there are also a number of doubters, who feel it lacks culinary finesse ("I was pleasantly surprised that it wasn't quite as extortionately priced as we'd anticipated. We shared the famous lobster pie (£96)… to be honest it was a bit disappointing. The remainder of the meal was competent if a bit unexciting"). / W1K 3AH; mountstrestaurant.com; mountstrestaurant; Mon-Sat 10 pm, Sun 4.45 pm.

Mountain W1 NEW
16-18 Beak Street   020 7437 6138   4–2B
Gwynedd meets Catalonia and beyond at Tomos (Brat) Parry's hotly anticipated summer 2023 newcomer: potentially one of Soho's brightest foodie sparks. A "wood grill and wine bar", Tomos channels the native cuisine of his upbringing on Anglesey (with nearby Snowdonia) through the lens of his travels across Spain. Supplied by farmers and fisherman in Wales and Cornwall, whole roast bream will be a feature as will lamb chops, and Anglesey lobster – all emerging, as at Brat, from an open kitchen and with a good deal of counter seating. / W1F 9RD; mountainbeakstreet.com; mountain.restaurant; Mon-Thu 11 pm, Fri & Sat 3 am, Sun 10 pm.

Mr Bao SE15   £36   3 3 3
293 Rye Lane   020 7635 0325   1–4D
This "buzzy Taiwanese café" in Peckham is a "friendly neighbourhood joint" that does a good trade in "reliably tasty bao buns"; and has a "wonderful" brunch menu at weekends ("spicy beans with hash browns; kimchi pancake with onsen egg and smoked salmon and egg bao buns are all 'must-tries"). There's also a Daddy Bao in Tooting and a Master Bao in Westfield Shepherd's Bush. / SE15 4UA; www.mrbao.co.uk; mrbaouk; Sun-Thu 10 pm, Fri 11.30 pm, Sat 11 pm.

Mr Falafel W12   £9   5 4 2
15 Uxbridge Road   07307 635548   8–1C
"The best falafel in town!" is a claim regularly made for this family-run gaff, to be found amongst the mêlée of Shepherd's Bush Market. Motto: 'We Speak Falafel Fluently' – you can order the dish in the style of Syria, Iran, Lebanon or the owners' native Palestine. / W12 8LH; www.mrfalafel.co.uk; mr_falafel_london; Mon-Thu, Sat 6 pm.

Mr Ji NW1   £39   3 3 3
63-65 Parkway   07857 592575   9–3B
With the closure of its Soho branch, this "creative and fun modern Chinese restaurant recently opened in Camden Town", in November 2022, complete with funky, hard-edged decor and serving an East-meets-West style of Asian cuisine, washed down with cocktails. "Not all the dishes are entirely successful but some are delicious. Service is sweet natured, helpful and knowledgeable". / NW1 7PP; mrji.co.uk; mrjirestaurant; Tue-Sat 10 pm, Sun 5 pm.

Mriya SW5   £64   3 3 3
275 Old Brompton Road   020 3089 4640   6–3A
Slava Ukraini! "Behind a scruffy streetscape" on the edge of Earls Court (near the Troubadour), this "enjoyable, if cramped and noisy" yearling was created by Ukrainian refugees, led by chef Yurii Kovryzhenko and his partner, Olga Tsybytovska. "It's a great project – a good cause, with charming service and distinctive cooking": "a modern and rather lighter interpretation of East European cuisine (e.g. courgette flowers used instead of cabbage leaves for golubtsi: the Ukrainian take on the Polish golabki)". "Well worth a visit and supporting the Ukrainian refugees who work there". Top Menu Tip – "deep-flavoured bortsch". / SW5 9JA; mriya_neo_bistro; Tue, Wed, Sun 11 pm, Fri 1 am, Sat midnight.

mu E8
432-434 Kingsland Road   020 7209 4187   14–1A
On a site that was Rotorino (RIP), this two-year-old music venue (named for a jazz album) is from the brothers behind Hackney's 'Brilliant Corners'. It has yet to generate much in the way of survey feedback, but London needs more jazz diners; and its Japanese-inspired robata cuisine received a big shout out from the Guardian's Grace Dent in November 2022, who found it be "far grander and ornately executed than it needs to be". / E8 4AA; mu-ldn.com; mu.ldn; Tue-Thu 11.30 pm, Fri & Sat 12.30 am, Sun 11 pm.

Murano W1 £129 **4 4 3**
20-22 Queen St   020 7495 1127   3–3B
"One of the best value top-end restaurants in London" – Angela Hartnett's London flagship (celebrating its fifteenth anniversary) scored consistently highly in this year's annual diners' poll and is the rare kind of fancy Mayfair destination where folks like spending their own money rather than needing corporate plastic. The Italian-inspired cuisine is "very accomplished", with "flavours seemingly so simply presented, you know the effort that must have gone into each elegant dish". Staff are "helpful but unobtrusive" and contribute to an overall experience that "never fails to hit the spot". In August 2023, the establishment announced a total refurb (complete with glass chandelier from Venice), and the appointment of George Ormond as Head Chef, who takes over from Emily Brightman. / W1J 5PP; www.muranolondon.com; muranolondon; Mon-Sat 10 pm.

Muse SW1 £215 **5 4 4**
38 Groom Place   020 3301 2903   6–1D
"Tom Aikens is back to his brilliant best!" at his "chic little Belgravia mews house", where he's created "an outstanding small restaurant with open kitchen". Set on two floors, "tables are a bit close", but the "intimate" style is a selling point for most diners (especially at the chef's counter), as is the fact that there's "plenty of interaction with the chefs including patron Tom", all of whom "serve and explain with a remarkable personal touch". The menu – "exquisite food, delivered with passion and skill" – draws on Tom's upbringing – "love the story-telling… a truly special experience". / SW1X 7BA; www.musebytomaikens.co.uk; musebytomaikens; Tue-Sat 11 pm.

Myrtle SW10 £84 **5 4 3**
1a Langton Street   020 7352 2411   6–3B
Dublin-born Anna Haugh "has created a fabulous local restaurant which is nowadays a destination" at her "warm and welcoming" Chelsea Townhouse. Her "imaginative" tasting menu provides "fine, Irish-influenced modern European cuisine": "brilliantly executed food which doesn't take itself too seriously whilst being superb" and "worth every penny in this challenging economic environment". Michelin continues to show they have no brain by failing to even list the place, never mind giving it the star it deserves! / SW10 0JL; www.myrtlerestaurant.com; myrtlerestaurant; Tue-Sat 10 pm.

Nakanojo W1
13-14 Thayer Street   020 7993 4321   3–1A
This high-street Nikkei hangout's first Chelsea branch opened in 2021 and shut in mid 2023 in favour of a new Marylebone location. No feedback as yet on either site, which purveys a trendy fusion of sushi, tacos, ceviche and robata bites, and of course pisco sours, sakes and cocktails aplenty. / W1U 3JR; www.nakanojo.com; nakanojouk; Sun-Thu 10 pm, Fri & Sat 11 pm.

Nammos SW7 NEW
13-17 Montpelier Street   no tel   6–1C
Mykonos, it is promised, will come to Knightsridge in autumn 2023, with the opening of this self-consciously glam newcomer – a spin-off from the celeb-filled Greek island original, which is jetting into the Harrods hinterland via Cannes and Dubai to create 'a new dining concept with a relaxed neighbourhood atmosphere'. It's on a site that was for decades Montpeliano, and – with its reservations-only (no walk-ins) policy – seems to be aiming to capture the same supercar-driving set as its predecessor did in its heyday. If the advance visuals are any guide, the bright interior will be rather gorgeous, in which to enjoy a sharing plates menu of Med-inspired surf 'n' turf. / SW7 1HF; www.nammosneighbourhood.com.

Nandine SE5 £36 3 3 3
45 Camberwell Church Street   020 7703 3221   1–3C

The name means 'kitchen' in Kurdish – Pary Baban's Camberwell café reproduces the dishes of her homeland, to the satisfaction of reporters. Top Tips – brunch is a highlight; you can BYO at her simpler nearby outlet at 82 Vestry Street (but the branch at Peckham Levels is no more). / SE5 8TR; nandineuk; Mon-Sun 11 pm.

Naughty Piglets SW2 £55 5 4 4
28 Brixton Water Ln   020 7274 7796   11–2D

"As brilliant as ever" – Joe Sharratt and Margaux Aubry's "unassuming space" in Brixton is "everything you'd want from a local and more" – making it stand out on the South London gastronomic scene. The "laid-back vibe belies a serious approach to food and wine", resulting in French-inspired "plates of pure pleasure" – "so much better than the fancy fly-by-night trendy places that are all queues, instagram and foam". Top Menu Tip – "they serve the BEST butter you will ever taste". / SW2 1PE; www.naughtypiglets.co.uk; naughtypiglets; Tue-Thu 9.15 pm, Fri & Sat 11 pm.

Nautilus NW6 £38 4 4 2
27-29 Fortune Green Rd   020 7435 2532   1–1B

This "classic family-run chippy" in West Hampstead has served "top-notch fish 'n' chips or any grilled fish alternative at a more than fair price" for longer than anyone can remember. "George the owner is lovely" and "the staff welcome you like you're family – once you've been a couple of times they'll know your order off by heart". "The dining room, though, is very basic and has the atmosphere of a station waiting room, with its fluorescent lighting". Top Menu Tip – "the matzo meal batter is really light". / NW6 1DU; nautilusfishandchip; Mon-Sat 10 pm, Sun 9 pm.

Nessa W1 £70 3 3 4
1 Warwick Street   020 7337 7404   4–3B

"A beautiful setting in a new members' club" adds lustre to this autumn 2022 newcomer in Soho: a stylish co-working space complex that's a sibling to fashionable Mortimer House, and with ex-Duck & Waffle chef, Tom Cenci at the stoves. On its bistro menu "some quite traditional dishes are given modern makeovers" which err on the hearty side (Chicken Cordon Bleu, 'Nessabocker Glory') and fans say results, especially at brunch, are "fantastic". Ratings are limited, though, by the odd reporter who feels the cooking's little more than "food assemblage at top prices". (Many newspaper critics have rushed along, and the consensus is also somewhat mixed – Giles Coren of The Times – a member of Mortimer House – thought some of the cooking "epochal", while the Telegraph's William Sitwell found the whole enterprise a "public-facing cash cow" with a "total charisma bypass"). / W1B 5LR; www.nessasoho.com; nessasoho; Mon-Wed midnight, Thu-Sat 1 am, Sun 6 pm.

NEST EC1 £105 4 3 3
374-378 Old Street   020 8986 0065   13–1B

"One of the best neighbourhood restaurants in London", this "bold" and "inspirational" outfit "creates dishes out of a tiny kitchen that puts a lot of better-known places to shame – the menu, centred around using as much of one main ingredient as possible and changing every few weeks, is always creative and thought-provoking". BREAKING NEWS: we've maintained ratings from the original Hackney site, but in September 2023 they closed the "uncomfortable" digs of five years' standing, so gaining more space in a new double-fronted Victorian location by Shoreditch Town Hall. / EC1V 9LT; www.nestfood.co.uk; nest_food; Mon-Sat 11 pm.

Newens: The Original Maids of Honour TW9 £43   3 4 3
288 Kew Road   020 8940 2752   1–3A
"Like taking tea in olden days" – this mock-Tudor tea room opposite Kew Gardens was built in the 1940s and is splendidly unmodernised. The Newens have been baking here since the Victorian era while their signature Maids of Honour tarts are said to have originated under the Tudors. Yes, it's "touristy – but very atmospheric, and the afternoon teas are good". / TW9 3DU; theoriginalmaidsofhonour.co.uk; theoriginalmaidsofhonour; Mon-Sun 6 pm.

1905 W1 NEW   £69   3 4 5
40 Mortimer Street   020 7436 8090   3–1C
This "interesting new Cretan" (named after Crete's 1905 revolution) in Fitzrovia claims to be the first Cretan restaurant anywhere outside Greece, and presents the island's distinctive version of eastern Mediterranean cuisine, along with natural wines from some of the world's oldest wine-producing regions. / W1W 7RQ; www.1905.london; 1905.london; Sun-Thu 11 pm, Fri & Sat 11.45 pm.

The Ninth London W1   £116   5 3 3
22 Charlotte Street   020 3019 0880   2–1C
"Exceptional food and an approach that's attentive and friendly but never overbearing or distant" wins nothing but high praise for Jun Tanaka's "consistently excellent and very enjoyable" HQ, on Fitzrovia's restaurant row. "It was closed from summer last year until mid March 2023 owing to a fire – post re-opening, the cuisine is of just the same standard as before". / W1T 2NB; www.theninthlondon.com; theninthlondon; Mon-Wed 9 pm, Thu-Sat 9.30 pm.

No. Fifty Cheyne SW3   £116   3 3 5
50 Cheyne Walk   020 7376 8787   6–3C
"An excellent venue for an intimate date…" – this beautiful and comfortable grill, just off Chelsea Embankment (with river views from its top-floor bar) is full of atmosphere. It's owned by Sally Green – who also owns Ronnie Scott's – who is celebrating her 10th year as proprietor in 2024. The menu focus is on grilled protein and Sunday roast is also a feature: results are very good, but some would still say it's "overpriced". / SW3 5LR; www.fiftycheyne.com; 50cheyne; Wed-Sat midnight, Sun 6 pm.

Noble Rot WC1   £78   3 4 5
51 Lamb's Conduit Street   020 7242 8963   2–1D
A "magnificent" operation – Mark Andrew and Dan Keeling's first venture has become one of the most popular destinations in London, hitting our Top 10 most-mentioned entries for the first time this year. Opened in 2015 – and named for the wine and food magazine they started in 2013 – it inhabits the "characterful" Bloomsbury premises that were for decades 'Vats', and its "dark, cosy spaces" are perfect for working through the "terrific wine list" they have assembled: very arguably "the best by-the-glass list in town", with many "rarities preserved by the Coravin system". The cooking is overseen by afar by executive chef, Stephen Harris of Seasalter fame: "slip soles in butter are almost as good as at The Sportsman, but the other dishes are a bit more standard" – the "food can be unexpectedly accomplished, but it's really all about the wine list which caters to all tastes and budgets". Service is "superb, passionate and friendly" ("but can be patchy during busy periods"). Fans say, of the three branches it's "the original and the best", but – though slightly less commented-on – its more recent spin-offs now actually outscore the mothership. / WC1N 3NB; www.noblerot.co.uk; noblerotbar; Mon-Sat 9.30 pm.

Noble Rot Mayfair W1 [NEW] £61 [4][5][4]

5 Trebeck Street 020 7101 6770 3–4B

"What a fabulous new bar and restaurant where Boudin Blanc (RIP) was" – this latest, April 2023 member of the well-known, wine-led group has been instantly hailed as a "wonderful addition" to picturesque Shepherd Market. "Thoroughly grown-up in style, it feels a bit more professional and slick than the lovely Holborn original". In particular, the superior bistro cooking is "more interesting than in WC1": "no culinary fireworks or cheffy tricks" but "worth it even for non-wine drinkers" and "reasonably priced considering the neighbourhood". As you might hope, there's an "exceptional" list of vintages "across a wide range of price points" with "random treasures at reasonable prices", delivered by "charming and engaged staff" who "can actually have a conversation about a given bottle". "Can't recommend it more highly!" / W1J 7LT; noblerot.co.uk; noblerotmayfair.

Noble Rot Soho W1 £64 [4][5][4]

2 Greek Street 020 7183 8190 5–2A

"Replacement for the beloved Gay Hussar" – Dan Keeling and Mark Andrew's 2021 resurrection of this famous Soho site has pulled off the amazingly difficult task of being almost as popular as their Bloomsbury original. "Everything about this establishment is wonderful, but the wine list elevates it to the exceptional" – "the care that goes into it is astonishing" ("I could happily spend the rest of my life working through it!"). The hearty food is "always enjoyable" too and "expertly served" by particularly "knowledgeable" and "friendly staff" in "the delightful atmosphere of this gorgeous old restaurant, which has been brought back to life by the Noble Rot team". Top Top – "amazing value set lunch". / W1D 4NB; noblerot.co.uk; noblerotsoho; Mon-Sat 9.30 pm.

Nobu,
Metropolitan Hotel W1 £134 [4][3][2]

19 Old Park Lane 020 7447 4747 3–4A

"Still the best Nobu for food in my opinion" – many "superb" meals are still reported at Nobu Matsuhisa's first London outpost: the first floor of a boutique hotel on Park Lane (famous, in part, for Boris Becker once having fathered a child here in between courses in a cupboard off the main dining room). "The original black cod is definitely better than the many rip offs that abound" and its mix of sushi, tacos, steak, raw seafood and other luxurious Nikkei bites inspires uniformly high ratings. "The uninviting room undeniably needs a make-over"... but people have been saying that almost since it first opened. / W1K 1LB; www.noburestaurants.com; nobuoldparklane; Sun-Wed 10 pm, Thu-Sat 10.30 pm.

Nobu Portman Square W1 £114 [4][3][3]

22 Portman Square 020 3988 5888 2–1A

Nobu Matsuhisa's Marylebone three-year-old is higher-rated but less well-known than the original Nobu in Park Lane. Decor-wise, it's more modern in style. Food-wise, it purveys the same, wizard Japanese-fusion cuisine for which the brand is internationally famous: most notably mesmerising sushi plus sensational signature dishes such as Black Cod. Practically all reports acknowledge the essential trade-off here: "it really cannot be beaten for deliciousness... but boy do you pay for it!" / W1H 7BG; london-portman.nobuhotels.com; nobulondonportman; Sun-Thu 10 pm, Fri & Sat 10.30 pm.

Nobu Shoreditch EC2   £127
10-50 Willow St   020 3818 3790   13–1B
Despite its famous brand, this chic Shoreditch-fringe boutique hotel has struggled to make waves since its 2017 launch (no survey feedback this year), and in summer 2023 relaunched (re-relaunched?) its basement restaurant with adjoining sunken garden as a 'destination bar', complete with 'world-renowned Nobu signature dishes, small plates and sushi' and a regular DJ. As well as the wizard Nikkei bits, options include the 'newly launched Monaka… a lightweight flat rice crispbread, branded with the Nobu logo and stuffed with fresh toppings'. / EC2A 4BH;
london-shoreditch.nobuhotels.com; nobulondonshoreditch; Mon-Wed 10 pm, Thu-Sat 10.30 pm, Sun 11 am.

Noci   £45   3 2 3
4-6 Islington Green, N1   020 3937 5343   9–3D
Circus Road West, SW11   020 3540 8252   11–1C NEW
The Bower, 211 Old Street, EC1   020 3780 0750   13–1A NEW
"The best vitello tonnato ever tasted" was one fan's recommendation at Louis Korovilas's Islington yearling, which serves a range of affordable pasta alongside Italian street-food dishes. Another supporter "raved about Noci last year, but found a recent lunch a little disappointing with cooking lacking the earlier refinement"; but even they still thought "this is a cut above the usual Italian fare and still something of a find". In any case, Korovilas must be doing something right, as in May 2023 (too late for our survey) he launched a new offshoot in Battersea Power Station; to be followed swiftly in August 2023 by one in Shoreditch.

Noizé W1   £105   4 5 3
39 Whitfield St   020 7323 1310   2–1C
"Hidden in a quiet street in Fitzrovia", Mathieu Germond "continues to oversee a brilliant operation", on the site that was once Dabbous, RIP. An "imaginative French-orientated menu" is well-realised ("but not exceptional or pointlessly innovative") and service is "truly exemplary". "But the real bonus is the interesting wine list expertly put together and presented by Mathieu himself", who is "not only completely charming but also hugely knowledgeable" and "it always includes something new and unusual to try". / W1T 2SF; www.noize-restaurant.co.uk; noize_restaurant; Wed-Fri, Tue, Sat 10 pm.

NoMad London WC2   £124   2 2 5
4 Bow Street   020 3906 1600   5–2D
The 2021 opening of a London branch of New York's hip NoMad hotel brought a "wonderful transformation" of Covent Garden's Bow Street Magistrates' Court "into a bright, airy venue with lots of choice" for eating and drinking. Its "fab main dining room", 'The Atrium', is a three-storey-high glass-ceilinged space with an extra-glam atmosphere, although "sometimes the food doesn't match the setting", being merely "OK, but no more than that". The appointment of Lancashire-born chef Michael Yates, formerly of Northcote and Holland's famous Oud Sluis, may lift its game. / WC2E 7AH; www.thenomadhotel.com; thenomadhotel; Mon-Sat 10.30 pm, Sun 5 pm.

Noodle & Snack W1   £33   4 4 2
145 Cleveland Street   020 3161 0735   2–1B
"Please whatever you do, don't dress up to dine here!" – "This is a tiny, cheap hole-in-the-wall" near Great Portland Street tube, serving "comfort noodles for Chinese students and others": "magical broth that feels utterly authentic and packed with flavour (we absolutely wolfed ours down!)". "Everyone gets a warm welcome" too! (The Times's Giles Coren is also a fan – "it drew tears of nostalgia for a 1970s Shenyang childhood that I never had"). / W1T 6QH; Mon-Sun 9 pm.

Noor Jahan £52 3 4 3
2a Bina Gardens, SW5   020 7373 6522   6–2B
26 Sussex Place, W2   020 7402 2332   7–1D
This family-run "stalwart" of the Earl's Court-South Ken dining scene (and its 'Noor Jahan II' Bayswater offshoot) has built a strong following for its "consistently good" Indian dishes over the past 60 years – and the smattering of celebs and royals among its guests (Angelina Jolie, Prince William…) has not gone to its head: "after all this time it remains your typical curry house". / www.noorjahansw5.co.uk.

Nopi W1 £97 3 2 2
21-22 Warwick St   020 7494 9584   4–3B
The Soho flagship of Israeli writer/chef Yotam Ottolenghi is conceived as a step up from his deli-diners, and the food is generally considered "wonderful". But a note of disappointment has crept in with complaints along the lines of "bad service" or "overpriced vegetables and wine" – "I really don't know what all the fuss is about". / W1B 5NE; ottolenghi.co.uk; nopi_restaurant; Mon-Sat 10.30 pm.

The Norfolk Arms WC1 £53 3 3 2
28 Leigh St   020 7388 3937   9–4C
"Looking like a typical London pub, but serving a good range of tapas" makes this Victorian boozer in the backstreets between King's Cross and Russell Square a little out of the ordinary. But "while some dishes are very good, others can be a bit hit and miss". / WC1H 9EP; www.norfolkarms.co.uk; Tue-Sat, Mon 11 pm, Sun 10.30 pm.

Norma W1 £89 4 3 4
8 Charlotte Street   0203 995 6224   2–1C
"Feeling like a serious step up from your run-of-the-mill Italian, but not breaking the bank" – this unusual and stylish venture is a spin-off from the Stafford Hotel. There's a Sicilian focus to the menu and the food is "absolutely delicious". "Booths make it a great spot for a business lunch – intimate enough to be quiet in a bustling restaurant", with very attentive service. Top Menu Tip – "dangerously delectable focaccia". / W1T 2LS; www.normalondon.com; norma_ldn; Mon-Sat 10.30 pm.

Normah's W2 £29 3 3 2
23-25 Queensway Market   07771 630828   7–2C
"If you love Malaysian food, head for Normah's" – "a small and basic café serving street food at incredibly low prices". It's "a little difficult to find in a nondescript Bayswater market, but so worth the effort" as your host, Normah Abd Hamid, "is likely to both greet you and cook your meal" – taking "great care to produce delicious food". / W2 4QP; www.normahs.co.uk; normahs_place; Tue-Sat 9 pm.

Normans Cafe N19 £27 4 4 4
167 Junction Road   no tel   9–1C
"Proper caff food done right" in Tufnell Park by two highly skilled chefs "will whizz you back in time to your school days or nursery – except I don't remember it ever tasting this good!". Elliot Kaye and Richard Hayes quit their jobs at Leroy and Lyle's four years ago to "make the best fry-up in London" at this "utterly brilliant" re-creation of the traditional greasy spoon. Top Tip – "arrive early as there is no booking system, so the queue is often around the corner for this tiny cafe". / N19 5PZ; www.normanscafe.co.uk; normanscafelondon; Wed-Sun 3 pm.

El Norte W1 £108 3 3 3
19-20 Dover Street   020 3154 8182   3–3C
Madrid-born Arian and Alberto Zandi added this new Mayfair venture to their portfolio (alongside Zuaya and Como Garden) in November 2021. On the plus side, results from the Spanish menu can be excellent. On the downside, the bill here can mount and feedback is sufficiently up-and-down to preclude a fully wholehearted endorsement. / W1S 4LP; el-norte.co.uk; elnortelondon; Sun-Thu 12.30 am, Fri & Sat 1.30 am.

North China W3 £43 3 3 3
305 Uxbridge Rd   020 8992 9183   8–1A
"The venerable kingpin of Chinese food in this part of west London is not giving up its crown easily" – opened by the Lou family in the outer reaches of Acton in 1976, it has served "exceptionally tasty Peking-style cuisine" with "considerate service and warm atmosphere" for almost 50 years. / W3 9QU; www.northchina.co.uk; northchinafood; Tue-Sun 10.30 pm.

North Sea Fish WC1 £52 3 2 2
7-8 Leigh St   020 7387 5892   9–4C
"A hidden gem in the back streets of Bloomsbury" – this traditional chippie has been owned and run by the Beauchamp family for the best part of 50 years, and excels for its "exceptionally good grilled fish" and "super-generous portions" of "normal fish 'n' chips". / WC1H 9EW; www.northseafishrestaurant.co.uk; thenorthseafish; Mon-Sat 9.30 pm.

The Northall,
Corinthia London WC2 £143 3 3 3
10a Northumberland Ave   020 7321 3100   2–3C
"Incredible flower displays" add to the airy and gracious style of this comfortable dining room, within the plush five star near Embankment station. Partly because of the fame of Kerridge's next door, it has struggled over the years to raise its profile, but can be a handy option for a stately, high-quality West End setting. Top Top – in particular, "the set lunch is excellent value". / WC2N 5AE; www.corinthia.com; corinthialondon; Tue-Sat 9.30 pm, Sun 4 pm, Mon 10.30 am.

Notto W1 NEW £62 4 3 3
198-200 Piccadilly   020 3034 2190   3–3D
"It seems unlikely to find such good food at such a touristy location", but "the lovely homemade pasta" at Phil Howard and Louis Korovilas's bright and efficient new pasta spot is "a revelation" – "very tasty Italian small plates at astonishingly reasonable prices for Piccadilly", from a "focused menu of pastas and dessert". (It was originally to be known as Otto – after Howard's lockdown pasta business – but lost a legal battle with 'an unnamed existing venture with a similar name'). / W1J 9EZ; www.nottopastabar.com; nottopastabar; Tue-Sat 10 pm, Sun 8 pm.

Novikov (Asian restaurant) W1 £140 2 2 4
50a Berkeley Street   020 7399 4330   3–3C
Thin feedback this year on this glossy Eurotrash playground in Mayfair – London outpost of Arkady Novikov's large restaurant empire (fun fact – according to Forbes in Nov 2022, this includes what used to be the Krispy Kreme Russian franchise, rebranded post-sanctions as 'Krunchy Dream'). Its sushi, seared seafood and other luxe Pan-Asian bites remain well-rated, if at prices designed for oligarchs. (There's also an imposing, ambitious dining room with an Italian menu to the rear that no-one mentions much). / W1J 8HA; www.novikovrestaurant.co.uk; novikovrestaurant; Mon-Sun midnight.

Numa NW7 £42 3 4 2
8 The Broadway 020 8912 1678 1–1A
*This "Middle Eastern small plates sharing concept" is a "fantastic addition
to Mill Hill Broadway", with "loads of veggie options" and "really tasty food"
from brunch through to dinner. Founder Tomer Vanuna and head chef
Michael Levi were school friends in Israel; Numa apparently means 'so what'
in Hebrew. / NW7 3LL; www.numacafe.co.uk; numacafe; Tue-Sat 11 pm, Sun 10 pm.*

Numero Uno SW11 £69 2 4 2
139 Northcote Road 020 7978 5837 11–2C
*"Engaging service" is the strong suit at this "solid neighbourhood Italian"
that has been a fixture on Clapham's Northcote Road for many years. The
menu offers "no surprises", but the cooking is "more than adequate".
/ SW11 6PX; www.numerounorestaurant.co.uk; numerounoclapham; Mon-Sun 11 pm.*

Nuovi Sapori SW6 £57 3 3 3
295 New King's Rd 020 7736 3363 11–1B
*Small and family-owned, this "always reliable quality Italian" near Parsons
Green wins consistently high ratings for its "friendly service" and "cheerful
ambience". / SW6 4RE; www.nuovisaporilondon.co.uk; Mon-Sat 11 pm.*

Nusr-Et Steakhouse,
The Park Tower Knightsbridge SW1 £194 1 1 1
101 Knightsbridge 01821 687738 6–1D
*With the closure of Nusret Gökçe's NYC branch, the vultures have started to
gather around this Knightsbridge venture ('Is Salt Bae's empire beginning to
crumble?' – Daily Mail, June 2023). The outlook is not super-positive. Our
review last year suggested it was "suitable only for chavs and vulgarians"
and our volume of reports this year was significantly reduced; while in
summer 2023, the venue was close to being London's lowest-ranking
restaurant on TripAdvisor (quite an achievement!). In a sign that suggests
management also think change is needed, in July 2023 they cut prices with
the introduction of a set lunch menu from £39 per person and burger and
fries for 'just' £45. / SW1X 7RN; www.nusr-et.com.tr; nusr_et_steakhouse__;
Mon-Sat 1.30 am, Sun 1 am.*

O'ver £68 3 3 2
1 Norris Street, St James's Market, SW1 020 7930 9664 4–4D
44-46 Southwark Street, SE1 020 7378 9933 10–4B
*"Bouncy, chewy, doughy deliciousness – the crust is to die for" at this pizzeria
that uses seawater to make its dough. "The lovely little restaurant in Borough
doesn't look anything special during the day, but in the evening it's very
romantic with candles and soft lighting". Some reckon "the food in St James's
is nothing like as good as the original in Borough". / www.overuk.com; over_uk.*

Oak £68 3 3 3
243 Goldhawk Rd, W12 020 8741 7700 8–1B
137 Westbourne Park Rd, W2 020 7221 3355 7–1B
*"Great Roman-style crispy pizzas" along with a full selection of tapas,
starters, "ever-changing Italian main courses" and a "fun Notting Hill vibe"
ensure that this smart pub conversion is "a definite step up from the pizza
chains" while "still reasonable value". Two offshoots further west – the Oak
W12 near Ravenscourt Park and the Bird in Hand at Brook Green – repeat
the trick. / www.theoaklondon.com; theoaklondon.*

Oak & Poppy NW3 NEW £67 3 4 3
48 Rosslyn Hill   020 3479 4888   9–1A
"A useful, casual-dining addition to the area" – this old Hampstead village pub (formerly the Rosslyn Arms) was brought back to life in Autumn 2022, with a "stylish fit out" featuring a retractable glass ceiling. Fans say it's now the "perfect neighbourhood café/restaurant", with "the loveliest staff and reliably good food". / NW3 1NH; www.oakandpoppy.co.uk; oakandpoppyhampstead; Mon-Sat 11 pm, Sun 10.30 pm.

Obicà Mozzarella Bar,
Pizza e Cucina £61 3 3 2
19-20 Poland St, W1   020 3327 7070   4–1C
1 West Wintergarden, 35 Bank St, E14   020 7719 1532   12–1C
Unit 4 5-7 Limeburners Lane,, EC4   020 3327 0984   10–2A
These "upscalish Italians" – part of an international chain – serve pizza, pasta and other lighter dishes, featuring the trademark ingredient. It can be that the "quality of the food is a pleasant surprise"; they inspired nothing but positive feedback this year. / obica.com; obicamozzarellabar; E14 & EC4 Closed Sun.

Oblix,
The Shard SE1 £116 3 3 4
31 St Thomas St   020 7268 6700   10–4C
"You book for the view, which is obviously incredible" at this 32nd-floor venue, run by Rainer Becker (of Zuma and many other top London restaurants). Like most places with a stunning outlook and "special occasion" suitability, it often takes flak for its sky-high pricing to match. This was absent in (admittedly thin) feedback this year, though, and the luxurious outputs from its open kitchen (with Josper oven, charcoal grill and rotisserie) were well-rated. (For cocktails or afternoon tea, head to Oblix East). / SE1 9RY; www.oblixrestaurant.com; oblixrestaurant; Mon-Sun 10.30 pm.

Ochre,
The National Gallery WC2 NEW £56 3 2 4
Trafalgar Square   020 7747 2525   2–2C
It's "nice to find a good restaurant in a museum", and the National Gallery's latest, year-old incumbent within its atmospheric ground floor dining room has provided a step-up just in time to compete with the revamped culinary offerings at the NPG next door. The snazzily updated interior by architects Red Deer makes a great setting for a "beautiful afternoon tea", and there's an opulent bar for stronger drinks. / WC2N 5DN; www.nationalgallery.org.uk; nationalgallery; Sun-Wed 6 pm, Thu-Sat 11 pm.

Odette's NW1 £83 3 3 2
130 Regents Park Road   020 7586 8569   9–3B
Chef-patron Bryn Williams produces a "small and well-executed menu" showcasing north Wales at this high-quality local in lovely Primrose Hill, which he's owned for over 15 years now. But while it still attracts many favourable reviews, the magical atmosphere that was a hallmark of its original incarnation (it was founded nearly 50 years ago) has "faded" in more recent times. / NW1 8XL; www.odettesprimrosehill.com; odettesrestaurant; Thu-Sat, Wed 9 pm, Sun 8.30 pm.

Ognisko Restaurant SW7 £63 **3 4 5**

55 Prince's Gate, Exhibition Road   020 7589 0101   6–1C

This "opulent, high-ceilinged dining room" within a Polish émigré club in South Kensington ("a stone's throw from the Royal Albert Hall") provides a "truly elegant" backdrop for a meal. "Inviting and cosmopolitan in atmosphere", it is "unusually, equally good in summer and winter" thanks to its "delightful" covered rear outside terrace, which provides "a memorable location on a warm day". "Delicious" Polish fodder comes in "hearty" portions and "without any grand prices despite the grand setting"; there's a wide range of affordable central and eastern European wines; and "the cocktails and vodkas are well worth a shout out". / SW7 2PG; www.ogniskorestaurant.co.uk; ogniskorestaurant; Mon-Sat 9.45 pm, Sun 8.45 pm.

Oka £57 **3 4 2**

Kingly Court, 1 Kingly Court, W1   020 7734 3556   4–2B
19 New Cavendish Street, W1   020 7486 4388   3–1A
251 King's Road, SW3   020 7349 8725   6–3C
71 Regents Park Rd, NW1   020 7483 2072   9–3B
88 Church Road, SW13   020 8741 8577   11–1A

"A top tip for sushi and other interesting Japanese dishes" – this 11-year-old group from Israeli-born Ohad Kastro offers an "excellent quality and variety of options" that are "so much better than standard rivals" – and each branch "manages to feel like a comfy 'local', despite there being others around town". / www.okarestaurant.co.uk; okarestaurant.

The Old Bull & Bush NW3 £59 **2 2 4**

North End Rd   020 8905 5456   9–1A

This renovated Victorian tavern makes a "great location" for refuelling "if you've been walking on Hampstead Heath". Its fame rests on Florrie Forde's music-hall song from the Edwardian era, when day-tripping Cockneys would visit, not on its cooking – the latter does have its fans, but there is also the view that it is "standard pub grub and rather indifferent" at that. Top Tip – "if you use the car park, make sure you check-in with the computer screen at the bar or risk a penalty charge". / NW3 7HE; www.thebullandbush.co.uk; oldbullandbush; Mon & Tue, Thu-Sat 11 pm, Wed 10 pm, Sun 10.30 pm.

Oliveto SW1 £78 **3 3 2**

61 Elizabeth St   020 7730 0074   2–4A

Whether you choose pizza, pasta or a main dish, this all-rounder in Sardinian Mauro Sanna's smart Belgravia group "never disappoints". Following a fire, it has moved a few doors to the premises formerly occupied by stablemate Olivocarne (RIP). A major attraction is the "wine list to delight lovers of off-beat, small producer wines". / SW1W 9PP; www.olivorestaurants.com; olivorestaurants; Mon-Sun 10.30 pm.

Olivo SW1 £87 **3 3 2**

21 Eccleston Street   020 7730 2505   2–4B

In its day a pioneer of Italian 'peasant' cuisine in the capital, Mauro Sanna's original Belgravia Sardinian remains "steady and always reliable" in its 35th year – "this restaurant has never disappointed". If it's "quite pricey", that has never been an issue for the well-heeled locals who ensure it is perennially busy. / SW1W 9LX; www.olivorestaurants.com; olivorestaurants; Tue-Sun 10.30 pm.

Olivomare SW1 £89 **4 3 2**

10 Lower Belgrave Street   020 7730 9022   2–4B

"Reliable Sardinian shellfish and pasta" win consistent high marks for this seafood specialist in Mauro Sanno's smart Belgravia group, which has been feeding well-heeled locals for 15 years. The pavement seating in the summer is a better bet than the sleek but stark modern interior. / SW1W 0LJ; www.olivorestaurants.com; olivorestaurants; Mon-Sun 10.30 pm.

Olley's SE24 £39 3 4 2
65-69 Norwood Rd   020 8671 8259   11–2D
"Love coming here", say fans of the *"excellent fish 'n' chips"* served for 36 years by Harry Niazi opposite Brockwell Park – where it's *"great to eat a takeaway"*. It takes its name from Oliver Twist, in which Dickens refers to Londoners' favourite dish. / SE24 9AA; www.olleys.info; olleysfishexperience; Tue-Sun 9.30 pm.

Olympic Studios SW13 £59 2 2 3
117-123 Church Road   020 8912 5170   11–1A
For *"Barnes at brunch"* – or as a *"very useful and convenient place to eat before a film"* – the *"family-friendly"* dining room in the *"nice surroundings"* of Barnes's iconic recording-studio- turned-indie-cinema *"serves its purpose"* (and the outdoor terrace further adds to its appeal as a social hub in decent weather). But the menu is *"disappointingly limited and dull, even if pretty well executed"*. / SW13 9HL; www.olympiccinema.co.uk; olympicstudios; Mon-Thu 10 pm, Fri & Sat 10.30 pm, Sun 9 pm.

Olympus Fish N3 £44 3 4 2
140-144 Ballards Ln   020 8371 8666   1–1B
"Always fresh and good-value fish 'n' chips" – cooked *"over charcoal as an alternative"* and backed up by a selection of Turkish small plates – ensures this 25-year-old family-run operation remains *"an attractive option"* for eating in Finchley. / N3 2PA; www.olympusrestaurant.co.uk; Mon-Sun 9.30 pm.

Ombra E2 £62
1 Vyner St   020 8981 5150   14–2B
A superb location – on the Regent's Canal and complete with heated terrace – helps justify the continued inclusion of this Hackney Italian. Feedback is too thin and nuanced for a full rating this year – according to one fan it's *"still good all round, but the ratio of hype to expectations is high"*. / E2 9DG; www.ombrabar.restaurant; ombrabar.restaurant; Mon, Thu-Sat 10 pm, Sun 3 pm.

108 Brasserie W1 £77 2 3 2
108 Marylebone Lane   020 7969 3900   2–1A
This *"well-run spot"* with outdoor seating attached to a hotel on Marylebone Lane makes a *"very useful venue for lunch when in the vicinity"*, with an offering that *"seems to have something for everyone"*. *"It's nothing exceptional in one sense, but a menu of properly prepared classics is the sort of thing that sounds easy but needs to be done well… and it is"*. / W1U 2QE; www.108brasserie.com; 108marylebonelane; Mon-Sat midnight, Sun 6 pm.

104 Restaurant W2 £129 5 4 4
104 Chepstow Road   020 3417 4744   7–1B
A focused menu of *"high-quality ingredients with excellent provenance and preparation"* together with *"attentive and adaptive service"* continue to win praise for Richard Wilkins's small (seating a maximum of 16) venue, which has an unobtrusive frontage on a corner-site in the Notting Hill/Bayswater borders. It has a comprehensive wine list, running to the likes of clarets and burgundies at over £1,000 per bottle. / W2 5QS; www.104restaurant.com; 104restaurant; Wed-Sun 9.30 pm.

101 Thai Kitchen W6 £42 3 3 2
352 King St   020 8746 6888   8–2B
This *"exciting local gem"* near Stamford Brook serves *"excellent Thai cuisine in a no-nonsense setting"*, attracting aficionados from far and wide who warm to an *"authenticity"* that makes it *"almost an 'in-country' experience"*. The uninitiated may miss the point other than the good prices. Top Tip – *"if they say something is hot, believe them!"* / W6 0RX; www.101thaikitchen.uk; 101thaikitchen; Tue-Sun 10.30 pm.

1 Lombard Street EC3 £94
1 Lombard St   020 7929 6611   10–3C

"For a dependable City business breakfast or lunch venue", Soren Jessen's stalwart brasserie, in the beating heart of the Square Mile, is the epitome of a useful amenity for dealmakers, even if *"the large, cavernous space remains a little tricky"* (*"the room is bright and airy, but depending on your table can feel cramped and noisy"*). *"Its modern European menu covers all the bases reliably. It does what it's meant to, but you are never coming away with a knockout meal. BTW, that's an observation not a criticism"*. / EC3V 9AA; www.1lombardstreet.com; 1lombardstreet; Mon-Fri 11 pm.

123V,
Fenwick W1 £60
63 New Bond Street   020 8132 9088   3–2B

"The vegan sushi is a work of art" at this outlet in the basement of Fenwick's department store in Mayfair from Alexis Gauthier (the French fine-dining-chef-turned-evangelist for plant-based eating). He has raided global cuisines for his concoctions – *"the vegan burgers are gorgeous"* – but it's the Japanese specials which elicit the most feedback, including *"all-you-can-eat sushi"* (in two hours). / W1S 1RQ; 123vegan.co.uk; 123vegan_w1; Mon-Wed 6 pm, Thu-Sat 9.30 pm, Sun 3.30 am.

Only Food and Courses WC2 £72
5 Little Essex Street   07949 259067   2–2D

Robbie Lorraine has upped sticks from Brixton with his Del Boy-inspired pop-up – a witty, multi-course trip back in time to the cuisine of the 80s and 90s (duck-liver paté, prawn cocktail…). This new home is part of a Grade II listed pub just off the Strand: not to be confused with Ye Olde Cheshire Cheese on Fleet Street, which is about ten minutes' stroll away (although both claim Dickens as a former patron). No survey feedback as yet – reports please! / WC2R 3LD; www.onlyfoodandcourses.com; onlyfoodandcourses; Thu-Sat 10.30 pm.

Les 110 de Taillevent W1 £90
16 Cavendish Square   020 3141 6016   3–1B

"If you love wine… heaven!" – a *"huge list (almost 2,000 bins)"*, *"some with no mark-up from merchant prices"* and including 110 available by the glass (hence the name), is the big attraction at this plush Cavendish Square venue from a famous Parisian operation. It *"finally seems to have found its footing as a real restaurant, not just somewhere that serves food as an afterthought to the wine list – there's some very good cooking here"*. / W1G 9DD; www.les-110-taillevent-london.com; 110london; Mon-Sat 10.30 pm.

Opera Tavern WC2 £60
23 Catherine Street   020 7836 3680   5–3D

"Handily located near the Royal Opera House", this converted pub serves Spanish and Italian-style small plates of *"food that's just a bit better than its local competition"* in the heart of Covent Garden. It is *"not the best of the Salt Yard chain, but good for a quick pre-show meal"*. / WC2B 5JS; www.saltyardgroup.co.uk; operatavernldn; Mon-Sat 11 pm, Sun 8 pm.

Opso W1 £101
10 Paddington St   020 7487 5088   2–1A

"Posh Greek food" – *"very nice sharing plates"* from a *"well-designed menu"* where *"delicious moussaka"* rubs shoulders with *"caviar"* and top steaks – wins praise for this Marylebone venture, as does its *"great wine list"*. It's a sibling to INO (see also), and likewise run by an Athens-based team who hold a Michelin star for that city's 'Funky Gourmet'. / W1U 5QL; www.opso.co.uk; opso_london; Mon-Fri 11.30 pm, Sat 10.30 pm, Sun 10 pm.

Orange Pekoe SW13 £40 **3 4 3**
3 White Hart Ln 020 8876 6070 11–1A
This pretty and professionally run tea shop close to the Thames in Barnes excels for its cakes and afternoon teas (for which booking is essential at busy times), although it no longer generates the copious feedback of earlier years. / SW13 0PX; www.orangepekoeteas.com; orangepekoeteas; Mon-Sun 5 pm.

The Orange Tree N20 £63 **2 2 3**
7 Totteridge Village 020 8343 7031 1–1B
This smart 'country pub' overlooking the village pond in Totteridge, far North London, boasts a menu that ranges from steaks to sourdough pizza. But marks suffered this year on the basis of one or two reports saying recent standards have been "all a bit 'meh'". / N20 8NX; www.theorangetreetotteridge.co.uk; Mon-Sat 11 pm, Sun 10 pm.

The Orangery Bar & Kitchen EC2 NEW
5 Sun Street 020 3988 7709 13–2A
A glass-roofed atrium dining room that's part of a new boutique hotel (created from six Georgian townhouses) on the City/Shoreditch fringes, that opened last year. No survey feedback as yet, but it looks well styled and potentially a useful option in the area either for a cocktail, or for a meal with a flexible all-day menu served: first a breakfast selection; later in the day of small and sharing dishes. (There's also a restaurant here serving South East Asian food called Quercus). / EC2A 2EP; www.sunstreethotel.com; sunstreetlondon; Mon-Fri 10 pm, Sat & Sun 2.45 pm.

Orasay W11 £63 **5 4 4**
31 Kensington Park Road 020 7043 1400 7–1A
"Jackson Boxer's sublime Notting Hill outpost remains an out-and-out favourite, from the laid-back vibe to the small but perfectly formed menu" – that's the unanimous view on his "beautifully lit and cosy" four-year-old: a "consistent and fantastic neighbourhood restaurant" serving superb, "inventive" small plates all at a "very reasonable price". Top Menu Tip – "special kudos has to go to the caviar served simply with potato chips and sour cream just as it should be". / W11 2EU; orasay.london; orasay.london; Tue-Sat 10 pm.

Oren E8 £70 **4 4 2**
89 Shacklewell Lane 020 7916 6114 14–1A
"Lovely and adventurous", Tel Aviv-style small plates "zinging with flavour" draw a busy crowd to Israeli chef Oden Oren's 30-seater in Dalston – an immediate hit from its opening in 2019. It's a "charming" place, but there's one catch: "it's hard to hear your companions over the din". A spin-off deli opened at Broadway Market in early 2023. / E8 2EB; www.orenlondon.com; Tue-Sat 11 pm.

Orient London W1 £55 **4 4 3**
15 Wardour Street 020 7989 8880 5–3A
With its "marvellous selection of dim sum" raised to a "fantastic" level; "amicable and chatty service"; and its "well-spaced tables", this low-key-looking venue "stands a cut above the usual Chinatown standard" in all respects. / W1D 6PH; www.orientlondon.com; orientlondon; Sun-Thu 11 pm, Fri & Sat 11.30 pm.

Ormer Mayfair by Sofian, Flemings Mayfair Hotel W1 £149 443
7-12 Half Moon Street   020 7016 5601   3–4B

Although this luxurious Mayfair hotel dates from the 1850s, its swish basement dining room owes its looks to the 1930s. Under chef Sofian Msetfi, the "fabulous" cuisine (choose either a 6-course 'market' menu or 9-course 'tasting' option) continues to achieve high ratings and even the weakest report this year awarded "full marks for presentation and service". "A friend of mine who swears not to visit hotel dining rooms granted it high praise after our dinner there!" / W1J 7BH; www.flemings-mayfair.co.uk; flemingsmayfair; Tue-Sat 9 pm.

Oro Di Napoli W5 £41 442
6 The Quadrant, Little Ealing Lane   020 3632 5580   1–3A

"The pizza is phenomenal" – "always tasty, with fresh ingredients well cooked" – at this popular Ealing independent, whose offerings are named after Neapolitan heroes ranging from Maradona to Bud Spencer (the spaghetti western actor born Carlo Pedersoli in Naples). / W5 4EE; www.lorodinapoli-ealing.com; lorodinapoliealing; Tue, Sat, Wed-Fri 10 pm.

Orrery W1 £100 224
55 Marylebone High St   020 7616 8000   2–1A

A "gorgeous bright room, overlooking a churchyard" – "especially lovely on sunny days when you can get a terrace seat on the roof" – this D&D London property above Marylebone's Conran shop provides a classy and intimate setting. It's no longer seen as a particularly gastro destination, as once it was, but the kitchen is currently putting in an "expensive but reliable" performance that avoids criticism and makes it a potentially useful choice, especially for a slightly "formal" or upscale occasion. / W1U 5RB; www.orrery-restaurant.co.uk; the_orrery; Mon-Sat 10 pm, Sun 9 pm.

Oscar Wilde Lounge at Cafe Royal W1 £101 335
68 Regent St   020 7406 3333   4–4C

"Gorgeous finger sandwiches, very pretty patisserie" and "fantastic staff" are all par for the course at an upscale afternoon tea, but it's "the opulent surroundings that make it special" in this "beautiful room" – the architecturally dazzling, rococo former Grill Room from 1865, now named after its most famous denizen and a must-visit for gastronomic history buffs. / W1B 4DY; www.hotelcaferoyal.com; hotelcaferoyal; Wed-Sun 5.30 pm.

Oslo Court NW8 £78 355
Charlbert Street   020 7722 8795   9–3A

"For a birthday there's nowhere better to come, whether you're 80, 90… or older!" – this "fun trip down memory lane" at the foot of a Regent's Park apartment block just goes on and on. A perfectly preserved time capsule from the 1970s ("from the salmon tablecloths and napkins to the recently departed ruched curtains"), you "sit down to crudités with a garlic dip and Melba toast then move onto a three-course meal from an extensive Italian-biassed English menu": "it's the most comforting of comfort food" ("Steak Diane as a main… wonderful!"). Service-wise, it's "a well-oiled machine": "all ages are well looked after, especially the oldest and youngest" and it's a "go-to venue for family celebrations" for a large slice of north London. "Portions are huge" ("even the teenagers in the party struggle with the quantities"), but you must leave space for pud, delivered by Neil "the fabulous dessert waiter, who always 'saves his favourite just for you'!" / NW8 7EN; www.oslocourtrestaurant.co.uk; oslocourt; Mon-Sat 11 pm.

Osteria Antica Bologna SW11 £67 3 3 2
23 Northcote Rd 020 7978 4771 11–2C
This rustic Italian trattoria is a "reliable local favourite" which has fed generations of families in Clapham's 'Nappy Valley' over the past 30 years. The hearty cuisine "rarely disappoints", although the venue "can get extremely loud on a busy night (speaking volumes for its popularity!)". / SW11 1NG; www.osteria.co.uk; osteriaanticabologna; Tue-Fri 21.45 pm, Sat 10 pm, Sun 8.45 pm.

Osteria Basilico W11 £78 3 3 3
29 Kensington Park Rd 020 7727 9957 7–1A
A "local favourite" in Notting Hill for more than 30 years on account of its "always-consistent" cooking, this rustic Italian is the sort of place with something for "every member of the family". It has spawned two offspring in the same street, Essenza and Mediterraneo – an indication of how well it suits the neighbourhood. / W11 2EU; www.osteriabasilico.co.uk; osteriabasilico; Mon-Sun 10.30 pm.

Osteria Tufo N4 £66 3 4 3
67 Fonthill Rd 020 7272 2911 9–1D
"Crowded, buzzy and fun" – this "atypical Italian" ("one of the waiters even breaks into operatic arias") "round the back of Finsbury Park station is a real neighbourhood gem". "Owned and run by the incredibly friendly and attentive Paola", its "cuisine ranges across Neapolitan and southern Italian in general and is totally unpretentious – it could be described as a little rustic". "No dish disappoints but to nit-pick, the menu hardly changes". / N4 3HZ; www.osteriatufo.co.uk; osteriatufo; Mon-Fri 10.30 pm, Sat 22.30 pm, Sun 8.30 pm.

Otto's WC1 £103 5 5 4
182 Gray's Inn Road 020 7713 0107 2–1D
"For extravagant excellence", look no further than this "quirky", "proper old-school French" establishment near Gray's Inn, where "splendidly off-the-wall" patron, Otto Tepasse, "is at times both chef, sommelier and confidant". "Old-fashioned silver service, rich dishes (including the signature 'canard à la presse'), a wine cellar that seems to have no limits, and waiters who prep the sauces in front of you" all make for "great theatre and superb food. It's slightly bonkers, but brilliant. Maybe wear elasticated trousers!" Top Menu Tip – "the scallops sealed in their shells, with the obligatory caviar, with puff pastry is a dish of the year". / WC1X 8EW; www.ottos-restaurant.com; ottos_restaurant; Wed-Fri, Tue, Sat 10 pm.

Ottolenghi £71 3 3 3
28 Pavilion Road, SW1 020 3824 2818 6–2D
63 Marylebone Lane, W1 020 3148 1040 2–1A
63 Ledbury Rd, W11 020 7727 1121 7–1B
287 Upper St, N1 020 7288 1454 9–2D
50 Artillery Pas, E1 020 7247 1999 10–2D
"Stunning salads, amazing pastries" and a "lovely variety of interesting prepared dishes" have stood the test of time at Yotam Ottolenghi's "vibrant" deli-cafés – still hugely popular 22 years on from the launch of the first in Notting Hill. The Israeli-born chef and writer has had an enormous influence on the way people shop, eat and cook, helping to create a whole category of modern Middle Eastern cookery and "totally living up to his reputation as a leading expert in vegetarian cuisine" – even though his premises serve meat and fish. An occasional quibble – "the prices? Too high for a few stalks of broccoli even taking into account the undoubtedly skills of the Chef!" / www.ottolenghi.co.uk; ottolenghi.

The OWO SW1
57 Whitehall Place   Awaiting tel   2–3C

A mega new hotel for London sees the Old War Office on Whitehall – in which Winston Churchill made many of the most important decisions of World War II – being taken over by Raffles, no less (their first venture in Europe) and the Hinduja Group, to open in late 2023 as a new 125 bedroom property. It will have nine new restaurants, of which we list the five most notable individually: Café Lapérouse, Endo Kazutoshi, Langosteria, Mauro Colagreco and Paper Moon (see also). Other options include Mauro's Table and a fine high-ceilinged brasserie called 'Saison' – which fall under the Colagreco umbrella – as well as The Drawing Room (lounge and all-day dining) and Guards Bar. / SW1A 2EU; www.theowo.london; theowo.london.

Oxo Tower,
Restaurant SE1   £113   🎬🎬🎬
Barge House St   020 7803 3888   10–3A

"The view is incredible, especially in the evening" from the posh section of this South Bank landmark – "anything with a view of St Paul's wins high marks in the romantic stakes". But too many of those acknowledging the "wonderful location" feel it "needs a revamp", or find the experience "very overpriced for the quality of food and service… One can't help but feel that OXO Tower trades off of its name and outlook rather than the actual virtues of its offering". / SE1 9PH; www.harveynichols.com; oxo_tower; Mon-Sun 9.30 pm; SRA-3 stars.

Oxo Tower,
Brasserie SE1   £92   🎬🎬🎬
Barge House St   020 7803 3888   10–3A

"A table right by the windows here – overlooking the river – is frankly still one of the best restaurant views to be had in London"; and some diners feel that the brasserie at this long-established Art Deco landmark provides a good all-round experience. It still gives rise to more than its fair share of disappointments, though, and the perennial complaint that "you get a wonderful vista but a very disappointing experience". / SE1 9PH; www.oxotowerrestaurant.co.uk; oxo_tower; Mon-Sun 9.30 pm; SRA-3 stars.

The Oystermen Seafood Kitchen & Bar WC2 £79   🎬🎬🎬
32 Henrietta St   020 7240 4417   5–3D

"Constantly updated on blackboards, you find a selection of fresh oysters, crab, lobster, other seafood, and fish to choose from" at this "brilliant little place" in Covent Garden, which "despite its location in the central touristic area, doesn't feel expensive". "Tables and chairs are a bit basic" though – it's "pleasant and convivial" enough, but "you do pretty much have to accept being part of the next table's conversation". / WC2E 8NA; oystermen.co.uk; theoystermen; Tue-Sun, Mon 10 pm.

Ozone Coffee Roasters   £45   🎬🎬🎬
Emma Street, E2   020 7490 1039   14–2B
11 Leonard Street, EC2   020 7490 1039   13–1A

A "spectacular breakfast" – "the options are hard to choose from, but none are a poor choice" – is the top culinary feature at these Kiwi haunts, whose zeitgeisty vibe and in-house roasting (omg the smell in Shoreditch!) makes them a magnet for a "top notch coffee" at any time of day. / ozonecoffee.co.uk.

Pachamama £76 **3 3 3**
18 Thayer Street, W1   020 7935 9393   3–1A
73 Great Eastern Street, EC2   020 7846 9595   13–1B
"A super choice to explore Peruvian cuisine with a wide variety of dishes available on their tapas-style menu" (ceviche, croquetas, churros…) – these noisy and atmospheric, cocktail-fueled operations in Marylebone and Shoreditch make for a fun night out: "a great evening was had by all!" / www.pachamamalondon.com; pachamamalondon/.

Padella £44 **4 3 4**
6 Southwark St, SE1   no tel   10–4C
"Love Padella! Both the one in Borough Market and the one in Shoreditch". "It doesn't need any review as everyone seems to already know it" – a "go-to Italian" with "simple, perfect portions whose comforting flavours just sing" (freshly made every morning on the premises) all at "amazing value" prices. "It's so busy, you need to book way in advance (at least in EC2, unlike SE1 where you need to queue)". "All in all, the whole experience is devoid of pretence: nothing tries to be fancy, it is just damn good." "I take all my friends, all of whom have been impressed… and many have subsequently returned for themselves. Says it all!" / /padella_pasta.

Pahli Hill Bandra Bhai W1 £83 **3 3 2**
79-81 Mortimer Street   020 8130 0101   3–1C
"Authentic high-quality Indian food", including some "inventive and interesting dishes", are on the menu at the first London venture from New Delhi's Azure Hospitality, on the former site of veteran curry house Gaylord (RIP) near Selfridges. Named after a smart Mumbai district and with the 'Bandra Bhai' cocktail bar downstairs, it's definitely "worth remembering". A chef's counter – launched in summer 2023 – is a new addition. / W1W 7SJ; www.pahlihillbandrabhai.com; pahlihillbandrabhaiuk; Mon-Sat 10 pm.

Paladar SE1 £66 **4 4 4**
4-5 London Road   020 7186 5555   10–4A
"Amazing artworks on the walls" and "great, unobtrusive music" set the tone for an enjoyable and "easygoing" meal at this "fun" Latino in the "increasingly Bohemian neighbourhood" of St George's Circus (not far from Elephant & Castle), which offers "superb South American fusion food" and "lovely Argentinian wines". Founder Charles Tyler was also behind Malay-Asian restaurant Champor-Champor near London Bridge. / SE1 6JZ; www.paladarlondon.com; paladarlondon; Tue-Fri 9.45 pm, Mon 9 pm, Sat 10 pm, Sun 8 pm.

The Palomar W1 £81 **3 3 2**
34 Rupert Street   020 7439 8777   4–3D
"Fabulous and unusual Middle East food" has carved a major reputation for Zoë and Layo Paskin's Tel Aviv-inspired grill, on the fringes of Chinatown (where the perches at the counter are the best seats in the house). Since its recent refurb, new menu and expansion, however, ratings have taken a knock: "service is still good and professional, but doesn't seem as cheerful as it used to be, and the new price tags on the dishes may blow your socks off!" / W1D 6DN; www.thepalomar.co.uk; palomarsoho; Mon-Sat 11 pm, Sun 9 pm.

Paper Moon, The OWO SW1 NEW
57 Whitehall Place   Awaiting tel   2–3C
One of the first restaurants to be announced at this major new five star in Whitehall, this Italian venue is part of a luxurious international chain that originated in Milan's fashion district in 1977. Nowadays with eight branches such as Doha, Istanbul and the Algarve, the promised offering here is a conventional chic Italian one. / SW1A 2EU; Tue-Sat 10.30 pm.

Papi E8 NEW £51 4 2 3
If Mentmore Terrace 07961 911500 14–2B
"Any restaurant with five orange wines gets my vote!" – initial reports give a green light to this early 2023 newcomer in London Fields: the successor to 'Hot 4 U', a wacky former meal delivery service for hipsters that was born of the pandemic. "The small menu highlights some imaginative dishes" from chef Matthew Scott and there's an "extensive wine list" curated by Charlie Carr. / E8 3PN; papi.restaurant; Wed & Thu 10 pm, Fri & Sat 10.30 pm, Sun 4 pm.

Paradise W1 £65 4 3 3
61 Rupert Street no tel 4–2D
The "fantastic Sri Lankan food" served at this brutalist-style Soho venue (formerly Spuntino, RIP) is part of the new wave of Asian restaurants, combining inspiration, spices and ancient-grain rice from Sri Lanka with high-quality British ingredients and natural wines from organic producers. Manager Sam Jones used to play rugby for Wasps. / W1D 7PW; www.paradisesoho.com; paradisesoho.

Paradise Hampstead NW3 £36 3 4 3
49 South End Rd 020 7794 6314 9–2A
"Consistently wonderful food and service" ensure that a loyal Hampstead crowd keeps coming back to this 55-year-old curry house, now run by the founder's son. It's "full of staff from the local hospital", who clearly know a good thing when they see it. / NW3 2QB; www.paradisehampstead.co.uk; Mon-Sun 11.30 pm.

The Parakeet NW5 NEW £71 5 4 3
256 Kentish Town Road 020 4599 6302 9–2C
"All the food is wood-grilled and tastes fantastic" at this exciting March 2023 newcomer – a converted boozer (a Victorian hostelry, previously called The Oxford Tavern) from former Brat chefs Ben Allen and Ed Jennings that's not just "a welcome addition to Kentish Town" but widely hailed from more distant postcodes as "the perfect gastropub". The "original" if quite limited menu is extremely highly rated in a slew of early reports (and just about every newspaper restaurant critic has waxed lyrical over it); there's also a "superb and well-priced wine list, plus great beers on tap". / NW5 2EN; theparakeetpub.com; the_parakeet; Mon-Sat midnight, Sun 10.30 pm.

The Park W2 NEW
123 Bayswater Rd Awaiting tel 7–2C
Jeremy King is back! (with a vengeance?) at this big, bold newcomer in a landmark new development opposite Kensington Gardens and on the corner of Queensway. Apparently it will be "very much within the 'Grand Cafés & Brasseries' mould that [he] love[s] so much but it is however very much of the early 21st Century rather than 20th". Perhaps that means less of the Edwardian (Ivy, Wolseley, Delaunay) or Victorian (Sheekeys) style that has characterised his earlier openings. BREAKING NEWS. In September 2023, King announced he is returning to the original site of Le Caprice, where he found fame. He sold the name long ago, but it's already being talked of as Le Caprice 2.0. / W2 3JH; Mon-Sat 11 pm.

Park Chinois W1 £156 221
17 Berkeley Street 020 3327 8888 3–3C
An "extravagant setting" is central to the approach of this showy Chinese venue in Mayfair, whose website promises 'the ultimate Asian restaurant' and a 'world of hedonism' including 'devilishly curious entertainment' (such as burlesque). Its "excruciating prices" have always been an issue, but the view that the food (from a very wide-ranging menu, including dim sum, caviar, steak, noodles…) is "nothing special" gained ground this year, as did the concern that "I just didn't enjoy the experience" – "the shows are at least a distraction from what is a pretty lacklustre meal…" / W1S 4NF; parkchinois.com; parkchinois; Tue-Sat 2 am, Sun midnight.

Park Row W1 £114
77 Brewer Street 02037 453 431 4–3C
Despite the larger-than-life Marvel theme (enter through a bookcase in a library) and big backing (including the involvement of DC Comics and Warner Bros), this sizable basement two-year-old near Piccadilly Circus doesn't make many waves – too few reports for a rating, although such feedback as we did receive was positive. That some aspects of its approach are surprisingly upmarket perhaps actually limits its appeal: instead of being a fun, cartoony schlockfest, the decor is in fact rather classy; and although there's now a cheap set menu option (including for 'Little Gothamites'), the à la carte or Monarch Theatre experience are priced beyond the reach of 'casual dining'. Still, with extensive AV in some areas, for a themed, business-related event it can be a natural. / W1F 9ZN; www.parkrowlondon.co.uk; parkrowlondon; Mon-Wed 1 am, Thu-Sat 1, Sun 9 pm.

Parlour Kensal NW10 £67 334
5 Regent St 020 8969 2184 1–2B
Jesse Dunford Wood's quirky former pub in Kensal Rise "never disappoints". It's open for "lovely meals all day long" (from 10am), delivering a versatile set of dishes from "an ever-changing seasonal menu" made "with fresh ingredients and imaginative preparation". "Sunday lunch for both vegetarians and meat-lovers is a particular highlight". / NW10 5LG; www.parlourkensal.com; parlouruk; Mon-Sun 10 pm.

Parrillan £123 333
Coal Drops Yard, N1 020 7018 3339 9–3C
Borough Yards, 4 Dirty Lane, SE1 no tel 10–4C
"Taking the good bits from Parrillan Coal Drops Yard and improving on it X 2" – the attractive Borough Yards branch of the Hart Bros Hispanic duo has eclipsed its N1 sibling in terms of feedback. At both sites, the parrilla grill is a DIY job if you sit outside (you order para picar, and then chicken, seafood and meat for the BBQ); but at SE1 there's also a stylish, brick-lined interior section, complete with chefs and a more conventional menu-style service. The younger branch is not beyond criticism though: as in CDY it can seem "a good all-round experience, but overpriced" and the odd reporter finds it all too "hyped". / www.parrillan.co.uk; parrillanlondon.

Parsons WC2 £71 432
39 Endell Street 020 3422 0221 5–2C
"By no means a flashy restaurant and fairly cramped, but some of the very best fish that you will find in London" – this immensely popular Covent Garden fixture is a "premier choice" despite its humble looks thanks to a "daily changing menu dependent on the morning's catch" that's "accurately and sometimes interestingly, sometimes classically cooked" and delivered at a "really good-value" price. "The inside space is tiny, but they have managed to expand into an outside area which they heat on the pavement". / WC2H 9BA; www.parsonslondon.co.uk; parsons_london; Mon-Sat 10 pm.

Pascor W8   **£63**   3 2 2
221 Kensington High Street   020 7937 3003   8–1D
"Terrific posh Levantine food with a twist" is the story of this Kensington High Street three-year-old, whose kitchen is run by former Palomar head chef Tomar Amedi. The menu can seem "confusing" to first-timers ("what's a starter? a main? a side? did we order enough?") but the small plates are "interesting and all very tasty". / W8 6SG; www.pascor.co.uk; pascor_restaurant; Tue-Sun 11 pm.

Pastaio W1   **£57**   3 2 3
19 Ganton Street   020 3019 8680   4–2B
"Fantastic pasta" is the USP at high-profile chef Stevie Parle's Soho venue. In particular, it's "a top spot with kids, thanks to the fun and friendly staff and a notably good children's menu option". / W1F 7BU; www.pastaio.london; pastaiolondon; Mon-Thu 10.30 pm, Fri & Sat 11 pm, Sun 10 pm.

Patara   **£74**   3 3 2
15 Greek St, W1   020 7437 1071   5–2A
7 Maddox St, W1   020 7499 6008   4–2A
181 Fulham Rd, SW3   020 7351 5692   6–2C
9 Beauchamp Pl, SW3   020 7581 8820   6–1C
82 Hampstead High St, NW3   020 7431 5902   9–2A
18 High St, SW19   020 3931 6157   11–2B
"Generous portions" of "reliably excellent Thai food" have kept the six London branches of Khun Patara Sila-On's international group busy for more than 30 years. Although known for its value for money, there were one or two grumbles about "price increases" this year, but full agreement that you get "a consistently great bargain on their lunch deal". / www.pataralondon.com; pataralondon.

Paternoster Chop House EC4   **£74**   2 3 2
1 Warwick Court   020 7029 9400   10–2B
Punters are often drawn to this D&D London operation because of its association with TV show 'First Dates', for which it was famously the location. Originally it was conceived by the group as a classic City steakhouse kind of place, but has never really made waves in that department. Still, the odd report says it's a "useful" option in the area (although, note, if you haven't visited for a little while, it's moved – it's no longer overlooking St Paul's from Paternoster Square and is now on Ludgate Hill). / EC4M 7DX; www.paternosterchophouse.co.uk; paternosterchophouse; Mon-Fri 10 pm, Sat 10.30 pm, Sun 4.30 pm.

Patri   **£49**   3 3 2
139 Northfield Avenue, W13   020 3981 3388   1–3A
103 Hammersmith Grove, W6   020 8741 1088   8–1C
This West London pair of Indian street-food canteens, in Ealing and Hammersmith, elicits little in the way of commentary this year but wins its usual solid ratings for food and service.

Patty and Bun   **£44**   3 2 2
18 Old Compton St, W1   020 7287 1818   5–2A
26 Kingly Street, W1   020 7287 9632   4–2A
54 James St, W1   020 7487 3188   3–1A
19 Borough High Street, SE1   020 7407 7994   10–4C
12 Northcote Road, SW11   020 7223 0900   11–2C
15 Park Drive, E14   020 3951 9715   12–1C
2 Arthaus Building, 205 Richmond Road, E8   020 8525 8250   14–1B
22-23 Liverpool St, EC2   020 7621 1331   10–2D
"So tasty and messy – I love it", say fans of this 12-year-old London operation who insist it's the "best burger restaurant in town – others copy

but this is consistently the best" "for when you want a full-on dripping burger and to hell with the diet!". Expansion of the chain has proved difficult in the last year, with the Notting Hill branch shutting up shop just months after its summer 2022 opening. / www.pattyandbun.co.uk; pattyandbun.

Pavyllon,
The Four Seasons Hotel W1 NEW   £140
Hamilton Place   020 7319 5200   3–4A
Parisian uber-chef Yannick Alléno – who holds a total of 15 Michelin stars at 17 restaurants across the globe – made his London debut this summer at this July 2023 launch. Since the days of Bruno Loubet in the early '90s, the quietly glamorous Four Seasons has – for all its other virtues – lacked a high profile flagship eatery. Let's hope that this newcomer inspires more local excitement than its more established near neighbour on Park Lane, run by the holder of the world's most Michelin Stars (in that case 21): Alain Ducasse at the Dorchester. With main dishes around £50, the à la carte pricing here is a little vertigo-inspiring, but the offering of a set two-course lunch option under £50 and a tasting menu under £100 suggest a desire to tempt the locals to try it out. / W1J 7DR; www.pavyllonlondon.com; pavyllon_london.

Pearl Liang W2   £54   3 2 2
8 Sheldon Square   020 7289 7000   7–1C
"Authentic and sensibly priced dim sum, a cut or two above the quality of many traditional Soho joints" (and with "some stand out dishes") has carved a good reputation for this Cantonese basement, below the shiny new towers of Paddington Basin. (Its ratings, though, are not as high as once they were; and one or two reporters feel "it still hasn't fully recovered its shine post pandemic"). / W2 6EZ; www.pearlliang.co.uk; pearl_liang_restaurant; Mon-Sun 10.30 pm.

Peckham Bazaar SE15   £61   4 3 3
119 Consort Rd   020 7732 2525   1–4D
The "great and original menu" at Albanian-born John Gionleka's Peckham pub conversion is inspired by the cuisine of the former Ottoman Empire, stretching across the Balkans to Greece and Anatolia, with an emphasis on cooking over a charcoal grill. Ingredients change daily with seasonal availability. See also its sister restaurant, Dulwich Lyceum. / SE15 3RU; www.peckhambazaar.com; peckhambazaar; Mon-Sat 11 pm, Sun 4 pm.

Peckham Cellars SE15   £60   3 4 3
125 Queens Road   020 7207 0124   1–4D
This "exceptional local wine room", one of the prime movers and shakers in the Peckham foodie scene, presents an "interesting list of wines" in a "fun and unpretentious atmosphere". There's also a short but well-received menu of modern European nibbles and larger plates. A long-heralded spin-off called 'Little Cellars' was due to open in Camberwell in 2023. / SE15 2ND; peckhamcellars.co.uk; peckhamcellars; Tue-Sat 11 pm.

The Pelican W11   £69   3 3 4
45 All Saints Rd   020 4537 2880   7–1B
"A winner if only for people-watching" – "the great and the good-looking of Notting Hill gather in the beige but tasteful surroundings" of this year-old pub, whose popularity is such that it's regularly "heaving". "It's not that cheap", but all reviews applaud Owen Kenworthy's "top-end pub good", from an "interesting menu" of "reinvented pub classics". Top Menu Tips – mince on toast is a staple here; "bar snacks of crab and cheese on toast are a delicious counterpoint to the drinks". / W11 1HE; thepelicanw11.com; thepelican_w11; Mon-Sat midnight, Sun 10.30 pm.

E Pellicci E2 £23 3 5 2
332 Bethnal Green Rd   020 7739 4873   13–1D

"Unbeatable for a classic full English breakfast" – but perhaps most popular for the accompanying baps – this Bethnal Green café, notable for its Grade II-listed Art Deco interior, has been run by four generations of the Pellicci family since 1900 – Maria, the current boss, has cooked here since 1966. / E2 0AG; epellicci.has.restaurant; pelliccicafe; Mon-Sat 4 pm.

The Pem,
Conrad London St James SW1 £101 4 4 3
22-28 Broadway   020 3301 8080   2–3C

Sally Abé's accomplished traditional British cuisine has rightfully succeeded in bringing media attention to this rather hotel-y chamber, in a comfortable but anonymous five-star a short walk from St James's Park tube. (Indeed, in his September 2022 review, the FT's Tim Hayward declared it "absolutely bloody cracking… some of the best food in town"). It still doesn't attract the volume of reports in our annual diners' poll we would like, but most (if not quite all) proclaim it "outstanding all round". BREAKING NEWS: in July 2023, the restaurant closed, for the installation of a new kitchen. We've left it with its former rating, but apparently on re-opening in autumn 2023 it will have an amended offering. Abé commented: 'We'll be back all guns blazing'! / SW1H 0BH; thepemrestaurant.com; thepemrestaurant; Tue, Sat, Wed-Fri 9.30 pm.

Pentolina W14 £67 4 5 4
71 Blythe Road   020 3010 0091   8–1C

A "perfect neighbourhood spot" near Brook Green – "Michele and Heidi's wonderful home from home" thrives on their "warm welcome", "honest" and "reasonably priced" Italian food and "lovely wine list". Most fans are local, but one or two cross London to visit. / W14 0HP; www.pentolinarestaurant.co.uk; pentolina_london; Tue-Sat 9.30 pm.

Perilla N16 £82 3 3 3
1-3 Green Lanes   020 7359 0779   1–1C

This "cosy yet elegant" neighbourhood restaurant overlooking Newington Green serves a "delicious and inventive menu" from highly rated young chef Ben Marks, who has The Square, Noma and Claridges on his impressive CV. Ratings have slipped slightly this year, but all reports here say it's a very good all-round experience. / N16 9BS; www.perilladining.co.uk; perilladining; Fri & Sat, Tue-Thu 11 pm, Sun 6 pm.

Persian Palace W13 £34 4 2 2
143-145 Uxbridge Road   020 8840 4233   1–3A

"Huge portions of very good Persian cuisine" are served at this Ealing local, where "very little has changed over the last ten years" – and it remains "excellent value". The menu encompasses kebabs, grills and traditional stews, while the decor adds to the authentic atmosphere. / W13 9AU; www.persianpalace.co.uk; persianppalace; Mon-Thu 10.30 pm, Fri-Sun 11 pm.

The Petersham WC2 £102 2 2 3
Floral Court, off Floral St   020 7305 7676   5–3C

"One of the prettiest restaurants in London – charmingly tucked away in Floral Court, Covent Garden" – this is the in-town offshoot of the famous Richmond plant nursery, and in fact houses two establishments – "La Goccia is the better of the two" (see also). There's "a lovely atmosphere in this light and bright room – it's the sort of place you might take your rich aunt to for lunch". The food, though, is "not especially memorable" and "weirdly expensive for average fare". / WC2E 9DJ; petershamnurseries.com; petershamnurseries; Mon-Sat 9.30 pm, Sun 4 am.

Petersham Nurseries Cafe TW10   £123   2 2 5
Church Lane (signposted 'St Peter's Church'), off Petersham Road
020 8940 5230   1–4A
A series of converted greenhouses makes an "eccentric but wonderfully romantic setting" for a meal at this posh garden centre, near Ham Polo Club. A shabby-chic culinary hit when it opened under chef Skye Gyngell 20 years ago, it has often stood accused of "hype over substance" – but remains a "personal favourite" to many, especially for the "quite delicious reinvention of afternoon tea". / TW10 7AB; www.petershamnurseries.com; petersham nurseries; Tue-Thu, Sun 5 pm, Fri & Sat 11 pm.

The Petersham Restaurant TW10   £83   2 2 4
Nightingale Lane   020 8003 3602   1–4A
The "stunning dining room with spectacular views, high above the Thames" at this grand mid-Victorian hotel in Richmond "retains a fine atmosphere", and it serves "delicious cakes" at afternoon tea. "Many chefs have been through the kitchen here" and where more serious culinary occasions are concerned, verdicts are split: fans say it is "currently undergoing a renaissance", but others feel (as they have for years) that "the food is only average and the service likewise". / TW10 6UZ; petershamhotel.co.uk; thepetershamhotel; Mon-Sun 6 pm.

Le Petit Beefbar SW3   £106
27 Cale Street   020 4580 1219   6–2C
On the backstreet Chelsea site that was Tom's Kitchen (RIP) – this import from Monte Carlo via Dubai and Méribel (which may sum-up its patrons too) opened in late 2021. For a second year, its meaty offering still hasn't generated a huge volume of feedback in our annual diners' poll, even if such as we have is all positive. But they must be doing something right, as a spin-off sprang up in Edinburgh too in mid 2023. / SW3 3QP; lepetit.beefbar.com; beefbar_official; Sun-Thu 10.30 pm, Fri & Sat 11 pm.

Le Petit Citron W6   £58   3 3 3
98-100 Shepherds Bush Road   020 3019 1175   8–1C
This "dependable neighbourhood bistro", on a busy stretch linking Hammersmith and Shepherd's Bush, combines classic gingham tablecloths with a menu inspired by Provence – favoured holiday destination for proprietors Lawrence & Emily Hartley, who previously operated the site as Mustard. / W6 7PD; lepetitcitron.co.uk; lepetitcitronw6; Mon-Sat 10 pm, Sun 4 pm.

Petit Ma Cuisine TW9   £62   3 4 3
8 Station Approach   020 8332 1923   1–3A
This "retro neighbourhood French bistro" in a parade of shops near Kew station is "massively popular with the locals due to its competitive prices" for "Gallic classics with a little twist" (and gets "very crowded at lunchtimes"). / TW9 3QB; www.macuisinebistrot.co.uk; Tue-Sun 10 pm.

La Petite Auberge N1   £56   3 3 2
283 Upper St   020 7359 1046   9–2D
"Calves' liver, perfect coq-au-vin, deeply flavourful venison stew" – this Gallic venue in Islington doesn't aim for foodie fireworks, but fans like its traditional approach, "warm" atmosphere and "willing" service. The less rosy view is that the cooking is "rather standard French food, if good enough for an evening with friends". Top Tip – the interior is split level in some areas and regulars say "the top section especially feels romantic". / N1 2TZ; www.petiteauberge.co.uk; lapetiteauberge_en4; Mon-Fri 10 pm, Sat 10.30 pm, Sun 9.30 pm.

Pétrus SW1 £167 ②③③
1 Kinnerton St 020 7592 1609 6–1D

"Interesting vintages, well introduced by the sommelier" helped win renewed praise this year for this slick, luxurious Belgravian (built around a central wine cage), which was also sometimes nominated for its "romantic" potential. However – as it approaches its 14th year – although its modern French cuisine was often favourably rated this year, there's little of the excitement in feedback that once distinguished it as one of the flagships of Gordon Ramsay's restaurant portfolio. / SW1X 8EA; www.gordonramsayrestaurants.com; petrusrestaurant; Wed-Sat 11 pm, Sun 6 pm.

Pham Sushi EC1 £53 ②③②
159 Whitecross St 020 7251 6336 13–2A

"There are so few dining choices near the Barbican, it's worth knowing that you can get decent sushi and other obvious Japanese options here at Pham", a short walk away; which particularly benefits from "fast and attentive" service. Some critics, though, feel that "evening visits without an expense account cannot justify the prices here". There's also a caution that "you should skip the house specials and stick to the simpler choices" as "several of the fancier options seem excessively performative". / EC1Y 8JL; www.phamsushi.com; phamsushi; Mon-Sat 9 pm.

Phat Phuc,
Chelsea Courtyard SW3 £41 ③③③
151 Sydney Street 020 7351 3843 6–3C

"Authentic street food at great prices" makes this Vietnamese noodle bar one of the better cheap grazing options in Chelsea. The name translates as 'happy Buddha' – which would not have sold many T-shirts. / SW3 6NT; www.phatphucnoodlebar.co.uk; phat_phuc_noodle_bar; Mon-Sun 6.30 pm.

Phoenix Palace NW1 £70 ③②②
5-9 Glentworth St 020 7486 3515 2–1A

This "reliable old-school Chinese" near Baker Street tube is "great for big family lunches" – with its sheer scale, traditional décor and eight menus, "one could be in Hong Kong of old". It's also "pretty good value for money" for its address. / NW1 5PG; www.phoenixpalace.co.uk; thephoenixpalace; Mon-Sat 11.30 pm, Sun 10.30 pm.

Piazza Italiana EC2 £74 ③③②
38 Threadneedle Street 020 7256 7223 10–2C

This "beautiful old banking hall" in Threadneedle Street makes for a "decent business venue" in the heart of the City, with "a well-executed if limited Italian menu, and wines priced for expense accounts". On a quiet evening, though, it can "lack atmosphere". / EC2R 8AY; www.piazzaitaliana.co.uk; piazzaitalianauk; Mon-Wed 10 pm, Thu-Sat 11 pm.

Pidgin E8 £87
52 Wilton Way 020 7254 8311 14–1B

No journalistic round-up of East End restaurants is complete without mention of this unassuming-looking Hackney eight-year-old (est 2015), which has been a darling of London's fooderati ever since winning (and quickly losing) a Michelin star in the years after its opening. But feedback in our annual diners' poll – while positive – was, surprisingly, too limited this year for a reliable rating on its experimental tasting menu of funky small plates. / E8 1BG; www.pidginlondon.com; pidginlondon; Wed-Sun 11 pm.

Pied à Terre W1 £151 4 3 3
34 Charlotte St   020 7636 1178   2–1C

"Over 30 years on this is still a class act" – David Moore's Fitzrovia townhouse has proved one of London's enduring temples of top gastronomy – currently under chef Asimakis Chaniotis – and "this old favourite has also evolved over the years": "the introduction of a vegan alternative menu is pure genius (as an unreformed eater of meat and fish, I was well-and-truly wowed by the plant-based version)"; and "as always the wine list is a treasure trove". There are a few quibbles: that "commercial pressure seems to have limited choice" a little of late; the odd "unexceptional" meal is reported; and its "long and thin" premises can feel "a little crowded". But overall feedback is sunny, helped by "thoroughly welcoming and unobtrusive service" which also helps make it a strong "romantic" bet. / W1T 2NH; www.pied-a-terre.co.uk; piedaterrerestaurant; Thu-Sat, Tue, Wed 10 pm.

Pierre Victoire W1 £56 3 2 3
5 Dean St   020 7287 4582   3–1D

"A teleport into France" is easily achieved at "this unfussy, efficiently run" operation off Soho Square, noted for its "good honest classics done well" at "very reasonable prices". "Service can suffer when busy, which it often is, but no matter". / W1D 3RQ; www.pierrevictoire.com; Sun-Wed 11 pm, Thu-Sat 11.30 pm.

Pig & Butcher N1 £69 4 3 3
80 Liverpool Road   020 7226 8304   9–3D

This "great neighbourhood gastropub" in Islington is "very strong all-round", and the in-house butchery means it delivers a "stunning roast". It's still winning excellent ratings after a dozen years, with just a single gripe this year – "they only had one vaguely interesting beer on tap". / N1 0QD; www.thepigandbutcher.co.uk; pigandbutcher; Mon-Sat 10 pm, Sun 9 pm.

The Pig's Head SW4 £78 3 4 4
87 Rectory Grove   020 4568 5830   11–1D

This two-year-old conversion of a "grand old barn of a tavern in Clapham" into a "beautiful city-rustic gastropub with very good food" has been a real success for the team behind Smokehouse and the Princess of Shoreditch. "So happy to have a local worth staying near home for", purr fans of its "meat-friendly menu that's packed with flavour". "Wide veggie options available", too. / SW4 0DR; www.thepigshead.com; thepigshead; Mon-Fri 10 pm, Sat 10.30 pm, Sun 9 pm.

Pique Nique SE1 £79 2 3 3
32 Tanner Street   020 7403 9549   10–4D

Converted from a building in Tanner Street Park, this Gallic fixture in Bermondsey is sibling to nearby Casse-Croûte and known as a culinary bright spark in the area. It can be a tad "inconsistent" though ("three servings of the same dish (saddle of lamb) produced one that was very good; one that was reasonable; and one that had to be returned to the kitchen!") / SE1 3LD; pique-nique.co.uk; piquenique32; Mon-Sat 11 pm, Sun 5 pm.

El Pirata W1 £57 2 4 4
5-6 Down St   020 7491 3810   3–4B

A "buzzy" atmosphere and "decent wine list" are strengths of this "reliable, traditional Spanish tapas bar"; and prices that represent "great value for Mayfair" have helped sustain the jolly venue from its founding decades before the current vogue for Hispanic cuisine. Notable fans include Fred Sirieix and Caribbean pirate Johnny Depp. / W1J 7AQ; www.elpirata.co.uk; elpiratamayfair.

Pivot by Mark Greenaway WC2 £96 3|3|3
3 Henrietta Street   020 3325 5275   5–3D
Scottish chef Mark Greenaway's two-year-old 'British bistro', set in the first-floor drawing room of an elegant Georgian townhouse overlooking Covent Garden piazza, flies somewhere under the radar given its grand address. (The name apparently refers to the way the menu 'pivots' with the changing seasons). Its pre-theatre options are useful for the area, while Sunday lunch is also favourably mentioned. / WC2E 8LU; 3henrietta.com; pivotbarandbistro; Mon-Sat 11 pm, Sun 9 pm.

Pizarro SE1 £66 4|4|4
194 Bermondsey St   020 7256 5333   10–4D
"Stunning and authentic" Spanish food in a "beautiful, always-convivial setting, and with a wine list to die for" is the attractive proposition of José Pizarro's massively popular Bermondsey restaurant. Its ratings are a shade below those of José, its older sister (by a few months) tapas bar across the road, due to a minority sentiment that it's "good rather than great". / SE1 3TQ; josepizarro.com; josepizarrorestaurants; Mon-Sat 10.45 pm, Sun 8.45 pm.

Pizza East E1 £59 3|2|3
56 Shoreditch High St   020 7729 1888   13–1B
"Great pizzas in the heart of buzzing Shoreditch" made this "cool and buzzy", post-industrial pizza joint an early player in the area's rise as a gastronomic hub when it was opened by Soho House in 2009. The venue was taken over by Gordon Ramsay after closing briefly in early 2023 (a sister site in Portobello has closed permanently), so there may be changes afoot. It's in the 'Tea Building', whose "concrete interior makes the place pretty noisy, but isn't that why you go to Shoreditch?". / E1 6JJ; www.pizzaeast.com; Mon-Sat 10.45 pm, Sun 8.45 pm.

Pizza Metro SW11 £60 3|2|2
64 Battersea Rise   020 7228 3812   11–2C
Now 30 years old, this battered Battersea Neapolitan helped introduce the capital to the delights of pizza sold by the metre. Others, perhaps, have overtaken it over the decades, but for a good laugh and some very decent pizza, it still has a fan club. / SW11 1EQ; www.pizzametropizza.com; pizzametropizza; Tue-Thu 10 pm, Fri, Sun 11.30 pm, Sat midnight.

Pizza Pilgrims £41 3|3|2
Branches throughout London
"The best whistle-stop pizza in London" for its army of fans – the Elliot brothers' successful chain continues to grow, with their latest opening in Queen's Park in June 2023. But even if "you can't knock the food" or the "realistic prices", the rest of the experience is somewhere between "pleasant" and "a bit underwhelming". / pizzapilgrims.co.uk; pizzapilgrims.

PizzaExpress £57 2|3|3
Branches throughout London
Is this venerable high-street brand (est. 1965) finally getting back on track? Owned by its creditors since 2021, its volume of feedback and ratings rebounded significantly this year, with particular improvement in its "efficient and welcoming" service and the "pleasant ambience" for which the chain was previously known. And, although its food rating remains washed out, it does retain many fans (including Marcus Wareing apparently!) who feel a pizza here is "always enjoyable". Parents still love it – "they are very friendly and kind to kids" and "you know what you are going to get". / www.pizzaexpress.co.uk; pizzaexpress/.

Pizzeria Mozza,
Treehouse Hotel W1   **£48**   4 3 3

14-15 Langham Place   020 3988 4273   3–1C

"Miss it and miss out!" – the first UK venture from legendary LA baker-chef Nancy Silverton (founder of La Brea Bakery and a James Beard Award winner) is "this pizza joint, tucked away in a hotel opposite Broadcasting House". It's "just the best", with "fab sourdough crust and great toppings" – altogether "very special!" / W1B 2QS; www.treehousehotels.com; pizzeriamozzalondon; Mon-Sat 10 pm.

Planque E8   **£80**   3 4 4

322 Acton Mews   020 7254 3414   14–2A

An "incredible wine list from a seriously passionate and knowledgeable team" is backed up by "lovely modern food" in this hip 'wine drinkers' clubhouse' set in a pair of Haggerston railway arches. "The restaurant has been designed beautifully and it feels like serious money has been spent on the project", even if wine is the primary focus. (Members enjoy priority booking and can store their reserves in the cellar.) / E8 4EA; www.planque.co.uk; _planque_; Wed & Thu 9 pm, Fri & Sat 9.30 pm, Sun 3 pm.

Plaquemine Lock N1   **£46**   4 3 4

139 Graham St   020 7688 1488   9–3D

"Amazing Creole food" including such delights as po'boys, gumbo and jambalaya liven up any meal at this Islington pub from Jacob Kenedy (of Bocca di Lupo) – a tribute to his Louisiana forebears. "If you're looking for something fun, lively and different without having to compromise on the cooking, Plaquemine Lock is an awesome night out". Top Tip – "great jazz at Sunday brunch". / N1 8LB; plaqlock.com; plaqueminelock; Sun & Mon 10 pm, Tue-Fri 11 pm, Sat midnight.

Plaza Khao Gaeng,
Arcade Food Hall WC1   **£36**   4 3 2

103-105 Oxford Street   no tel   5–1A

"Not a place to linger" – this "busy, basic and noisy" canteen from JKS Restaurants is a highlight of the Arcade Food Hall (see also) at Centrepoint. "Styled as street food" – it's "several notches above a typical Thai offering" and bangs out dishes that aficionados claim "are reminiscent of actually eating in the lesser-known corners of Thailand" (some of them "rip-your-face-off" spicy). Top Menu Tip – "sea bass in chilli and holy basil is just epic". / WC1A 1DB; plazakhaogaeng.com; plazakhaogaeng; Tue-Sat 10 pm, Sun 7.30 pm.

The Plimsoll N4   **£61**   5 4 3

52 St Thomas's Road   no tel   9–1D

"Legendary Dexter cheeseburgers and well-flavoured small plates" of "delicious, unfussy grub" hit the jackpot at this "crowded Finsbury Park local" near the old Arsenal stadium, "if you want to eat down-to-earth cooking, served up with charm in a proper boozer". "With the exception of the burgers the menu changes constantly", and "attention is on the food not the decor" – although the 'Four Legs' duo, Jamie Allan & Ed McIlroy, did strip out the previous incarnation's Oirish-themed interior before launching here two years ago. / N4 2QW; theplimsoll.com; the.plimsoll; Mon-Fri 11 pm, Sat & Sun midnight.

The Plough SW14 £58 2️⃣2️⃣3️⃣
42 Christ Church Rd   020 8755 7444   11–2A

This attractive eighteenth-century inn is a short stroll from Sheen Gate and a good option following a walk in Richmond Park (especially in summer on the terrace). On the downside, "the cooking can be a bit hit and miss" – it's "under new management" since Fuller's fell out with the previous landlord a couple of years back, "so perhaps hasn't found its stride yet". / SW14 7AF; www.plougheastsheen.co.uk; ploughsheen; Mon-Fri 9 pm, Sat 10 pm, Sun 8 pm.

Ploussard SW11 NEW £34 4️⃣3️⃣3️⃣
97 Saint John's Road   020 7738 1965   11–2C

"A more-than-welcome addition to Battersea Rise, with a Continental-style vibe" that opened in April 2023 (a revamp of the "small", 35-cover site that Tommy Kempson and chef Matt Harris used to run the as a branch of their Brixton-based 'Other Side Fried'). The eclectic menu is short but interesting, and accompanied by a selection of low-intervention vintages. "Grab a seat by the window to watch the world go by whilst enjoying delicious plates of food" – crumpet with lamb and anchovy is a prime example – plus a small-but-good wine list. / SW11 1QY; ploussardlondon.co.uk; ploussardlondon; Tue, Wed 10 pm, Fri & Sat 11 pm, Thu 10.30 pm, Sun 6 pm.

PLU NW8 £213 5️⃣4️⃣4️⃣
12 Blenheim Terrace   020 7624 7663   9–3A

"If I won the lottery I would eat at PLU at least once a month!" – Elliot Moss has created something "so special" with this "cosy-yet-super-elegant" venue in St John's Wood: "a small luxurious room with impeccable attention from the single front-of-house person" (Helen, his wife). "The best part is the food": "dishes should score 10 out of 5 for their flavours, textures, aromas, presentation, anticipation, fun and excitement"; and "betray a lovely sense of humour too". "How on earth Michelin continually fails to recognise PLU is a travesty of justice!'" / NW8 0EB; www.plurestaurant.co.uk; plurestaurant; Thu-Sat 10 pm.

Plum Valley W1 £51 3️⃣2️⃣2️⃣
20 Gerrard St   020 7494 4366   5–3A

"The dim sum is pretty good for this price range" ("all the stalwarts are available" as well as one or two "unusual/Hakkasan-like creations") at this Cantonese stalwart in Chinatown. / W1D 6JQ; plumvalley.co.uk; plumvalleyrestaurant; Mon-Sun 10 pm.

Pollen Street Social W1 £160 3️⃣3️⃣3️⃣
8-10 Pollen St   020 7290 7600   3–2C

"Jason Atherton's original solo venture in Mayfair remains a star" and it's "good to see him still at the helm and running the pass". His cuisine is "immaculately presented" with "many little delights in between courses" and "the wine list is special (not cheap but with some good bargains to be had if you look carefully"). The stylish interior can seem a fraction "soulless" for some tastes however; and there was the odd incident of "unhelpful" service this year. And even those acknowledging the "beautiful-looking and generally excellent cuisine" can go "Oh… the bill.....wow!!" Maybe that's why – as our survey was in progress – Jason slashed his prices, taking the tasting menu down from £185 to £145 per person; and the set lunch from £75 per person to £39.50 per person. The latter in particular is stunning value! / W1S 1NQ; www.pollenstreetsocial.com; pollen_street_social; Tue-Sat 9.30 pm.

Le Pont de la Tour SE1 £96 2 2 3
36d Shad Thames 020 7403 8403 10–4D

"An outside table on the lovely riverside, complete with the spectacular and iconic view of Tower Bridge" is the best way to visit this D&D London venue (where the Blairs once entertained the Clintons, when both were in office). With its modern French cuisine and heavyweight wine list, there was a time when this was both the jewel in the crown of the late Sir Terence Conran's restaurant empire and the City of London's favourite entertaining spot. Times have moved on, though, and nowadays its middling performance gives it a dwindling reputation. For fans, it's still *"worth it for a really special treat"*. Others, though, *"won't be rushing back: the interior ambience is nothing to write home about and the food is pricey for what's served up"*. / SE1 2YE; www.lepontdelatour.co.uk; lepontdelatourldn; Mon-Sat 10 pm, Sun 9 pm.

Popolo EC2 £61 3 3 2
26 Rivington Street 020 7729 4299 13–1B

"A find!" – *"Sit at the ground-floor kitchen bar for a fun, close up experience"* at this sophisticated Shoreditch joint, where Jon Lawson and his team provide accomplished sharing plates (often with Moorish touches) and deliver them in a *"knowledgeable and friendly"* manner. But ratings took a hit this year, with the odd review referring to cost-of-living concerns: *"most of the food is excellent but the size of the portions for the price charged was ridiculously small and felt like a starter at the price of a main. For the premium cost, you might expect comfy seating too!"* / EC2A 3DU; popoloshoreditch.com; popoloshoreditch; Mon-Wed 10.30 pm, Thu-Sat 11 pm.

Poppy's £36 3 2 3
129-131 Brackenbury Road, W6 020 8741 4928 8–1C
30 Greyhound Road, W6 020 7385 9264 8–2C
78 Glenthorne Road, W6 020 8748 2351 8–2C

"Good home-cooked Thai food" at *"bargain"* prices keeps guests coming back to this trio of Hammersmith neighbourhood cafés, distinctively crammed full of retro bric-a-brac. They serve English breakfasts and afternoon teas by day.

Porte Noire N1 £56 3 4 4
Unit A Gasholder 10, 1 Lewis Cubitt Square 020 7930 6211 9–3C

Within the foot of one of King's Cross's historic gasholders – just behind Coal Drops Yard – this handsome wine bar boasts a celeb investor (Idris Elba) as well as a large terrace with peaceful views over the canal and landscaped greenery. The business also makes Champagne and other vintages under the 'Porte Noire' brand and *"an interesting wine list"* is a key strongpoint, alongside its *"buzzy"* atmosphere and staff who are *"well-balanced, friendly and knowledgeable"*. The food is relatively *"basic"*, but some of the more ambitious dishes can really shine. / N1C 4BY; www.portenoire.co.uk; portenoirekx; Mon-Sat 11.30 pm, Sun 5.30 pm.

Il Portico W8 £74 2 3 3
277 Kensington High St 020 7602 6262 8–1D

"Such traditional, family-run restaurants are quite a rarity in London these days"; and the Chiavarinis have maintained this *"quintessential"*, *"old-fashioned"* trattoria, opposite the Design Museum, for over 50 years. Fans say the food is *"terrific, albeit a bit pricey probably because of its posh postcode"*. But there is a less charitable school of thought, which says results are *"uninspired, but it's always busy, possibly because the locals don't know how to cook…"* / W8 6NA; www.ilportico.co.uk; ilportico.kensington; Mon-Sat 11 pm.

Portland W1 £98   4️⃣4️⃣2️⃣
113 Great Portland Street 020 7436 3261 2–1B

Will Lander and Daniel Morgenthau have created an understated classic at this Fitzrovia fixture, with open kitchen on view. No-one minds that the "informal atmosphere is nothing particularly special" or that "tables are too close together" – they value the positive vibes generated by "low-key, friendly and unobtrusive staff who are helpful without hovering or being overly servile". Most importantly, "if the decor is slightly bland, the food is anything but": it can be "outstanding"; comes at "a very reasonable price given the location and quality"; and is backed up by "unusual and excellent wines". / W1W 6QQ; www.portlandrestaurant.co.uk; portlandrestaurant; Tue-Sat 9.45 pm.

Portobello Ristorante Pizzeria W11 £75   3️⃣3️⃣4️⃣
7 Ladbroke Road 020 7221 1373 7–2B

"Make sure you sit in the front garden" or the "nice covered terrace" to get the most out of this "lovely local", not far from Notting Hill Gate. Despite the "fresh fish on display", lots of regulars "only ever have pizza, which is very good indeed with lots of very fresh-tasting toppings". "Nice gelato" too. And it's "excellent value for the quality and area". / W11 3PA; www.portobellolondon.co.uk; portobello_ristorante_pizzeria; Mon-Sun 11 pm.

The Portrait Restaurant by Richard Corrigan, National Portrait Gallery WC2 NEW
St Martin's Place 020 7306 0055 5–4B

Dazzling rooftop views accompany a trip to this landmark chamber overlooking the rooftops of Trafalgar Square towards Parliament. As part of the NPG's refurb it has been re-designed by design studio Brady Williams and re-opened in early July 2023 with acclaimed chef, Richard Corrigan at the helm. The bar operation has been beefed up and offerings will include a light afternoon tea and chef's dining counter (plus launch set lunch and pre-theatre menus from £29 per head). / WC2H 0HE; www.npg.org.uk; Mon & Tue, Sun 5.30 pm, Wed & Thu 9.30 pm, Fri & Sat 9.45 pm.

Postbox SW13 £43   3️⃣4️⃣3️⃣
201 Castelnau 07424 339379 11–1A

This yearling on the Barnes approach to Hammersmith Bridge is a "lovely little neighbourhood eatery" serving "amazing and homely fresh Indian dishes". Founder Leo Noronha, originally from Goa, presides over a "short menu of family recipes" – of the type jotted down on postcards to remind travellers of the food from home. / SW13 9ER; www.postboxrestaurantlondon.com; postbox_ldn; Tue-Thu 10 pm, Fri & Sat 10.30 pm, Sun 9.30 pm.

Potli W6 £55   4️⃣3️⃣3️⃣
319-321 King St 020 8741 4328 8–2B

"An interesting street-food menu is very well executed" at this "real treat" of a Hammersmith café, with a comfortable, atmospheric interior and "friendly service". "It's not as flash as Indian Zing across the road, but dishes are full of flavour and good value!" / W6 9NH; www.potli.co.uk; potlirestaurant; Mon-Thu 10 pm, Fri & Sat 10.30 pm, Sun 9 pm.

La Poule au Pot SW1 £76 345
231 Ebury St 020 7730 7763 6–2D
Dark and candle-lit, this "unchanging French" old charmer in Pimlico has "lots of tiny tables squeezed into its intimate nooks"; and yet again comes highly recommended for a steamy date in our annual diners' poll. The very Gallic service "can be a bit hit 'n' miss (it helps if they know you)" but typically "makes you feel so cosseted and looked after". "There aren't so many restaurants left in Paris serving such traditional bistro fare" (Tarte à l'Oignon, Beef Bourguignon, Crème Brûlée…), all served in "very generous portions" and "with a sensibly priced wine list". Top Tip – "great terrace for al fresco dining" in summer. / SW1W 8UT; www.pouleaupot.co.uk; lapouleaupotrestaurant; Mon-Sun 11 pm.

Prawn on the Lawn N1 £72 432
292-294 St Paul's Rd 020 3302 8668 9–2D
This 10-year-old fishmonger-turned-restaurant near Highbury Corner is a "great all-rounder", with "fresh fish" from Devon or Cornwall (it has another branch in Padstow) "often cooked originally". Even after a move to "slightly larger premises on St Paul's Road" it's still "a simple space, so the ambience is not highly rated given the expense" – "shame it's so small that you can't always get a booking". / N1 2LH; prawnonthelawn.com; prawnonthelawn; Wed-Sat 10 pm, Sun 5 pm.

Primeur N5 £65 334
116 Petherton Rd 020 7226 5271 1–1C
A retro shopfront (left behind by a 1940s car showroom) adds to the street cred of this well-known East End foodie hotspot (linked to Westerns Laundry and Jolene). Its fashionable combination of small plates served with natural wines doesn't inspire as much feedback in our annual diners' poll as its fooderati renown might imply, but is all positive. / N5 2RT; www.primeurN5.co.uk; menuprimeur; Mon-Sat 11 pm, Sun 9 pm.

The Princess Royal W2 £84 333
7 Hereford Road 020 3096 6996 7–1B
"A very solid offering in a great space" – this restored late-Victorian tavern in Notting Hill provides "delicious food from Ben Tish", culinary director of the smart Cubitt House group. This extends from breakfast via a £15 'worker's lunch' to more sophisticated evening dining. / W2 5AH; www.cubitthouse.co.uk; princessroyalnottinghill; Mon-Sat 10 pm, Sun 9 pm.

The Princess Victoria W12 £55 323
217 Uxbridge Road 020 8749 4466 8–1B
This big, smartly restored 1829 gin palace in deepest Shepherd's Bush features a horseshoe bar stocking 100 different gins, and a modern gastropub menu appealing to all age groups – "kids love their pizzas and we love their Sunday roasts". / W12 9DH; www.princessvictoria.co.uk; threecheerspubs; Mon-Thu 11 pm, Fri & Sat midnight, Sun 10.30 pm.

Prix Fixe W1 £49 332
39 Dean St 020 7734 5976 5–2A
For a "really good-value meal" (including a "pretty decent steak-frites") "in the heart of the West End" it's hard to beat this Soho brasserie. "The simplicity of the menu" and "wide variety of choices" mean "there's something for everyone", so it's "a real go-to", especially for its set-price lunch or pre-theatre deals. / W1D 4PU; www.prixfixe.net; prixfixesoho; Mon-Sun 11.30 pm.

The Promenade at The Dorchester W1 £141 ③④④
53 Park Lane 020 7629 8888 3–3A

Following the refurb of the hotel's extremely plush lounge bar, fans hail it as "the most amazing new tea salon in London" thanks to its "elegant and tasty" afternoon teas. Pastry chef Michael Kwan's creations take centre stage, and range from 'Champagne' to 'vegan' options. / W1K 1QA; www.dorchestercollection.com; thedorchester; Mon-Sun 10.30 pm.

Provender E11 £46 ③④②
17 High St 020 8530 3050 1–1D

"Typical French cuisine perfectly cooked" has won a solid reputation for this "great Wanstead local" – a traditional-ish Gallic bistro, with terrace. Veteran restaurateur Max Renzland, who founded it in 2011, stepped down in 2021, with no evident change in its performance. / E11 2AA; www.provenderlondon.co.uk; provenderwanstead; Tue-Thu 10 pm, Fri & Sat 11 pm, Sun 9 pm.

Prufrock Coffee EC1 £15 ③③③
23-25 Leather Ln 020 7242 0467 10–2A

Caffeine aficionados beat a path to the Leather Lane premises of "one of the early champions of speciality coffee", where they imbibe information from the "friendly and knowledgeable staff" along with their brews. It's a "comfortable refurbished space", and there are "great pastries" and breakfast/brunch options to munch on. / EC1N 7TE; www.prufrockcoffee.com; prufrockcoffee; Mon-Fri 4.30 pm, Sat & Sun 5 pm.

Punjab WC2 £49 ③④③
80 Neal St 020 7836 9787 5–2C

"It ain't Bibi or Tamarind, but it's less than half the price and it's jolly good" – this "ever-reliable" Covent Garden institution has earned devotion from generations of fans for its "authentic" Punjabi curries and "great staff" ("I've been coming here for excellent meals for over 40 years"). Founded in 1946 – the year before Indian independence – it claims to have been the UK's first north Indian restaurant and is now run by the fourth generation of the founding family. It's run with a conscience too – "during lockdown they served over 45,000 meals to the needy and homeless". / WC2H 9PA; www.punjab.co.uk; punjabcoventgarden; Mon-Sat 11 pm, Sun 10 pm.

Pure Indian Cooking SW6 £56 ④④③
67 Fulham High Street 020 7736 2521 11–1B

There's "always something new and original to tempt you" at this understated and "very good value" contemporary Indian on Fulham High Street near Putney Bridge. Chef-owner Shilpa Dandekar (who trained with both India's Taj Group and Raymond Blanc) "proves you can give a nod to tradition while being a little more modern, and not have to pay Mayfair prices to get it". Husband Faheem Vanoo ensures the front of house "always provides courteous service". Top Menu Tip – "the best black dhal". / SW6 3JJ; www.pureindiancooking.com; pureindiancooking; Mon-Wed, Sat, Thu & Fri 11 pm, Sun 10.30 pm.

Quaglino's SW1 £93 ②③④
16 Bury St 020 7930 6767 3–3D

Thirty years ago, this vast basement – a 1929 ballroom which later fell on hard times to be rescued and relaunched with a tsunami of hype by the late Sir Terence Conran – was emblematic of the sweeping improvements in the capital's dining out scene. Nowadays run under the flag of D&D London, it's largely forgotten by the locals and most frequented for special occasions by out-of-towners and tourists, for whom its attractions include a large bar and regular live music. Reports on the food used to be awful, but have improved in recent years and although feedback on its posh-brasserie cuisine is limited it's much more upbeat than it once was. Top Menu Tip – good value prix-fixe options for brunch (£39 for two courses, with bottomless bubbles for £35); and dinner Mon-Thu till 7pm then after 8.30pm (£38 for three courses and a glass of fizz). / SW1Y 6AJ; www.quaglinos-restaurant.co.uk; quaglinos; Mon-Thu midnight, Fri & Sat 1 am, Sun 7 pm.

The Quality Chop House EC1 £106 323
88-94 Farringdon Rd   020 7278 1452   10–1A
"So what if the benches aren't that comfortable!" – the bum-numbing seating at Will Lander and Daniel Morgenthau's "characterful and closely packed" Clerkenwell institution is part of its proud history as a 'Progressive Working Class Caterer', built in 1869 to feed the masses. Nowadays, "as the name suggests", it mainlines on "butchery and quality of the meat" ("you can pop into their nextdoor butcher's shop to buy too"). Most reviewers feel it is "a great London venue and long may it continue", but it can also seem "a slightly odd mix of traditional English food with the tasting plate craze" and "some dishes can fall into the cracks between the price charged and their quality". / EC1R 3EA; thequalitychophouse.com; qualitychop; Tue-Sat 10 pm, Sun 3.15 pm.

Le Querce SE23 £58 342
66-68 Brockley Rise   020 8690 3761   1–4D
Diminishing feedback in recent years makes it hard to recommend this "noisy and fun", family-run Sardinian on Brockley Rise quite as resoundingly as we used to. Fans, though, still say it's "a super, local Italian trattoria, with a great menu: especially the quirky ice cream and sorbet flavours". / SE23 1LN; www.lequerce.co.uk; le_querce; Wed-Sat 8.30 pm, Sun 5.30 am.

Quilon SW1 £92 432
41 Buckingham Gate   020 7821 1899   2–4B
"Delicate flavours" from dishes rooted in southwest Indian coastal cuisine establish this blandly luxurious hotel venue, near Buckingham Palace, as "the most interesting of London's Indians" for some of its fans. You wouldn't go there for riotous ambience though, particularly in the "gloomy back of the dining room". Top Tip – "the set lunch menu is great value considering its location" and there's also a "great weekend brunch". / SW1E 6AF; www.quilon.co.uk; thequilon; Tue-Thu, Sun 10 pm, Fri & Sat 10.30 pm.

Quo Vadis W1 £90 445
26-29 Dean St   020 7437 9585   4–1D
"One of the legends of the London food scene" – the Hart Bros' 'Grande Dame of Dean Street' is some reporters' "all-time favourite in the capital – especially now the dining room has been enlarged and transformed to feel much comfier". (At the end of 2022, the Harts reclaimed the space in this "beautiful, historic building" that had been given over to Barrafina for a few years, to return QV back to its former capacity). "Now with the refit, the environment has caught up with Jeremy Lee's dishes" – "fine British fare using seasonal ingredients" that's "top cuisine, without feeling too 'restaurantly'" – all delivered in a "convivial atmosphere which takes us back to classic Soho days". "Superb all round" and "low-key in a good way, so ideal for business". Top Menu Tip – "that eel sandwich is still a winner". / W1D 3LL; www.quovadissoho.co.uk; quovadissoho; Mon-Sat 10 pm; SRA-2 stars.

Rabbit SW3 £71 222
172 King's Rd   020 3750 0172   6–3C
The Gladwin family's faux-rustic, field-to-fork spot in quirky premises on the King's Road still scores more hits than misses, thanks to the "care taken sourcing the ingredients" and its "buzzy" atmosphere. It's perennially a "crowded" venue however, and a slip in ratings supports the odd reporter who feels that food-wise, its British small plates are "not quite punching up there like they used to". / SW3 4UP; www.rabbit-restaurant.com; rabbit_resto; Mon-Sat 10.30 pm, Sun 8 pm.

Ragam W1 £36 4 2 1
57 Cleveland St   020 7636 9098   2–1B
"The rather cramped interior isn't great but Keralan food is exceptional" at this "really good local independent Indian", near the Telecom Tower, which has delivered "very decent value for money" for four decades. ("More than a quarter of a century after my first visit, the dosas are still worth the trip. I think it's been redecorated as well!") / W1T 4JN; www.ragamindian.co.uk; Mon-Thu 11 pm, Fri & Sat 11.30 pm.

Rambutan SE1 £41 5 3 3
10 Stoney Street   no tel   10–4C
"A fantastic new Sri Lankan restaurant that really does things differently!": cookbook author Cythia Shanmugalingham opened her Borough Market newcomer in late 2022, and the dishes from its open kitchen – with much use of open grills – generated excellent ratings in our annual diners' poll. The press have utterly raved too: The Standard's Jimi Famurewa discovered a "buzzy, tropical playground" and had "an unforgettable, palate-rattling trip"; The Times's Giles Coren was "mesmerised by watching the chefs" and "such great use of different kinds of fire"; and the FT's Tim Hayward thought the food "so good it could heal wounds". / SE1 9AD; www.rambutanlondon.com; rambutan_ldn; Wed-Sat, Tue 10 pm.

Randall & Aubin W1 £86 3 3 4
14-16 Brewer St   020 7287 4447   4–2D
"A glorious spot for a boozy seafood bite, watching Soho stroll past" – this "always busy" and "buzzy" venue was converted over 25 years ago from an atmospheric old butcher's shop (est 1911) and oozes quirky Edwardian charm. Perch on a stool, and "exuberant staff" will serve you fizz and "expert fish dishes" ("simple, but cooked beautifully – fruits de mers, oysters, pints of prawns"). "It's not the most comfortable time, but worth it for the quality of the food and general ambience". "Long live R&A". / W1F OSG; www.randallandaubin.com; randallandaubin; Mon-Thu 11.30 pm, Fri & Sat midnight, Sun 10.30 pm.

Rasa N16 £46 4 3 3
55 Stoke Newington Church St   020 7249 0344   1–1C
Still regarded as a "benchmark" for vegetarian cuisine – not just of the south Indian variety – Das Sreedharan's bright pink Stoke Newington fixture has for 30 years showcased the Keralan home cooking he grew up with. At one stage the flagship of a small group, these days the fleet is limited to here and its new 'Rasa Street' spin-off across the, er, street. / N16 0AR; www.rasarestaurants.com; Mon-Sat 11 pm, Sun 9.30 pm.

Rasa Sayang W1 £51 4 3 2
5 Macclesfield Street   020 7734 1382   5–3A
Ellen Chew's "always reliable" Chinatown outfit celebrates the Chinese-Malay street food she sold as a hawker in her Singapore youth, and is widely held to be "one of the better Malaysian restaurants" in town. Opened in 2008, it is now the flagship of her Chew On This group, with outlets across England. / W1D 6AY; www.rasasayangfood.com; rasasayang_london; Mon-Sat 10 pm, Sun 9 pm.

Rasa Street N16 NEW £24 3 3 2
60-62 Stoke Newington Church Street   020 7254 8882   1–1C
"Well done Rasa!" – the revered veggie Keralan has "opened up a new restaurant in Stokey": opposite the original bright-pink Rasa, now in its 30th year, the latest venture from Das Sreedharan "stays true to the original, but also offers yummy fish dishes" with "a whole array of beautiful and tasty new options" – and "it's already a local hit". / N16 0NB; www.rasastreet.com; rasastreet; Tue-Sun 10 pm.

Ravi Shankar NW1 £35 322
133-135 Drummond St   020 7388 6458   9–4C

"Very well-priced vegetarian Indian thalis" have brought a steady ants' trail of diners to this fixture of the 'Little India' dining enclave behind Euston station for more than 40 years. "The buffets offer real value and choice". / NW1 2HL; www.ravishankarbhelpoori.com; Mon-Sun 11 pm.

The Red Lion & Sun N6 £63 333
25 North Road   020 8340 1780   9–1B

"In an area where there's lots of options for dining out, it's not easy to get a reservation – that says it all" about this well-known Highgate gastropub – which serves "good seafood in addition to the usual pub favourites" and benefits from "an owner (Heath Ball) who knows his wine, with an excellent selection from his native NZ". It's also "rather grand" and "old established" – there's been a pub on the site for 500 years – and there are two gardens for eating al fresco. / N6 4BE; www.theredlionandsun.com; theredlionandsun; Mon-Sun 11 pm.

Regency Cafe SW1 £15 335
17-19 Regency Street   020 7821 6596   2–4C

A definitive London caff – this Westminster institution has hardly changed since opening in 1946, and provides "the best fry-up you'll likely have had in years, with quality ingredients, well cooked and served in an iconic Art Deco setting". Breakfast here is "an experience every Londoner should try at least once in their life: consistent, quick and heavy" – and it's "as good as ever, even if there are lots of tourists now" ("you'll totally understand why people join the long queue"). / SW1P 4BY; regencycafe.co.uk; Mon-Fri 7.15 pm, Sat 12 pm.

Le Relais de Venise L'Entrecôte £57 333
120 Marylebone Ln, W1   020 7486 0878   2–1A
5 Throgmorton St, EC2   020 7638 6325   10–2C

"So long as you don't mind queuing and the fact that there's just one item on the menu" – "entrecôte, salad, secret sauce and sublime frites" – this Gallic duo in Marylebone and the City can offer "a wonderful evening of no-frills dining", and it's an "obsession" to more ardent fans . "The only pressing question is 'house red or Bordeaux'" – while the "hugger-mugger seating and bustle is all part of the charm". The original Paris branch opened 60 years ago in a bankrupt Italian restaurant – hence the name. / www.relaisdevenise.com; lerelaisdeveniseofficial.

Republic W4 £49 433
301-303 Chiswick High Road   020 8154 2712   8–2A

"Luscious, carefully spiced and original food" wins high ratings for this "very good upmarket Indian" in deepest Chiswick. Founders Kuldeep Mattegunta and Mustaq Tappewale (ex- Kricket, Amaya, Benares among others) took over the venue from the brilliant, much lamented Hedone (RIP), whose open kitchen makes it a "great place for chef watching". / W4 4HH; republicw4.com; republic_chiswick; Tue-Sat 10 pm.

Restaurant 1890 by Gordon Ramsay WC2 £211 344
Strand   020 7499 0124   5–3D

"Beautifully decorated", this small, gold-decorated jewel box of a restaurant in the Savoy opened in 2022 (a location that in days gone by was a cheaper eatery called 'Upstairs', long RIP). A major plus is its bird's-eye view of the comings and goings at the hotel's main entrance, providing a superb talking-point for your date: the best use for the place as its few tables are mostly doubles and space is tight. The main kitchens are elsewhere in the building, so the menu is "limited" but "very good if you like what you receive". / WC2R 0EZ; www.gordonramsayrestaurants.com; restaurant1890gordonramsay; Tue-Sat 11 pm.

The Restaurant at The Capital SW3 £98 **3**3**2**
22-24 Basil Street   020 7591 1202   6–1D

Back in the day, this small chamber – in a luxury five-star near the back of Harrods – was a much stiffer and foodie affair. In recent times the style has become laid-back – bare tables and an all-day menu (much of it from a Josper grill). Feedback is a little up-and-down, but even a reporter who was "a little disappointed" ultimately rated the experience as "good all-round". / SW3 1AT; www.therestaurantatthecapitallondon.com; thecapitalhotel; Mon-Sun 9.30 pm.

The Restaurant at The Twenty Two W1 £62 **344**
22 Grosvenor Square   020 3988 5022   3–2A

A "stunning dining room" – stylishly decked out in an elegant, traditional fashion – helps inspire good vibes for this recently opened, "understated-but-great" hotel (launched in spring 2022), just around the corner from the former American Embassy in Mayfair. Chef Alan Christie aims for a 'Mediterranean flourish to modern British fare': the result is "a cute menu that's expertly cooked". "Prices are steep but locally acceptable!" / W1K 6LF; www.the22.london; the22.london; Mon-Sun midnight.

Restaurant St. Barts EC1 £173 **545**
63 Bartholomew Close   020 4547 7985   10–2B

Johnnie Crowe, Luke Wasserman and Toby Neill – "the team from Nest and Fenn – have brought their A-game" to this "beautiful" Smithfield yearling, which opened in September 2022. "No expense can have been spared in the design and fit-out of this wonderful space, atmospherically situated with a floodlit view of St-Bartholomew-the-Great through the massive windows". The "ambitious menu focuses on British ingredients" and each "adventurous" course is "cleverly delivered" and "with marvellous, personal service". "It's the finest of fine dining with some original and exceptional tastes from a fixed multi-course tasting menu". / EC1A 7BG; www.restaurant-stbarts.co.uk; restaurantstbarts; Wed & Thu, Tue 7.30 pm, Fri & Sat 8 pm.

Reubens W1 £48 **3**2**3**
79 Baker St   020 7486 0035   2–1A

"Perennially popular and always great fun" – there's "nowhere better for excellent salt beef and chicken soup", say fans, than this classic Jewish deli in Baker Street – Britain's longest-running kosher restaurant, having opened (on a different site) in 1973. Restaurateur Lee Landau saved it from closure four years ago with plans for a revival of the basement fine-dining space, scheduled to open in late 2023. / W1U 6RG; www.reubensrestaurant.co.uk; reubens_restaurant; Sun-Thu 10 pm, Fri 2 pm.

Rhythm & Brews W4 £25 **334**
22 Walpole Gardens   020 7998 3873   8–2A

"Brilliant vinyl in the background" – you can choose the records, and in the evenings listen to live music while sipping drinks from the licensed bar – sets the tone at this "wonderful and very relaxed neighbourhood café" not far from Turnham Green church. The coffee is notably good, staff are "lovely" and they "serve the best breakfast – complete with edible flowers!". / W4 4HA; rhythmandbrews.co.uk; rhythmandbrewscafe; Sun, Sat 5 pm, Mon-Fri 5pm.

The Rib Man E1 £11 44–
Brick Lane Market no tel 13–2C
"Messy but worthwhile!" – a trip to Mark Gevaux's acclaimed pitch on Sundays at Brick Lane, for his BBQ ribs and pork rolls from pigs reared outdoors in Norfolk and Suffolk. But the creator of 'Holy Fuck' hot sauce suffered an aneurism and underwent surgery in summer 2023 – wishing him all the best for a speedy recovery… not only is he a top bloke, but we all need him back at work… / E1 6HR; www.theribman.co.uk; theribman; Sun 2 pm.

Riccardo's SW3 £54 343
126 Fulham Rd 020 7370 6656 6–3B
This "fun" Tuscan tapas bar on a Chelsea corner is, say fans, "everything a local Italian should be", and celebrates its 30th anniversary next year. "It knows what it's good at and does it very, very well" – "though not exceptional, it's reasonably priced for SW3; and always relaxed and informal". / SW3 6HU; www.riccardos.it; riccardoslondon; Mon-Sun 11.30 pm.

Richoux W1 £56 333
172 Piccadilly 020 3375 1000 3–3D
Decked out in cosy period style, this "slightly touristy"-looking Mayfair stalwart was rescued from administration in 2021 and is the surviving member of a now-defunct tearoom chain. Traditionally an afternoon tea place, there's more of an emphasis these days on its menu of "well-presented brasserie classics". At worst it's a "safe bet" for "a good pre-theatre supper", but some would argue that its "excellent offerings and well-spaced tables" means it can be more highly recommended. / W1Y 9DD; www.richoux.co.uk; richouxrestaurants; Tue-Sat 11 pm, Sun 5 pm.

Rick Stein SW14 £90 222
Tideway Yard, 125 Mortlake High St 020 8878 9462 11–1A
A "lovely location on the river" with "vistas over the Thames" is an uncontested attraction of the London outpost of the famous TV chef, near Barnes Bridge. It's not a huge advertisement for choosing a place according to the celebrity name over the door, as results are "hit and miss" to the extent that many diners view it as "consistently disappointing", "especially given the elevated prices". / SW14 8SN; www.rickstein.com; ricksteinrestaurants; Sun-Thu 9 pm, Fri & Sat 10 pm; SRA-accredited.

Riding House £64 223
43-51 Great Titchfield St, W1 020 7927 0840 3–1C
The Brunswick Centre, Bernard Street, WC1 020 3829 8333 2–1D
The "good-looking decor" and "varied menu with an enticing range of small plates, bowls and skewers" bring customers back to this well-established Fitzrovia haunt, now with a popular sibling in Bloomsbury's modernist Brunswick Centre ("nice place with lots of plants, like a conservatory"). They're a big hit for "a long lazy brekkie"; at other times the cooking can seem rather "uninspiring".

The Rising Sun NW7 £70 343
137 Marsh Ln 020 8959 1357 1–1B
"A true treasure in the leafy suburbs", this "small and quirky" 16th-century pub operates as a "restaurant spread over different rooms", "delivering a consistently high standard of high-quality British/Italian cooking". "Luca (Delnevo) and the team treat you as part of the extended family". / NW7 4EY; www.therisingsunmillhill.com; therisingsunmillhill; Tue-Sat 9.30 pm, Sun 8 pm.

Ristorante Frescobaldi W1 £89 233
15 New Burlington Place   020 3693 3435   4–2A

This sumptuous Mayfair outpost from a Florentine banking dynasty offers a "great location"; "an atmosphere ideal for hedge fund types"; and wines "straight from the vineyards in Tuscany" (the family estates date back to 1308). There's also a "super outdoor space when the weather cooperates". Fans say the Italian cooking is "solid" – foes that it's "just not good enough – let alone for the price". / W1S 5HX; www.frescobaldi.london; frescobaldi_london; Mon-Sat 11 pm.

The Ritz W1 £195 455
150 Piccadilly   020 7300 2370   3–4C

"Like a holiday in heaven!" – this "simply wonderful" Louis XVI-style chamber is known for its "OTT but magnificent" decor, and creates an "unbeatable location" for a special celebration, particularly an important date. John Williams commands a brigade of 60 chefs in the kitchen to provide "absolutely wonderfully executed, classic dishes, some using gueridon service – so rare now – and always adding a sense of occasion". It's "some of the best cooking in London", and though "horrendously expensive" is justified by the "utterly sensational" all-round level of performance, which also includes "professional and kind" service and a wow of a wine list. "The Ritz is unusual in still having a jacket-and-tie dress code (about the only time I wear a tie these days!)". "A band provides music, for dancing, at dinner on weekends (although there is a significant supplement for this)". / W1J 9BR; www.theritzlondon.com; theritzlondon; Mon-Sun 9 pm.

The Ritz, Palm Court W1 £134 345
150 Piccadilly   020 7493 8181   3–4C

"A truly iconic experience all round" – this "world famous", gilt chamber is "renowned for its elegant and sophisticated atmosphere" and provides "exactly what everybody expects from an Afternoon Tea", for which it remains London's No.1 choice: "a great treat for your mum on her birthday, with super sandwiches (loads of 'em – they don't scrimp here) and lots of tea options and other yummy bites"; "pricey and extravagant but worth it!". / W1J 9BR; www.theritzlondon.com; theritzlondon; Mon-Sun 7.30 pm.

Riva SW13 £82 542
169 Church Rd   020 8748 0434   11–1A

"Really special cooking" – "simple, seasonal northern Italian dishes with excellent daily specials" – has won a star-studded following amongst food writers for Andreas Riva's Barnes fixture of over 30 years standing (Fay Maschler, Nigella Lawson and the late AA Gill have all cited it as a favourite). The uninitiated sometimes find its attractions pass them by and even fans admit that the "ambience, while OK, could do with a bit of a spruce up". "This is such an iconic restaurant" for its fan club though that all is easily forgiven – "I keep coming back year in year out and the quality of the food has not diminished and speaks for itself. Looking forward to our next meal already!" / SW13 9HR; Tue-Sat 10 pm, Sun 9 pm.

The River Café W6 £150 323
Thames Wharf, Rainville Rd   020 7386 4200   8–2C

"Just keeping on delivering outstanding quality, year after year, with the highest-quality seasonal Italian food that's not over-elaborate" – Ruth Rogers' iconic Thames-side café in an obscure Hammersmith backstreet remains one of the most talked-about destinations in our annual diners' poll. Since its debut in 1987, it has helped drive culinary fashion. "They take the best fresh ingredients and the open-plan kitchen allows you to watch them work their magic" – an "exceptional" ingredient-led approach that's now practically ubiquitous in top kitchens. And it popularised the idea that top-notch food can be enjoyed in a "casual" setting, without flunkies and flummery: the bright, "noisy", "packed-in" space having originally been created as the canteen for her late husband's architectural practice (it helps that "it has a gorgeous riverside setting, especially outside on the terrace on a summer's day"). But, "while it's simply great, my God, do you pay for that simplicity". Yet again, it tops our list of 'most overpriced' restaurants as its "absurd prices seem to be multiplied by the number of years it has been open". As always our reporters have mixed feelings on this question of value. Some are unquestioning ("it's expensive, but you never feel ripped off"). For others, it's a struggle ("it never disappoints... so long as the heart attack when you get the bill doesn't end the evening prematurely"). And this year, those who "find it increasingly difficult to justify the expense" are gaining ground, particularly as the "beautiful" servers have seemed "very flakey" or "impersonal" on numerous occasions this year. "If you live near an airport, consider a day trip to Milan for lunch instead: it would work out cheaper...". Top Tip – "the winter weekday lunch is absolutely fantastic value and so delicious". / W6 9HA; www.rivercafe.co.uk; therivercafelondon; Mon-Sat 9 pm, Sun 3 pm.

Riviera SW1
23 St James's Street   020 7925 8988   3–4D
Aiming to bring Côte d'Azur style to stuffy old St James's – Arian & Alberto Zandi launched this bar and lounge in April 2023 on the interesting if offbeat 120-cover site (now with an open kitchen) that was formerly Sake no Hana (RIP). A 60-cover ground floor bar opened subsequently, together with a similarly sized terrace. Too few reports as yet for any rating – little in the MSM to-date either. / SW1A 1HA.

Roast SE1 £80   ②②**4**
Stoney St   0845 034 7300   10–4C
The dramatic setting of a wrought-iron and glass portico – originally part of Covent Garden's Royal Opera House and now overlooking Borough Market – makes this "a great place for breakfasts or business lunches". More generally, though, its retro-British cuisine generates limited enthusiasm (the main problem is "it costs too much!"). / SE1 1TL; www.roast-restaurant.com; roast_restaurant; Tue-Fri, Mon, Sat 10 pm, Sun 6.30 pm.

Rocca £51   ②②**3**
73 Old Brompton Rd, SW7   020 7225 3413   6–2B
75-79 Dulwich Village, SE21   020 8299 6333   1–4D
With their "decent menu of Italian food at good prices" and terraces for al fresco dining, this low-key duo can be useful options – the South Ken branch is "perfect for a pre-museum or Sunday grazing trip", while its bigger Dulwich Village sibling is "filled with families and dogs". "You wouldn't make a special journey, but they're reliably pleasant". / www.roccarestaurants.com.

Rochelle Canteen E2 £70   ②**33**
16 Playground Gardens   020 7729 5677   13–1C
Melanie Arnold and Margot Henderson's (wife of St John's Fergus) not-so-secret venue near Spitalfields was converted in 2006 from the bike sheds of a former school. Aided by its hipster credentials, it has long been a regular inclusion on top-10 round-ups by food journalists. Feedback this year, however, invariably came with a catch: "good, but not quite as good as expected...", "food went downhill after the scrummy starters...", "overhyped and too cool for school...". / E2 7ES; www.arnoldandhenderson.com; rochelle canteen; Mon-Wed 2.45 pm, Thu-Sat 7.30 pm.

Rock & Rose £67 ②②③
270-272 Chiswick High Road, W4 020 8948 8008 8–2A
106-108 Kew Road, TW9 020 8948 8008 1–4A
"Wonderful décor, a nice mix of cocktails and a lively buzz make this a very good local" that works equally *"for a romantic meal or for celebrating a special event"*. The new branch in Chiswick generates most of the feedback this year, but Lorraine Angliss (also owner of Annie's and Little Bird) has run the Richmond original for 15 years.

Rock & Sole Plaice WC2 £64 ③②②
47 Endell St 020 7836 3785 5–1C
A classic *"cheap eats place"* on the fringe of Covent Garden that's particularly handy for feeding groups on a budget, with *"very good fish 'n' chips"* that are *"great for eating outside with the sun shining"*. There's been a chippie on the site since 1871 – although not under the current very 1970s name. / WC2H 9AJ; www.rockandsoleplaice.com; rockandsolelondon; Tue-Sat 11.30 pm.

Roji W1 ③④②
56b South Molton Street no tel 3–2B
One of London's top omakase-style experiences is provided by husband and wife chef team, Tamas Naszi and Tomoko Hasegawa, at this small 10-seater counter experience, in a yard just off Mayfair's pedestrianised South Molton Street. Feedback in its first year of operation has been limited, so our rating is a conservative one. / W1K 5SH; ro-ji.co.uk; ro_ji_ldn; Wed-Sat 8.30 pm.

Roka £91 ③②③
30 North Audley St, W1 020 7305 5644 3–2A
37 Charlotte St, W1 020 7580 6464 2–1C
Aldwych House, 71-91 Aldwych, WC2 020 7294 7636 2–2D
Unit 4, Park Pavilion, 40 Canada Sq, E14 020 7636 5228 12–1C
"The pan-Asian food is yummy... the black cod is exceptional" and the *"buzzy"* atmosphere is *"stunning"*, say fans of Arjun Waney and Rainer Becker's svelte Japanese-inspired venues, where *"you can either sit at the counter watching the kitchen (great if you're just two), or at a table"*; and where *"a typical meal is sushi or sashimi as a starter then a robata (charcoal grill) dish for a main"*. Its ratings slid this year, though. Never cheap, prices are becoming *"sky high"*; the cooking is *"not as reliably good as it once was"*; and there was the odd incident of *"shocking"* service. / www.rokarestaurant.com; rokarestaurant.

Roketsu W1 £294 ⑤④③
12 New Quebec Street 020 3149 1227 2–2A
This *"completely original"* two-year-old Japanese restaurant in Marylebone offers *"a great and authentic kaiseki experience"* with *"luxury ingredients and amazing presentation"* from chef-patron Daisuke Hayashi, who trained at Kyoto's famous Kikunoi. The interior, complete with 10-seater counter, was tailor-made in the Sukiya style from 100-year-old hinoki wood in Kyoto and shipped over, which means *"being in the dining room is like being transported to Japan"*. A la carte dining is also available in the Bo-sen 'wine and dining room', where guests relax over a light meal in mid-century European armchairs, with a choice of 500 wines and sakes. / W1H 7RW; www.roketsu.co.uk; roketsulondon; Tue-Sat 10 pm.

Romulo Café W8　　　　　£64　🄷🄸🄷

343 Kensington High Street　020 3141 6390　8–1D

"A pioneer in championing dishes from the Philippines" – this Kensington feature opened in 2016 and helped pave the way for what's nowadays a healthy level of interest in the cuisine in the Capital. It's named for a well-known Filipino diplomat whose grandchildren own the venture; and who also run a number of similarly branded cafés back home in Asia. / W8 6NW; www.romulocafe.co.uk; romulocafelondon; Wed-Sun 9.30 pm.

Roof Garden at Pantechnicon SW1　　£90　🄸🄸🄷

19 Motcomb St　020 7034 5426　6–1D

"Costa del Belgravia anyone? On a sunny day, you're entirely justified eating in your sunnies" in this "roof-top bar/restaurant" with a retractable glass ceiling on top of the landmark Pantechnicon building. But while all agree on the merits of the stunning location, views on the food range from "great" via "fairly standard" to frankly "awful": at the very least, it is inconsistent. / SW1X 8LB; www.pantechnicon.com; Tue, Wed 11 pm, Thu & Fri 00 , Sat 00 pm, Sun 10 pm.

The Rosendale SE21　　　　£56　🄷🄷🄷

65 Rosendale Road　020 8761 9008　1–4D

"Brilliant pub grub" wins a nod at this Victorian former coaching inn in West Dulwich, with plenty of outdoor space that is covered and heated in winter. It's family-friendly, so gets "a bit noisy" at times. / SE21 8EZ; www.therosendale.co.uk; therosendalepub; Mon-Thu 11 pm, Fri & Sat midnight, Sun 10.30 pm.

Rosmarino SW17　　　　　£46　🄷🄷🄷

23 Trinity Road　020 8244 0336　11–2C

"Tiny, buzzy and authentic Italian" in Tooting Bec – on the fringe of the area's burgeoning gastro zone – that's "a bit of a neighbourhood gem", with its smart modern styling and "some unusual menu offerings that lift it a cut above average". Owner-operators Daria & Giovanni set up on their own account five years ago after establishing themselves in the industry. / SW17 7SD; www.rosmarinorestaurant.co.uk; rosmarinorestaurant; Tue-Sat 10.30 pm, Sun 10 pm.

Rosslyn Coffee EC4　　　　£8　🄷🄸🄷

78 Queen Victoria Street　no tel　10–3B

This five-year-old in the City (now with three outlets) has won international recognition for its "exceptional" coffee, sourced from some of the world's leading independent roasteries. The name? Founders James Hennebry and Mat Russell picked up the caffeine habit in Melbourne, location of Rosslyn Street. / EC4N 4SJ; Mon-Thu 10.30 pm, Fri-Sun 11 pm.

Roti Chai W1　　　　　£48　🄷🄸🄸

3 Portman Mews South　020 7408 0101　3–1A

"There's a wide range of options to explore" on the extensive menu of this "Indian street-food" café, in a side-alley near Selfridges: "great simple food at reasonable prices" and cooked to a "consistently high level". Upstairs makes a "perfect location for lunch". There's a more formal basement dining room, better suited to evening meals. / W1H 6AY; www.rotichai.com; rotichai; Mon-Sat 10 pm, Sun 9 pm.

Roti King £15 5️⃣2️⃣2️⃣
Ian Hamilton House, 40 Doric Way, NW1 020 7387 2518 9–3C
Battersea Power Station, SW8 020 4580 1282 11–1C
"Huge queues are par for the course but worth it in spades", when visiting this "sensational" basement – "a great, basic pit stop" on "a dodgy street near Euston station" where you "pack in tight" for the "amazing, fresh and feather-light rotis", "excellent laksa" and other "stalwart Malaysian dishes". "For a satisfying, cheap meal" many would say this is "the best value in town". There's also now a larger spin-off in the Battersea Power Station development – "it's good, but the original is still the favourite". / rotikinguk.

Rotunda Bar & Restaurant,
Kings Place N1 £62 2️⃣2️⃣4️⃣
90 York Way 020 7014 2840 9–3C
At the foot of the King's Place arts centre – a "lovely space overlooking water" with a glorious canal-side terrace – Green & Fortune's stylish venue offers a "good selection of small plates and excellent, if pricey, beef and lamb" from its own farm in Northumberland. "The pre-concert set menu is super value, but best of all is the Sunday roast lunch". / N1 9AG; www.rotundabarandrestaurant.co.uk; rotundalondon; Tue-Sat midnight, Mon 11 pm, Sun 9 pm.

ROVI W1 £89 3️⃣3️⃣3️⃣
59-65 Wells Street 020 3963 8270 3–1D
"I don't know how Ottolenghi comes up with those flavour combinations but the result is genius!", say fans of Yotam O's Fitzrovia flagship, which lives up to his renown for "exceptionally varied and delicious food with a focus on the Middle East (but also with some oriental influences)". "Served mostly as small plates so great for sharing", they're "particularly talented at vegetable dishes, but overall everything tastes good". There's also a "short but interesting wine list". It would score even higher but for the odd niggle: be it about "erratic, if charming" service; or toppish prices. Top Menu Tip – "in a high-quality field, the celeriac shawarma really stands out". / W1A 3AE; www.ottolenghi.co.uk; rovi_restaurant; Sun-Fri & Sat 10.30 pm.

Rowley's SW1 £93 2️⃣2️⃣3️⃣
113 Jermyn St 020 7930 2707 4–4D
"Steak, as many hot chips as you can handle, good claret... and that's about it really" – sums up the appeal of this "traditional" St James's steakhouse that occupies the site where Wall's became famous for their sausages. "Does exactly what it says on the tin", although it's seen as "rather overpriced" – "you're paying for the name and the location". / SW1Y 6HJ; www.rowleys.co.uk; rowleys_restaurant; Tue-Sat 11.30 pm.

Royal China £67 3️⃣2️⃣2️⃣
24-26 Baker St, W1 020 7487 4688 2–1A
805 Fulham Rd, SW6 020 7731 0081 11–1B
30 Westferry Circus, E14 020 7719 0888 12–1B
"Sunday dim sum lunch is always full of happy families" at this popular Cantonese group with 1980s-nightclub decor – an occasion for which they "cannot be beaten" for many diners: so "arrive around 10:45 to join queue for 11am opening". With the closure of its Bayswater branch a few years ago, Baker Street and Canary Wharf are its preeminent spots (and SW6 can be "disappointing" by comparison). All feedback is about the lunchtime service – "the evening offering is a bit ordinary". / www.royalchinagroup.co.uk.

Royal China Club W1 £76 4 3 2
38-42 Baker Street   020 7486 3898   2–1A

*"Best dim sum I've had in a long time – everything was best-in-class":
reporters are unanimous in their praise for the "always great" Cantonese
cooking at the Marylebone flagship of the Royal China group. But there's
some pushback against the prices: "eye-wateringly expensive, compared to
the standard competition, if comparable to their Hakkasan/Yauatcha-peers".
/ W1U 7AJ; www.royalchinagroup.co.uk; Mon-Sun 9 pm.*

Rudy's W1 £34 3 4 3
80-82 Wardour St   020 7734 0195   4–2D

*From Naples via Manchester to Soho – this "really top-quality joint in a
former Wahaca is definitely a positive addition to the London pizza scene".
"The smiley, friendly service" and "big portions" – legacies perhaps of its
Northern origins – "make the opposition look second rate". It's part of
Manchester's expanding Mission Mars stable, which is planning more Rudy's
and Albert's Schlosses in the capital and beyond. / W1F 0TG;
www.rudyspizza.co.uk; wearerudyspizza; Sun-Thu 9 pm, Fri & Sat 10.30 pm.*

Rules WC2 £83 3 3 5
35 Maiden Ln   020 7836 5314   5–3D

*"What's not to like about the oldest restaurant in London?" – in continuous
operation on the same Covent Garden site since 1798. Of course, it's
"popular with tourists", but its "quintessentially British" style makes it an
"old favourite" for many Londoners too, and it provides "a beautiful,
traditional experience". The atmosphere of the beautiful dining room is
"exceptional" and the "old school cuisine, with an emphasis on meat and
game", is very dependable; and backed up by an "extensive, if quite
expensive wine list". Top Menu Tip – "lovely steak 'n' kidney pie".
/ WC2E 7LB; www.rules.co.uk; rules_restaurant; Mon-Sat 11.30 pm, Sun 10 pm.*

Sabor W1 £68 5 5 5
35 Heddon St   020 3319 8130   4–3A

*"Just wonderful: fresh… lively… exciting and always interesting!" – that's this
year's worst (!) report of many lauding Nieves Barragan and José Etura's
phenomenal slice of Spain, just off Regent Street. "A seat at the counter, if
you can snag one (get there early, or be prepared to queue – it's well worth
it) transports one to Andalucia or Castile, and the assured food is as good as
it is there". Or "eat upstairs at the El Asador dining room" (which is
bookable nowadays). "Seating can be a little cramped but it all adds to the
atmosphere". Top Menu Tip – "crisp piglet never disappoints". / W1B 4BP;
www.saborrestaurants.co.uk; sabor_ldn; Tue-Sat 10.30 pm.*

Le Sacré-Coeur N1 £50 3 3 2
18 Theberton St   020 7354 2618   9–3D

*"French comfort food in a cosy setting in the heart of Islington" is just the
ticket at this long-serving outfit, where "both cuisine and ambience resemble
a bistro in France two or three decades ago". "Wines have a restrained
mark-up", and there's a "super-value set lunch which is also available on
Saturdays". Top Menu Tip – "boeuf bourguignon is particularly good".
/ N1 0QX; lesacrecoeurbistro.co.uk; lesacrecoeurfrenchbistro; Mon-Sun midnight.*

Sacro Cuore £43 3 3 2
10 Crouch End Hill, N8   020 8348 8487   1–1C
45 Chamberlayne Rd, NW10   020 8960 8558   1–2B

*"Top Neapolitan pizza", say fans of this Kensal Rise 11-year-old and its
Crouch End offshoot, which offers a "limited and delicious menu (they stick
to what they know) in cool surroundings". / www.sacrocuore.co.uk;
sacrocuorepizza.*

Sagar £45 **3**|**3**|**2**
37 Panton Street, SW1   020 3093 8463   5–4A
17a Percy St, W1   020 7631 3319   3–1D
31 Catherine St, WC2   020 7836 6377   5–3D
157 King St, W6   020 8741 8563   8–2C
The "absolutely delicious" South Indian vegan and vegetarian food at this
quintet of low-key cafés – stretching from Harrow to Covent Garden – is
"good enough to keep carnivores quiet": in particular "the dosas, which are
just what you want from a dosa: crispy, tender, flavourful". The formula is
"simple but it works, even if the menu is always the same"; and it helps that
the experience comes at "very reasonable prices". / www.sagarrestaurant.co.uk.

Saint Jacques SW1 £87 **4**|**3**|**4**
5 St James's St   020 7930 2030   3–4D
This "delightful" and "very trad (in a good way) French resto" in St James's
thrives on its "unpretentious, classic cooking delivered by efficient and
accommodating waiting staff" under an "entertaining boss who seems to
know everyone". "There have been several very good restaurants on this site
(Boulestin and L'Oranger inter alia) and Saint Jacques is up there with any of
them". Top Menu Tip – "the theatre of crêpes Suzette cooked by the table
is highly recommended". / SW1A 1EF; www.saintjacquesrestaurant.com;
saintjacquesrestaurant; Mon-Fri 22, Sat 10 pm.

St John Bread & Wine E1 £74 **4**|**3**|**3**
94-96 Commercial St   020 7251 0848   13–2C
"Wearing the 'nose-to-tail' mantle a little more lightly" than the Smithfield
original, Trevor Gulliver and Fergus Henderson's Spitalfields canteen hits the
nail on the head for many diners. Its robust British small plates are "seriously
good – different, and utterly delicious with plenty of offal" – and "the wine
list with lesser known bottles is also interesting". "The room may be clinical"
but "its basic style is attractive… if you like that sort of thing". Top Menu
Tip – "the best bacon butty in London!", plus "mega Eccles cakes with
Lancashire cheese to fill you up". / E1 6LZ; www.stjohngroup.uk.com;
st.john.restaurant; Mon-Sun 9.30 pm.

St John Smithfield EC1 £82 **4**|**4**|**3**
26 St John St   020 7251 0848   10–1B
"Still love the place…" – Trevor Gulliver and Fergus Henderson's icon of
British cuisine coined the concept of 'nose-to-tail dining' and hasn't missed a
beat since it opened in 1994, in a "stark-but-chic" ex-smokehouse, near
Smithfield Market. Known for its "sometimes challenging menu (not least for
its selection of offal dishes)", it continues to deliver "totally brilliant",
"straightforward" dishes ("the cuts may be humble, but the results are of the
highest grade") from "good old-fashioned recipes" in its distinctive "white-
walled, down-to-earth" setting, whose ultra-utilitarian style is livened up by
"entertaining" service that's "very kind and personable". Top Menu Tip –
"puddings are to die for (I don't have a sweet tooth but this is the only
restaurant where I ALWAYS have a pudding)". / EC1M 4AY; stjohnrestaurant.com;
st.john.restaurant; Mon-Sat 10.30 pm, Sun 4 pm.

St Johns N19 £66 **3**|**3**|**4**
91 Junction Rd   020 7272 1587   9–1C
Fans hail this Archway tavern as "the best for miles around" (it was George
Michael's favourite back in the day) – "always welcoming", and with a
"terrific menu of mainly British cuisine" served in the dining room, which has
"some charm as a former ballroom". Top Menu Tip – the "great roast beef"
is a treat for Sunday lunch. / N19 5QU; www.stjohnstavern.com; stjohnstavern;
Tue-Sat 10 pm, Sun 6 pm.

St Moritz W1 £66 3|3|3
161 Wardour Street 020 7734 3324 4–1C

That "you could almost be in the Alps" is the raison d'être of this chalet-style veteran in Soho, celebrating its half-century this year. There is the odd long-term visitor who feels its performance is so-so nowadays, and that it's "time to call it a day on this long-time institution". But in general, reviews are positive for its "traditional Swiss menu which caters for all lovers of the country's food". "It may be described as looking old-fashioned, but I have eaten in many restaurants in Switzerland which look exactly like this; absolute classics!" / W1F 8WJ; www.stmoritz-restaurant.co.uk; st.moritzsoho; Mon-Sat 11.30 pm, Sun 10.30 pm.

Sakonis £34 3|3|2
127-129 Ealing Rd, HA0 020 8903 9601 1–1A
330 Uxbridge Road, HA5 020 8903 9601 1–1A

An all-you-can-eat buffet – with options at breakfast, lunch and dinner – is a longstanding feature of this no-frills veggie veteran: a family business that started out as a market stall in 1984. It also offers an à la carte menu, which includes a significant Indo-Chinese section. No alcohol, so knock yourself out on the array of milkshakes and lassis. (It also has offshoots in Hatch End and Kingsbury). / sakonis.co.uk; sakonis_uk.

Sale e Pepe SW1 £83
9-15 Pavilion Road 020 7235 0098 6–1D

Retired maître d' Tony and his team created an atmosphere that was "mad, crowded, noisy yet still great fun" at this fifty-year-old Trattoria (est. 1974), long known for providing relatively good value for somewhere not far from the back door of Harrods. In February 2023, it was taken over by The Thesleff Group, whose press release promises 'a revitalised energy and subtle changes' to this old groover, which includes a trendified menu. No reports from the old regulars as yet on the new regime so we've left it un-rated for the time being. / SW1X 0HD; www.saleepepe.co.uk; saleepepelondon; Mon-Sat 10.30 pm, Sun 10 pm.

Le Salon Privé TW1 £73 3|3|3
43 Crown Rd 020 8892 0602 1–4A

For a quality meal out St Margaret's way, this conventional French restaurant – set in agreeably old-fashioned Victorian premises – provides a traditional and enjoyable experience that's consistently well-rated in our annual diners' poll. Top Tip – good-value 'menu du jour' available at lunch and at dinner early in the week. / TW1 3EJ; lesalonprive.net; lesalon_prive; Tue-Sat 21.30 pm, Sun 4 pm.

Salt Yard £61 3|2|2
54 Goodge St, W1 020 7637 0657 2–1B
The Southern Terrace, Ariel Way, W12 020 7749 3834 1–3B
New Hibernia House, Winchester Walk, SE1 020 8161 0171 10–4C

"The original Salt Yard in W1 used to be one of London's best new tapas restaurants" – but it opened over 15 years ago and "the subsequent roll-out of the brand as multiple branches" under Urban Pubs & Bars "has seen quality drop quite a lot". As "a pleasant option for well-produced Med-inspired dishes", they maintain a fair number of fans, if without the pizzazz once conjured by the name. The year-old branch near the entrance to Westfield is the highest rated, and the newest near Borough Market is also seen as "a handy addition to the group". / www.saltyardgroup.co.uk; saltyardgroup.

Saltie Girl W1 £75 **3** **4** **3**
15 North Audley Street 020 3893 3000 3–2A

"You will not believe how good canned fish can be!" – this late 2022 newcomer from a Boston chain maxes out on luxurious seafood treats ("delicious oysters, caviar, premium tinned seafood and of course lobster rolls!") and provides both "a nice change of pace" and also "a great addition to the Mayfair food scene". "The fresh fish is excellent. The dozens of tinned fish options are surprisingly varied and tasty – like having a North Sea picnic when you don't want a full meal". / W1K 6WZ; www.saltiegirl.com; saltiegirl.london; Mon-Sat 11 pm, Sun 4 pm.

Salut N1 £79 **4** **4** **4**
412 Essex Road 020 3441 8808 9–3D

This "lovely neighbourhood restaurant" in Islington from brothers Martin & Christoph Lange thrives thanks to a "really good all-round menu" fusing Nordic, French and German influences, and a "New York-style ambience". / N1 3PJ; www.salut-london.co.uk; salut.restaurant; Mon-Thu 9.30 pm, Fri & Sat 10 pm, Sun 9 pm.

Sam's Café NW1 £28 **3** **2** **2**
40 Chalcot Road 020 7916 3736 9–3B

"This upmarket local café" with artistic leanings in Primrose Hill has a "great vibe, relaxed-yet-warm service and consistently good food". Founded by actor Sam Frears and novelist Andrew O'Hagan, who live nearby, it has an artist-in-residence programme and hosts readings, live music and community supper clubs. / NW1 8LS; www.samscafeprimrosehill.com; samscafeprimrosehill; Mon & Tue, Thu-Sun 10 pm, Wed 5 pm.

Sam's Kitchen W6 NEW
17 Crisp Road 020 8237 1020 8–2C

Just behind Sam's Riverside, on the site that was Café Plum (RIP) – Sam Harrison's vision of a 'perfect little local corner café' offers a full English breakfast and all-day bacon rolls alongside more contemporary dishes such as beetroot with halloumi and za'atar on sourdough with goat's cheese, crushed nuts, pickled red onion, roasted garlic confit and poached eggs. It opened in summer 2023, too late for feedback in our annual diners' poll. / W6 9RL; samsriverside.co.uk; samskitchenw6; Mon-Sun 4 pm.

Sam's Riverside W6 £81 **3** **5** **5**
1 Crisp Walk 020 8237 1020 8–2C

"Sam himself is very much in evidence" at his "glamourous" brasserie, which has an "ideal location on the Thames" – "with a close-up view of Hammersmith Bridge" – and whose popularity is making it "a destination restaurant" for a huge fan club spread across west London. "You could describe it as the perfect local – but it's smarter than that", with a "lovely" (and expensively decorated) interior and "super vibe". "The menu is full of well-crafted crowd- pleasers" and – though not hugely 'gastro' – its "seafood orientation" (and "wonderful seafood platters") makes anything pescatarian a top choice. "Packed to the rafters", it's "a great night out". / W6 9DN; samsriverside.co.uk; samsriversidew6; Mon-Sat 10 pm, Sun 4 pm.

Sam's Waterside TW8
Catherine Wheel Road Awaiting tel 1–3A

Restaurateur Sam Harrison's smart neighbourhood restaurant and bar is designed to help anchor the new Brentford Project – an upscale, mixed-use development beside the River Brent, open in summer 2023. It follows the success of Sam's Riverside at the re-opened Riverside Studios by Hammersmith Bridge, although it doesn't have the sweeping Thames -side vistas of the original. (There is also a Sam's Larder opposite). / TW8 8BD.

Sambal Shiok N7   £47   3 2 2
171 Holloway Road   020 7619 9888   9–2D
"Fantastic laksa – available in vegetarian versions" – is a crowd-pleaser at Mandy Lim's hawker-style Malaysian spot on the Holloway Road. Her authentic version is in the 'campur' style found in Malacca – combining Kuala Lumpur's curry laksa with Penang's fiery assam. If you don't like noodles, rice bowls are also on offer. / N7 8LX; www.sambalshiok.co.uk; sambalshiok; Tue-Thu 9 pm, Fri & Sat 9.30 pm.

San Carlo SW1   £82   3 3 3
2 Regent Street Saint James's   020 3778 0768   4–4D
"The warmth of the welcome and quality of the food can come as something of a surprise at such a central and well-known location" as this West End branch (just north of Pall Mall) of the national group, created by Sicilian-born Carlo Distefano and now with over 20 locations nationwide. Perhaps it's the "lovely atmosphere for either a business or social lunch or dinner" that's its key strength, but all reports suggest the "great and varied menu" is also "consistently good". / SW1Y 4AU; sancarlo.co.uk; sancarlorestaurants; Mon-Sun 11.30 pm.

San Carlo Cicchetti   £68   3 4 4
215 Piccadilly, W1   020 7494 9435   4–4C
30 Wellington St, WC2   020 7240 6339   5–3D
6 Hans Road, SW3   020 7846 7145   6–1D
"Don't be put off by the tourist location or the gold frontage" if you visit the flagship branch of this successful Italian chain near Piccadilly Circus (which is due to double in size over 2023). For a national group, it and its siblings deliver a surprisingly high-quality formula that mixes "a great range of Venetian-style small plates" with "friendly and efficient" service and "bright and vibrant interiors" which create a "wonderful and buzzing atmosphere". Top Tip – "super for pre-theatre eating". / www.sancarlocicchetti.co.uk; sancarlorestaurants.

San Pietro W8   £56   3 3 4
7 Stratford Road   020 7938 1805   6–1A
"A wonderful display of fresh fish on ice" ("including the biggest scallops with the coral attached") greets diners arriving at this "unique Italian" in a quiet corner of Kensington, whose "cooking is precise with a light touch". / W8 6RF; www.san-pietro.co.uk; sanpietro7; Mon-Sun 10 pm.

Santa Maria   £47   4 2 3
160 New Cavendish St, W1   020 7436 9963   2–1B
92-94 Waterford Road, SW6   020 7384 2844   6–4A
11 Bond Street, W5   020 8579 1462   1–3A
189 Upper Street, N1   020 7288 7400   9–2D
"Glorious-tasting authentic Neapolitan pizza", "with interesting toppings that are quite unique", is the USP of this Ealing-based operation launched in 2010 by Naples-born duo Angelo and Pasquale, which has grown in recent years into a small group with outlets as far away as Islington and Fitzrovia. Their "aim is to transport you to Naples, and the pizzas live up to the ambition". / www.santamariapizzeria.com; santamariapizza.

Santa Maria del Sur SW8   £60   3 3 2
129 Queenstown Road   020 7622 2088   11–1C
"Friendly" Argentinian steakhouse that's clocked up 18 years in Battersea, with well-priced cuts of beef complemented by empanadas at lunchtime and a list of South American wines. Top Tip – on Sundays you can bring your own wine, with no corkage fee. / SW8 3RH; www.santamariadelsur.co.uk; stamariadelsur; Mon-Sun 10 pm.

Santini SW1 £116 2 3 3

29 Ebury St   020 7730 4094   2–4B

Food writer Laura Santini nowadays oversees this datedly chic Belgravia Italian founded by her father Gino in 1984, and which had quite a celebrity following back in the day (Frank Sinatra was a fan). Ever since we started our guide in 1991, it's been priced for the rich residents of SW1 (a bowl of pasta is about £30), and most years don't see a huge volume of reports. Representative of feedback this year: "OK food on the whole (if unexciting)… and big wine list mark-ups". / SW1W 0NZ; www.santinirestaurant.com; santinirestaurant; Mon-Sat 11.30 pm.

Santo Mare W1 £97 3 4 3

87-89 George Street   020 7486 0377   2–1A

High-quality Italian seafood (some of it fresh from the tank) and elegant decor help win solid ratings for Andrea Reitano's Marylebone fixture, which is about to enter its fifth year. But there's the odd cavil from diners who say it has "excellent food and good service but is more expensive than it should be". / W1U 8AQ; www.santomare.com; santomare; Mon-Sun 11 pm.

Santo Remedio £72 3 3 2

152 Tooley Street, SE1   020 7403 3021   10–4D
55 Great Eastern Street, EC2   020 7403 3021   13–1B

"Proper home-made nachos" backed up by "awesome margaritas" top the "short but focused menu" at Edson & Natalie Diaz-Fuentes's authentic Mexican cantina in Bermondsey (with an offshoot in Shoreditch). Top Tip – "the reasonably priced pre-theatre menu is perfect before going to the Bridge Theatre".

Saravanaa Bhavan HA0 £53 4 2 2

531-533 High Rd   020 8900 8526   1–1A

"It feels like being transported to SB in Chennai", according to well-travelled fans of the Wembley branch of this global vegetarian chain offering "reasonably priced South Indian food", who say that "if you're hankering for a masala dosa, this is the place". There are actually seven branches around the capital (including Leicester Square and Tooting), but this is the most commented-on. (Historical footnote: P Rajagopal, who founded SB in 1981, died five years ago after being imprisoned for the murder of an employee whose wife he wanted to marry.) / HA0 2DJ; saravanabhavanlondon.co.uk; saravanaa bhavan london; Mon-Sun 10.30 pm.

Sartoria W1 £94 3 3 3

20 Savile Row   020 7534 7000   4–3A

This classic Italian set among the tailors of Savile Row (for which it is named and themed) serves "outstanding" dishes – most notably seafood – at admittedly "expensive" prices. Celebrity chef Francesco Mazzei departed in early 2023, leaving the D&D London venue lacking a high-profile figurehead, but thus far, this has seemingly had little effect on the quality of the cooking. / W1S 3PR; www.sartoria-restaurant.co.uk; sartoriarestaurant; Mon-Sat 10 pm.

(The River Restaurant)
The Savoy WC2 £103 2 2 3

91 The Strand   020 7499 0122   5–3D

Gordon Ramsay's two-year-old tenure has yet to dazzle at this Thames-side dining room (which, two years ago – when Gordon took it over – returned to the name under which it was launched in 1890 and has traded under for much of the last century). From its days as Kaspar's (RIP), it continues a fish and seafood theme – now with a fashionable raw bar – and there are also a few meat grills on the menu. But few dishes catch the eye from the somewhat "unremarkable" selection and it can be "difficult to find something you fancy". And, when they arrive, too often results are "only moderately good" or plain "disappointing". / WC2R 0EU; www.gordonramsayrestaurants.com; riverrestaurantbygordonramsay; Mon-Sat midnight, Sun 11.30 pm.

The Savoy Hotel,
Savoy Grill WC2   **£154**   2️⃣2️⃣4️⃣
Strand   020 7592 1600   5–3D
A two-month closure facilitated a 'Gatsby makeover' this year at this elegant and famous grill room, which for the last 20 years has been part of Gordon Ramsay's culinary empire. (It now incorporates a chef's table, and a walnut wood-lined wine experience room for eight). With its Beef Wellington, Dover Sole and Lobster Thermidor – plus also a selection of steaks from now de rigueur charcoal grill – fans say it's "superb all round for celebrating that special occasion". Doubters, though, continue to focus on its "extortionate prices and very uninspired menu in this newly redecorated Art Deco space". / WC2R 0EU; www.gordonramsayrestaurants.com; savoygrillgordonramsay; Mon-Sat midnight, Sun 11.30 pm.

The Savoy Hotel,
Thames Foyer WC2   **£115**   2️⃣4️⃣5️⃣
91 The Strand   020 7420 2111   5–3D
"Is there a better way to spend the afternoon?", query fans of the "beautiful" foyer of this famous hotel – "a wonderful room with the piano playing and where the sandwiches just keep coming!" Supporters say "nothing can compare to the high level of cakes" and that service is "above par" too. Ratings are capped, though, by one or two more cautious reports, from those who "were expecting more of the tea" (too weak) and/or the victuals. When it comes to the music, there's also some debate – "I hated the Disney tunes being played on the piano, although admittedly I was tempted to stand and join in when it moved on to Les Mis!" / WC2R 0ER; www.thesavoylondon.com; thesavoylondon; Mon & Tue 4 pm, Wed-Sun 6 pm.

Scalini SW3   **£95**   3️⃣4️⃣3️⃣
1-3 Walton St   020 7225 2301   6–2C
This "really good old-school Italian" in Knightsbridge is a perfect fit for the Harrods shopping crowd it feeds, and "has hardly changed in 30 years". Expansion in recent years has seen spin-offs open in Cannes and the Middle East, which gives a clue to the prices charged. Top Menu Tip – "the bruschetta they give you as you sit down is great, but make sure you ask for cheese as well". / SW3 2JD; www.scalinilondon.co.uk; scaliniuk; Mon-Sat 10.45 pm, Sun 10 pm.

The Scarsdale W8   **£67**   2️⃣3️⃣5️⃣
23a Edwardes Sq   020 7937 1811   8–1D
On one level it's like any other "friendly local", but few pubs have such a picturesque location as this popular tavern, on the kind of Regency square in Kensington that makes tourists swoon (and with its own cute outside terrace). "Great pub-like food" (without any gastro pretensions) is served in its "lively" dining room. Piers Morgan throws an annual Christmas party here, hosting celeb pals from TV and politics, with Gary Lineker in regular attendance… well, nowhere's perfect… / W8 6HE; www.scarsdaletavern.co.uk; scarsdalew8; Mon-Sat 11 pm, Sun 10.30 pm.

Schnitzel Forever N16 £51 3|3|2

119 Stoke Newington Church Street   020 7419 0022   1–1C

"Literally the size of a dinner plate", the schnitzels at this tiled Stoke Newington two-year-old are "freshly made", "tender & super-tasty", and come with "great sides – especially the pickled cucumber salad". The classics (veal, pork, chicken) take their cue from German-speaking central Europe, but the menu strays as far as Mexico and Japan to up the variety. A spin-off opened in Hoxton under the name Schnitzel Heaven in early 2023. / N16 0UD; www.schnitzelforever.co.uk; schnitzel_forever; Mon, Wed & Thu, Sat 10 pm, Fri 10.30 pm, Sun 9.30 pm.

Scott's W1 £113 3|3|4

20 Mount St   020 7495 7309   3–3A

"Always sparkling" – this "glamorous" Mayfair "classic" (007's favourite) is nowadays second only to its Theatreland stablemate Sheekeys in terms of the total number of nominations it receives in our annual diners' poll; and likewise in the rankings as a "go-to place for fish". More "sophisticated" (and expensive) than its rival, the crowd is better heeled and more A-lister here than in WC2 (and also, perhaps, with a greater share of "flash Harrys"). "Excellent Dover Sole", "the best crab" and "top-quality fruits de mer" are typical of the "superb seafood", "classily" delivered by "professional" staff, all of which make it popular for most occasions, including business entertaining. "It slipped down in the estimations" of one or two reporters this year due to general concerns that it risks becoming "overrated and overpriced". But for the vast majority, the feeling is still that although "it's obviously not cheap, it's a real treat and a totally reliable one at that". / W1K 2HE; www.scotts-restaurant.com; scottsmayfair; Mon-Sat 1 am, Sun 9.30 pm.

Scott's Richmond TW9 £113 2|3|4

4 Whittaker Avenue   020 3700 2660   1–4A

"They must have spent a fortune on the decor" of this "absolutely stunning" Richmond newcomer, with a "terrace overlooking the Thames": Richard Caring's first spin-off from Mayfair's legendary Scott's. But while everyone is sold on the "wonderful dining room with its riverside view", views on the cuisine diverge. Fans say its luxurious seafood menu "has transferred very well" delivering "top-quality" Fruits de Mer, Lobster Bisque and other fishy delights. But its ratings in our annual diners' poll are not nearly as strong as in W1. Firstly, there are numerous reservations about it being "totally overpriced". Secondly, it can seem like a poor substitute ("I was excited to visit the newly opened Scott's in Richmond, a great addition to the area, so I thought. But this version is nothing like the original, it is like an Ivy Café under another name"). / TW9 1EH; www.scotts-richmond.com; scottsrichmond; Mon-Sat 12.30 am, Sun midnight.

Scully SW1 £91 4|4|2

4 St James's Market   020 3911 6840   4–4D

"Ramuel Scully gets flavour out of ingredients like no one else" at his ambitious St James's Market fixture, where he and his team serve a "wacky and interesting menu based on ferments and underused ingredients" from their open kitchen. Its ratings are not as stratospheric as when it first opened, due to the odd doubt that "the quality of foodstuffs can be lost in the plethora of flavourings". But the balance of feedback this year was highly enthusiastic: "it's my London go-to" with a "very different menu that changes enough to warrant a return". / SW1Y 4QU; www.scullyrestaurant.com; scully_chef; Tue-Sat 11 pm.

The Sea, The Sea   **£175**   5 4 4
174 Pavilion Road, SW3   020 7824 8090   6–2D
337 Acton Mews, E8   020 7824 8090   14–2A
"Incredible seafood in the most unique of settings" inspires outstanding feedback on chef Leandro Carreira and restaurateur Alex Hunter's "amazing and inventive" 14-seater chef's table experience under Haggerston railway arches, where the moodily-lit counter looks onto the gleaming open kitchen. A 12-course tasting menu involving every type of sustainable sea creature is presented at £150 per person. (Very good all-round ratings too for the original branch – a simpler and cheaper seafood bar in the bouji backstreets, off Sloane Street). / www.theseathesea.net; theseathesea_.

Sea Containers,
Mondrian London SE1   **£83**   2 2 3
20 Upper Ground   020 3747 1000   10–3A
This swish and "buzzy" hotel dining room on the South Bank walkway – designed by Tom Dixon with full-height windows and a terrace overlooking the river – makes a most "enjoyable place to meet friends" – "and there's a great bar" by Ryan Chetiyawardana, aka Mr Lyan. On the debit side, it's certainly "not cheap", and the food "could be so much better". / SE1 9PD; www.seacontainerslondon.com; seacontainersldn; Mon-Sun 9.30 pm.

Seabird at The Hoxton,
Southwark SE1   **£90**   4 3 5
40 Blackfriars Road   020 7903 3000   10–4A
"Fresh fish and shellfish" – including "oysters to die for" from what is billed as 'London's longest oyster list' – make this glamorous modern venue in Southwark a genuine rarity: a swish rooftop restaurant worth visiting for its food. Set on the 14th floor of a hip hotel, it has "great panoramas over the capital, and the large terrace is a top spot in good weather" – "loved the atmosphere, views and food". / SE1 8NY; thehoxton.com; thehoxtonhotel; Sun-Thu midnight, Fri & Sat 1 am.

The Seafood Bar W1   **£87**   3 4 2
77 Dean Street   020 4525 0733   4–1D
This "clean and spare-looking seafood restaurant" from Amsterdam's De Visscher family is a "super addition to Soho", with "platters both raw and roasted that are generous, super-fresh, tasty and not exorbitantly pricey". It's also "a great place just to drop in for a martini and some oysters at the bar". / W1D 3SH; www.theseafoodbar.com; theseafoodbar; Sun-Thu 10 pm, Fri & Sat 10.30 pm.

Seafresh SW1   **£60**   3 2 2
80-81 Wilton Rd   020 7828 0747   2–4B
This "absolutely reliable" chippie has done sterling service in Pimlico for 59 years, with a recent refurb enabling it to live up to its name. "Dishes range from excellent fish 'n' chips to more complex and flavourful fare" – and it's "reasonably priced". / SW1V 1DL; seafreshrestaurant; Mon-Sun 10.30 pm.

Searcys St Pancras Grand NW1   **£77**   2 2 3
Upper Concourse   020 7870 9900   9–3C
With its gracious styling, this handsome brasserie (with a neighbouring Champagne bar overlooking the Eurostar tracks) is extremely comfortable and its location – and all-day service from early morning onwards – certainly means "it's a very convenient place for folk from around the country to meet up". But while it is tipped for business, breakfast and afternoon tea, it's hard to give it a ringing endorsement: to some diners, it feels like "everything is average, apart from the price…" / NW1 2QP; stpancrasbysearcys.co.uk; searcystpancras; Mon-Sat 9 pm, Sun 4 pm.

The Sea Shell NW1 £59 3 2 2
49-51 Lisson Grove 020 7224 9000 9–4A

The very "essence of chip shop" – this century-old Lisson Grove institution serves "lovely fresh fish" with a "great choice" of preparation ("plain grilled or deep-fried in batter or breadcrumbs") and "LOTS of chips – it's bottomless and they mean it!". "Staff can be a bit pressurised on a busy service, and not terribly engaged with customers". / NW1 6UH; www.seashellrestaurant.co.uk; seashellrestaurant; Tue-Sat 10 pm, Sun 7 pm.

Sessions Arts Club EC1 £62 3 4 5
24 Clerkenwell Green 020 3793 4025 10–1A

"A very special venue"; "hidden behind a nondescript door in Farringdon and accessed by an ancient brass lift, you pass beyond the heavy black curtain to a breathtaking dining room" at this "wonderfully atmospheric" two-year-old. "A historic setting" (mentioned in Dickens's 'Oliver Twist') – its "high ceilings, distressed walls and candle light" come highly recommended for "an illicit date". Fans of Florence Knight's "inventive" cuisine say it "holds its own in the space" – is "magical" even – but to others it is "unspectacular" in comparison to the backdrop. "Booking a table requires military advance planning but it's worth it". / EC1R 0NA; sessionsartsclub.com; sessionsartsclub; Tue-Sat 10 pm.

Seven Park Place SW1 £170 3 2 2
7-8 Park Pl 020 7316 1621 3–4C

A "real favourite" of well-heeled foodies, this classy if relatively unsung Mayfair hotel dining room boasts in "William Drabble, the most underrated of chefs – and one of great longevity" after 15 years at the helm. There is an eight-course 'Menu Gourmand' (for £125), but also à la carte options (starting in the evening with a two-course meal for £82 – lunchtimes are cheaper). / SW1A 1LS; www.stjameshotelandclub.com; sevenparkplace; Thu-Sat, Tue, Wed 9 pm.

Sexy Fish W1 £104 1 1 2
1-4 Berkeley Square 020 3764 2000 3–3B

"Full of Eurotrashy tourists taking selfies" – if that's not you, a visit to Richard Caring's glitzy and "superficial" Mayfair seafood scene may be "an unhappy experience". True, fans do claim it can be a "very buzzy and atmospheric" place to try "for the people-watching and sushi" (plus other luxurious fishy treats). But 70% of reporters feel it's "overpriced"; and its "loud, echo-chamber" styling, "offhand service" and "food that – particularly given the cost – is terrible" can all grate. ("I'm surprised there isn't a tanning booth in the loos so the clientele can top up in between courses…"; "I get forced to go there on business: why anyone would go of their own free will is a mystery"). / W1J 6BR; www.sexyfish.com; sexyfishlondon; Sun-Wed 1 am, Thu-Sat 2 am.

Shahi Pakwaan N2 £36 3 2 2
25 Aylmer Parade, Aylmer Road 020 8341 1111 1–1B

"You go for the food not the location" to this family-run Indian café, rated by locals as one of the best options for a curry in the purlieus of East Finchley. / N2 0PE; www.shahipakwaan.co.uk; shahi_pakwaan009; Mon-Sat 11 pm, Sun 10 pm.

The Shed W8 £83 3 2 4
122 Palace Gardens Ter 020 7229 4024 7–2B

This "noisy, fun" and "quirky little place" – just off Notting Hill Gate – was the first of the Sussex-based Gladwin brothers' 'farm-to-fork' restaurants to open in the capital, a dozen years ago, and is applauded for the "fresh ingredients" that one might hope for. One reporter feels that it's "not as good as it was", but ratings have held up decently over the years. / W8 4RT; www.theshed-restaurant.com; theshed_resto; Tue-Sat, Mon 11.30 pm.

J Sheekey WC2 £93 3 3 4
28-34 St Martin's Ct   020 7240 2565   5–3B

Black & white pictures of actors past and present line the "iconic panelled dining rooms" of this "absolute classic" in Theatreland (est. 1896) – "still the benchmark for fish and seafood" in London; and still the capital's No.1 most-mentioned entry in our annual diners' poll; and still "always packed". Located in an unpromising back alley off St Martin's Lane, you navigate past the uniformed doorman and opaque windows to the "very classy" and "old school" interior, which is "divided into smaller rooms, lending a degree of privacy and keeping the noise down" (not always successfully). A superb variety of fresh dishes is "impeccably" (if "unadventurously") realised, with Dover Sole ("cooked on the bone then prepared by the waiter") and Fish Pie most often featuring in reports. This year, there's a feeling that "though very good, it's now relatively expensive for quality versus its peers": a particular gripe is the "rather overpriced" wine. / WC2N 4AL; www.j-sheekey.co.uk; jsheekeyldn; Mon-Sat 11 pm, Sun 10 pm.

J Sheekey Atlantic Bar WC2 £89 4 2 2
28-32 St Martin's Ct   020 7240 2565   5–3B

"Pre or post-theatre, very much a favourite over many years" – this elegant seafood bar was added adjacent to the main restaurant fifteen years ago, and its more laid-back style means it's tailor-made for a luxurious bite and glass of fizz. That said, it becomes "quite pricey" over time, and doesn't have quite the dazzling golden glow of yesteryear. / WC2N 4AL; www.j-sheekey.co.uk; jsheekeyldn; Mon-Sat 11 pm, Sun 10 pm.

Sheesh W1 NEW
1 Dover Street   020 8559 1155   3–3C

TOWIE comes to Mayfair at Dylan Hunt's March 2023 newcomer: a spin-off from his Chigwell original notorious for its crowd of Essex royalty from Harry Kane to Rod Stewart, and visitors including the Gypsy King himself, Tyson Fury. It also imports its luxurious comfort food menu ('let's begin', 'the main event', 'a bit on the side',…) to a prime spot on Piccadilly. Feedback is too limited for a rating but our first report is not encouraging: "unbelievably over-priced… only the briefest nod to Turkish cuisine… all in all, very disappointing". There is also much outrage online at the restaurant's unusual practice of presenting prices ex VAT (so, be prepared for them to whack 20% on your bill…) / W1S 4LD; sheeshrestaurant.co.uk; sheesh_uk.

Shikumen,
Dorsett Hotel W12 £73 4 2 2
58 Shepherd's Bush Green   020 8749 9978   8–1C

"Some of the best dim sum in London" and "outstanding, delicious Peking duck" is an unexpected find in this anonymous modern hotel dining room overlooking trafficky Shepherd's Bush Green. It's "good enough to impress visitors from the Far East" and has built a sufficiently strong reputation in its 10 years to be extremely busy at times. / W12 5AA; www.shikumen.co.uk; shikumen.w12; Mon-Sun 11 pm.

Shilpa W6 £37 4 2 2
206 King St   020 8741 3127   8–2B

Its "appearance is very basic", but this "slightly shabby" Hammersmith pit-stop is acclaimed by its local fans as "still some of the best Indian food in London, regardless of price". "The host in charge is very charming", too. / W6 0RA; shilpahammersmith.co.uk; Sun-Wed 11 pm, Thu-Sat midnight.

Ship Tavern WC2 £71 3 4 5

12 Gate Street   020 7405 1992   2–1D

This historic Holborn tavern – dating from 1549, if rebuilt a century ago – deploys its wood-panelled Dickensian atmosphere to good effect, with appetising bites served in the bar and a more involved menu in the upstairs Oak Room, complete with dining booths and an open fireplace. / WC2A 3HP; www.theshiptavern.co.uk; theshiptavern; Mon-Sun 11 pm.

Shiro EC2 NEW

100 Liverpool Street   020 3873 8252   13–2B

Neither its prime City location – overlooking Broadgate Circle – nor its experienced heritage (the Hong Kong-based Aqua group, with their Aqua-branded operations in the Shard and on Oxford Street) have helped garner huge attention for this glossy December 2022 newcomer: a minimalist Japanese, where chef Ken Miyake offers 'crystal sushi' (draping sushi rolls in coloured jelly slices with kimchi, ponzu or mint and sake favouring) plus robata-grilled meats and noodles. The exception is a January 2023 review from the Independent's Lucy Thackray, who said the "dizzying" selection of dishes "hit the mark, when it comes to the trifecta [of] presentation, flavour, quality". She also noted, though, that portions are "petite"; and that it's "easy to rack up quite a bill". / EC2M 7RH; www.shirosushi.co.uk; shirosushilondon; Mon-Sat 9.30 pm.

Shoryu Ramen £59 3 2 2

9 Regent St, SW1   no tel   4–4D
3 Denman St, W1   no tel   4–3C
5 Kingly Ct, W1   no tel   4–2B
35 Great Queen Street, WC2   no tel   5–1D
190 Kensington High Street, W8   no tel   8–1D
45 Great Eastern Street, EC2   no tel   13–1B
Broadgate Circle, EC2   no tel   13–2B

"The ramen is excellent" at this West End-based group from the Japan Centre's Tak Tokumine – although "the rest of the menu is not as good" and the venues tend to be "too cramped and/or noisy to be ideal". A drive to expand via franchise operations has apparently stalled since the summer 2022 opening of a branch in Kensington High Street – a possible sign that "we may have passed peak noodle". / www.shoryuramen.com; shoryu_ramen.

The Sichuan EC1 £50 3 2 2

14 City Road   020 7588 5489   13–2A

"Authentically fiery dishes" light up the menu at this City Road restaurant where head chef Zhang Xiao Zhong hails from Chengdu, the capital of Sichuan – a third-generation chef, his grandfather was personal chef to Deng Xiaoping, China's leader through the 1980s. / EC1Y 2AA; www.thesichuan.co.uk; Mon-Sun 11 pm.

Silk Road SE5 £28 4 3 2

49 Camberwell Church St   020 7703 4832   1–3C

This "rapid-fire" canteen in Camberwell serves up "pungent and fiery spiced dishes" from Xinjiang in northwest China, homeland of the Muslim Uigurs. The food is "relatively cheap" and "a cut above" what you might expect – which makes a visit "well worth sharing a table and being hurried out afterwards". / SE5 8TR; silkroadlondon.has.restaurant; Mon-Sun 11 pm.

The Silver Birch W4 £86 4 3 2
142 Chiswick High Road   020 8159 7176   8–2A
"Great to have this restaurant on our doorstep" – Kimberley Hernandez's
superior fixture is easily missed in the strip of pizza-stops and cafés on
Chiswick's main drag; but it's well worth discovering for its *"interesting, very
well-prepared and presented"* (and relatively healthy) cuisine. And in April
2023, they appointed Nathan Cornwell (recently of The Barn at Moor Hall)
as head chef who has, if anything, further stepped up its performance. Not
sure about the home-made elderflower wine though… / W4 1PU;
silverbirchchiswick.co.uk; silverbirchchiswick; Tue-Sat 9 pm.

Simpson's in the Strand WC2 £100
100 Strand   020 7420 2111   5–3D
*This legendary temple to roast beef (opened in 1828) closed in March
2020 and has yet to re-open. In August 2023, the Savoy (of which it's a
part) auctioned off many of the antiquities relating to the site, including
fireplaces, furniture, crockery and its renowned carving trolleys. It has also
posted on its website its 'intention to announce a re-opening date in 2024'.
Clearly it will be a new non-heritage-based departure for this famous name,
so, watch this space.* / WC2R 0EW; www.simpsonsinthestrand.co.uk; simpsons1828.

Singapore Garden NW6 £59 3 3 3
83a Fairfax Rd   020 7624 8233   9–2A
"This place has not changed in 30 years, thank goodness!" – a Swiss
Cottage *"stalwart"* that *"packs 'em in every night"* (*"it gets very loud"*) with
"slick service and consistently good cooking" from *"an excellent range of
Chinese and SE Asian specialities"*, all at very *"reasonable prices"*. Top Menu
Tip – *"laksa is a favourite"*. / NW6 4DY; www.singaporegarden.co.uk;
singapore_garden; Mon-Thu 10.30 pm, Fri & Sat 11 pm, Sun 10 pm.

Singburi Royal Thai Café E11 £28 4 2 2
593 Leytonstone High Rd   020 8281 4801   1–1D
"Just go!" say fans of this *"wildly popular"* shopfront Thai BYO in
Leytonstone, which *"deserves a medal"* for the *"fabulous flavours"* on its
"authentic menu". Top Tip – *"book in person for weeks ahead – no phone
bookings"*. / E11 4PA; singburi_e11; Wed-Sat 10.30 pm, Sun 9.30 pm.

Six by Nico £70 3 3 3
33-41 Charlotte Street, W1   020 7580 8143   2–1C
6 Chancellor Passage, E14   020 3912 3334   12–1C
*Glasgow chef Nico Simeone's distinctive concept has grown into a national
chain with 11 restaurants (including Fitzrovia and Canary Wharf) in just six
years, offering a quick-changing succession of themed six-course menus for
under £50 a head. It's widely seen as "fantastic value" and has a sizeable
fanbase amongst reporters ("every six weeks, the menu renews and for me,
it is something to look forward to…"; "we simply love it and we've yet to
miss a menu!" – "the Tokyo menu was so good we went back a second
time"). Only a tiny few say, "you can feel you're on a conveyor belt with lots
of upsells"; or that the whole thing is "a dystopia of where restaurants will
evolve".* / www.sixbynico.co.uk; sixbynico.

Six Portland Road W11 £83 3 3 3
6 Portland Road   020 7229 3130   7–2A
*Nowadays owned by Jesse Dunford Wood, this "beauty of a local restaurant"
is a "gem worth travelling to Holland Park for" – "with a warm welcome,
efficient staff and a regularly changing menu". It's notably "small and cosy",
which most reporters "love".* / W11 4LA; www.sixportlandroad.com;
sixportlandroad; Mon-Sun 10 pm.

64 Goodge Street W1 NEW
64 Goodge Street   020 3747 6364   2–1C
The team behind highly regarded central London trio Portland, Clipstone and the Quality Chop House is to open what promises to be a smart French bistro in Fitzrovia, in August 2023. Chef Stuart Andrews's knowledge of Gallic cuisine stems from his 18 months working in Paris, and he aims to offer 'French cooking from an outsider's perspective'. / W1T 4NF; 64goodgestreet.co.uk; Mon-Sat 11 pm.

Skal Nordic Dining N1   £38   3 4 3
149 Upper Street   07308 031151   9–2D
"Tasty and authentic" Scandinavian dishes including "excellent fish" are on the menu at this "surprisingly cosy and stylish" Nordic outfit in Islington, where "attentive service" ensures an enjoyable meal. Top Menu Tip – "the venison meatballs with lingonberry sauce deserve a special mention". / N1 1RA; www.skalnordicdining.co.uk; skalnordic; Fri & Sat, Tue-Thu 11 pm.

Sketch,
The Lecture Room and Library W1   £245   4 4 5
9 Conduit St   020 7659 4500   4–2A
This "simply stunning" fairytale chamber on the top floor of the well-known Mayfair palazzo won many 5/5 reviews this year, while avoiding the brickbats often thrown at it in former years. "In these curious post-Covid times, where even the most indifferent restaurants are charging hard, this one now seems good value", despite its notoriously vertiginous prices. Overseen by Gallic über-chef Pierre Gagnaire – Daniel Stucki provides a "divine" selection of intriguing modern French dishes, be it from the £190 tasting menu or £210 three-course à la carte. If this venue continues on its current "outstanding" form, we will have to finally agree that it is "deserving of its three Michelin stars". / W1S 2XG; sketch.london; lrl.sketchlondon; Fri & Sat, Wed & Thu 9 pm.

Sketch,
Gallery W1   £101   2 3 4
9 Conduit St   020 7659 4500   4–2A
A gorgeous, Grade II Palladian Mansion… glowing pink-hued walls, high ceilings, glam banquettes… incredible artworks from Yinka Shonibare… über-chef Pierre Gagnaire's menu… what's not to like about this famous Mayfair venue? The fact that it's seen as being mightily "overpriced" with forgettable food is the chief fault, which means that few other than fashionistas and first-timers are prepared to make the investment… even to go to the bog in a WC shaped like an egg! / W1S 2XG; sketch.london; sketchlondon; Sun-Thu 10 pm, Fri & Sat 11 pm.

Skewd Kitchen EN4   £70   4 3 3
12 Cockfosters Parade   020 8449 7771   1–1C
This "fantastic upscaled-local Turkish restaurant" in Cockfosters gives the traditional North London Anatolian grill a modern makeover – and fans say it's "wonderful to see it so deservedly busy" on account of its "excellent food and service". "They've just expanded", but it's "harder than ever to get a table on a Saturday night". / EN4 0BX; www.skewd.com; skewdkitchen; Mon-Sun midnight.

Skylon,
South Bank Centre SE1 £80 2 1 2
Belvedere Road   020 7654 7800   2–3D
"With spectacular views of London over the Thames, this is the place to
bring out-of-towners", say fans of this huge, Brutalist chamber, built in the
1950s as the South Bank's original destination restaurant (when it was
known as 'The People's Palace'). Supporters – particularly those on business
– say the food is "perhaps a little formulaic, but reliably good too". This is
not a universal experience, though, and too often this D&D group venue
suffers from "complacent service" and "below-average cooking". (Some
reports do also tip it as "a very nice spot to eat before a concert". But others
have had a bad pre-show trip… "what we ordered never arrived in time").
/ SE1 8XX; www.skylon-restaurant.co.uk; skylonrestaurant; Mon & Tue 9 pm, Wed-Sat
10 pm, Sun 5 pm.

Skylon Grill SE1 £72 2 3 5
Belvedere Rd   020 7654 7800   2–3D
"Still adore the room but the food should get a leg up at that price" – a
verdict that has for many years dogged this landmark venue. Even though it's
the cheaper section of the large operation run by D&D London, "you're most
certainly paying for the location, when there are similarly priced restaurants
along the South Bank which are much better". / SE1 8XX;
www.skylon-restaurant.co.uk; skylonrestaurant; Mon-Sat 10.30 pm, Sun 4 pm.

Smith & Wollensky WC2 £112 2 2 2
The Adelphi Building, 1-11 John Adam St   020 7321 6007   5–4D
Despite a fine NYC pedigree; a selection of top-quality imported USDA
steaks; and a 'prestige' location, at the foot of the Adelphi (just off the
Strand), this US steakhouse has never made waves in the capital. When it
does, it's often for the wrong reasons, with too many complaints either that
it's "overpriced" or "very disappointing". / WC2N 6HT;
www.smithandwollensky.co.uk; sandwollensky; Mon-Thu 11.30 pm, Fri & Sat midnight,
Sun 10 pm.

Smith's Wapping E1 £82 4 3 4
22 Wapping High St   020 7488 3456   12–1A
"A top selection of fish" – "simple and so fresh" – is served at this smart,
white-tablecloth restaurant in a "fantastic setting, on the Thames at
Wapping, with great views of Tower Bridge". "Service is slick and the
atmosphere reflects the bright, buzzy feel of the whole place". The only
drawback is that "it's always full and difficult to get into". The original
Smith's was founded 66 years ago in Ongar, Essex. / E1W 1NJ;
www.smithsrestaurants.com; smithsofwapping; Mon-Sat 10 pm, Sun 9 pm.

Smiths of Smithfield,
Top Floor EC1 £88 3 3 3
67-77 Charterhouse St   020 7251 7950   10–1A
"Amazing steak (though the rest of menu is good too)" and terrific views
over the City and St Paul's share top billing at the flagship restaurant at the
top of a handsome Grade II-listed former Smithfield market warehouse. It
can be "a bit noisy", but it makes for a "solid dining experience" that's
"always good for business". / EC1M 6HJ; www.smithsofsmithfield.co.uk; thisissmiths;
Mon-Fri 9.30 pm, Sat 9 pm.

Smoke & Salt SW17 £53 5 4 3
115 Tooting High St   no tel   11–2C
Another year of stellar ratings confirms that Remi Williams and Aaron Webster's former pop-up in Tooting is no flash in the pan, offering "fine food in a bustling, vibrant atmosphere" and "set menus of delicious sharing plates" for which they make clever use of European salting, curing and smoking techniques. They made a name for themselves at Pop Brixton before moving to this permanent site in 2020. / SW17 0SY; www.smokeandsalt.com; smokeandsaltldn; Tue-Sat 10 pm.

Smokestak E1 £56 4 3 3
35 Sclater Street   020 3873 1733   13–1C
"Boldly seasoned, flavourful — unashamedly meat-heavy" – dishes are the simple hallmark of BBQ obsessive David Carter's moodily dim-lit Brick Lane operation, inspired by the smokehouses of the American South. "Some interesting options on the menu" include salt-baked beetroot or charred greens with tahini and pomegranate. / E1 6LB; www.smokestak.co.uk; smokestakuk; Mon-Thu, Sat, Fri 11 pm, Sun 10 pm.

Smoking Goat E1 £62 5 3 3
64 Shoreditch High Street   no tel   13–1B
"Thailand meets Shoreditch" at Ben Chapman's "still exciting" BBQ, with its "deliciously different", "confident and bold spicing" creating "amazingly flavoursome food". If there's a downside, it's "cramped" tables and that it becomes "understandably noisy", but regulars "love eating here whether solo or with friends". / E1 6JJ; www.smokinggoatbar.com; smokinggoatbar; Mon-Sat 11 pm, Sun 10 pm.

Smokoloko E1 £18 4 3 3
Old Spitalfields Market, Bethnal Green Road   07508 675363   13–2B
Meaty street-food dishes, smoked in an oven shaped like the boiler of an old steam engine, produce "fabulous food" in the "great setting" of Spitalfield Market. (In August 2023, they graduated to include a small unit with a few seats in the section of the market on Lamb Street.) / E1 6EW; smokoloko.uk; smokolokobbq; Mon-Fri 3 pm, Sat & Sun 5 pm.

Socca W1 £114 3 3 3
41 South Audley Street   020 3376 0000   3–3A
"Deliciously light and fluffy food" inspired by the sunshine cuisine of the south of France lights up the menu at this Mayfair yearling – a collaboration between Lyonnais-born chef Claude Bosi of Bibendum and restaurateur-du-moment Samyukta Nair (it's named after the chickpea flour flatbread made in Nice). Sadly, they have brought with them "plain ludicrous" Riviera-style pricing, which sours the tone of otherwise positive reports. (The Observer's March 2023 review from Jay Rayner was not-dissimilar: "I wanted that utter fabulousness to mitigate the price. But it was strange and uneven rather than the perfect it should be".) / W1K 2PS; soccabistro.com; soccabistro; Mon-Sun 10.30 pm.

Social Eating House W1 £97 3 2 2
58-59 Poland Street   020 7993 3251   4–1C
Having put in over ten years of services, the chilled Soho outpost of Jason Atherton's 'Social' brand no longer attracts a huge volume of feedback. But the food remains good, and the chef's table on the lower ground floor is particularly recommended as a "truly personal and excellent" (if "rather noisy") experience. / W1F 7NR; www.socialeatinghouse.com; socialeathouse; Tue-Sat 10 pm.

Soffice London SW15 £47 3️⃣3️⃣2️⃣
236 Upper Richmond Road   020 3859 4335   11–2B
*"In Putney's fairly indifferent restaurant scene, this is a welcome addition" –
a Sicilian 'gastro-bakery' with an interesting selection of pastries from that
sweet-toothed island, plus pasta and pizza. / SW15 6TG; www.sofficelondon.com;
soffice_london; Mon-Sat 11 pm, Sun 5 pm.*

Soif SW11 £66 3️⃣2️⃣2️⃣
27 Battersea Rise   020 7223 1112   11–2C
*With its charcuterie, gutsy small plates, cheese and wacky vintages, this
venture from Les Caves de Pyrène (est 2011) helped inspire the current
vogue for low intervention wine bars in the capital. Feedback is scarce
nowadays, but still suggests it's worth a try if you're in the vicinity of
Battersea Rise. / SW11 1HG; www.soif.co; soif_sw11; Wed-Sat, Tue 11 pm, Sun
5 pm, Mon 9 pm.*

SOLA W1 £210 5️⃣3️⃣2️⃣
64 Dean Street   020 7734 8428   5–2A
*"Slightly unorthodox" but "exceptional" Californian food "made with super,
luxury ingredients" and backed up by "an interesting and mainly Californian
wine list" mean Victor Garvey's acclaimed four-year-old is "the place to head
for in Soho for an out-of-the-ordinary meal"; and some believe "it should
have two stars from the tyre men". ("Highlights included flambéed
langoustines with a dashi broth and foie gras; and that rare thing, a
grapefruit dessert with jelly, sorbet, consommé and meringue"). If there's a
reservation, it's about the "small and cramped-feeling" space, which critics
feel "for a VERY expensive meal has really no sense of occasion at all" ("it is
essentially an unremarkable café in Soho with staff who might have been
officiating at some kind of sacred ceremony in a High Temple!"). / W1D 4QQ;
solasoho.com; solasoho; Wed-Fri, Tue 8.30 pm, Sat 9 pm.*

Sollip SE1 £107 5️⃣4️⃣3️⃣
8 Melior Street   020 7378 1742   10–4C
*"Perfect French cuisine with a Korean twist" has built an impressive
reputation for Woongchul Park and Bomee Ki's ambitious and highly
accomplished three-year-old – a patch of serenity in the gritty streets
surrounding Guy's Hospital. The main event is an 8-9 course tasting menu,
which is exciting in the freshness of its ideas and with "faultless" realisation.
Top Tip – Bomee trained as a pastry chef so pace yourself for dessert.
/ SE1 3QQ; www.sollip.co.uk; sollip_restaurant; Tue-Sat 9 pm.*

Som Saa E1 £48 4️⃣3️⃣3️⃣
43a Commercial Street   020 7324 7790   13–2C
*"Full of a young crowd who really want to enjoy the flavours of Thailand" –
this "noisy" former factory near Spitalfields Market has won renown for
offering "a unique flavour of 'real' Thai cuisine with a wonderful selection of
zingy, spicy, aromatic and refreshing dishes". Top Menu Tip – "nothing can
beat the whole deep-fried seabass with crunchy bones, and sitting at the
counter they'll do half portions for a single diner. Excellent!" / E1 6BD;
www.somsaa.com; somsaa_london; Mon-Wed 10 pm, Thu-Sat 10.30 pm, Sun 9 pm.*

Sông Quê E2 £41 3️⃣2️⃣2️⃣
134 Kingsland Rd   020 7613 3222   14–2A
*"Some of the best Vietnamese food on Kingsland Road" is to be found at
this "no-frills dining room" in Shoreditch – everything is "fresh and fragrant":
no wonder "they're always so busy". / E2 8DY; www.songque.co.uk; songquecafe;
Mon-Sat 11 pm, Sun 10.30 pm.*

Sorella SW4 £69 3 2 2
148 Clapham Manor Street   020 7720 4662   11–1D
An "interesting range of modern, high-quality Italian dishes" means this
"buzzy" Clapham Old Town venue – inspired by chef-patron Robin Gill's
experience of working on the Amalfi coast – draws a more-than-local
clientele. The Dairy, its influential older 'sister' around the corner, closed down
in 2020. Top Menu Tips – "superb octopus arancini, fresh gnocchi and
pappardelle ragu". / SW4 6BX; www.sorellarestaurant.co.uk; sorellaclapham; Tue-Sat
10 pm.

Soutine NW8 £67 2 2 4
60 St John's Wood High Street   020 3926 8448   9–3A
"Safe food and lovely decor" help maintain fans for this "beautifully
decorated" and "quintessentially French" brasserie – part of the Wolseley
Group, and – according to such supporters – "everything you could want
from a neighbourhood restaurant". However, even those who say it's "one of
the only decent options for a meal in St John's Wood", can feel that "it's
really gone downhill since the departure of the Corbin & King founders"; and
a slip in ratings can be ascribed to "inconsistent" standards here this year.
Top Tip – popular for breakfast. / NW8 7SH; soutine.co.uk; soutinestjohn; Mon-Sat
10 pm, Sun 9 pm.

Souvlaki Street SE22 NEW
18 North Cross Road   no tel   1–4D
After nine years in various street markets including Pop Brixton (which came
to an end in late 2022), Greek street-food specialists Evi Peroulaki and
Conor Mills are moving into permanent premises on North Cross Road in
East Dulwich. Expect Aegean classics using prime British ingredients such as
rare-breed Old Spot pork, plus Greek lager and cola. / SE22 9EU;
www.souvlakistreet.co.uk; souvlakistreet.

Spagnoletti NW1 £49 3 4 3
23 Euston Road   020 7843 2221   9–3C
"A great little find right opposite King's Cross". "The location is not the best"
– immediately off a busy pavement and bordering the trafficky Euston Road
– but, if you want a good-value refuel before you hop on a train (especially
with family in tow), this bright pitstop at the foot of a boutique hotel is trying
hard: "service is good and they obviously care". Pasta (the main event) is
made in-house: if it lacks anything in terms of finesse, it compensates with
ample portions and "the food is very nice". In case you've been wondering,
the place is named after the 19th-century Anglo-Italian inventor of the
railway signalling system. / NW1 2SD; www.spagnoletti.co.uk; spagnoletti_; Mon-Fri
9.30 pm.

The Spaniard's Inn NW3 £59 2 3 5
Spaniards Rd, Hampstead Heath   020 8731 8406   9–1A
This "ancient characterful tavern" by Hampstead Heath has hosted an
impeccable list of literary tipplers in its long history from 1585, from Byron
and Dickens to Bram Stoker and local poet John Keats, who listened to a
nightingale in the walled garden. These days it serves "good fish 'n' chips"
and other pub staples, and an "excellent Sunday lunch!" / NW3 7JJ;
www.thespaniardshampstead.co.uk; thespaniardsinn; Mon-Sat 11 pm, Sun 10.30 pm.

Sparrow Italia W1 3 2 4
1-3 Avery Row   020 3089 9501   3–2B
"Request the elegant first-floor dining room" when you dine at this large
Italian in Mayfair, imported from LA (there's also a ground-floor bar). It
opened in late 2022 and reports are still not as numerous as we'd like; but
early diners are wowed by the classily ritzy decor and high-quality cuisine.
There's also a cigar lounge and terrace. / W1K 4AJ; www.sparrowitalia.com;
sparrowitalia; Mon-Sat midnight.

Speedboat Bar W1   **£54**   4 4 4
30 Rupert Street   no tel   4–3D
"They rock a vibrant, kitsch, Thai-sports-bar style beautifully" at JKS
Restaurants's zany and "buzzy" Chinatown yearling, which is "very casual"
and "great fun". "Full-flavoured dishes are authentically and unashamedly
packed with the core Thai flavours of sweet, sour, fire and salt" – it's
"fantastic, authentic, good-value" food, washed down with funky cocktails
and a wide variety of other libations (you can just drink here). / W1D 6DL;
speedboatbar.co.uk; speedboatbar; Fri & Sat 1 pm, Mon-Thu midnight.

Spring Restaurant WC2   **£123**   4 4 4
New Wing, Lancaster Place   020 3011 0115   2–2D
"Simplicity and style are in abundance" at Skye Gyngell's dining room in
Somerset House – not only "an absolutely beautiful space", but whose
"seamless service" and "wonderful food" make it "a delightful experience
from start to finish". Skye's cuisine has a deft delicacy of touch, but the most
popular option is the 'Scratch' menu – "lovely reimagined 'leftovers' from
earlier services, provided from a no-choice menu between 17.30 and 18.30
at £25 for three courses" ("designed to reduce food waste, it's a great idea
and useful for a post-shopping pick-me-up before the train home or a pre-
theatre supper"). Although this is the kind of venue that's "gorgeous for
lunch with a visiting mother", it's actually most nominated as either a
gastronomic highlight or for client-entertaining: "the slightly zen nature of the
food and purist environment makes it a brilliant choice for a certain type of
business"; and "clients are always impressed with Spring". / WC2R 1LA;
www.springrestaurant.co.uk; spring_ldn; Tue-Sat 9.30 pm.

St John Marylebone W1   **£67**   4 3 2
98 Marylebone Lane   020 7251 0848   3–1A
Nose-to-tail dining returns to the West End, with Fergus Henderson and
Trevor Gulliver's first opening in seven years (their Leicester Square project, St
John's Hotel, closed in 2013). It's on a two-floor Marylebone site with a short
menu of trademark punchy British dishes and baked items (for example:
deep-fried rarebit, ox heart, Eccles cake and cheese). Ratings are high for the
food, but also support the view that – as yet – it's "not as good as in
Smithfield" or Spitalfields. More problematic is the interior, which echoes the
stark utilitarian approach of its siblings: here it can seem merely "cold" or
"dreary" ("like the 1960s!"). / W1U 2JE; stjohnrestaurant.com; st.john.restaurant;
Mon-Sun 10 pm.

Stanley's SW3   **£100**   3 2 2
151 Sydney Street   020 7352 7664   6–3C
This "pleasant spot off the King's Road" in Chelsea is at its "romantic best if
you're sitting outside in the summer", in one of the courtyard booths. The
seasonal British menu is well executed, if lacking real excitement. / SW3 6NT;
www.stanleyschelsea.co.uk; stanleys_chelsea_; Mon-Sat 11.30 pm, Sun 7.30 pm.

Steven Edwards Bingham Riverhouse TW10 £86   4 2 4
61-63 Petersham Road   020 8940 0902   1–4A
"An incredible setting overlooking The Thames at Richmond" anchors the
appeal of this "relaxing and enjoyable" dining room, with terrace: part of a
small boutique hotel set in gardens right by the river. The "competent and
consistent" realisation of high-quality dishes wins nothing but praise for
cuisine created by chef Steven Edwards (winner of Masterchef: The
Professionals a decade ago), which makes it one of this swanky borough's
top culinary venues. / TW10 6UT; www.binghamriverhouse.com; binghamriverhouse;
Wed-Sat 11 pm.

Stick & Bowl W8 £20 4 2 2

31 Kensington High Street 020 7937 2778 6–1A

With its "delicious cheap 'n' cheerful Chinese food in an area of overpriced restaurants", this "brisk" family-run spot on Kensington High Street is "always popular and rightly so", including with "many Asian clients, which tells you everything you need to know". ("I've been coming for almost 30 years, and they recently updated the interior while remaining true to their unique concept of barstool dining tables"). / W8 5NP; stickandbowl.has.restaurant; stickandbowl; Mon-Fri 10.45 pm.

Sticks'n'Sushi £72 3 2 2

3 Sir Simon Milton Sq, Victoria St, SW1 020 3141 8810 2–4B
40 Beak Street, W1 020 3141 8191 4–2C
11 Henrietta St, WC2 020 3141 8810 5–3D
113-115 King's Road, SW3 020 3141 8181 6–3C
1 Nelson Road, SE10 020 3141 8220 1–3D
58 Wimbledon Hill Rd, SW19 020 3141 8800 11–2B
1 Crossrail Place, E14 020 3141 8230 12–1C

"Expensive, but high-quality yakitori skewers and sushi" are a "delicious and original offering that suit all ages", and win little but praise for this "very consistent" chain, whose minimalist Scandi style reflects its origins in Copenhagen. Success continues to bring fast expansion, with recent openings in Westfield W12 (in December 2022) and Shoreditch (in March 2023) and more soon to follow in Richmond (October 2023) and Kingston (early 2024). Phew! Top Menu Tip – "truffle paste cauliflower side dish to die for (who knew?)". / www.sticksnsushi.com; sticksnsushi.

Sticky Mango £61 3 2 2

33 Coin Street, SE1 020 7928 4554 10–4A
36c Shad Thames, SE1 020 7928 4554 10–4D NEW

"A well composed panoply of flavours from Southeast Asia" – curry puffs, crab dumplings, lobster, ox cheek Penang curry – have won a loyal following for Peter Lloyd's South Bank fixture, and over time fans "have become enamoured, and no longer mourn the loss of RSJ" (which preceded on the site for over 20 years). "Nothing is extraordinary, but it is our current first choice pre the National Theatre". He must be doing something right, as expansion is coming fast, with a sibling to open in July 2023 on the former site of Cantina del Ponte, RIP, with a large terrace overlooking Tower Bridge; and another in Islington later in the year.

Story SE1 £272

199 Tooley St 020 7183 2117 10–4D

"Quite an experience" – Tom Sellers has established his unique foodie temple near Tower Bridge as one of a kind. Each quixotic menu relates a culinary 'story' which unfolds over numerous courses and the "fabulous" results mean that quibbles regarding the mind-numbing prices – though often present – were a minor theme this year in diner feedback compared with satisfaction with the overall stellar performance. Just after our survey concluded in May 2023, the restaurant closed for the addition of a second floor, outside terrace, and the promise of new areas in which to dine. TS has also been busy with the openings of Dovetale and Story Cellar – hence for the time being we've left it unrated. / SE1 2UE; www.restaurantstory.co.uk; rest_story; Mon-Sun 11 pm.

Story Cellar WC2 NEW £83 **3** **3** **4**
17 Neal's Yard   020 7183 0021   5–2C
A back-to-basics offshoot of Tom Seller's celebrated Restaurant Story, this new Covent Garden venue opened in April 2023, inspired by his love of Parisian brasseries. Dine on rotisserie chicken (the big deal here) or other brasserie fare including large cuts of meat from the grill to share. Most of the ground floor is counter seating, with more conventional tables in the cellar. It's an atmospheric winner on most accounts, and – when it came to the food – The Standard's Jimi Famurewa awarded it full marks, applauding "a careful Jenga tower of elements" that transforms "a deceptively basic concept" into "stylish, subtly affecting excellence". Not all our early reporters are quite as wowed though – it can also seem "perfectly good if expensive; and unclear what the Michelin background really adds to this type of cooking". / WC2H 9DP; storycellar.co.uk; story_cellar; Tue-Sat 10 pm.

Straker's W10 £87 **3** **3** **5**
91 Golborne Road   020 3540 8727   7–1A
"A hot new ticket north of the Portobello Road" – Insta fave-rave, Thomas Straker's "super-busy" new 40-seater opened in November 2022 and has a "brilliant atmosphere" driven by "passionate chefs creating unusual food in a sharing plates concept". At their best, results are electrifying, but the odd misfire is not unknown: "the famed butter-drenched flatbreads were over burnt, so the waiters trying to upsell us was annoying… the doughnuts and langoustines were heaven though!" / W10 5NL; www.strakers.london; strakers__; Tue-Sun 11 pm.

Street Burger £51 **3** **2** **2**
13-14 Maiden Lane, WC2   020 7592 1214   5–3D
24 Charing Cross Road, WC2   020 7592 1361   5–4B
222 Kensington High Street, W8   020 7592 1612   8–1D
341 Upper Street, N1   020 7592 1355   9–3D
Entertainment District, The O2, SE10   020 7352 2512   12–1D
26 Cowcross Street, EC1   020 7592 1376   10–1A
One New Change, EC4   020 7592 1217   10–2B
The "fancy burgers" usually hit the spot this year at TV chef Gordon Ramsay's growing diffusion chain, with nine sites in the capital as of mid-2023 (and where the frozen chips are provided by another prominent chef now retired from front-line stove action: the venerable Pierre Koffmann). The odd "mixed experience" or "haphazard service" was still reported, but overall ratings were up. / www.gordonramsayrestaurants.com/street-burger; gordonramsaystreetburger.

**Studio Frantzén,
Harrods SW1** £160 **3** **4** **5**
87-135 Brompton Road   020 7225 6800   6–1D
"A beautiful space with a Michelin three-star chef overseeing the kitchen" – Harrods continues to reinvent itself as a gastronomic hub with this blockbusting 2022 debut from an acclaimed Nordic chef. It occupies a newly constructed site on the top floor of the world famous department store. "Surprisingly spacious with a very high ceiling": inside you can get a "nice view of the sparkling clean kitchen"; and outside there's a glam roof terrace overlooking the Knightsbridge rooftops. The cooking combines Asian and Scandi influences and most reports are rapturous. Top marks are only missed due to the odd more nuanced account – "I had palpable excitement to try this Swede's food, but was let down by ridiculous pricing and the mixture of some exquisite and some dud options". Top Menu Tip – "they are justifiably proud of their milk bread: a crisp crust similar to croissant and a fluffy centre like the Japanese variety, served with miso butter and borage

honey" ("the best bread I have – dare I say – ever had!"). The 'Sweden vs Japan' menu option "allows you to compare meats prepared in the style of each cuisine. Both are good but there is a significant contrast in textures". / SW1X 7XL; www.harrods.com; Mon-Sat 11.30 pm, Sun 10.30 pm.

Studio Gauthier W1 NEW
21 Stephen Street   020 8132 9088   5–1A

Renowned vegan chef-patron, Alexis Gauthier has spun out his meat-free cuisine with the June 2023 opening of two new venues in the BFI Building in Stephen Street, north of Oxford Street. Studio Gauthier is a more relaxed showcase for the upmarket veggie cooking featured at his Soho flagship (Gauthier), while 123V Bakery offers lighter bites to eat in or take away. / W1T 1LN; studiogauthier.co.uk; gauthierinsoho; Mon-Fri 11 pm.

Sucre London W1   £83   3 3 4
47b Great Marlborough Street   020 3988 3329   4–1B

A "great vibe" is the key selling point of this "large", "buzzing" chandeliered venue, where Latino chef, Fernando Trocca aims to import the glam of Buenos Aires. Most reports also applaud its "ace take on Argentinian cuisine, with the asado fired up at the back of the room" delivering "a real variety of options, not just beef" in a "tasty tapas style". A minority of diners, though, are "a little disappointed" by the size of the bill: "not terrible, but at the prices I won't be rushing to return". Top Tip – the basement bar is excellent. / W1F 7HS; www.sucrerestaurant.com; sucre.london; Mon-Sat 1 am, Sun midnight.

SUDU NW6   3 4 3
30 Salusbury Road   020 7624 3829   1–2B

"Really succulent rendang" is a menu highlight at this "great new Malaysian eatery": a 'kopitiam' (café-style) venture which opened in Queen's Park in late 2022. It's the creation of siblings Fatizah and Irqam Shawal, whose parents opened London's most venerable Malaysian – Satay House – in 1973. / NW6 6NL; sudu.ldn; Mon-Sun 10.30 pm.

Sukho Fine Thai Cuisine SW6   £55   4 4 2
855 Fulham Rd   020 7371 7600   11–1B

The "delicious and beautifully prepared Thai food" at this Fulham shop conversion makes it a "great local restaurant" that attracts diners from across London. The surroundings are nothing special, but everything is "served with charm". / SW6 5HJ; www.sukhogroups.com; sukho_thairestaurant_fulhamsw6; Mon-Sat 10.30 pm, Sun 9.30pm.

Sumak N8   £44   3 4 2
141 Tottenham Lane   020 8341 6261   1–1C

"One of the reasons we've yet to move house from Crouch End!" – local fans are sold on the virtues of this "stubbornly traditional Turkish restaurant (with murals on every wall depicting famous Turkish and other global tourist destinations… at least a step up from the glitzy establishments on Green Lane)". "Despite recent price hikes, they are still very fair considering the high standard of cooking, as well as the warm welcome". / N8 9BJ; sumakrestaurants.com; sumakrestaurant; Sun-Thu 11 pm, Fri & Sat 11.30 pm.

Sumi W11   £103   4 4 3
157 Westbourne Grove   020 4524 0880   7–1B

"Incredible sushi in an environment that is more relaxed and fun than many sushi joints of this quality" is a potent recipe for success at Endo Kazutoshi's "welcoming" venture ("all the more enjoyable as it affords the opportunity to people-watch in the rarefied atmosphere of Notting Hill"). "A simple menu is very well realised; service is good and friendly"; and since it expanded in late 2022 "the extra floor-space has made for a better atmosphere". / W11 2RS; www.sushisumi.com; sumilondon; Tue-Sat 10 pm, Sun 5 pm.

The Summerhouse W9 £84 2 3 5
60 Blomfield Rd   020 7286 6752   9–4A

"Sitting by the canal is relaxing, and in cooler weather the heaters are turned on and the entire experience is warm and welcoming" at this *"beautiful"* spot by the Regent's Canal in Little Venice. Views diverge on the fish-centric cooking: to fans it produces *"well-cooked staples"*, to the odd harsh critic the performance is verging on *"unskilled"*. All agree, though, that *"personal and un-rushed service"* contributes to its appeal. / W9 2PA; www.thesummerhouse.co; the_summerhouse; Mon-Sat 11 pm, Sun 10.30 pm.

Sunday in Brooklyn W2 £73 2 2 4
98 Westbourne Grove   020 7630 1060   7–1B

If it didn't attract quite a few reports in our annual diners' poll, we might be tempted to overlook this NYC-import on a corner in Notting Hill, named for its fashionable elder sibling in Williamsburg. Mostly, feedback is from locals, who feel the place is "fun", but too often "very disappointing"; a natural choice for an authentic American brunch, but where "only the pancakes are above average". / W2 5RU; sundayinbk.co.uk; sundayinbrooklyn_ldn; Mon-Wed 4.30 pm, Thu-Sat 10 pm, Sun 8 pm.

Supa Ya Ramen £33 3 3 2
191 Rye Lane, SE15   020 7358 0735   1–4D NEW
499 Kingsland Road, E8   07440 066900   14–1A

Chef Luke Findlay brings his 'traditionally inauthentic' cult ramen (using ingredients such as Parmesan cheese or Cumberland sausages) to a duo of functionally kitted-out venues. First honed as a supper club, the Dalston original opened in March 2000, and a Peckham spin-off in late 2022. Not a huge volume of feedback, but all good for the big-flavoured bowls that had The Independent's Kate Ng hail "a perfectly imperfect take on fusion food" in January 2023.

Supawan N1 £58 5 4 4
38 Caledonian Road   020 7278 2888   9–3D

Some of the "most authentic Thai food you could ever experience in UK is prepared by a Thai chef and team" in the bizarre but *"beautiful"* surroundings of a florist's shop, near King's Cross station, where *"the flowers are put aside in the evening to make room for extra tables"*. Chef Wichet Khongphoon delivers *"incredible"* and *"powerful"* flavours and the *"attentive staff give helpful and useful guidance as to the potentially obscure treats"* from the *"interesting and deeply satisfying"* menu. *"You can get a green curry (a really good one!), but alongside more unusual starters, there are salads and slow-cooked meats, plus good vegan options with clear allergy pointers too"*. *"Book well ahead: and you may have to wait for your table even so, as the place is very busy and popular"*. / N1 9DT; www.supawan.co.uk; supawan_thaifood; Tue-Sat 11 pm, Sun 10.30 pm.

Super Tuscan E1 £70
8a Artillery Passage   020 7247 8717   13–2B

Post pandemic, the feedback on this small, quirky, City-fringe Italian (in the characterful tangle of streets near Spitalfields) has become more patchy. Fans still say its interesting wines and authentic cuisine are outstanding, but we don't have sufficient volume of reports for a reliable rating. / E1 7LJ; www.supertuscan.co.uk; enoteca_super_tuscan; Mon-Fri 9 pm.

The Surprise SW3 £82 3 3 4
6 Christchurch Terrace   020 7351 6954   6–3D
"A gem of a place hidden away" in a quiet corner of SW3 close to Chelsea's 'Physic Garden', this "traditional" 1853 pub – a classic watering hole in the area – has been transformed by landlord Jack Greenall (scion of the Lancashire brewing dynasty), and now serves a high standard of "very reasonable value" British dishes, accompanied by "sensibly priced" Bibendum wines. "Service is spot-on, too". / SW3 4AJ; www.thesurprise-chelsea.co.uk; Tue-Sat 9.30 pm, Sun 8.30 pm.

Sushi Atelier W1 £70 4 3 3
114 Great Portland Street   020 7636 4455   2–1B
Sit on the ground floor at the counter and watch the chefs in action to get the most out of this clean-lined Japanese (part of the Chisou group) near Oxford Circus. The food here is consistently well-rated: choose from modern sushi options, ceviches, fish carpaccios and other Japanese-inspired bites like wagyu sliders. / W1W 6PH; www.sushiatelier.co.uk; sushiatelierlondon; Tue-Sat 11 pm.

Sushi Bar Makoto W4 £44 4 3 1
57 Turnham Green Terrace   020 8987 3180   8–2A
While you probably wouldn't cross town for it, this basic pit-stop near Turnham Green tube is worth remembering – the sushi is a cut-above what you'd expect from the nondescript exterior. / W4 1RP; sushi_makoto; Mon-Sat 10 pm, Sun 9 pm.

Sushi Kanesaka W1 NEW
45 Park Lane   020 7319 7466   3–4A
Aiming for 'a new benchmark for omakase dining in the city' – certainly when it comes to price… – this Dorchester Collection property (opposite the mothership itself across the road) opened in July 2023. It's a spin-off from Shinji Kanesaka's Tokyo Michelin two-star and will seat just 13 diners (9 at a counter, 4 in a separate room). Perhaps the UK's most expensive set menu: it offers a 20-course omakase experience for £420 per head, plus paired saké at £150 per head. Go easy on the Coco Mademoiselle though: 'we kindly request that you refrain from wearing perfume'. / W1K 1PN; www.dorchestercollection.com; 45parklane; Tue-Sun 11.30 pm.

Sushi Masa NW2 £47 3 3 2
33b Walm Lane   020 8459 2971   1–1A
With its "surprisingly high-quality Japanese cooking for a nondescript suburban strip" in Willesden Green, this accomplished local spot offers a "delicious omakase experience in a calm environment" – making it an adequate replacement for its predecessor Sushi-Say (the epitome of a wonderful, family-owned Japanese, which inhabited this out-of-the-way site for over 30 years). / NW2 5SH; sushimasa_id; Tue-Sat 10 pm.

Sushi Murasaki W9 £58 4 4 2
12 Lauderdale Road   020 3417 8130   7–1C
"Tucked away in an unassuming suburban street, this Maida Vale Japanese is firmly established as a local favourite" for its "inventive and original" dishes that are "excellently executed" using "high-quality ingredients". "Standards are much higher than the dining room decor might suggest – it's somewhat functional!" / W9 1LU; sushi-murasaki.co.uk; sushimurasakiuk; Mon-Sat 11 pm, Sun 10.30 pm.

Sushi Revolution SW9   £39   4 4 2
240 Ferndale Road   020 4537 4331   11–1D
This "really impressive" two-year-old from Aidan Bryan & Tom Blackshaw in Brixton's former Bon Marché department store is a "catch-all Japanese restaurant delivering high-quality, tasty dishes" that are "quirky, in a good way": "while not the most authentic sushi for the purists" – the clue is in the name – "it's definitely worth a visit". / SW9 8FR; www.sushirevolution.co.uk; sushirevolution; Mon-Sun 10 pm.

Sushi Tetsu EC1   £167   5 5 4
12 Jerusalem Passage   020 3217 0090   10–1A
"Still a top omakase experience in a very relaxed environment" – Toru Takahashi does not exactly need to go out of his way to attract customers to this tiny (7 seat) venue. You can only book online on Monday at 12:00pm onwards. There are no event bookings (max 4 in a party). There's no concession to vegans or vegetarians. No kids under 12. No Insta (yay!!) – photography and video are not permitted. No scent is to be worn by diners. The full shebang costs £167 per person and takes 3-4 hours, although he also does a shorter 2 hour version early on Saturday evenings for £117 (June 2023 prices). Everyone loves it… / EC1V 4JP; www.tetsusushibar.com; tetsusushibar_van; Tue-Sun 9.30 pm.

Sushisamba   £117   2 2 3
Opera Terrace, 35 The Market, WC2   020 3053 0000   5–3D
Heron Tower, 110 Bishopsgate, EC2   020 3640 7330   10–2D
Zooming up to the 38th floor of the Heron Tower in one of Europe's fastest lifts… looking out with a cocktail on an open terrace overlooking the scrapers of the City, it's easy to get swept up by the glamour of the original, "buzzy" branch of this US-based chain. And its popular WC2 spin-off is also "always a pleasure to visit": looking out onto the back of the Royal Opera House from the huge terrace on the top of Covent Garden Market. Fans say the luxe, Japanese/South American fusion cuisine in both locations – taquitos, sushi, steaks, samba rolls, black cod from the robata – is "delicious and remarkably inventive" too. But ratings for it have sunk post-Covid, and while pricing here has always been toppy, there is a growing gripe that "food which is average at best is accompanied by a bill that's distinctly not average!" / sushisamba.com; SUSHISAMBA.

Sussex W1   £81   2 2 3
63-64 Frith Street   020 3923 7770   5–2A
This Soho outpost from the Sussex-based Gladwin Brothers was launched in 2019 in the stylish quarters vacated by Arbutus (long RIP). As at the Gladwins' five other venues across London, feedback was somewhat limited and a little up-and-down this year. A particular plus is the "valiant focus on locally sourced produce" and a "friendly" approach. Negatives include meals that can be "pleasant but unmemorable" and the odd incident of "haphazard" service. / W1D 3JW; www.sussex-restaurant.com; sussex_resto; Tue-Fri, Mon, Sat 10.30 pm.

Suzi Tros W8   £88   4 4 3
18 Hillgate Street   020 7221 2223   7–2B
The "delicious and interesting modern Greek food" is enjoyed by all who visit this "fun" if "slightly cramped and noisy" Notting Hill four-year-old – the "less formal sister to Mazi" nearby. (Founders Christina Mouratoglou and Adrien Carre were inspired by the cuisine of northern Greece, and named it after a film character who has passed into contemporary Greek folklore.) / W8 7SR; suzitros.com; suzitros; Mon-Sun 11 pm.

The Swan W4 £67 **3 4 4**
1 Evershed Walk, 119 Acton Ln   020 8994 8262   8–1A
A "top pub garden" is the trump card of this handsome, green-tiled tavern on the Chiswick-Acton border, and it's backed up by "super-attentive service, great food" and "a lively buzz". It's been "consistently good" in its current guise for more than 20 years. / W4 5HH; www.theswanchiswick.co.uk; theswanchiswick; Sun-Thu 10 pm, Fri 10.30 pm, Sat 11 pm.

The Swan at the Globe SE1 £70 **2 2 4**
21 New Globe Walk   020 7928 9444   10–3B
The "unforgettable setting" of this pub and restaurant adjoining Shakespeare's Globe theatre, "with a lovely view over the river" to St Paul's, provides much of the draw, although its food and service are (just about) up to scratch too. The wide range of menus makes it a "flexible option", providing afternoon teas, brunches, drinks and meals before and after performances. / SE1 9DT; www.swanlondon.co.uk; swanglobe; Mon-Sat 9 pm, Sun 6 am.

Sweet Thursday N1 £52 **3 2 2**
95 Southgate Rd   020 7226 1727   14–1A
This lively bottle shop and local in De Beauvoir Town does a good trade in Neapolitan-style pizzas and a small selection of Italian starters and mains – not surprisingly, it attracts "loadsa families, so choose your time carefully". / N1 3JS; www.sweetthursday.co.uk; sweetthursdaypizza; Mon-Thu 10 pm, Fri & Sat 10.30 pm, Sun 9 pm.

Sweetings EC4 £92 **3 2 4**
39 Queen Victoria St   020 7248 3062   10–3B
"It's as though time was paused 100 years ago" at this Square Mile legend, founded in the 1830s and on its current site since the 1920s. Arrive early if you want to beat the City pinstripes to a table or a spot at the counter, although "it's worth the wait for a seat while sipping a tankard of Black Velvet". "Traditional, hearty British fish is served in a manner unchanged by time" – oysters, smoked eel, whitebait – and "the fish pie is still good and not too expensive". "Longstanding staff add to its stalwart appeal". / EC4N 4SA; sweetingsrestaurant.co.uk; sweetingslondon; Mon-Fri 3 pm.

Sycamore Vino Cucina, Middle Eight Hotel WC2 £76 **2 2 2**
66 Great Queen Street   020 7309 9300   5–1D
The timing of its debut, during Covid 19, couldn't have been harder for this Covent Garden three-year-old, and it has yet to attract a huge volume of feedback or a settled view from diners. One fan says "you get a twist on Italian cooking, and boy do they get it right" in a "superb, light and airy space that's ideal for a business meal". To a critic it's "bizarre eating in what feels like, and actually is, a hotel lobby, with some dishes very clumsily seasoned". / WC2B 5BX; www.middleeight.com; middle_eight_hotel; Mon-Sat 10 pm, Sun 5 pm.

Ta Ke Sushi W5 £45 **4 3 2**
3-4 Grosvenor Parade   020 8075 8877   1–3A
"A favourite of local Japanese expats", this Ealing three-year-old offers a wide range of fresh-made dishes, including sushi, ramen, soba and udon. It's "not so cheap, but excellent value, and definitely cheerful". Top Tip – "the daily lunch special is a steal, with plenty of change from a tenner". / W5 3NN; take-sushi.co.uk; Mon-Sat 10.30 pm, Sun 10.30pm.

Tab X Tab W2 £38 343
Westbourne House, 14-16 Westbourne Grove   020 7792 3445   7–1B
This "great meeting spot" in Bayswater is "ever-popular" for its "excellent coffee and snacks" served in immaculate minimalist surroundings, from founders Mathew and Charmaine Tabatabai. The menu stretches from breakfast/brunch dishes to afternoon cocktails. / W2 4UJ; tabxtab.com; tabxtablondon; Mon-Sun 4 pm.

Table Du Marche N2 £65 332
111 High Road   020 8883 5750   1–1B
"This better-than-solid bistro" in East Finchley offers "excellent value and sound cooking – the very strong local following is justified". It's old-school in the best way – and "the staff are charming". / N2 8AG; tabledumarchelondon.co.uk; tabledumarche; Mon-Sat 11 pm, Sun 10.30 pm.

Taka Marylebone W1 £100 323
109 Marylebone High Street   020 3637 4466   2–1A
An "upscale Japanese/fusion place" – "a modern take on Nipponese cuisine in a light and airy venue in the heart of Marylebone High Street". It scores higher this year: even those who consider it "overpriced" still say the culinary results are "very good". / W1U 4RX; takalondon.com; takarestaurants; Fri & Sat, Tue-Thu 10 pm.

Takahashi SW19 £62 553
228 Merton Road   020 8540 3041   11–2B
"The omakase experience borders on the sublime" – "it's food as art" – at this "hidden gem" of a Japanese restaurant, tucked away in an unpromising shopping parade near South Wimbledon tube for almost a decade now. Former Nobu chef Taka and his wife Yuko preside over a "very personalised food offering", with their "delightful and kind service". / SW19 1EQ; www.takahashi-restaurant.co.uk; takahashi_wimbledon; Wed-Sat 10.30 pm, Sun 7.30 pm.

TAKU W1 NEW £378 533
36 Albemarle Street   no tel   3–3C
Japanese chef Takuya Watanabe transfers his high-end skills from Paris (where he spent 10 years at restaurant Jin) to Mayfair, for this November 2022 debut. A visit is an investment – lunch is £130 per head, dinner £280 per head, or £380 for the 'prestige' offering. We have had limited but outstanding feedback to date in our annual diners' poll; Michelin rushed to award it an early star after less than six months in operation; and veteran blogger Andy Hayler – who knows his way around a chopstick – declared it "definitely some of the best sushi to be found in the capital" after an April 2023 visit. / W1S 4JE; www.takumayfair.com; takumayfair; Tue-Sat 11 pm.

Tamarind W1 £87 433
20 Queen St   020 7629 3561   3–3B
The world's first Indian restaurant to bag a Michelin star (in 2001) – this "sophisticated and glamorous" Mayfair linchpin has neither lost its way, nor remained pre-eminent: it just continues to plough its own distinctive path. The kitchen "always finds a neat twist to traditional favourites" and succeeds in delivering "stunning presentation and wonderful flavours". And "despite its top quality food and location, the bill isn't bad either". Top Tips – "the vegetarian fare is particularly delicious"; and "the lunchtime menu is great value". / W1J 5PR; www.tamarindrestaurant.com; tamarindofmayfair; Mon-Sat 10.15 pm, Sun 9.15 pm.

Tamarind Kitchen W1 £81 4 3 3
167-169 Wardour St   020 7287 4243   4–1C
"A gem in Soho" – this large and stylish spin-off from the famous Mayfair mothership is "a very reasonable (and reasonably priced) option" that takes inspiration from regional cuisines across India. "The tasting menu is particularly good value by London standards". / W1F 8WR;
tamarindkitchen.co.uk; tamarindkitchenlondon; Mon-Thu 10 pm, Fri & Sat 10.30 pm, Sun 9.30 pm.

The Tamil Prince N1 £48 4 3 3
115 Hemingford Road   020 7062 7846   9–2D
"Truly brilliant" – this desi pub (formerly the Cuckoo) in Barnsbury is one of the most talked-about openings of 2022 thanks to "stellar" cooking that's "expertly spiced and oh-so-moreish", washed down with "great cocktails and beers on tap". On the downside, it is "squashed" and "oh-so-noisy" ("they won't turn the music down!") but most folks like its "bustling" style. "You have to plan ahead" – "it's very difficult to get a reservation unless you book four weeks in advance" – but "well worth the effort". / N1 1BZ;
www.thetamilprince.com; the_tamil_prince; Tue-Sat, Mon 10 pm, Sun 9 pm.

Tamp Coffee W4 £29 3 4 3
1 Devonshire Road   no tel   8–2A
Superb in-house roasted coffee and scrumptious pastries (speciality Portuguese Pastel de Nata) – made daily on the premises – make for a superior breakfast at this Chiswick café, just off the main drag. / W4 2EU;
www.tampcoffee.co.uk; tampcoffee; Mon-Fri 3.30 pm, Sat & Sun 4 pm.

Tandoor Chop House WC2 £60 4 3 3
8 Adelaide Street   020 3096 0359   5–4C
"Tandoor as it is meant to be", with "bursts of authentic, deep and rich smoky flavours", earns an emphatic thumbs-up for this "energetic" operation just off Trafalgar Square. The "menu is limited but compelling, with bold and memorable spicing", "mouthwatering chicken and duck" and "well made naan", while "desserts are the weakest element". / WC2N 4HW;
tandoorchophouse.com; tandoorchop; Mon-Thu 11 pm, Fri & Sat 11.30 pm, Sun 10 pm.

Tapas Brindisa £68 2 2 2
46 Broadwick St, W1   020 7534 1690   4–2B
7-9 Exhibition Rd, SW7   020 7590 0008   6–2C
18-20 Southwark St, SE1   020 7357 8880   10–4C
Battersea Power Station, SW11   020 8016 8888   11–1C
Hotham House, 1 Heron Square, TW9   020 8103 8888   1–4A
"An excellent location overlooking the River Thames makes the Richmond branch very special if you are able to bag one of its outside tables on a balmy summer evening"; and it's a highpoint of this chain run by a firm of well-known Iberian food importers. On the plus-side, its branches are generally "buzzy", with "tasty" and "authentically flavoured" tapas. On the minus-side, for all the "high quality ingredients", dishes can end up "indifferent" and "pricey for the size of the portions"; and "service can be a little too uneven". / www.brindisakitchens.com; brindisaspanishfoods; SRA-accredited.

Taqueria £45 3 3 3
141-145 Westbourne Grove, W11   020 7229 4734   7–1B
8-10 Exmouth Market, EC1   020 3897 9609   10–1A
"Really tasty Mexican food in a fairly spartan setting" established this Notting Hill venue as one of London's original taco specialists, and 20 years on it remains on some accounts "possibly the best". Now with an offshoot in Exmouth Market, it continues to serve "excellent mojitos" which makes it "a good choice for lunch… if one has nothing else planned for the afternoon". / taqueria.co.uk; taqueriauk.

Taro £39 3 3 2
I Churton Street, SW I 020 7802 9776 2–4B
61 Brewer Street, W I 020 7734 5826 4–3C
356 Regents Park Road, N3 020 4531 9124 I–1B
414 Kennington Road, SE11 020 7735 7772 I–3C
193 Balham High Road, SW12 020 8675 5187 11–2C
76 High Street, E17 020 8520 2855 I–1D
"Well produced, tasty morsels of delight" including *"ace lunchtime bento boxes"* are served at these *"pared down"* Japanese canteens, which provide *"good value for money for what is generally an expensive cuisine"*. Founder Mr Taro is not one for fast food: he conceived the idea of opening an 'everyday dining room' on a visit to London in 1979 and launched it in Soho 20 years later. Two decades on he is in expansion mode, and in February 2023 opened a sixth branch in a former Manze Pie & Mash shop in Walthamstow, with a Grade II listed interior now restored to its previous glory. / tarorestaurants.uk; tarorestaurants.

**Tate Modern Kitchen & Bar,
Level 6 SE1** £51 3 3 5
Level 6 Boiler House, Bankside 020 7401 5108 10–3B
With its *"great view over the river"*, the sixth-floor restaurant in this converted power station opposite St Paul's Cathedral is a *"really rather splendid place for a decent set lunch"*. The food is *"better than expected, perhaps better than it needed to be"* – *"appropriately arty"*, too, with dishes inspired by artists on display in the gallery. (Over at Tate Britain, *"the Rex Whistler dining room is sorely missed and a real loss"* – its closure brought about by a combination of Covid and dilemmas about the depiction of slavery in its Whistler murals, nowadays deemed 'unequivocally… offensive'.) / SE1 9TG; www.tate.org.uk; tate; Mon-Sun 6 pm.

Tattu London WC2 £120 2 3 3
The Now Building Rooftop, Denmark Street 020 3778 1985 5–1A
Considering its prominent location in 'The Now Building' on Oxford Street, this glossy two-year-old from an Insta-friendly Manchester-based group inspires surprisingly little feedback. Most are positive, but it's not without the one or two disappointments, and some ongoing concern about high prices. / WC2H 8LH; tattu.co.uk; tattulondon; Tue-Sun 1 am, Mon midnight.

Tavernaki W11 £30 3 2 3
222 Portobello Road 07510 627752 7–1A
"An excellent Greek, with a brilliant, relaxed atmosphere. Being Mediterranean, the staff love children. Highly recommended!" – In the thick of Portobello, this cosy spot is only three years old, but fairly conventional in style, complete with 'traditional comfort cuisine' and live Greek music. / W11 1LJ; www.tavernakiportobello.co.uk; tavernaki.portobello; Mon-Sun 11 pm.

Tavolino SE1 £67 2 2 3
Unit 1, 2 More London Place 020 8194 1037 10–4D
"Fabulous views of the Thames" from this modern Italian in the new development next to City Hall make it *"perfect for giving out-of-town guests the full London experience"*. *"The food has sufficient interest, but the real draw is the panoramic view from HMS Belfast to Tower Bridge"*. / SE1 2JP; www.tavolino.co.uk; tavolinokitchen; Sun-Wed 10 pm, Thu-Sat 10.30 pm.

Tayyabs E1 £36 4 3 2
83 Fieldgate St 020 7247 6400 10–2D
"The grilled lamb chops are worth a visit in their own right" to this *"affordable and ever-reliable Punjabi institution in Whitechapel"* whose 500 seats are *"guaranteed to be jam-packed on any particular evening"*. *"BYOB means it is even better value for money"*. / E1 1JU; www.tayyabs.co.uk; 1tayyabs; Mon-Sun 11.30 pm.

Tehran Berlin
(fka The Drunken Butler) EC1   £167   3 4 4
20 Rosebery Avenue   020 7101 4020   10–1A
"What a find! Chef Yuma (Hashemi) produces the most amazing plates of delicious food which reflect his heritage and upbringing" at this quirky Clerkenwell operation, whose decor is akin to a retro Tehran living room. The menu plays out in 'four acts', with shifts of gear in the background music to enhance the experience. All this plus "great staff and a fabulous vibe". / EC1R 4SX; www.tehranberlin.com; tehran_berlin; Tue-Sat 11 pm.

The Telegraph SW15   £54   3 4 5
Telegraph Road, Putney Heath   020 8194 2808   11–2A
Few London pubs enjoy as leafy a setting (complete with "lovely garden") as this "spacious" and "friendly" tavern on Putney Heath, which is "suitable for all ages" and makes a "good destination for Sunday lunch". Now capably run by Chester-based Brunning & Price, it takes its name from the visual shutter telegraph that linked the Admiralty in London with Portsmouth in the Napoleonic era. / SW15 3TU; www.brunningandprice.co.uk; telegraphputneyheath; Sun-Thu 11 pm, Fri & Sat midnight; SRA-3stars.

temper   £58   2 1 2
25 Broadwick Street, W1   020 3879 3834   4–1C
5 Mercers Walk, WC2   020 3004 6669   5–2C
78 Great Eastern Street, EC2   020 3758 6889   13–1B
Angel Court, EC2   020 3004 6984   10–2C
An "open-plan kitchen" complete with fire pit is the theme unifying Neil Rankin's four-strong BBQ-group, which takes all its supplies of beef, pork, lamb and chicken from Yorkshire farmer Charles Ashbridge. Despite some favourable steak suppers being reported, ratings took a further dive in our latest poll, continuing last year's themes of "chaotic" service and a feeling that the overall experience can "promise more than it delivers". Lack of value, in particular, inspires repeated gripes ("plates were minuscule at ridiculous prices…"; "we joked that you needed a microscope to find the portions…") / temperrestaurant.com; temperlondon.

The 10 Cases WC2   £82   3 4 3
16 Endell St   020 7836 6801   5–2C
With its "unusual and interesting wines" (only 10 cases of each one are ordered, to ensure a steady turnover), "well complemented by delicious small bites to eat", this is "the wine bistro you want in your street". The fact that they can combine this with a "great, busy and bustling neighbourhood vibe in the middle of Covent Garden" is "simply astonishing", making it both "a pre-theatre restaurant and a destination in its own right". / WC2H 9BD; www.10cases.co.uk; 10cases; Mon-Sat midnight.

10 Greek Street W1   £70   4 4 3
10 Greek St   020 7734 4677   5–2A
A "reliable Soho favourite", where results from its blackboard menu are "always solidly good and can be excellent" – the same can be said of its handwritten 'little black book' of wines. "Small, relaxed and friendly", it "can become pretty noisy, but that's part of the fun". / W1D 4DH; www.10greekstreet.com; 10greekstreet; Tue-Sat 10.30 pm.

Tendido Cero SW5   £71   3 3 3
174 Old Brompton Road   020 7370 3685   6–2B
"Every dish is good" at this long-running tapas bar in South Kensington. Regulars, though, reckon it's "not quite up to the experience" of its sibling opposite, Cambio de Tercio, with which it shares a list of "excellent" Spanish wines ("it's clearly tapas from a chef more familiar with fine dining, leaning towards the elegant rather than a solid punch of flavour"). / SW5 0BA; cambiodeterciogroup; Mon-Sun 11.30 pm.

Tendril W1 £58 433
5 Princes Street   07842 797541   4–2C
The "interesting, unusual" and "occasionally really great" vegan cuisine at this "romantic and candle-lit restaurant close to Oxford Circus" has won enough fans to crowdfund its transformation from pop-up to permanent status at the same address. "The best test is that it continues to attract non-vegetarians because the food is so good". Former Fat Duck and Chiltern Firehouse chef Rishim Sachdeva was a committed meat-eater before challenging himself to create knock-out veggie dishes (with some cheese permitted). / W1B 2LQ; www.tendrilkitchen.co.uk; tendril_kitchen; Mon-Sat 10 pm, Sun 5 pm.

Terra Moderna NW3 NEW
2b Englands Lane   020 4568 8525   9–2A
Modern Italian cuisine with Antipodean influences – including an impressive list of Australian and New Zealand wines – is to be found at this new venture in the heart of Belsize Park from Aussie founder and coffee entrepreneur Jeffrey Young, who is also behind the England's Lane café next door. It opened in April 2023, too late to inspire survey feedback, but early online buzz suggests it's worth giving it a go. / NW3 4TH; www.terramodernalondon.com; terramodernaldn; Tue-Sat 11 pm.

Terra Rossa £67 444
139 Upper Street, N1   020 7226 2244   9–3D
62 Carter Ln, EC4   020 7248 6600   10–2A NEW
"What a find!" – this Puglian specialist close to Islington's Almeida Theatre (it takes its name from the Salento peninsula's red earth) is "a cheap 'n' cheerful favourite", thanks to its "generous portions of absolutely delicious and comforting Italian food". It may "lack kerb appeal, but once inside you find an attractive dining room with quite a buzz" – making it a "classic and authentic neighbourhood restaurant". Since spring 2023, founder François Fracella also has now opened a second site near St Paul's.

Thai Tho SW19 £22 333
20 High St   020 8946 1542   11–2B
"Wimbledon Village may have three Thai restaurants, but this independent family business is our favourite!" Nicky Santichatsak's "traditional" operation sits "in the centre of the village" and is a "preferred choice for celebs during the tennis". (There's also a long-established Soho sibling that inspires no feedback). / SW19 5DX; www.thaitho.co.uk; Tue-Sat 10.30 pm.

Thali SW5 £53 333
166 Old Brompton Rd   020 7373 2626   6–2B
With its "good North Indian cooking" from family recipes, this well-established venue with Bollywood posters lining the walls is these days a rival to veteran Noor Jahan for bragging rights on Earl's Court's "curry corner". / SW5 0BA; thali_london; Mon-Sat midnight.

Theo Randall at the InterContinental London Park Lane W1 £90 543
1 Hamilton Place   020 7318 8747   3–4A
"As good as anything you might experience in Verona or Florence" – Theo Randall's "divine, monthly regional tasting menus" produce "consistently great" results as well as adding interest to his Mayfair HQ, just off Hyde Park Corner. "There's the option of wine matches" and "a good cocktail bar (especially the design-your-own-Negroni option!)". "Ok, the space isn't terrific" – windowless, and off the foyer of a large 1970s hotel – but "it is one of the very few celebrity chef restaurants where the chef is frequently to be seen". "Theo always seems to be there and comes out into the dining

room most times you visit", helping create an overall atmosphere that was surprisingly well-rated this year. Top Tip – "Sunday brunch at £65 including unlimited Prosecco, Negroni or Aperol Spritz is particularly good value".
/ W1J 7QY; www.theorandall.com; theo.randall; Tue-Sat 10 pm, Sun 6 pm.

Theo's SE5 £41 3 3 2

2 Grove Lane 020 3026 4224 1–3C
The "doughy, chewy, charred base is a winner" at this "excellent quality" pizzeria duo in Camberwell and Elephant & Castle, whose "pared-back toppings deliver great tastes". They're backed up by a short but sharp selection of cocktails, craft beers and organic or skin-contact wines. / SE5 8SY; www.theospizzeria.com; theospizzeria; Tue-Thu 10.30 pm, Sun & Mon 10 pm, Fri & Sat 11 pm.

34 Mayfair W1 £133 2 3 2

34 Grosvenor Sq 020 3350 3434 3–3A
Richard Caring's American-style grill near the former US Embassy in Mayfair wins praise as "an all-rounder, with a menu to suit all tastes"; and as "a busy, vibrant place with attentive and knowledgeable staff". "The wine list (book really) is endless and if you want to be extravagant, very expensive"… in keeping with the general approach. / W1K 2HD; www.34-restaurant.co.uk; 34mayfair; Mon-Sat 11 pm, Sun 10 pm.

The Thomas Cubitt Pub Belgravia SW1 £80 2 2 3

44 Elizabeth St 020 7730 6060 2–4A
"Consistent over many years", this smart (and "not particularly cheap") Belgravia gastropub is named after the master-builder who developed the area in the Georgian era, and is the flagship of the ambitious Cubitt House group, which has hired chef-director Ben Tish (ex-Salt Yard, The Stafford and Norma) and food journalist/hospitality expert Joe Warwick to bolster its standards. / SW1W 9PA; www.thethomascubitt.co.uk; cubitt house london; Mon-Sat 10 pm, Sun 8.45 pm.

Three Falcons NW8 £48 4 3 2

1 Orchardson Street 020 7724 8928 7–1C
"Under the radar of most who are not in the know" – this large tavern and hotel off Edgware Road incorporates some "excellent Indian food" into a more conventional gastropub offering. "A number of TV screens to watch sports" are also a feature. / NW8 8NG; threefalcons.com; threefalcons.

Three Uncles £37 5 2 2

Unit 199 Hawley Wharf, 2nd Fl. Foodhall, NW1 07597 602281 9–2B
Unit 19&20, Brixton Village, SW9 020 3592 5374 11–2D
12 Devonshire Row, EC2 020 7375 3573 10–2D
"Fantastic roast duck" and quite possibly "the best chicken rice in London" earn full marks for this Cantonese roast meat specialist with outlets near Liverpool Street, in Hawley Wharf, Camden, and Brixton Market. Founders Pui Sing, Cheong Yew and Mo Kwok were inspired by childhood memories of eating sui mei near Wan Chai market in Hong Kong. Their venues may be "cramped and busy", but the cooking is "consistently delicious, generously portioned and great value". / three.uncles.

Tila SE8 £74 3 3 3

14 Deptford Broadway 020 8692 8803 1–3D
"Have been walking by literally for years… tonight we took the plunge for dinner… my goodness… the food was superb! Every dish used herbs to provide intense bursts of flavour. Thoughtful, exciting cooking, both tasty and well presented…" – Thumbs up for this brick-lined bar/restaurant between Deptford High Street and Deptford Bridge, which is heavily influenced by the Eastern Med, with lots of preparation over fire. "The charred aubergine is a must!" / SE8 4PA; www.tiladeptford.com; tila.deptford; Wed-Sat 10 pm, Sun 5 pm.

TING,
The Shard SE1   **£95**   3️⃣3️⃣5️⃣
31 St Thomas St   020 7234 8108   10–4C
"What could be nicer than sitting on the 38th floor of the Shard with
fantastic views of London", while lingering over a "lovely unrushed afternoon
tea" or – later in the day when the mood is "very romantic" – sampling its
"fresh Asian-inspired dishes". Not a huge volume of feedback, but ratings are
better this year as it escaped the customary complaints for overpricing.
/ SE1 9RY; www.ting-shangri-la.com; tinglondon; Mon-Sun 10.15 pm.

Tish NW3   **£91**   3️⃣2️⃣3️⃣
196 Haverstock Hill   020 7431 3828   9–2A
An "attractively presented dining room" is the setting for "excellent kosher
food" at David Levin's modern brasserie in Belsize Park. "Usually the culinary
experience is firmly in the back seat at kosher restaurants, but not here".
/ NW3 2AG; www.tish.london; tish_london; Sun-Thu midnight.

Toba SW1 NEW
1 St James's Market   020 3583 4660   4–4B
In slick-but-stilted St James's Market, this February 2023 newcomer inhabits
the site that till recently housed Ikoyi (nowadays on The Strand). It's from
Pino Edward Sinaga, and – like his successful Camden Market operation –
serves Indonesian street food inspired by family recipes. For this posh SW1
locale, prices are very approachable. No survey feedback as yet, but in a
March 2023 review, The Guardian's Grace Dent thought results were
incentive enough to visit this "soulless" SW1 development. / SW1Y 4AH;
tobalondon.co.uk; toba.london; Tue-Fri 11 pm, Sat 11.30 pm, Sun 4 pm.

Toff's N10   **£54**   3️⃣4️⃣2️⃣
38 Muswell Hill Broadway   020 8883 8656   1–1B
"Sensationally good grilled plaice" and the "freshest fish and prawns" help
make this 55-year-old north London chippy a "favourite place to go to be
cheered up" ("my partner and I think it's well worth catching the two buses
needed to get there!"). "Snooker legend Ronnie O'Sullivan is known to
frequent it when playing in the Masters Championships at nearby Ally Pally".
Top Menu Tip – "always order the delicious Greek salad, with the family's
own-recipe dressing". / N10 3RT; www.toffsfish.co.uk; toffsfish; Mon-Sat 10 pm.

Tofu Vegan   **£23**   4️⃣3️⃣2️⃣
105 Upper Street, N1   020 7916 3304   9–3D
28 North End Road, NW11   020 8922 0739   1–1B
54 Commercial Street, E1   020 7998 6640   13–2C NEW
This "great vegan" with branches in Islington, Golders Green and Spitalfields
Market "beats the hell out of anything left in Chinatown" with its
"interesting Chinese options", full of "flavour and texture" and "leaning
towards Sichuan peppercorns" (it's from the team behind non-vegan Xi'an
Impression). "Go with half-a-dozen friends so you can try plenty of dishes" –
"you won't miss the meat". / tofuveganlondon.

Tokimeite W1   **£104**
23 Conduit St   020 3826 4411   3–2C
Since its founding in 2015, this ambitious Japanese – created with
investment from Zen-Noh (Japan's agricultural cooperative) has struggled to
make waves. Although Zen-Noh remains involved, ownership was taken over
a couple of years ago by London food importers Atariya, whose sound
restaurants elsewhere should underpin a decent level of performance here.
Feedback in our annual diners' poll is still too thin for a proper rating, but we
do receive the odd very favourable report. / W1S 2XS; www.tokimeite.com;
tokimeitelondon; Tue-Sat 10.30 pm.

Toklas WC2 £84 3️⃣3️⃣3️⃣
1 Surrey Street   020 3930 8592   2–2D
Who knew Arthur Andersen's previous HQ (also apparently a former car park) could look so chic! The founders of Frieze art fair are behind this "stylish and buzzing" yearling in a Modernist building, off the Strand – "an interesting mid-century space", which is "spacious" and "with a lovely secluded outside terrace". Chef Yohei Furuhashi delivers an "on-trend concept": "ingredients so fresh and of superior quality" are interfered with as little as possible: "this is how delicious food should taste, with flavours bursting in one's mouth, not dishes laced with salt lazily passed off as a meal in most restaurants" ("impeccable…. I'm still dreaming about the artichoke and pea salad"). "Prices seem to have jumped up in recent months" though, placing it in value terms as "pricey, but worth it". / WC2R 2ND; www.toklaslondon.com; toklas_london; Tue-Sat 11 pm.

Tommi's Burger Joint £36 3️⃣3️⃣2️⃣
30 Thayer St, W1   020 7224 3828   3–1A
37 Berwick Street, W1   020 7494 9086   4–2D
"Well priced, tasty" burgers make this long-running Icelandic chain (with two outlets in London and one in Oxford; as well as Berlin and Copenhagen) a "cheap 'n' cheerful favourite" for some reporters. Veteran burger-slinger Tómas Tómasson founded the group 43 years ago, and in 2021 was elected to Iceland's parliament, the Althing, at the age of 72. / www.burgerjoint.co.uk; burgerjointuk.

Tomoe SW15 £43 4️⃣4️⃣2️⃣
292 Upper Richmond Road   020 3730 7884   11–2B
This "outstanding family Japanese" in Putney has attracted a strong following across southwest London for its fresh and authentic cooking, presented in deceptively – but authentically Japanese – modest surroundings. / SW15 6TH; tomoe.london; Wed & Thu 9 pm, Fri & Sat 9.30 pm.

Tonkotsu £50 3️⃣3️⃣3️⃣
Branches throughout London
"Tasty, good-value noodles" in a "relaxed environment" make this 12-year-old London chain (14 branches, plus Brighton and Brum) "worth a visit". The "ramen is deep and fabulous" if "limited in range (no fish-based dishes except prawn)", and is augmented by "quite acceptable katsu curry". Aficionados should head to the Haggerston branch to watch the noodles being made. / www.tonkotsu.co.uk; tonkotsulondon.

Tosa W6 £40 3️⃣3️⃣2️⃣
332 King St   020 8748 0002   8–2B
This "very decent" small café near Stamford Brook tube makes "a good change from the usual Japanese", with "yakitori grilled skewers the real draw". "The room is a little jaded but a seat at the grilling bar is an entertaining winner" ("the friendly chef chats all through the meal"). Top Menu Tip – "the grilled mackerel is truly holy". / W6 0RR; www.tosa.uk; tosa_authentic_japanese ??; Wed-Sun 11.30 pm.

Toulouse Lautrec SE11 £69 3️⃣3️⃣3️⃣
140 Newington Butts   020 7582 6800   1–3C
This wood-panelled French brasserie with an "excellent fixed-price menu" of Gallic classics is particularly "useful in the location" – close to the Imperial War Museum in Kennington – and provides its own entertainment in the form of its upstairs jazz club. / SE11 4RN; www.toulouselautrec.co.uk; tlvenue; Mon-Sat midnight, Sun 10.30 pm.

Townsend @ Whitechapel Gallery E1 £59 3|3|2
77-82 Whitechapel High Street   020 7539 3303   10–2D
One of London's most appealing museum or art gallery dining rooms – this "cheerful operation with a small but delightful menu" presents chef Nick Gilkinson's "well sourced, flavoursome dishes", distinguished by the way the "clean, simple flavours of the ingredients come though". Named in celebration of the turn-of-the-century building's architect, Charles Harrison Townsend, "the room is lined with light wood and mirrors (which some may think a bit stark)". / E1 7QX; www.whitechapelgallery.org; whitechapelgallery; Tue, Sun 6 pm, Wed-Sat 11 pm.

Tozi £65 2|1|3
8 Gillingham St, SW1   020 7769 9771   2–4B
3a Electric Boulevard, SW11   020 38 338 200   11–1C NEW
All-day Italian-style eating, inspired by the grand cafés of Europe and the culinary traditions of Venice, is the aim at this ground-floor venue in a hotel near Victoria station and its sibling in the Battersea Power Station development's new art'otel. Both can still be an "asset to the area", offering a "buzzing" setting, "amazing breakfasts" and "decent dining proposition", but there was also a high proportion of disappointments this year – in particular, poor service in both locations.

The Trafalgar Tavern SE10 £62 3|3|5
28 Park Row   020 8858 2909   1–3D
"On the river, next to the Royal Naval College buildings in the heart of Greenwich", this massive old tavern opened in the year of Queen Victoria's coronation, and its "period design, position and aspect give it a unique selling point". Perhaps because it doesn't have to try too hard, its culinary offering has fluctuated in quality over the years, but the view that "it's a mechanism to fleece tourists" took more of a back seat this year, with most reports being of "pub staples and British classics" that are "full of flavour". / SE10 9NW; www.trafalgartavern.co.uk; trafalgartaverngreenwich; Sun-Thu 11 pm, Fri & Sat midnight.

Trinco SE22 NEW
20 Lordship Lane   020 8638 7812   1–4D
In East Dulwich's restaurant row, Vibushan Thirukumar launched this 'community focused, sustainable restaurant' in April 2023 – too late for feedback in our annual diners' poll – inside the co-working and wellness hub Oru Space (which he co-founded with business partner Paul Nelmes in 2020). Named for his seaside home town back in Sri Lanka, its vegan and vegetarian cuisine is rooted in Tamil culture. / SE22 8HN; www.trinco.restaurant; Thu-Sat 11 pm.

Trinity SW4 £103 3|3|2
4 The Polygon   020 7622 1199   11–2D
"A perfect mix of fine dining and neighbourhood restaurant" – Adam Byatt's celebrated flagship on Clapham Common has won renown as one of the most notable destinations south of the River, and a strong rival to Chez Bruce ten minutes away thanks to its "exquisite evolving menu" and "personal" service. But while still much-vaunted this year by very many reporters, its ratings slipped noticeably due to an unusual number of downbeat reports ("I can't understand why Trinity is so highly rated… I found the experience underwhelming"; "expensive and can lack atmosphere"; "until recently, this was a favourite, but it's now fallen out of my top ten"). In July 2023 – after our annual diners' poll had finished – a former member of the team, Harry Kirkpatrick, returned to the kitchen after stints at a number of top establishments having been appointed as a new head chef. Taking into account owner Adam Byatt's impressive track record

here, our best bet is a swift return to form. And, still for the majority of diners in this year's poll, this is "a place we go to again and again for special occasions and it never disappoints us". / SW4 0JG; www.trinityrestaurant.co.uk; trinityclapham; Mon-Sun 8 pm.

Trinity Upstairs SW4 £70 **4 4 3**
4 The Polygon 020 3745 7227 11–2D

"Wonderful food", delivered in the format of "innovative and interesting sharing plates", is the draw at chef-patron Adam Byatt's casual option, upstairs from his Clapham flagship Trinity. The "high stool seating" doesn't please everyone, but that's more than made up for by the "good-value, high-class victuals" and "friendly and knowledgeable staff". / SW4 0JG; www.trinity-upstairs.co.uk; trinityclapham; Tue-Sat 8.30 pm, Sun 4 pm.

Trishna W1 £81 **5 3 2**
15-17 Blandford St 020 7935 5624 2–1A

"Wonderfully scented dishes" are "delicately and expertly prepared" at JKS Restaurants' exceptional Marylebone flagship, just off the high street, which fans claim "surpasses the Indian original" in Mumbai (which inspired it). But while its culinary performance impressively lives up to its reputation, perceptions of its "oddly shaped and slightly claustrophobic" premises are deteriorating. Top Menu Tip – "definitely get the Duck Keema Naan if it's on the menu". / W1U 3DG; www.trishnalondon.com; trishnalondon; Mon-Sat 10.15 pm, Sun 9.45 pm.

Trivet SE1 £147 **3 3 3**
36 Snowsfields 020 3141 8670 10–4C

The Bermondsey location is "not the easiest to get to", but many reporters make the effort for this "very accomplished" four-year-old. Chef Jonny Lake provides "absolutely first-rate cooking" with "refined and exciting flavours" and sommelier Isa Bal curates a "fantastic and eclectic" wine list. But even numerous fans feel a tad daunted by the pricing – "I thought it well worth the trip and deserving of its reputation, but the bill here makes it a treat rather than just a meal out..."; "it was very good... luckily I wasn't paying!". / SE1 3SU; trivetrestaurant.co.uk; trivetrestaurant; Wed-Sat, Tue 11 pm.

La Trompette W4 £111 **3 3 3**
5-7 Devonshire Rd 020 8747 1836 8–2A

This "absolute gem of a neighbourhood restaurant" sits on a side street off Chiswick's bustling main drag, and – like its cousin Chez Bruce – has earned a London-wide reputation over the years thanks to its "fine modern British dining", "well-drilled service with a smile" and "comprehensive list of fine wines". There's been some "changing of the guard in the kitchen" in the last 12 months with Greg Wellman, formerly of The Glasshouse, Kew, taking over at the stoves. But whereas some fans say "it hasn't undermined what remains a very strong offering", others are less certain and ratings are not what they were: "I'm still the 'fan from E18' who schleps across town to go here, and remain a supporter, but it seems to have lost some of that elusive lustre that previously made it so special". / W4 2EU; www.latrompette.co.uk; latrompettechiswick; Wed & Thu 9 pm, Fri & Sat 10 pm, Sun 3 pm.

Trullo N1 £78 **4 3 3**
300-302 St Paul's Rd 020 7226 2733 9–2D

"The neighbourhood Italian everyone would want to have" – Tim Siadatan and Jordan Frieda's "low-key and lovely" Islington fixture "feels like a special meal every time", with "amazing pasta" and other "delicious" dishes prepared from "excellent ingredients". "Choose upstairs in summer for lunch, and downstairs in winter for a romantic dinner". "Just wish they weren't so dog-friendly!". / N1 2LH; www.trullorestaurant.com; Mon-Sat 10.30 pm, Sun 9.30 pm.

Tsiakkos & Charcoal W9   **£74**   **3** **4** **3**
5 Marylands Road   020 7286 7896   7–1B
"Great hosts and a wonderful bubbly venue" – not to mention affordable
prices for its simple food, much of it from the charcoal grill – underpin the
appeal of this cosy Greek-Cypriot café, off the Harrow Road in Maida Vale. A
couple of newspaper articles in 2022 have brought it to the attention of
more people of late, but it's been there for yonks. / W9 2DU; tsiakkos.co.uk;
Tue-Sat 11 pm.

Tsunami SW4   **£57**   **3** **2** **3**
5-7 Voltaire Rd   020 7978 1610   11–1D
This "modern Japanese" with a "clubby and bouncy vibe" has been a hit on
Clapham High Street since three former Nobu chefs opened it 23 years ago,
and it remains a "very popular" destination for cocktails and fusion bites.
Always "a slightly idiosyncratic" place – this issue was more to the fore this
year with incidents of "erratic" or "uncoordinated" service, and one or two
fears that the "huge" menu is being "dumbed down". / SW4 6DQ;
www.tsunamirestaurant.co.uk; tsunami_restaurants; Sun-Thu 10.30 pm, Fri & Sat
11.30 pm.

Turnips with Tomas Lidakevicius SE1   **£137**   **4** **3** **3**
43 Borough Market, Off Bedale Street   020 7357 8356   10–4C
"A unique experience!" – "For a dinner with a twist, sit 'outside' within
Borough Market and enjoy a set menu with wine pairing" at Tomas
Lidakevicius's offbeat venture, attached to a greengrocer's stall. "You've no
need to choose anything and everything is good": "the lovely setting helps for
sure, but the great food from a tasting menu with seasonal veg as its
centrepiece speaks for itself". "Loved it!". / SE1 9AH;
www.turnipsboroughmarket.com; turnipsborough; Tue-Sat 11.30 pm.

12:51 by chef James Cochran N1   **£71**   **4** **3** **2**
107 Upper Street   07934 202269   9–3D
"Fantastically fun and fabulous food" from accomplished chef, James
Cochran, is the pay-off for a visit to his Islington venue. "It's definitely not a
posh night out" – "the room is tiny" and it's "a tricky and very cramped
space" – but "the vibe is very upbeat and the meal is great value and highly
recommended". Top Menu Tip – "best fried chicken ever". / N1 1QN;
www.1251.co.uk; 1251_twelve_fifty_one; Tue-Sat 10 pm, Sun 8 pm.

20 Berkeley W1 🆕
20 Berkeley Street   020 3327 3691   3–3C
Misha Zelman's (Goodman, Burger & Lobster) Creative Restaurant Group
(Endo at the Rotunda; Humo; Sumu) opened this luxurious May 2023
newcomer on a Mayfair site that's never been previously used as a
restaurant. Online articles around its launch have recycled the PR claims to
'English Manor House' styling – but the reality seems to be nothing like a
creaky old country home, other than in the names of rooms like 'pantry' and
the addition of lots of posh finishes. Executive chef Ben Orpwood sources
ingredients at the height of their short seasons to emphasise the cuisine's
local British focus. No survey feedback or significant press reviews as yet.
/ W1J 8EE; www.20berkeley.com; 20berkeleylondon; Mon-Thu 9.30 pm, Fri & Sat
10 pm.

28 Church Row NW3   **£61**   **4** **4** **4**
28 Church Row   020 7993 2062   9–2A
Under a picturesque Georgian terrace, close to St John-in-Hampstead
church, this basement tapas bar is a prime destination in the area thanks to
its "consistently delicious food, attentive staff" and "lovely atmosphere". The
menu adds Italian elements to its Spanish core, and there's a "very good
wine selection". / NW3 6UP; www.28churchrow.com; 28churchrow; Mon-Sat
10.30 pm, Sun 9.30 pm.

28-50 £90 ②②❸
15-17 Marylebone Lane, W1   020 7486 7922   3–1A
4 Great Portland Street, W1   020 7420 0630   3–1C
300 King's Road, SW3   020 7349 9818   6–3C
96 Draycott Ave, SW3   020 7581 5208   6–2C
A "fabulous wine list with so many wines available by the glass" is the key
draw to this trio of wine-bar/kitchens from the West End to Chelsea (the
Draycott Avenue branch closed this year). Dining can seem "quite pricey" for
what it is, but most diners say they "love the food as well". / www.2850.co.uk;
2850marylebone.

24 The Oval SW9 £62 ❸❹❸
24 Clapham Road   020 7735 6111   11–1D
In the thin area near Oval tube, this neighbourhood bistro is worth
remembering. A sibling to Knife in Clapham, its "old-fashioned modern
British cooking" puts a similar emphasis on steak and other grills, but there's
a good selection of dishes and – albeit on limited feedback – it wins praise
for "excellent all-round value". / SW9 0JG; www.24theoval.co.uk; 24theoval;
Fri & Sat, Wed & Thu 9.30 pm, Sun 4.30 pm.

Twist Connubio W1 £69 ❸❸②
42 Crawford Street   020 7723 3377   2–1A
"Tucked away in Marylebone, with a friendly vibe and tasty food", this
creative outfit marries flavours from Spanish, Italian and Japanese cuisine.
"Some of the tapas are very good indeed", and they are supported by a
serious wine list focused on Spain and Italy. / W1H 1JW; www.twistconnubio.com;
twistconnubio; Mon-Sat 10 pm.

Two Brothers N3 £40 ❸②②
297-303 Regent's Park Rd   020 8346 0469   1–1B
"The fish is always fresh and the staff are friendly" at this "good local fish 'n'
chip place" that has been a fixture in Finchley for three decades. "Best fish
and chips in London?" – probably not, but just what you want in your
neighbourhood. / N3 1DP; www.twobrothers.co.uk; Tue-Sun 10 pm.

222 Veggie Vegan W14 £46 ❸❸❸
222 North End Road   020 7381 2322   8–2D
Celebrating its 20th anniversary this year, chef Ben Asamani's "very good
vegan" on Fulham's trafficky North End Road (near its crossroads with the
Lillie Road) provides "a lovely dining experience" – "you certainly don't miss
eating fish or meat". Top Menu Tip – the "veggie burgers" – made with
asparagus and petits pois on gluten-free bread – "are the best!". / W14 9NU;
www.222vegan.com; 222vegancuisine; Wed-Sun 9 pm.

2 Veneti W1 £59 ②❸②
10 Wigmore Street   020 7637 0789   3–1B
Handy as a "welcoming" spot near the Wigmore Hall – this straightforward
Italian delivers "an enjoyable experience" at "surprisingly reasonable prices
for a smart restaurant in a smart district". Some reports also applaud its
"really good and authentically Venetian dishes", but a fair summary might be
that the overall performance is "pleasant". / W1U 2RD; www.2veneti.com;
2veneti; Mon-Fri 9.45 pm, Sat 10 pm.

Uli £78 ❹❸❹
15 Seymour Place, W1   020 3141 5877   2–2A **NEW**
5 Ladbroke Road, W11   020 3141 5878   7–2B
"Relaxed and busy", Michael Lim's Notting Hill venue is "always a treat",
with "great Singaporean and other Asian dishes". It has notched up 26
years, first in All Saints Road and more recently in smart new premises on
Ladbroke Road. A second branch opened in Seymour Place, Marylebone, in
June 2023. Top Tip – "fantastic in the summer with the roof open".

Umu W1 £166 | 3 | 4 | 4 |
14-16 Bruton Pl   020 7499 8881   3–2C
Opened 20 years ago as London's first exponent of Kyoto-style kaiseki dining (Japan's most refined cuisine), this low-key Mayfair fixture remains a key foodie destination under Ryo Kakatsu, who joined 10 years ago and was appointed executive chef in 2020. It also has one of the most extensive sake lists in Europe. While the occasional reporter flinches at the "incredibly expense and very small portions", nobody complains about the quality of the food. / W1J 6LX; www.umurestaurant.com; umurestaurant; Tue-Sat 10 pm.

Upstairs at The George W1 £86 | 3 | 2 | 3 |
55 Great Portland Street   020 3946 3740   2–1B
This "grand but friendly" tavern, in "magnificent" 18th-century premises a short walk from Oxford Circus, offers Kitchen Table chef "James Knappett's take on traditional pub classics with inventive twists". In the main bar you'll find elevated snacks, while a "concise British menu" is served in the upstairs dining room, including "incredible roast dinners – huge slices of beef with what can only be described as a chimney-sized Yorkshire pudding!". / W1W 7LQ; thegeorge.london; thegeorgepublichouse; Tue-Sat 11 pm, Sun 7 pm.

Le Vacherin W4 £77 | 3 | 4 | 4 |
76-77 South Parade   020 8742 2121   8–1A
"The French bistro at its best", this "reliable" Gallic fixture by Acton Green is "a small bit of Paris in Chiswick", with "perfect food (including oysters) and an atmosphere for romance". Top Menu Tip – "delicious soufflés". / W4 5LF; www.levacherin.com; le_vacherin; Mon-Sat 10.30 pm, Sun 9 pm.

Vardo SW3 £75 | 2 | 2 | 3 |
9 Duke of York Square   020 7101 1199   6–2D
Set in a striking purpose-built circular pavilion in Duke of York Square, this family-friendly venture is part of the Caravan group (it's named after the Romany travelling wagon). The menu of global favourites is "very good value for Chelsea" (but, in gastronomic terms, perhaps a bit "dull"). / SW3 4LY; vardorestaurant.co.uk; vardorestaurant; Tue-Thu, Sun 10 pm, Fri & Sat 10.30 pm, Mon 9.30 pm.

Vasco & Piero's Pavilion W1 £75 | 3 | 4 | 3 |
11 D'Arblay Street   020 7437 8774   4–1C
"Still a special place even though it's moved site" – this veteran Soho Italian was evicted from its previous Poland Street home over Covid, and found these new digs last year. It still "exudes old world charm" and has retained many of the former "delightful" staff, who are really at the heart of this "unpretentious" experience as much as the "reliable Umbrian/Italian cooking". / W1F 8DT; www.vascosfood.com; Tue-Sat 10 pm.

Veeraswamy W1 £101 | 4 | 3 | 4 |
Victory House, 99-101 Regent Street   020 7734 1401   4–4B
"First came here almost 60 years ago! And it's still one of my favourites" – London's oldest Indian restaurant "delivers fabulous food year after year". Opened in 1926, in a first-floor space at the Piccadilly end of Regent Street, it is nowadays part of the upmarket Amaya and Chutney Mary group who have ensured its offering has moved with the times. The decor is "lovely" but not old-fashioned, and the "imaginative food has lots of flavours". Top Menu Tip – "Rogan Josh on the bone". / W1B 4RS; www.veeraswamy.com; veeraswamy.london; Mon-Sat 10 pm, Sun 10.15 pm.

Via Emilia £48 **3 4 3**

10 Charlotte Place, W1T   020 8127 4277   2–1C **NEW**
37a Hoxton Square, N1   020 7613 0508   13–1B

"A relatively limited menu allows for a focus on quality" and authenticity at this duo showcasing the food of Emilia-Romagna: both the original "small and intimate" branch in Shoreditch; and the one "formerly known as 'In Parma by Food Roots' in Fitzrovia (since early 2023 now rebranded in line with its sister restaurant)". "Staff are very accommodating" and offer "Italian meats and cheeses and Bolognese/Emilian standbys, like Tagliatelle al Ragu (definitely not SpagBol!)". "Go back frequently as it's great value too".

Il Vicolo SW1 £72 **2 3 2**

3-4 Crown Passage   020 7839 3960   3–4D

Celebrating its 30th anniversary this year, this "family-owned Italian restaurant" has long seemed refreshingly down to earth for somewhere hidden in an alleyway in posh St James's: with its "simple Calabrian menu and good service", it's "especially good for lunch". As with many other central places, it has "appeared considerably more expensive" of late – perhaps they are saving up for a move to new premises: a relaunch a few doors down from its old site scheduled for September 2023. / SW1Y 6PP; www.ilvicolorestaurant.co.uk; ilvicolo_restaurant; Mon-Sat 10 pm.

The Victoria SW14 £66 **3 3 3**

10 West Temple Sheen   020 8876 4238   11–2A

"Love this pub", hailed by fans (often parents) for providing "one of the best Sunday lunches" in this part of southwest London, just outside Richmond Park in East Sheen. Over the years, TV chef Paul Merrett has transformed the rambling Victorian tavern into a boutique hotel with a large garden and spacious conservatory for dining. / SW14 7RT; victoriasheen.co.uk; thevictoriasheen; Wed & Thu, Sat, Fri 9 pm, Sun 7 pm.

Viet Food W1 £43 **3 2 3**

34-36 Wardour Street   020 7494 4555   5–3A

"Delicious morsels" of "good Asian food at low, low prices" ensure that ex-Hakkasan chef Jeff Tan's warehouse-style Chinatown operation is often packed to the rafters – it's a "fun, busy place" if you don't mind squeezing in. / W1D 6QT; www.vietnamfood.co.uk; vietfoodlondon; Sun-Thu 10.30 pm, Fri & Sat 11 pm.

Viet Garden N1 £36 **3 2 2**

207 Liverpool Rd   020 7700 6040   9–3D

"I couldn't love it more", say regulars of this Islington Vietnamese – "a family-run and family-oriented original, with reliable and delicious food". / N1 1LX; www.vietgarden.co.uk; vietgardenuk; Sun-Thu 11 pm, Fri & Sat 11.30 pm.

Vijay NW6 £41 **3 4 2**

49 Willesden Ln   020 7328 1087   1–1B

This "well-established" Kilburn curry house – purportedly the first to offer South Indian cuisine in the UK – celebrates its 60th anniversary this year. Little has changed since it opened, with its "plain good cooking", "authentic recipes" including dishes not found elsewhere and "lovely vegetarian meals" pleasing happy locals as well as a string of celeb visitors ranging from the late Michael Winner to Diana Ross, Harrison Ford and the Indian cricket team. / NW6 7RF; www.vijayrestaurant.co.uk; vijayindiauk; Sun-Thu 10.45 pm, Fri & Sat 11.45 pm.

Villa Bianca NW3 £75 334

1 Perrins Ct 020 7435 3131 9–2A

"There's an air of old-school sophistication as you enter" this "established Italian" with starched white linen "off an alleyway in Hampstead". It scored consistently well this year for its "charming and helpful" service and "fab food, without fab prices". Top Tip – "the wild boar ragu". / NW3 1QS; villabiancagroup.com; villabiancanw3; Tue-Sat 11 pm, Sun 10 pm.

Villa Di Geggiano W4 £93 344

66-68 Chiswick High Road 020 3384 9442 8–2B

This "beautiful courtyard" on the Chiswick High Road "feels like a little bit of (the expensive part) of Tuscany – but at least you've saved on the air fare", and the "delightful atmosphere, good fish and pasta" add to the impression. The Chianti estate it is named after has exported wine to London for 300 years. / W4 1SY; www.villadigeggiano.co.uk; villa_di_geggiano_london; Tue-Sat 10.30 pm, Sun 9 pm.

The Vincent Rooms, Westminster Kingsway College SW1 £46 334

76 Vincent Square 020 7802 8391 2–4C

One of "London's best kept foodie secrets", where you act as a guinea pig for the next generation of the UK hospitality trade within Westminster Kingsway College, on leafy Vincent Square. There are two restaurants: the relaxed 'Brasserie' and more formal 'Escoffier Room', where "the cooking by third-year students is often Michelin quality", while "the service by first years is lovely… if a bit rough at the edges". Not only is a meal here "terrific value (£35 for 5-course tasting menu, ditto wine pairings)", you also "support budding culinary careers". / SW1P 2PD; www.thevincentrooms.co.uk; thevincentrooms; Mon, Fri 3 pm, Tue-Thu 9 pm.

Vinoteca £62 222

18 Devonshire Rd, W4 020 3701 8822 8–2A
One Pancras Sq, N1 020 3793 7210 9–3C
Borough Yards, Stoney Street, SE1 020 3376 3000 10–4C
7 St John St, EC1 020 7253 8786 10–1B
Queen Victoria Street, EC4 awaiting tel 10–3C

"An exceptional list of wine with so many to choose by the glass that it's always possible to try something a bit different" is the key selling point of this popular modern wine bar chain. Its culinary attractions are less reliable – the food can be "surprisingly good" but is too often "essentially average"; service can be "accommodating" or "rushed"; and the ambience can be "better if you can sit outside". But its "excellent value" drinking and "lively" style carry the day. In particular, the "conveniently placed" King's Cross branch has a "great location, which makes it a winner". Top Tip – "creditable set lunch at a pretty restrained price". / www.vinoteca.co.uk; vinotecawinefood.

Vivat Bacchus £74 332

4 Hay's Lane, SE1 020 7234 0891 10–4C
47 Farringdon Street, EC4 020 7353 2648 10–2A

Now in its 21st year, this South African-owned duo in Farringdon and London Bridge thrive on their "good basics", including "delicious steaks" and a "lovely wine list" with a focus on South African vintages. Saffa-style dried meats and a dedicated cheese room complete the deal. / www.vivatbacchus.co.uk; vivatbacchus.

Volta do Mar WC2   £66   3 3 2
13-15 Tavistock Street   020 3034 0028   5–3D
A move to Notting Hill in summer 2023 after four years in Covent Garden should have put new wind in the sails of this culinary celebration of Portugal and its historical maritime links with Asia, Africa and South America – a project from Salt Yard founder Simon Mullins and his Portuguese wife Isabel Almeida Da Silva. The "fancy versions of Portuguese classic dishes" are generally "very good" (if, according to the odd critic, "too well behaved"), and there's a "well-priced Portuguese wine list". / WC2E 7PS; voltadomar.co.uk; voltadomar_ldn; Thu-Sat, Tue, Wed 10.30 pm.

Vori W11 NEW   £88   3 3 3
120 Holland Park Avenue   020 3308 4271   7–2A
Restaurateur Markos Tsimikalis closed his Shoreditch restaurant, Hungry Donkey, to open this brightly decorated Greek venue in Holland Park in late 2022. Our initial feedback is very upbeat all-round and – in April 2023 – The Independent's Kate Ng was likewise positive, including about the signature Cretan-style cheesecake made with sheep and goat's milk ("certainly up there with the greats"). / W11 4UA; vorigreekkitchen.co.uk; vorilondon; Tue-Sat 10.30 pm, Sun 9 pm.

VQ   £64   2 2 3
St Giles Hotel, 111a Great Russell St, WC1   020 7636 5888   5–1A
325 Fulham Rd, SW10   020 7376 7224   6–3B
9 Aldgate High Street, EC3   020 3301 7224   10–2D
"Open 24 hours, with flexible options for breakfast" – these round-the-clock cafés are worth remembering if you're out on the town and need to refuel. Only the SW10 original generates much in the way of feedback – "the cuisine is not fine food, but it's a convenient option that's good value" and "reliable". (Aldgate also has a standalone bar with a 24-hour alcohol licence). / www.vqrestaurants.com; vqrestaurants.

Wagamama   £58   1 1 2
Branches throughout London
As a "reliable standby", this Japanese-inspired ramen (noodle) chain still inspires many reports, and parents in particular see it as a "safe option". Even some fans, though, acknowledge that "it's not a gastronomic highlight" nowadays, and ratings are dragged significantly down by the few who feel it's "lost its way", with service that's "not the fastest" and "food that used to be nice, but which is now not so good". / www.wagamama.com; wagamama_uk; SRA-1 star.

Wahaca   £53   2 2 3
Branches throughout London
These "lively, colourful" Mexican street-food joints are, say fans, "great for a quick bite" – "the food remains pretty good (if not where it was several years ago)" and "you can't complain at the prices". That's the majority view anyway, although there is a small minority who feel it's "very average" now (and its ratings risk heading that way). Founded by MasterChef winner Thomasina Miers in 2007, the group hit the buffers during the pandemic and halved in size to 10 sites in London, with Dick Enthoven of Nando's taking a controlling stake. / www.wahaca.com; wahaca; SRA-3 stars.

The Wallace,
The Wallace Collection W1   £48   2 1 5
Hertford House, Manchester Square   020 7563 9505   3–1A
This "beautiful space in a covered courtyard" at the Wallace Collection museum and art gallery makes an unusually "delightful" rendez-vous for lunch or afternoon tea near Oxford Street… or it would if it were not for the "disappointing food and shambolic service". / W1U 3BN; www.peytonandbyrne.co.uk; peytonandbyrne; Mon-Sun 4 pm.

The Water House Project E2 — £197 — 4 5 4
1 Corbridge Crescent   07841 804119   14–2B
"Wow! Terrifically innovative, technical cooking and a lovely supper club concept of common tables, complete with a welcome and farewell from the chef" inspires ongoing acclaim for Gabriel Waterhouse's excellent Bethnal Green venture (which relocated a couple of years ago to an airy new space). It's £155 for his 10-course menu with drinks pairings (and on Wednesday nights and Saturday lunchtimes a shorter selection is served for £100): "for this standard of cuisine, it's a great price when so much London serious 'fine' dining is nowadays just unaffordable". / E2 9DS; www.thewaterhouseproject.com; thewaterhouseproject; Wed-Sat 11 pm.

The Waterman's Arms SW13 NEW
375 Lonsdale Rd   Awaiting tel   11–1A
Few pubs in London boast as fine a location as this riverside tavern, at the Thames-side end of Barnes High Street (and next to the also-picturesque Bull's Head). Abandoned to pizza and brasserie chains in recent decades, it's now to be relaunched as a passion project by Patty & Bun founder, Joe Grossmann; and with front of house from Simon Walsh, who filled the same role at Hammersmith's excellent Anglesea Arms. / SW13 9PY; Tue-Sat 10.30 pm.

The Wells Tavern NW3 — £74 — 3 4 4
30 Well Walk   020 7794 3785   9–1A
By many accounts "by far the best gastropub in the Hampstead area", this particularly "welcoming and charming" Georgian tavern has been run for two decades by Beth Coventry (sister of the doyenne of restaurant critics, Fay Maschler). "Great outside seating… if you can nab it". / NW3 1BX; thewellshampstead.london; thewellshampstead; Mon-Sat 10 pm, Sun 9.30 pm.

Westerns Laundry N5 — £73 — 3 3 3
34 Drayton Park   020 7700 3700   9–2D
"Heavily embracing the post-industrial vibe" – this "buzzy" hipster feature not far from the Emirates and Drayton Park station ("did they go out of their way to make it difficult to find?") makes elegant and appealing use of the high-ceilinged space it occupies (originally, of course, a laundry). Five years old now, it's something of a classic of the contemporary East End genre – "a small plates outlet of quality" combining funky tapas with low intervention wines. It does attract the odd more downbeat critique though: "the food, service and ambience are all fine but in no way justify the prices". / N5 1PB; www.westernslaundry.com; westernslaundry; Tue-Sat 10.30 pm, Sun 9 pm.

The Wet Fish Café NW6 — £57 — 3 3 3
242 West End Lane   020 7443 9222   1–1B
"A great local for brunch, quick lunchtime bite or impromptu dinner for two" – this "small and always friendly neighbourhood favourite" occupies atmospheric premises in West Hampstead that started life as a 1930s fishmonger (you can still buy fish retail here). "The food is consistently good", "service is speedy" and they do "excellent coffee" too. / NW6 1LG; www.thewetfishcafe.co.uk; thewetfishcafe; Mon-Sun 10.30 pm.

The Wigmore, The Langham W1 — £65 — 3 4 4
15 Langham Place, Regent Street   020 7965 0198   2–1B
Pub grub is elevated by Michel Albert Roux to great effect at this "posh pub", "handily close to the horrors of Oxford Circus" – a surprisingly "good place to meet for business" and "worth going out of your way for". Top Menu Tip – "take friends and order the cheese toastie on the sly, then watch their faces light up when the magnificent beast of a sandwich is presented". / W1B 3DE; www.the-wigmore.co.uk; wigmorelondon; Mon-Sat 11 pm.

Wild Honey St James SW1 £120 3️⃣2️⃣2️⃣
Sofitel, 8 Pall Mall   020 7389 7820   2–3C

Anthony Demetre's "combination of balance, tastes and textures" inspires fans of this "grand hotel dining room" off Trafalgar Square ("a far cry from his original restaurant of this name" in Mayfair). It's most nominated for a "solid business lunch" although "the tasting menu is lovely" and also wins recommendations for it as a foodie destination in its own right. A setting that's "classy" to supporters, though, can – to critics – seem "a little soulless"; and service doesn't always live up to the occasion. Top Tip – "the set lunch and early evening menus offer excellent value". / SW1Y 5NG; www.wildhoneystjames.co.uk; wildhoneystjames; Wed-Sat 9.30 pm, Tue 2.30 pm.

Wild Tavern SW3 £127 2️⃣2️⃣3️⃣
2 Elystan Street   020 8191 9885   6–2C

This Chelsea four-year-old (by Chelsea Green) with an Alpine-themed interior is from a duo involved in Beast and Burger & Lobster; and offers a raw bar along with prime cuts of steak and fish from the grill, sold per 100g – all of which attracts little commentary from reporters beyond the consistent complaint that it's "way over-priced". In September 2023, a new offshoot – Wild Notting Hill – will open on the site that was formerly 202 (RIP). / SW3 3NS; www.wildtavern.co.uk; wildtavern; Mon-Sat 10 pm, Sun 9.30 pm.

Wiltons SW1 £117 3️⃣3️⃣3️⃣
55 Jermyn St   020 7629 9955   3–3C

"A last redoubt of traditional gastronomy" – London's oldest restaurant in St James's (est. 1742, but on this site since the 1980s) maintains its "quiet" and "calm" style, with "understated but excellent service" and "booths that make a superb place to do business". Classic fish dishes – for example "very good Dover sole off the bone" – are the speciality and "ever-reliable". A less welcome constant are its "eye-watering prices": "everything was as I hoped it would be... apart from the bill!" / SW1Y 6LX; www.wiltons.co.uk; wiltons1742; Mon-Sat 10.30 pm.

The Windmill W1 £65 3️⃣2️⃣3️⃣
6-8 Mill St   020 7491 8050   4–2A

The "focus on home-made British pies" makes this trad Mayfair pub a crowd-pleaser, "tucked away" off Regent Street close to Oxford Circus. From the same stable as the Guinea Grill, it now has a smarter restaurant upstairs, along with a rooftop terrace. Top Menu Tips – "the pastry pies are best for hungry young adult males, while the shepherd's pie is excellent if you want something lighter". / W1S 2AZ; www.windmillmayfair.co.uk; windmill_pub; Mon-Sat 9 pm, Sun 7 pm.

The Wine Library EC3 £51 2️⃣3️⃣5️⃣
43 Trinity Sq   020 7481 0415   10–3D

"Back to being busy, bubbly and bright" after the bleak pandemic years – this vaulted 19th-century cellar near Tower Hill offers a "great and interesting selection of wine", served at retail prices plus £9.50 corkage, with "informative staff" to help you choose. A "help-yourself" menu of cheeses, cold meats and other nibbles is on hand to provide ballast. / EC3N 4DJ; www.winelibrary.co.uk; thewinelibrary; Tue-Fri 8 pm, Mon 6 pm, Sat 5.30 pm.

The Wolseley W1 £83 2️⃣2️⃣5️⃣
160 Piccadilly   020 7499 6996   3–3C

"Reports of the death of The Wolseley are greatly exaggerated". After a well-publicised boardroom battle in 2022 ousted its original co-founders, even though its long-term fans are "annoyed at the ousting of Christopher Corbin & Jeremy King", there is "no evidence on the floor of any impact": "it's as good as it ever was (and just as full!")". This Continental-style Grand Café, near The Ritz (originally built as a car showroom, for which it is named) is celebrating its 20th year, and remains a hub of metropolitan

living. The "impressive" and "always bustling" space is "one of the best dining rooms in London" and "if you want to wow a client or a foreigner, then bring them here": it remains London's No. 1 for business entertaining in our annual diners' poll. Its "great menu of classics" is executed to a "solid and reliable" if "lacklustre" standard, but you "go for the overall package and peerless people watching, not the food". The exception is "the most civilised breakfast anywhere on the planet" which is also our diners' poll's No. 1 choice in this category. The "varied menu, with something – and more – for everyone", helps "elevate the occasion to a special level"; and it is also "a power scene" amongst business-types. Top Tip – afternoon tea is also "always impressive with its elegance and high standards". / W1J 9EB; www.thewolseley.com; thewolseley; Mon-Sat 11 pm, Sun 10 pm.

The Wolseley City EC4 NEW
68 King William Street   Awaiting tel   10–3C
In Autumn 2023, the famous West End icon will start a new, ultimately global, roll-out. First stop is the City, with this conversion of the ground floor of the old House of Fraser building, near Monument tube and looking onto London Bridge. The site is considerably larger than that on Piccadilly and the website promise is of 'a younger sister to the original, not a replica'.
/ EC4N 7HR; thewolseleyhospitalitygroup.com; thewolseley; Mon-Sun 10 pm.

Wong Kei W1   £34   3 2 2
41-43 Wardour St   020 7437 8408   5–3A
"No frills, no smiles but always fast and reliable" – this "Chinatown standby" has fed generations of West End revellers and theatre-goers with "great cheap Cantonese food", serving up to 500 people at a time over several floors. "Service is not what it was – the staff are no longer rude!" – but "the speed with which scoff arrives at the table remains utterly predictable". Top Menu Tip – "still love their Singapore noodles". / W1D 6PY; Mon-Sat 11.30 pm, Sun 10.30 pm.

Wright Brothers   £72   3 3 3
56 Old Brompton Rd, SW7   020 7581 0131   6–2B
11 Stoney St, SE1   020 7403 9554   10–4C
26 Circus Road West, SW8   020 7324 7734   11–1C
"Crowded… slightly crazy-busy… top oysters supported by a changing menu of fish and crustacea" – that's the package at this trio of "busy" bistros in Borough Market, Battersea Power Station and South Kensington. "You come here for the seafood, not to be fawned over. The decor's a little rough and ready but the food's so fresh and delicious".
/ thewrightbrothers.co.uk; WrightBrosLTD.

Wulf & Lamb   £57   3 2 3
243 Pavilion Road, SW1   020 3948 5999   6–2D
66 Chiltern Street, W1   020 8194 0000   2–1A
"The food pleases everyone, vegan or not" at this duo of "comfortable" and "enjoyable" meat-free cafés which occupy chichi enclaves in Chelsea and Marylebone. "Vegan eaters are bewildered at the choice on offer" ("great curries, veggie burgers etc") and "whether or not you eat meat, it represents good value for lunch or a light dinner in an otherwise pricey part of town".
/ www.wulfandlamb.com.

Xi'an Impression N7   £44   4 2 1
117 Benwell Rd   020 3441 0191   9–2D
"I could eat here every day and die happy", say fans of this Shanxi street-food canteen opposite Arsenal's Emirates stadium – "the homemade dumplings and noodles are consistently superlative and soooo moreish". "Service is matter-of-fact Chinese, seating is short and tight", "but you go just for the food and you're not disappointed!" / N7 7BW; www.xianimpression.co.uk; xianimpression; Mon-Sun 10 pm.

Yaatra SW1 NEW   £85   4 4 2
Old Westminster Fire Station, 4 Greycoat Pl 020 4549 1906 2–4C
This "no-expense-spared upmarket Indian restaurant" in Grade II listed Old
Westminster Fire Station has impressed reporters with some "amazing and
interesting dishes" in its first year. It was launched as "Atul Kochhar's
Mathura, which didn't last long, but the new management has done some
great marketing with customer deals" – "I'd certainly go again". / SW1P 1SB;
www.yaatrarestaurant.com; yaatrawestminster; Tue-Sun 11 pm.

Yama Momo SE22   £65   3 2 3
72 Lordship Ln 020 8299 1007 1–4D
Buzzy Japanese in East Dulwich (younger sister of Clapham's long-
established Tsunami), that's "always busy due to the reliably tasty (and
never-changing) menu" of sushi and sashimi, plus more substantial fare,
backed up by "excellent cocktails". / SE22 8HF; www.yamamomo.co.uk;
yamamomo_eastdulwich; Mon-Thu 10 pm, Fri & Sat 10.30 pm, Sun 9.30 pm.

Yard Sale Pizza   £43   3 4 2
54 Blackstock Road, N4   020 7226 2651   9–1D
46 Westow Hill, SE19   020 8670 6386   1–4D
39 Lordship Lane, SE22   020 8693 5215   1–4D
393 Brockley Road, SE4   020 8692 8800   1–4D
63 Bedford Hill, SW12   020 8772 1100   11–2C
622 High Road Leytonstone, E11   020 8539 5333   1–1D
15 Hoe Street, E17   020 8509 0888   1–1D
184 Hackney Road, E2   020 7739 1095   14–2A
105 Lower Clapton Rd, E5   020 3602 9090   14–1B
"Delicious thin-crust pizzas" win consistently high ratings for this 10-strong
chain across north, east and south London. They are a socially conscious
bunch who contributed 8,000 meals to NHS staff during the pandemic.
/ yardsalepizza.com; yardsalepizza.

Yashin   £109   4 3 2
117-119 Old Brompton Rd, SW7   020 7373 3990   6–2B
1a Argyll Rd, W8   020 7938 1536   6–1A
This offbeat, "really high-quality Japanese" outfit in a Kensington backstreet
from Yasuhiro Minemo and Shinya Ikeda has carved out a niche for itself
over the last 13 years with its "delicious sushi" and "extremely attentive
staff". It's pricey, but "the lunch menu is great value". Its offshoot Ocean
House is in the former Brompton Library, while the latest addition from
2022, Sushi Kamon in Arcade Food Hall on Oxford Street, offers a cut-price
45-minute omakase experience. / yashinsushi.com.

Yauatcha   £105   3 2 2
15-17 Broadwick Street, W1   020 7494 8888   4–1C
Broadgate Circle, EC2   020 3817 9888   13–2B
"Cheung fun... just wow" – a highlight of the "brilliant" dim sum at this cool
modern take on Cantonese cuisine, created by Alan Yau, the restaurant
whizz behind Hakkasan and Wagamama. Now in its 20th anniversary year,
there are two sites in the capital – a Soho basement (with ground-floor tea
room) and a very much bigger and glossier venue in the City's Broadgate
development (plus satellites in the Middle East and India). But even fans of
the "delicious food" sometimes say, "I like it here, but the bill always
surprises me... not in a good way!" / www.yauatcha.com.

The Yellow House SE16 £53 **3 3 3**

126 Lower Rd 020 7231 8777 12–2A

"Thank the stars they survived the pandemic!" – nearby residents cherish this *"wonderful local"* near Surrey Quays station. *"Effectively, it has three menus – modern European, grill and pizza 'n' pasta – all are top-notch!"* / SE16 2UE; www.theyellowhouse.eu; theyellowhouserestaurant; Tue-Thu 9 pm, Fri & Sat 9.30 pm, Sun 5.30 pm.

Zafferano SW1 £116 **4 3 3**

15 Lowndes St 020 7235 5800 6–1D

"Top-notch food and great service" continue to win praise for this chic Belgravia Italian. Compared with its 1990s heyday (when under Giorgio Locatelli it reigned supreme as London's best) it doesn't attract nearly the same level of attention, partly because it is *"very, very expensive"*. But quality remains high and it's particularly popular amongst expense-accounters as a good way to *"impress clients"*. / SW1X 9EY; zafferanorestaurant.com; zafferanorestaurant; Mon-Sun 10 pm.

Zaibatsu SE10 £40 **4 3 2**

96 Trafalgar Rd 020 8858 9317 1–3D

"Small, rammed and pretty hectic, but that's all part of the charm" at this Japanese café on the edge of Greenwich, serving *"fantastic food that's insanely well priced"* – *"ribs in BBQ sauce, mixed tempura, cod in tempura, sushi, noodles... all amazing, fresh and such good value"*. *"A few things to note: it's cash only; BYO for booze; it can be a tad cold in winter"*. / SE10 9UW; www.zaibatsufusion.co.uk; Tue-Sat 11 pm, Sun 9 pm.

Zaika of Kensington W8 £79 **4 4 4**

1 Kensington High Street 020 7795 6533 6–1A

"Stunning food, service and ambience" make a meal at this upscale Indian near Kensington Gardens *"a special experience"*. Set in a *"beautiful ex-bank building with great art throughout"*, fans feel it is *"often overlooked given the location (i.e. not Mayfair) but up there with the best"* (*"I've tried several new Indian places, but keep returning to this one"*). / W8 5NP; www.zaikaofkensington.com; zaikaofkensington; Tue-Sat 10.15 pm, Sun 9.15 pm.

Zapote EC2 NEW £40 **4 4 4**

70 Leonard Street 020 7613 5346 13–1B

"Bringing an affordable higher-end Mexican experience to London, with inventive cuisine" – chef Yahir Gonzalez and co-founder Tony Geary have taken over the Shoreditch site that was St Leonards (RIP) to open this colourfully decorated and attractive 60-seater. It has received some up-and-down reports in the media (The Guardian's Grace Dent, a fan, thought it *"a date-night kind of place, or for dinner with a client you'd actually like to talk to"*; but it's *"a modern Mexican muddle"* according to the FT's Tim Hayward; or with *"basic errors"* in the view of online restaurant maven, Andy Hayler). But we've rated it positively on our initial reports of *"knockout Latino food with imaginative and perfectly judged sharing plates"*, *"interesting cocktails and wines"* and *"warm and attentive service"*. / EC2A 4QX; zapote.co.uk; Tue-Thu 10 pm, Fri & Sat 10.30 pm.

Zephyr W11 £80 **4 4 4**

100 Portobello Road 020 4599 1177 7–2B

This *"chic-casual"* venture from the Pachamama group in Notting Hill focuses on *"modern Greek fusion food"*, and has picked up plenty of fans in its inaugural year thanks to its *"sophisticated cooking"* and *"buzzy"* vibe. One repeated gripe: *"bringing dishes when the kitchen fancies can lead to an odd sequence to meals!"* / W11 2QD; www.zephyr.london; zephyrnottinghill; Mon-Sat 11 pm, Sun 10 pm.

Zheng SW3 £80 3 3 2

4 Sydney St   020 7352 9890   6–2C

Chelsea Malaysian whose menu mixes and matches Chinese dishes and other Asian inspirations. It's survived ten years on a site (off the King's Road) that was previously something of a restaurant graveyard, due to its straightforward if not earth-shattering virtues: "friendly service, good food, nice interior". / SW3 6PP; www.zhengchelsea.co.uk; Mon, Wed-Sun 11 pm.

Zia Lucia £53 3 3 2

61 Blythe Road, W14   020 7371 4096   8–1C
18 Olympic Way, HA9   020 3744 4427   1–1A
61 Stoke Newington High Street, N16   020 8616 8690   1–1C
157 Holloway Road, N7   020 7700 3708   9–2D
238 West End Lane, NW6   020 3737 9557   1–1B **NEW**
65 Balham High Road, SW12   020 3093 0946   11–2C
356 Old York Road, SW18   020 3971 0829   11–2B
75 Hampton Tower, E14   020 4503 8859   12–1C **NEW**
12a Piazza Walk, E1   020 7702 2525   10–2D

"It's hard to be 'special' with pizza these days with so much competition, but the eye-catching options give an edge" to this popular nine-strong chain, whose calling card is a choice of four different 48-hour fermented pizza bases, including the distinctive black vegetable charcoal. Their latest opening is in Canary Wharf. / zialucia.com; zialuciapizza.

Ziani's SW3 £58 3 4 3

45 Radnor Walk   020 7351 5297   6–3C

"Despite being off the beaten track" in Chelsea (albeit near the King's Road), this tiny trat' still packs 'em in. Founder Roberto Colussi died a few years back, but the front-of-house team has maintained his warm welcome and the very dependable cooking. / SW3 4BP; www.ziani.co.uk; Mon-Sun 10 pm.

Zoilo W1 £85 3 3 4

9 Duke St   020 7486 9699   3–1A

"Small, personal and romantic, with serious food for meat fans" – an Argentinian venue near the Wallace Collection in Marylebone, run by chef-patron Diego Jacquet, who trained in his native Buenos Aires under the legendary Francis Mallmann and worked at El Bulli in Spain and Aquavit in New York. Top Tip – "set lunch is a bargain". / W1U 3EG; www.zoilo.co.uk; zoilolondon; Tue-Sat midnight.

Zuma SW7 £115 4 4 4

5 Raphael St   020 7584 1010   6–1C

"Buzzy and still heaving" – Rainer Becker and Arjun Waney's happening Eurotrash magnet, a short walk from Harrods, is "still a firm favourite after all these years" (and was the original site of what's now a 20-strong global luxury chain). As well as its moody cocktail bar, the draw is "top-notch Japanese food" – sushi, tempura, robata grills, black cod, lobster – "if with prices to match". "I feel like a cheat putting this as my top choice again… but it never fails to deliver!" / SW7 1DL; www.zumarestaurant.com; zumalondonofficial; Mon-Sat 11 pm, Sun 10.30 pm.

AREA OVERVIEWS

CENTRAL

Soho, Covent Garden & Bloomsbury
(Parts of W1, all WC2 and WC1)

£240+	Frog by Adam Handling	*British, Modern*	4 4 3
£230+	Aulis London	*British, Modern*	5 4 3
£210+	SOLA	*American*	5 3 2
	Alex Dilling	*British, Modern*	5 4 3
	Restaurant 1890	*French*	3 4 4
£160+	Evelyn's Table	*British, Modern*	5 4 3
£150+	The Savoy Hotel	*British, Traditional*	2 2 4
£140+	The Northall	*International*	3 3 3
£120+	Gauthier Soho	*Vegan*	3 4 4
	NoMad London	*American*	2 2 5
	Spring Restaurant	*British, Modern*	4 4 4
	Kebab Queen	*Turkish*	4 4 3
	Tattu London	*Chinese*	2 3 3
£110+	Kerridge's Bar & Grill	*British, Modern*	3 3 4
	Park Row	*"*	– – –
	Sushisamba	*Fusion*	2 2 3
	Smith & Wollensky	*Steaks & grills*	2 2 2
	The Savoy Hotel	*Afternoon tea*	2 4 5
£100+	Christopher's	*American*	2 2 3
	Simpson's in the Strand	*British, Traditional*	– – –
	The River Restaurant	*Fish & seafood*	2 2 3
	L'Escargot	*French*	3 3 3
	Otto's	*"*	5 5 4
	The Petersham	*Italian*	2 2 3
	Oscar Wilde Lounge	*Afternoon tea*	3 3 5
	Yauatcha	*Chinese*	3 2 2
£90+	Bob Bob Ricard	*British, Modern*	2 4 4
	Clos Maggiore	*"*	3 4 5
	The Ivy	*"*	2 2 3
	Pivot by Mark Greenaway	*"*	3 3 3
	Quo Vadis	*"*	4 4 5
	Social Eating House	*"*	3 2 2
	J Sheekey	*Fish & seafood*	3 3 4
	Frenchie	*French*	3 3 3
	Margot	*Italian*	3 4 4
	Nopi	*Mediterranean*	3 2 2
	Decimo	*Spanish*	3 2 4
	Hawksmoor	*Steaks & grills*	3 3 2
	Roka	*Japanese*	3 2 3

£80+	Balthazar	British, Modern	1	2	3
	Cora Pearl	"	3	4	4
	The Ivy Market Grill	"	2	2	3
	Sussex	"	2	2	3
	Holborn Dining Room	British, Traditional	2	1	3
	The Ivy Soho Brasserie	"	2	2	3
	Rules	"	3	3	5
	Firebird	East & Cent. European	3	3	3
	Fishworks	Fish & seafood	3	3	2
	Randall & Aubin	"	3	3	4
	The Seafood Bar	"	3	4	2
	J Sheekey Atlantic Bar	"	4	2	2
	Blanchette	French	3	3	2
	Story Cellar	"	3	3	4
	The 10 Cases	International	3	4	3
	Toklas	Mediterranean	3	3	3
	Cakes and Bubbles	Spanish	3	4	3
	Maresco	"	3	3	3
	Cecconi's Pizza Bar	Pizza	2	3	3
	Sucre London	Argentinian	3	3	4
	The Barbary	North African	5	4	4
	The Palomar	Middle Eastern	3	3	2
	Tamarind Kitchen	Indian	4	3	3
£70+	Big Easy	American	2	2	3
	Andrew Edmunds	British, Modern	3	4	5
	Dean Street Townhouse	"	2	4	4
	Ducksoup	"	4	4	3
	The French House	"	4	4	5
	Ham Yard Restaurant	"	2	3	4
	Heliot Steak House	"	3	2	2
	Indigo	"	3	3	4
	Nessa	"	3	3	4
	Noble Rot	"	3	4	5
	Only Food and Courses	"	—		
	Ship Tavern	"	3	4	5
	10 Greek Street	"	4	4	3
	The Delaunay	East & Cent. European	2	4	4
	The Oystermen	Fish & seafood	4	3	2
	Parsons	"	4	3	2
	Mon Plaisir	French	2	3	4
	Café Murano	Italian	3	4	2
	Da Mario	"	2	3	3
	Sycamore Vino Cucina	"	2	2	2
	Vasco & Piero's Pavilion	"	3	4	3
	Lisboeta	Portuguese	4	3	2
	Barrafina	Spanish	5	4	4
	Il Teatro della Carne	Steaks & grills	2	2	3
	Burger & Lobster	Burgers, etc	4	3	2
	Barshu	Chinese	5	3	2
	The Duck & Rice	"	3	2	3
	Chotto Matte	Japanese	4	4	4
	Sticks'n'Sushi	"	3	2	2
	Jinjuu	Korean	3	2	2
	Patara Soho	Thai	3	3	2

£60+					
Paradise	Sri Lankan	4	3	3
Joe Allen	American	2	3	4
Café Deco	British, Modern	3	2	2
Caravan	"	2	2	2
Double Standard	"	3	5	5
Isla	"	3	5	4
Noble Rot Soho	"	4	5	4
Riding House	"	2	2	3
VQ	"	2	2	3
Cork & Bottle	British, Traditional	2	3	4
Brasserie Blanc	French	2	2	2
Brasserie Zédel	"	1	2	4
Cigalon	"	3	4	4
Le Garrick	"	3	3	3
Boulevard	International	2	3	3
Ave Mario	Italian	3	3	4
Bocca di Lupo	"	4	4	3
Dehesa	"	2	2	2
La Goccia	"	3	3	3
Luce e Limoni	"	3	3	2
Obicà Mozzarella Bar	"	3	3	2
San Carlo Cicchetti	"	3	4	4
Volta do Mar	Portuguese	3	3	2
Opera Tavern	Spanish	3	2	2
Tapas Brindisa Soho	"	2	2	2
St Moritz	Swiss	3	3	3
Haché	Burgers, etc	3	3	2
Rock & Sole Plaice	Fish & chips	3	2	2
L'Antica Pizzeria	Pizza	4	3	2
Homeslice	"	3	2	3
Monmouth Kitchen	Sandwiches, cakes, etc	3	4	3
Ceviche Soho	Peruvian	3	2	3
Le Bab	Middle Eastern	4	3	2
Berenjak	Persian	5	4	4
Lahpet	Burmese	4	3	2
Four Seasons	Chinese	4	1	1
Din Tai Fung	Chinese, Dim sum	2	2	2
Cinnamon Bazaar	Indian	5	4	3
Colonel Saab	"	4	3	4
Gunpowder Soho	"	4	3	3
Masala Zone	"	4	4	4
Tandoor Chop House	"	4	3	3
Flesh and Buns	Japanese	4	4	3
Inamo	Pan-Asian	3	2	4

£50+					
El Pastor Soho	Mexican	3	3	4
Tendril	Vegan	4	3	3
The Black Book	British, Modern	3	4	4
The Norfolk Arms	"	3	3	2
Ochre	"	3	2	4
Pierre Victoire	French	3	2	3
INO	Greek	3	4	4
La Fromagerie	International	3	3	3
Bancone	Italian	2	3	3
Ciao Bella	"	3	4	5
Cinquecento	"	3	3	3

Fumo	"		2 3 4
Lina Stores	"		2 2 3
Mele e Pere	"		3 3 3
Pastaio	"		3 2 3
Blacklock	Steaks & grills		3 4 4
Block Soho	"		2 2 2
Mildreds	Vegetarian		3 3 3
MEATliquor	Burgers, etc		3 2 2
Street Burger	"		3 2 2
North Sea Fish	Fish & chips		3 2 2
temper Covent Garden	Pizza		2 1 2
temper Soho	BBQ		2 1 2
Miznon London	Middle Eastern		3 2 3
Fatt Pundit	Chinese		3 2 3
Golden Dragon	"		3 2 2
Imperial China	"		3 2 2
Orient London	"		4 4 3
Plum Valley	"		3 2 2
Kasa & Kin	Filipino		3 4 3
Dishoom	Indian		3 4 5
Fatt Pundit	"		3 2 3
Kricket	"		5 4 4
Dipna Anand	Indian, Southern		– – –
Oka	Japanese		3 4 2
Shoryu Ramen	"		3 2 2
Rasa Sayang	Malaysian		4 3 2
Gura Gura	Pan-Asian		3 4 4
Kiln	Thai		5 4 4
Speedboat Bar	"		4 4 4
£40+ Hoppers	Sri Lankan		3 3 3
Milk Beach Soho	Australian		3 4 3
Chez Antoinette	French		3 3 2
Prix Fixe	"		3 3 2
Bar Italia	Italian		2 4 5
Patty and Bun Soho	Burgers, etc		3 2 2
50 Kalò di Ciro Salvo	Pizza		4 3 3
Chick 'n' Sours	Chicken		4 3 3
Barbary Next Door	North African		4 3 2
Bubala Soho	Middle Eastern		4 4 3
Dim Sum Duck	Chinese, Dim sum		5 2 2
Dumplings' Legend	"		3 2 1
Hankies	Indian		3 3 2
Punjab	"		3 4 3
Sagar	"		3 3 2
Bone Daddies	Japanese		3 2 2
Eat Tokyo	"		3 2 2
Jugemu	"		5 2 2
Kanada-Ya	"		4 2 2
Koya-Bar	"		4 4 3
Hare & Tortoise	Pan-Asian		2 3 2
Cay Tre	Vietnamese		3 3 2
Viet Food	"		3 2 3
Bao Soho	Taiwanese		3 4 4

£35+	Kolamba	Sri Lankan	4	3	2
	Café in the Crypt	British, Traditional	2	2	4
	Arcade Food Hall	International	2	2	2
	Fadiga	Italian	4	5	3
	Flat Iron	Steaks & grills	3	3	3
	Tommi's Burger Joint	Burgers, etc	3	3	2
	Coqfighter	Chicken	3	2	2
	The eight Restaurant	Chinese	3	2	2
	Baozi Inn	Chinese, Dim sum	3	2	2
	Humble Chicken	Japanese	4	3	4
	Taro	"	3	3	2
	C&R Café	Malaysian	4	2	2
	Plaza Khao Gaeng	Thai	4	3	2
£30+	Rudy's	Pizza	3	4	3
	Master Wei	Chinese	4	2	2
	Wong Kei	"	3	2	2
£25+	Imad's Syrian Kitchen	Syrian	3	4	4
	The Kati Roll Company	Indian	3	2	2
£20+	Bageriet	Sandwiches, cakes, etc	4	2	2
£15+	Maison Bertaux	Afternoon tea	3	3	5
£10+	Flat White	Sandwiches, cakes, etc	3	3	2
£5+	Monmouth Coffee Company	Sandwiches, cakes, etc	3	4	3

Mayfair & St James's (Parts of W1 and SW1)

£390+	The Araki	Japanese	4	5	3
£370+	TAKU	Japanese	5	3	3
£340+	Ikoyi	West African	2	3	2
£270+	Alain Ducasse	French	3	3	2
£260+	Maru	Japanese	5	4	3
£240+	Sketch (Lecture Rm)	French	4	4	5
£200+	The Ritz	British, Traditional	4	5	5
£180+	Bacchanalia	British, Modern	2	2	4
	Cut	Steaks & grills	2	3	2
£170+	Hide	British, Modern	3	2	3
	Hélène Darroze	French	3	3	2
	Seven Park Place	"	3	2	2

£160+	The Connaught Grill	*British, Modern*	–	–	–
	Pollen Street Social	"	3	3	3
	Umu	*Japanese*	3	4	4
£150+	Park Chinois	*Chinese*	2	2	1
£140+	The Grill by Tom Booton	*British, Modern*	–	–	–
	Ormer Mayfair by Sofian	"	4	4	3
	Estiatorio Milos	*Fish & seafood*	2	2	4
	L'Atelier Robuchon	*French*	–	–	–
	Pavyllon	"	–	–	–
	Amazonico	*International*	2	3	4
	The Promenade, Dorchester	*Afternoon tea*	3	4	4
	Novikov (Asian restaurant)	*Pan-Asian*	2	2	4
£130+	Corrigan's Mayfair	*British, Modern*	3	4	4
	Il Borro	*Italian*	2	3	3
	34 Mayfair	*Steaks & grills*	2	3	2
	Brown's Hotel	*Afternoon tea*	3	4	4
	The Ritz	"	3	4	5
	Kai Mayfair	*Chinese*	4	4	3
	Nobu	*Japanese*	4	3	2
	Jean-Georges, Connaught	*Pan-Asian*	2	3	3
£120+	Wild Honey St James	*British, Modern*	3	2	2
	The Game Bird	*British, Traditional*	3	3	4
	Bar des Prés	*French*	2	4	3
	LPM	"	3	3	3
	Murano	*Italian*	4	4	3
	Gouqi	*Chinese*	2	3	2
	Hakkasan Mayfair	"	4	2	3
£110+	Charlie's at Brown's	*British, Modern*	4	5	5
	Mount Street Restaurant	"	3	3	4
	Wiltons	*British, Traditional*	3	3	3
	Scott's	*Fish & seafood*	3	3	4
	Galvin at Windows	*French*	3	3	4
	Socca	"	3	3	3
	Bocconcino	*Italian*	–	–	–
	The Guinea Grill	*Steaks & grills*	2	1	3
	Claridges Foyer	*Afternoon tea*	3	4	4
	Coya	*Peruvian*	2	2	3
	China Tang	*Chinese*	3	3	4
£100+	Colony Grill Room	*American*	3	3	4
	Apricity	*British, Modern*	3	3	2
	The Maine Mayfair	"	2	2	3
	Bentley's	*Fish & seafood*	3	4	4
	Sexy Fish	"	1	1	2
	Sketch (Gallery)	*French*	2	3	4
	El Norte	*Spanish*	3	3	3
	Jeru	*Middle Eastern*	3	3	4
	Kanishka	*Indian*	3	2	2
	Veeraswamy	"	4	3	4
	Ginza	*Japanese*	3	3	3
	Koyn	"	3	4	4

			Ratings
Tokimeite		"	– – –

£90+

Name	Cuisine	Rating
The Barley Mow	British, Modern	3 3 3
Hush	"	2 3 4
Quaglino's	"	2 3 4
Butler's Restaurant	British, Traditional	3 3 3
GBR	"	3 2 3
Scully	International	4 4 2
Al Duca	Italian	3 2 3
Chucs Dover Street	"	2 2 3
Franco's	"	3 4 4
Sartoria	"	3 3 3
Theo Randall	"	5 4 3
Hawksmoor	Steaks & grills	3 3 2
Rowley's	"	2 2 3
Fortnum & Mason	Afternoon tea	3 3 4
MiMi Mei Fair	Chinese	3 4 4
Benares	Indian	4 3 2
Chutney Mary	"	4 4 4
Gymkhana	"	5 4 3
Humo	Japanese	5 5 4
Ikeda	"	4 3 2
Roka	"	3 2 3

£80+

Name	Cuisine	Rating
The American Bar	American	3 3 4
Bellamy's	British, Modern	3 4 4
45 Jermyn St.	"	2 3 3
Kitty Fisher's	"	3 4 3
Little Social	"	4 4 3
The Wolseley	"	2 2 5
Fishworks	Fish & seafood	3 3 2
Maison François	French	3 3 4
Saint Jacques	"	4 3 4
Cecconi's	Italian	2 3 3
Ristorante Frescobaldi	"	2 3 3
San Carlo	"	3 3 3
Goodman	Steaks & grills	3 4 3
Delfino	Pizza	3 3 2
BiBi	Indian	5 5 4
Jamavar	"	3 3 3
Tamarind	"	4 3 3
The Ivy Asia Mayfair	Pan-Asian	3 2 4
Lucky Cat	"	1 2 2

£70+

Name	Cuisine	Rating
Langan's Brasserie	British, Modern	2 2 3
Maddox Tavern	"	2 2 3
Saltie Girl	Fish & seafood	3 4 3
Café Murano	Italian	3 4 2
Il Vicolo	"	2 3 2
Burger & Lobster	Burgers, etc	4 3 2
Bombay Bustle	Indian	5 3 4
Chisou	Japanese	4 3 2
Kiku	"	4 4 2
Patara Mayfair	Thai	3 3 2

£60+	123V	Vegan	3	2	2
	Noble Rot Mayfair	British, Modern	4	5	4
	Restaurant at The 22	"	3	4	4
	The Windmill	British, Traditional	3	2	3
	Notto	Italian	4	3	3
	José Pizarro at the RA	Spanish	3	3	4
	Sabor	"	5	5	5
	O'ver	Pizza	3	3	2
	Manthan	Indian	3	3	2
£50+	The Audley	British, Modern	3	2	4
	Casa do Frango	Portuguese	3	3	5
	El Pirata	Spanish	2	4	4
	Richoux	Sandwiches, cakes, etc	3	3	3
	Shoryu Ramen	Japanese	3	2	2

Fitzrovia & Marylebone (Part of W1)

£290+	Roketsu	Japanese	5	4	3
£250+	Kitchen Table	British, Modern	4	4	4
£240+	Mayha	Japanese	4	4	4
£160+	Akoko	West African	4	4	3
£150+	Pied à Terre	French	4	3	3
£120+	Kol	Mexican	4	4	4
	Mere	East & Cent. European	3	4	3
	Hakkasan	Chinese	4	2	3
£110+	The Chiltern Firehouse	American	2	2	4
	The Ninth London	British, Modern	5	3	3
	Nobu Portman Square	Japanese	4	3	3
£100+	The Berners Tavern	British, Modern	3	4	5
	Clarette	French	2	3	3
	Noizé	"	4	5	3
	Orrery	"	2	2	4
	Opso	Greek	3	3	3
	Locanda Locatelli	Italian	3	3	2
	Arros QD	Spanish	2	3	2
	Palm Court	Afternoon tea	2	3	3
	Dinings	Japanese	5	3	2
	Taka Marylebone	"	3	2	3
£90+	Portland	British, Modern	4	4	2
	28-50 Marylebone	"	2	2	3
	Santo Mare	Fish & seafood	3	4	3
	Les 110 de Taillevent	French	4	4	4
	Ampéli	Greek	3	3	2
	Donostia	Spanish	3	2	2
	The Bright Courtyard	Chinese	3	2	2

	Roka	*Japanese*	3	2	3
£80+	Cavita	*Mexican*	3	2	3
	Brasserie of Light	*British, Modern*	2	3	4
	Clipstone	*"*	3	3	2
	The Ivy Café	*"*	1	1	2
	Upstairs at The George	*"*	3	2	3
	Fishworks Marylebone	*Fish & seafood*	3	3	2
	Meraki	*Greek*	4	3	4
	La Brasseria Milanese	*Italian*	2	2	2
	Caffè Caldesi	*"*	3	3	2
	Norma	*"*	4	3	4
	ROVI	*Mediterranean*	3	3	3
	Zoilo	*Argentinian*	3	3	4
	Jikoni	*Indian*	4	3	4
	Pahli Hill Bandra Bhai	*"*	3	3	2
	Trishna	*"*	5	3	2
£70+	The Lore of the Land	*British, Modern*	3	4	4
	108 Brasserie	*"*	2	3	2
	Chotto Matte	*Fusion*	4	4	4
	Carousel	*International*	4	4	2
	Six by Nico	*"*	3	3	3
	Blandford Comptoir	*Mediterranean*	3	4	3
	Ottolenghi	*"*	3	3	3
	Lurra	*Spanish*	4	3	3
	Burger & Lobster	*Burgers, etc*	4	3	2
	Daylesford Organic	*Sandwiches, cakes, etc*	1	2	2
	Pachamama	*Peruvian*	3	3	3
	Honey & Co	*Middle Eastern*	3	2	2
	Honey & Smoke	*"*	3	2	2
	Ishtar	*Turkish*	3	3	2
	Royal China Club	*Chinese*	4	3	2
	Junsei	*Japanese*	3	4	2
	Sushi Atelier	*"*	4	3	3
	Uli Marylebone	*Pan-Asian*	4	3	4
£60+	Granger & Co	*Australian*	2	2	3
	Caravan	*British, Modern*	2	2	2
	St John Marylebone	*British, Traditional*	4	3	2
	The Wigmore	*"*	3	4	4
	Fischer's	*East & Cent. European*	2	2	3
	Twist Connubio	*Fusion*	3	3	2
	1905	*Greek*	3	4	5
	Briciole	*Italian*	3	3	2
	Circolo Popolare	*"*	3	4	5
	Italian Greyhound	*"*	3	3	3
	Riding House Café	*Mediterranean*	2	2	3
	Ibérica	*Spanish*	2	2	2
	Salt Yard	*"*	3	2	2
	The Gate	*Vegetarian*	3	3	3
	Homeslice	*Pizza*	3	2	3
	Royal China	*Chinese*	3	2	2
	Chourangi	*Indian*	4	4	3
	Flesh and Buns	*Japanese*	4	4	3

£50+	Wulf & Lamb	Vegan	3	2	3
	La Fromagerie Café	International	3	3	3
	Lina Stores	Italian	2	2	3
	2 Veneti	"	2	3	2
	Le Relais de Venise	Steaks & grills	3	3	3
	MEATLiquor	Burgers, etc	3	2	2
	Golden Hind	Fish & chips	3	3	2
	Chishuru	West African	–	–	–
	Delamina	Middle Eastern	3	3	3
	The Gurkhas	Pan-Asian	3	4	3
	Oka	"	3	4	2
	Foley's	Thai	3	3	3
£40+	Hoppers	Sri Lankan	3	3	3
	The Wallace	French	2	1	5
	Via Emilia	Italian	3	4	3
	Patty and Bun	Burgers, etc	3	2	2
	Pizzeria Mozza	Pizza	4	3	3
	Santa Maria	"	4	2	3
	Reubens	Kosher	3	2	3
	Roti Chai	Indian	3	2	2
	Sagar	"	3	3	2
	Bone Daddies	Japanese	3	2	2
	Laksamania	Malaysian	3	2	2
	Bao Marylebone	Taiwanese	3	4	4
£35+	Flat Iron Marylebone	Steaks & grills	3	3	3
	Tommi's Burger Joint	Burgers, etc	3	3	2
	Ragam	Indian	4	2	1
	CoCoRo	Japanese	4	3	2
£30+	Noodle & Snack	Chinese	4	4	2
£15+	Icco Pizza	Italian	3	3	2
	Kaffeine	Sandwiches, cakes, etc	2	5	3
	Kiss the Hippo	"	3	4	3
	Marugame Udon	Japanese	3	3	2

Belgravia, Pimlico, Victoria & Westminster (SW1, except St James's)

£250+	A Wong	Chinese	5	2	2
£210+	Muse	British, Modern	5	4	4
£190+	Nusr-Et Steakhouse	Steaks & grills	1	1	1
£160+	Pétrus	French	2	3	3
	Studio Frantzén	Scandinavian	3	4	5
£150+	Dinner	British, Traditional	2	2	2
£140+	Imperial Treasure	Chinese	4	3	2

Price	Name	Cuisine			
£130+	The Collins Room	Afternoon tea	3	3	4
£120+	The Dining Room	British, Traditional	2	2	3
	Hunan	Chinese	4	2	1
£110+	Santini	Italian	2	3	3
	Zafferano	"	4	3	3
	Ekstedt at The Yard	Scandinavian	3	4	3
	Boisdale of Belgravia	Scottish	2	3	3
£100+	Fallow St James's	British, Modern	3	3	3
	The Pem	"	4	4	3
	Kerridge's Fish & Chips	Fish & seafood	2	3	4
	The Crystal Moon Lounge	Afternoon tea	3	4	4
£90+	The Lanesborough Grill	British, Modern	2	2	4
	Roof Garden, Pantechnicon	"	2	2	5
	Harrods Dining Hall	International	–	–	–
	Chucs	Italian	2	2	3
	Goya	Spanish	3	3	2
	Cedric Grolet	Sandwiches, cakes, etc	3	4	3
	Amaya	Indian	4	4	4
	Quilon	Indian, Southern	4	3	2
£80+	Blue Boar Pub	British, Modern	2	2	2
	Ganymede	"	3	3	3
	Hans' Bar & Grill	"	3	3	3
	The Ivy Victoria	"	2	2	3
	The Jones Family Kitchen	"	3	3	4
	The Thomas Cubitt	"	2	2	3
	Olivomare	Fish & seafood	4	3	2
	Colbert	French	2	2	3
	Olivo	Italian	3	3	2
	Sale e Pepe	"	–	–	–
	The Cinnamon Club	Indian	4	4	5
	Kahani	"	4	4	3
	Yaatra	"	4	4	2
£70+	Daylesford Organic	British, Modern	1	2	2
	Lorne	"	5	5	3
	La Poule au Pot	French	3	4	5
	Caraffini	Italian	2	4	3
	Drawing Room, Dukes	Afternoon tea	3	4	4
	Burger & Lobster	Burgers, etc	4	3	2
	Oliveto	Pizza	3	3	2
	Ottolenghi	Middle Eastern	3	3	3
	Ken Lo's Memories	Chinese	3	3	2
	Sticks'n'Sushi	Japanese	3	2	2
£60+	Granger & Co	Australian	2	2	3
	Grumbles	International	3	4	2
	Motcombs	"	2	2	4
	Gustoso	Italian	3	2	2
	Tozi	"	2	1	3
	Ibérica	Spanish	2	2	2
	Seafresh	Fish & chips	3	2	2

	Kazan	*Turkish*	**3** **3** 2
£50+	Holy Carrot	*Vegan*	**4** **4** **4**
	Casa do Frango	*Portuguese*	**3** **3** **5**
	Wulf & Lamb	*Vegetarian*	**3** 2 **3**
	Ma La Sichuan	*Chinese*	**4** **3** 2
£40+	The Vincent Rooms	*British, Modern*	**3** **3** **4**
	Chez Antoinette	*French*	**3** **3** 2
	Cyprus Mangal	*Turkish*	**3** **3** 2
	Aloo Tama	*Indian*	**4** **3** 2
	Sagar	*"*	**3** **3** 2
	Bone Daddies	*Japanese*	**3** 2 2
	Café Kitsuné	*"*	**3** **3** **4**
	Kanada-Ya	*"*	**4** 2 2
£35+	Taro	*Japanese*	**3** **3** 2
£25+	Bleecker Burger	*Burgers, etc*	**4** 2 2
£15+	Regency Cafe	*British, Traditional*	**3** **3** **5**

WEST

Chelsea, South Kensington, Kensington, Earl's Court & Fulham (SW3, SW5, SW6, SW7, SW10 & W8)

Price	Name	Cuisine	FSA
£230+	Gordon Ramsay	French	2 2 2
£220+	Bibendum	French	3 3 3
£200+	The Five Fields	British, Modern	4 4 3
£170+	The Sea, The Sea	Fish & seafood	5 4 4
£120+	Wild Tavern	Italian	2 2 3
£110+	Clarke's	British, Modern	4 5 3
	Medlar	"	4 4 3
	No. Fifty Cheyne	"	3 3 5
	Zuma	Japanese	4 4 4
£100+	Elystan Street	British, Modern	4 3 3
	Launceston Place	"	4 4 4
	Stanley's	"	3 2 2
	Le Petit Beefbar	Steaks & grills	– – –
	Min Jiang	Chinese	4 4 5
	Dinings	Japanese	5 3 2
	Yashin Ocean House	"	4 3 2
£90+	Bluebird	British, Modern	2 1 3
	Kitchen W8	"	4 4 3
	28-50 Chelsea	"	2 2 3
	Restaurant at The Capital	British, Traditional	3 3 2
	Le Colombier	French	2 4 4
	Chucs	Italian	2 2 3
	Daphne's	"	3 3 5
	Lucio	"	3 2 2
	Scalini	"	3 4 3
	Hawksmoor	Steaks & grills	3 3 2
	Chicama	Peruvian	3 3 3
	Bombay Brasserie	Indian	3 3 3
£80+	Harwood Arms	British, Modern	4 3 3
	The Ivy Chelsea Garden	"	2 2 3
	The Shed	"	3 2 4
	The Surprise	British, Traditional	3 3 4
	Bibendum Oyster Bar	Fish & seafood	3 3 4
	Suzi Tros	Greek	4 4 3
	Myrtle	Irish	5 4 3
	La Famiglia	Italian	2 3 4
	Manicomio Chelsea	"	2 2 3
	Cambio de Tercio	Spanish	3 3 3
	Koji	Japanese	4 4 4
	Zheng	Malaysian	3 3 2
	The Ivy Asia Chelsea	Pan-Asian	3 2 4

£70+					
Big Easy	American		2	2	3
Brinkley's	British, Modern		2	3	3
The Cadogan Arms	"		3	3	4
Daylesford Organic	"		1	2	2
The Enterprise	"		2	3	4
Kuro Eatery	"		4	4	3
Rabbit	"		2	2	2
Wright Brothers	Fish & seafood		3	3	3
Margaux	French		3	4	3
Mazi	Greek		4	4	3
Vardo	International		2	2	3
Jacuzzi	Italian		1	2	4
Il Portico	"		2	3	3
Belvedere	Mediterranean		3	3	4
Tendido Cero	Spanish		3	3	3
Macellaio RC	Steaks & grills		2	2	3
Alexandrie	Egyptian		3	3	3
Akub	Middle Eastern		2	3	4
Good Earth	Chinese		3	3	2
Kutir	Indian		4	4	4
Zaika of Kensington	"		4	4	4
Akira at Japan House	Japanese		3	3	2
Chisou	"		4	3	2
Sticks'n'Sushi	"		3	2	2
Huo	Pan-Asian		3	3	3
Patara	Thai		3	3	2

£60+					
The Abingdon	British, Modern		3	3	3
The Fox and Pheasant	"		3	3	4
Manuka Kitchen	"		3	3	3
VQ	"		2	2	3
Maggie Jones's	British, Traditional		3	4	4
Mriya	East & Cent. European	3	3	3
The Scarsdale	International		2	3	5
Cicchetti Knightsbridge	Italian		3	4	4
Frantoio	"		3	2	4
Pascor	Mediterranean		3	2	2
Daquise	Polish		2	3	4
Ognisko Restaurant	"		3	4	5
Tapas Brindisa	Spanish		2	2	2
Haché	Steaks & grills		3	3	2
Maroush	Lebanese		4	2	1
Royal China	Chinese		3	2	2
Romulo Café	Filipino		3	4	3
Flora Indica	Indian		3	3	3
Masala Zone	"		4	4	4

£50+					
The Holland	British, Modern		4	3	3
Los Mochis	Fusion		3	3	3
Aglio e Olio	Italian		3	3	2
Da Mario	"		3	2	3
Made in Italy	"		3	2	2
Maria G's	"		3	3	3
Nuovi Sapori	"		3	3	3
Riccardo's	"		3	4	3
San Pietro	"		3	3	4

	Ziani's	"	3	4	3
	The Atlas	Mediterranean	3	4	4
	Street Burger	Burgers, etc	3	2	2
	Cinquecento	Pizza	3	3	3
	Rocca	"	2	2	3
	Cocotte	Chicken	3	3	2
	Diba	Persian	2	2	2
	Best Mangal	Turkish	4	4	2
	Chakra	Indian	3	3	3
	Dishoom	"	3	4	5
	Noor Jahan	"	3	4	3
	Pure Indian Cooking	"	4	4	3
	Thali	"	3	3	3
	Oka	Japanese	3	4	2
	Shoryu Ramen	"	3	2	2
	Sukho Fine Thai Cuisine	Thai	4	4	2
	Go-Viet	Vietnamese	3	4	2
£40+	Churchill Arms	British, Traditional	3	2	4
	Big Fernand	Burgers, etc	3	3	2
	Fishers	Fish & chips	3	3	2
	Santa Maria	Pizza	4	2	3
	Ceru	Middle Eastern	3	2	2
	Bone Daddies	Japanese	3	2	2
	Bibida	Korean	3	4	2
	Freak Scene	Pan-Asian	4	4	3
	Phat Phuc	Vietnamese	3	3	3
£35+	Flat Iron	Steaks & grills	3	3	3
£20+	Stick & Bowl	Chinese	4	2	2
£15+	Hagen Chelsea	Sandwiches, cakes, etc	3	4	2

Notting Hill, Holland Park, Bayswater, North Kensington & Maida Vale (W2, W9, W10, W11)

£230+	Core by Clare Smyth	British, Modern	5	5	4
	The Ledbury	"	4	4	4
£130+	Caractère	Mediterranean	3	3	3
£120+	104 Restaurant	British, Modern	5	4	4
£100+	London Shell Co.	Fish & seafood	3	4	5
	Sumi	Japanese	4	4	3
£90+	Assaggi	Italian	4	5	3
£80+	The Princess Royal	British, Modern	3	3	3
	Six Portland Road	"	3	3	3
	Straker's	"	3	3	5
	The Summerhouse	Fish & seafood	2	3	5
	Vori	Greek	3	3	3

	Zephyr	"	4	4	4
	The Cow	Irish	3	2	4
	La Brasseria	Italian	2	2	2
£70+	Sunday in Brooklyn	American	2	2	4
	Daylesford Organic	British, Modern	1	2	2
	Gold	"	2	4	5
	The Ladbroke Arms	"	3	2	4
	Tsiakkos & Charcoal	Greek	3	4	3
	Mediterraneo	Italian	3	2	3
	Osteria Basilico	"	3	3	3
	Portobello Ristorante	"	3	3	4
	Ottolenghi	Mediterranean	3	3	3
	Farmacy	Vegetarian	4	3	4
	Mandarin Kitchen	Chinese	4	4	2
	E&O	Pan-Asian	3	3	3
	Uli	"	4	3	4
£60+	Granger & Co	Australian	2	2	3
	Caia	British, Modern	4	3	3
	Orasay	"	5	4	4
	The Pelican	"	3	3	4
	Hereford Road	British, Traditional	4	4	3
	Cepages	French	3	2	4
	Edera	Italian	3	4	3
	The Oak W2	"	3	3	3
	Maroush	Lebanese	4	2	1
	Four Seasons	Chinese	4	1	1
	Bombay Palace	Indian	4	4	2
£50+	Dorian	British, Modern	4	4	5
	The Cheese Barge	British, Traditional	2	3	3
	Cinquecento	Italian	3	3	3
	Haya	Mediterranean	3	4	3
	MEATliquor	Burgers, etc	3	2	2
	Cinquecento	Pizza	3	3	3
	Cocotte	Chicken	3	3	2
	Miznon	Middle Eastern	3	2	3
	Fez Mangal	Turkish	3	2	1
	Pearl Liang	Chinese	3	2	2
	Noor Jahan	Indian	3	4	3
	Sushi Murasaki	Japanese	4	4	2
£40+	Taqueria	Mexican	3	3	3
	Ceru	Middle Eastern	3	2	2
	Gold Mine	Chinese	3	2	2
	Durbar	Indian	3	3	2
	Eat Tokyo	Japanese	3	2	2
£35+	Tab X Tab	International	3	4	3
£30+	Tavernaki	Greek	3	2	3
£25+	Normah's	Malaysian	3	3	2
£15+	Layla	Sandwiches, cakes, etc	3	3	3

Hammersmith, Shepherd's Bush, Olympia, Chiswick, Brentford & Ealing (W4, W5, W6, W12, W13, W14, TW8)

Price	Name	Cuisine			
£280+	Endo at The Rotunda	Japanese	5	4	5
£150+	The River Café	Italian	3	2	3
£110+	La Trompette	British, Modern	3	3	3
£90+	Villa Di Geggiano	Italian	3	4	4
£80+	Sam's Riverside	British, Modern	3	5	5
	The Silver Birch	"	4	3	2
	Cibo	Italian	4	4	4
£70+	High Road Brasserie	British, Modern	3	2	4
	Le Vacherin	French	3	4	4
	Shikumen	Chinese	4	2	2
	Sticks n Sushi	Japanese	3	2	2
£60+	The Anglesea Arms	British, Modern	4	3	5
	City Barge	"	2	2	3
	The Duke of Sussex	"	2	2	3
	The Havelock Tavern	"	3	3	3
	Rock & Rose	"	2	2	3
	Vinoteca	"	2	2	2
	Brasserie Blanc	French	2	2	2
	Annie's	International	2	3	4
	L'Amorosa	Italian	4	4	3
	Giulia	"	4	3	2
	The Oak W12	"	3	3	3
	Pentolina	"	4	5	4
	The Carpenter's Arms	Mediterranean	3	3	3
	The Swan	"	3	4	4
	Salt Yard	Spanish	3	2	2
	The Gate	Vegetarian	3	3	3
	Homeslice	Pizza	3	2	3
	Indian Zing	Indian	4	3	3
£50+	Brackenbury Wine Rooms	British, Modern	2	4	4
	The Crabtree	"	2	2	4
	The Dartmouth Castle	"	3	2	3
	The Dove	"	3	4	5
	The Princess Victoria	"	3	2	3
	Le Petit Citron	French	3	3	3
	The Andover Arms	International	3	4	4
	Capri	Italian	3	3	3
	Maria G's	"	3	3	3
	Avanti	Mediterranean	2	2	3
	The Bird in Hand	Pizza	3	3	3
	Crisp Pizza	"	5	2	2
	Zia Lucia	"	3	3	2
	Chateau	Lebanese	3	4	2
	Best Mangal	Turkish	4	4	2

	Copper Chimney	*Indian*	3	3	3
	The Hampshire	"	3	3	3
	Kricket	"	5	4	4
	Potli	"	4	3	3
£40+	222 Veggie Vegan	*Vegan*	3	3	3
	Kindred	*British, Modern*	3	3	3
	Oro Di Napoli	*Pizza*	4	4	2
	Santa Maria	"	4	2	3
	North China	*Chinese*	3	3	3
	Patri	*Indian*	3	3	2
	Republic	"	4	3	3
	Sagar	"	3	3	2
	Eat Tokyo	*Japanese*	3	2	2
	Kanada-Ya	"	4	2	2
	Sushi Bar Makoto	"	4	3	1
	Ta Ke Sushi	"	4	3	2
	Tosa	"	3	3	2
	Hare & Tortoise	*Pan-Asian*	2	3	2
	Chet's	*Thai*	3	3	3
	101 Thai Kitchen	"	3	3	2
£35+	Base Face Pizza	*Pizza*	4	4	3
	Shilpa	*Indian, Southern*	4	2	2
	Poppy's Thai Eatery	*Thai*	3	2	3
£30+	Persian Palace	*Persian*	4	2	2
£25+	The Elder Press Café	*British, Modern*	3	3	4
	Bleecker Burger	*Burgers, etc*	4	2	2
	Rhythm & Brews	*Sandwiches, cakes, etc*	3	3	4
	Tamp Coffee	"	3	4	3
£5+	Mr Falafel	*Middle Eastern*	5	4	2

NORTH

Hampstead, West Hampstead, St John's Wood, Regent's Park, Kilburn & Camden Town (NW postcodes)

£210+	PLU	*French*	5 4 4
£90+	Tish	*Kosher*	3 2 3
£80+	Booking Office 1869	*British, Modern*	2 3 5
	The Ivy Café	"	1 1 2
	The Landmark	"	3 3 5
	Odette's	"	3 3 2
	L'Aventure	*French*	4 5 4
	Lume	*Italian*	3 2 2
	Magenta	"	3 4 3
	Cinder	*Mediterranean*	3 3 2
£70+	Bradley's	*British, Modern*	2 2 2
	The Parakeet	"	5 4 3
	Searcys St Pancras Grand	"	2 2 3
	The Wells Tavern	"	3 4 4
	Holly Bush	*British, Traditional*	3 2 3
	Michael Nadra	*French*	3 3 2
	Oslo Court	"	3 5 5
	Bull & Last	*International*	4 3 3
	Morso	*Italian*	3 2 2
	The Rising Sun	"	3 4 3
	Villa Bianca	"	3 3 4
	Skewd Kitchen	*Turkish*	4 3 3
	Good Earth	*Chinese*	3 3 2
	Kaifeng	"	4 4 3
	Phoenix Palace	"	3 2 2
	Patara	*Thai*	3 3 2
£60+	Greenberry Café	*British, Modern*	2 3 3
	Oak & Poppy	"	3 4 3
	Parlour Kensal	"	3 3 4
	Lemonia	*Greek*	2 3 3
	Soutine	*International*	2 2 4
	Carmel	*Mediterranean*	5 3 4
	28 Church Row	*Spanish*	4 4 4
	Haché	*Steaks & grills*	3 3 2
	L'Antica Pizzeria	*Pizza*	4 3 2
	Maroush Park Royal	*Lebanese*	4 2 1
	Bonoo	*Indian*	3 3 3
	Jin Kichi	*Japanese*	5 4 3
£50+	The Old Bull & Bush	*British, Modern*	2 2 4
	The Wet Fish Café	"	3 3 3
	Lure	*Fish & seafood*	3 2 3
	Authentique	*French*	3 3 3
	The Spaniard's Inn	*International*	2 3 5
	Anima e Cuore	*Italian*	4 3 2

	L'Artista	*"*	2	3	3
	Cinquecento	*"*	3	3	3
	Giacomo's	*"*	3	3	2
	Mildreds	*Vegetarian*	3	3	3
	The Sea Shell	*Fish & chips*	3	2	2
	Zia Lucia	*Pizza*	3	3	2
	Cocotte	*Chicken*	3	3	2
	Crocker's Folly	*Lebanese*	3	3	3
	Green Cottage	*Chinese*	3	2	2
	Saravanaa Bhavan	*Indian*	4	2	2
	Oka	*Japanese*	3	4	2
	Singapore Garden	*Malaysian*	3	3	3
£40+	Spagnoletti	*Italian*	3	4	3
	Berbere Pizza	*Pizza*	4	3	3
	Sacro Cuore	*"*	3	3	2
	Numa	*Middle Eastern*	3	4	2
	Great Nepalese	*Indian*	3	2	3
	Three Falcons	*"*	4	3	2
	Vijay	*"*	3	4	2
	Café Japan	*Japanese*	3	3	2
	Eat Tokyo	*"*	3	2	2
	Sushi Masa	*"*	3	3	2
	Bang Bang Oriental	*Pan-Asian*	3	2	2
£35+	Nautilus	*Fish & chips*	4	4	2
	Mr Ji	*Chinese*	3	3	3
	Three Uncles	*"*	5	2	2
	Paradise Hampstead	*Indian*	3	4	3
	Ravi Shankar	*"*	3	2	2
	Anjanaas	*Indian, Southern*	3	4	2
£30+	Diwana Bhel-Poori House	*Indian*	3	2	1
	Sakonis	*"*	3	3	2
£25+	Sam's Café	*British, Traditional*	3	2	2
	Chutneys	*Indian*	3	3	2
£20+	Tofu Vegan	*Chinese*	4	3	2
£15+	Icco Pizza	*Pizza*	3	3	2
	Ginger & White	*Sandwiches, cakes, etc*	3	3	3
	Roti King	*Malaysian*	5	2	2

Hoxton, Islington, Highgate, Crouch End, Stoke Newington, Finsbury Park, Muswell Hill & Finchley (N postcodes)

£120+	Parrillan	*Spanish*	3	3	3
£90+	Hot Stone	*Japanese*	2	2	2
£80+	The Baring	*British, Modern*	4	3	3
	Perilla	*"*	3	3	3

£70+					
	Frederick's	*British, Modern*	3	4	4
	Hicce	"	2	2	3
	12:51	"	4	3	2
	Westerns Laundry	"	3	3	3
	Prawn on the Lawn	*Fish & seafood*	4	3	2
	Les 2 Garcons	*French*	5	5	3
	Jiji	*Fusion*	3	3	3
	German Gymnasium	*German*	1	1	3
	Salut	*International*	4	4	4
	Trullo	*Italian*	4	3	3
	Coal Office	*Mediterranean*	4	4	4
	Ottolenghi	"	3	3	3
	Barrafina	*Spanish*	5	4	4
	Escocesa	"	3	3	2

£60+					
	Granger & Co	*Australian*	2	2	3
	The Bull	*British, Modern*	3	3	2
	Caravan King's Cross	"	2	2	2
	The Clarence Tavern	"	3	3	3
	The Drapers Arms	"	3	3	3
	Humble Grape	"	2	3	3
	Pig & Butcher	"	4	3	3
	The Plimsoll	"	5	4	3
	The Red Lion & Sun	"	3	3	3
	Rotunda	"	2	2	4
	St Johns	*British, Traditional*	3	3	4
	Lyon's	*Fish & seafood*	4	4	3
	Table Du Marche	*French*	3	3	2
	The Orange Tree	*International*	2	2	3
	Primeur	"	3	3	4
	Citro	*Italian*	4	4	2
	Osteria Tufo	"	3	4	3
	Terra Rossa	"	4	4	4
	Vinoteca	*Mediterranean*	2	2	2
	Bar Esteban	*Spanish*	3	4	4
	Camino King's Cross	"	2	2	2
	The Gatehouse	"	3	3	2
	Chuku's	*West African*	3	4	3
	Arabica KX	*Middle Eastern*	3	3	3

£50+					
	Casa Pastór	*Mexican*	2	2	2
	Granary Square Brasserie	*British, Modern*	2	3	4
	The Lighterman	"	2	2	2
	Porte Noire	"	3	4	4
	Kipferl	*East & Cent. European*	4	3	3
	Schnitzel Forever	"	3	3	2
	Bellanger	*French*	–	–	–
	La Petite Auberge	"	3	3	2
	Le Sacré-Coeur	"	3	3	2
	Kalimera	*Greek*	4	3	3
	FKABAM	*International*	4	2	3
	The Flask	"	2	3	4
	La Fromagerie	"	3	3	3
	500	*Italian*	3	4	2
	Lina Stores	"	2	2	3
	La Lluna	*Spanish*	3	3	2

	Mildreds	Vegetarian	3 3 3	
	MEATLiquor Islington	Burgers, etc	3 2 2	
	Street Burger	"	3 2 2	
	Toff's	Fish & chips	3 4 2	
	Sweet Thursday	Pizza	3 2 2	
	Zia Lucia	"	3 3 2	
	Cocotte	Chicken	3 3 2	
	Jam Delish	Caribbean	5 4 3	
	Gallipoli Again	Turkish	3 2 4	
	Kaki	Chinese	3 3 2	
	Dishoom	Indian	3 4 5	
	Bund	Pan-Asian	3 3 3	
	Farang	Thai	4 4 3	
	Supawan	"	5 4 4	
£40+	Frank's Canteen	British, Modern	3 3 2	
	Two Brothers	Fish & seafood	3 2 2	
	Caravel	French	4 4 4	
	Le Mercury	"	2 2 2	
	Noci	Italian	3 2 3	
	Via Emilia	"	3 4 3	
	Olympus Fish	Fish & chips	3 4 2	
	Sacro Cuore	Pizza	3 3 2	
	Santa Maria	"	4 2 3	
	Yard Sale Pizza	"	3 4 2	
	Plaquemine Lock	Cajun/creole	4 3 4	
	Gem	Turkish	3 3 3	
	Sumak	"	3 4 2	
	Xi'an Impression	Chinese	4 2 1	
	Delhi Grill	Indian	4 2 3	
	Hoppers	"	3 3 3	
	Jashan	"	3 3 2	
	Rasa	Indian, Southern	4 3 3	
	Akari	Japanese	4 3 3	
	Kanada-Ya	"	4 2 2	
	Sambal Shiok	Malaysian	3 2 2	
	The Tamil Prince	Pan-Asian	4 3 3	
	Cafe Bao	Taiwanese	3 4 4	
£35+	Skal Nordic Dining	Scandinavian	3 4 3	
	Flat Iron	Steaks & grills	3 3 3	
	The Dusty Knuckle	Sandwiches, cakes, etc	5 2 3	
	Afghan Kitchen	Afghani	3 2 2	
	Shahi Pakwaan	Indian	3 2 2	
	Taro	Japanese	3 3 2	
	Viet Garden	Vietnamese	3 2 2	
£25+	Normans Cafe	British, Modern	4 4 4	
	Bayleaf	Indian	4 3 3	
£20+	Tofu Vegan	Chinese	4 3 2	
	Rasa Street	Indian	3 3 2	

SOUTH

South Bank (SE1)

£270+	Story	British, Modern	– – –
£140+	Trivet	British, Modern	3 3 3
£130+	Turnips	British, Modern	4 3 3
	Hannah	Japanese	3 3 2
£120+	Parrillan	Spanish	3 3 3
	Hutong	Chinese	3 4 4
£110+	Aqua Shard	British, Modern	2 2 4
	Oblix	"	3 3 4
	Oxo Tower (Restaurant)	"	1 1 1
£100+	Sollip	French	5 4 3
£90+	Oxo Tower (Brasserie)	British, Modern	1 1 3
	TING	"	3 3 5
	Seabird at The Hoxton	Fish & seafood	4 3 5
	Le Pont de la Tour	French	2 2 3
	La Barca	Italian	3 3 3
	Hawksmoor	Steaks & grills	3 3 2
£80+	The Garrison	British, Modern	3 3 3
	The Ivy Tower Bridge	"	2 2 3
	Sea Containers	"	2 2 3
	Skylon	"	2 1 2
	Butlers Wharf Chop Hs	British, Traditional	2 2 3
	Roast	"	2 2 4
	The Coal Shed	Steaks & grills	3 2 2
£70+	Santo Remedio	Mexican	3 3 2
	Elliot's	British, Modern	3 3 2
	Skylon Grill	"	2 3 5
	The Swan at the Globe	"	2 2 4
	Applebee's Fish	Fish & seafood	3 3 2
	fish!	"	3 2 3
	Wright Brothers	"	3 3 3
	Vivat Bacchus	International	3 3 2
	Cafe Murano	Italian	3 4 2
	Macellaio RC	"	2 2 3
	Barrafina	Spanish	5 4 4
	Pique Nique	Chicken	2 3 3
	Bala Baya	Middle Eastern	4 3 3
	Baluchi	Indian	3 3 4
£60+	The Anchor & Hope	British, Modern	4 3 3
	The Boot & Flogger	"	3 3 4
	Caravan Bankside	"	2 2 2
	Garden Café, Garden Mus'	"	3 3 4
	Vinoteca Borough	"	2 2 2

	Brasserie Blanc	French	2️⃣ 2️⃣ 2️⃣
	Casse-Croute	"	4️⃣ 3️⃣ 4️⃣
	Borough Market Kitchen	International	4️⃣ 2️⃣ 2️⃣
	Tavolino	Italian	2️⃣ 2️⃣ 3️⃣
	José	Spanish	5️⃣ 3️⃣ 4️⃣
	Pizarro	"	4️⃣ 4️⃣ 4️⃣
	Salt Yard Borough	"	3️⃣ 2️⃣ 2️⃣
	Tapas Brindisa	"	2️⃣ 2️⃣ 2️⃣
	O'ver	Pizza	3️⃣ 3️⃣ 2️⃣
	Paladar	South American	4️⃣ 4️⃣ 4️⃣
	Arabica	Lebanese	3️⃣ 3️⃣ 3️⃣
	Berenjak Borough	Persian	5️⃣ 4️⃣ 4️⃣
	Gunpowder	Indian	4️⃣ 3️⃣ 3️⃣
	Sticky Mango	Pan-Asian	3️⃣ 2️⃣ 2️⃣
	Champor-Champor	Thai	3️⃣ 2️⃣ 4️⃣
	Sticky Mango	"	3️⃣ 2️⃣ 2️⃣
£50+	Mallow	Vegan	3️⃣ 3️⃣ 4️⃣
	El Pastór	Mexican	3️⃣ 3️⃣ 4️⃣
	40 Maltby Street	British, Modern	3️⃣ 3️⃣ 3️⃣
	Lupins	"	4️⃣ 4️⃣ 4️⃣
	Tate Modern	"	3️⃣ 3️⃣ 5️⃣
	Bancone	Italian	2️⃣ 3️⃣ 3️⃣
	Flour & Grape	"	3️⃣ 3️⃣ 4️⃣
	Legare	"	4️⃣ 4️⃣ 3️⃣
	Bar Douro	Portuguese	3️⃣ 3️⃣ 4️⃣
	Casa do Frango	"	3️⃣ 3️⃣ 5️⃣
	Andanza	Spanish	4️⃣ 3️⃣ 3️⃣
	La Gamba	"	3️⃣ 4️⃣ 2️⃣
	Mar I Terra	"	3️⃣ 3️⃣ 3️⃣
	Meson don Felipe	"	2️⃣ 2️⃣ 4️⃣
£40+	Rambutan	Sri Lankan	5️⃣ 3️⃣ 3️⃣
	Mercato Metropolitano	Italian	2️⃣ 2️⃣ 4️⃣
	Padella	"	4️⃣ 3️⃣ 4️⃣
	Patty and Bun	Burgers, etc	3️⃣ 2️⃣ 2️⃣
	Kin and Deum	Thai	3️⃣ 2️⃣ 3️⃣
	Bao Borough	Taiwanese	3️⃣ 4️⃣ 4️⃣
£35+	Flat Iron	Steaks & grills	3️⃣ 3️⃣ 3️⃣
	Baozi Inn	Chinese	3️⃣ 2️⃣ 2️⃣
£10+	Kappacasein	Swiss	5️⃣ 3️⃣ 2️⃣
£5+	Monmouth Coffee Company	Sandwiches, cakes, etc	3️⃣ 4️⃣ 3️⃣

Greenwich, Lewisham, Dulwich & Blackheath (All SE postcodes, except SE1; also BR1)

£70+	Coal Rooms	British, Modern	3️⃣ 3️⃣ 2️⃣
	Copper & Ink	"	3️⃣ 3️⃣ 3️⃣
	Llewelyn's	"	3️⃣ 3️⃣ 3️⃣
	Tila	"	3️⃣ 3️⃣ 3️⃣
	Sticks'n'Sushi	Japanese	3️⃣ 2️⃣ 2️⃣

			Ratings		
£60+	The Alma	*British, Modern*	3	3	4
	The Camberwell Arms	"	4	4	4
	Franklins	"	3	4	3
	The Guildford Arms	"	3	3	3
	Levan	"	3	2	2
	Toulouse Lautrec	*French*	3	3	3
	Peckham Bazaar	*Greek*	4	3	3
	The Trafalgar Tavern	*International*	3	3	5
	Artusi	*Italian*	3	3	2
	Forza Wine	"	3	4	3
	Luciano's	"	3	4	3
	Manuel's	"	4	4	4
	Peckham Cellars	*Spanish*	3	4	3
	Kudu	*South African*	4	4	3
	Dragon Castle	*Chinese*	3	2	2
	Yama Momo	*Japanese*	3	2	3
£50+	Dorothy & Marshall	*British, Modern*	2	3	3
	The Rosendale	"	3	3	3
	Brookmill	*International*	3	3	3
	The Yellow House	"	3	3	3
	Le Querce	*Italian*	3	4	2
	The Dartmouth Arms	*Burgers, etc*	3	2	2
	Street Burger	"	3	2	2
	Rocca	*Pizza*	2	2	3
	Kudu Grill	*South African*	4	4	3
	Babur	*Indian*	4	4	3
	Everest Inn	"	3	2	2
	Heritage	"	4	4	3
	Kennington Tandoori	"	3	4	3
£40+	Marcella	*Italian*	3	4	3
	500 Degrees	*Pizza*	3	2	3
	Theo's	"	3	3	2
	Yard Sale Pizza	"	3	4	2
	Ganapati	*Indian*	4	4	3
	Bone Daddies	*Japanese*	3	2	2
	Zaibatsu	"	4	3	2
£35+	Olley's	*Fish & chips*	3	4	2
	081 Pizzeria	*Pizza*	5	2	2
	Nandine	*Middle Eastern*	3	3	3
	Taro	*Japanese*	3	3	2
	Mambow	*Pan-Asian*	4	2	1
	Mr Bao	*Taiwanese*	3	3	3
£30+	Everest Curry King	*Sri Lankan*	3	3	2
£25+	Goddards At Greenwich	*British, Traditional*	3	4	3
	Silk Road	*Chinese*	4	3	2
£15+	La Chingada	*Mexican*	3	3	2
	Marugame Udon	*Japanese*	3	3	2
£5+	Monmouth Coffee Company	*Sandwiches, cakes, etc*	3	4	3

FSA Ratings: from **1** (Poor) to **5** (Exceptional)

**Battersea, Brixton, Clapham, Wandsworth
Barnes, Putney & Wimbledon
(All SW postcodes south of the river)**

£110+	Chez Bruce	*British, Modern*	5	5	3
	JOIA	*Portuguese*	3	3	4
£100+	Trinity	*British, Modern*	3	3	2
£90+	Rick Stein	*Fish & seafood*	2	2	2
£80+	Hatched	*British, Modern*	4	4	3
	The Ivy Café	"	1	1	2
	Darby's	*Irish*	3	3	4
	Riva	*Italian*	5	4	2
£70+	Church Road	*British, Modern*	3	4	2
	The Pig's Head	"	3	4	4
	Trinity Upstairs	"	4	4	3
	Wright Brothers	*Fish & seafood*	3	3	3
	Brinkley's Kitchen	*International*	2	2	3
	Archway	*Italian*	4	4	4
	Fiume	"	2	2	2
	The Fox & Hounds	*Mediterranean*	3	4	3
	Knife	*Steaks & grills*	4	4	3
	Macellaio RC	"	2	2	3
	Good Earth	*Chinese*	3	3	2
	Cilantro Putney	*Indian*	4	4	2
	Sticks'n'Sushi	*Japanese*	3	2	2
	Patara	*Thai*	3	3	2
£60+	The Laundry	*Australian*	3	4	4
	Bistro Union	*British, Modern*	3	3	2
	The Black Lamb	"	3	2	2
	Bottle & Rye	"	3	4	2
	The Brown Dog	"	3	3	4
	Brunswick House Café	"	3	2	5
	Coppa Club Putney	"	2	2	4
	Humble Grape	"	2	3	3
	24 The Oval	"	3	4	3
	The Victoria	"	3	3	3
	Canton Arms	*British, Traditional*	3	3	4
	Fox & Grapes	"	3	4	3
	Augustine Kitchen	*French*	3	2	3
	Gazette	"	2	2	3
	Soif	"	3	2	2
	The Light House	*International*	3	3	3
	Maremma	*Italian*	3	3	3
	Numero Uno	"	2	4	2
	Osteria Antica Bologna	"	3	3	2
	Pizza Metro	"	3	2	2
	Sorella	"	3	2	2
	Tozi Grand Cafe	"	2	1	3
	Lusitania	*Portuguese*	3	3	3
	Tapas Brindisa	*Spanish*	2	2	2
	Haché	*Burgers, etc*	3	3	2

	Restaurant	Cuisine			
	Santa Maria del Sur	Argentinian	3	3	2
	Le Bab	Middle Eastern	4	3	2
	Cinnamon Kitchen	Indian	4	3	3
	Evernight	Japanese	3	3	3
	Kibou London	"	2	2	3
	Takahashi	"	5	5	3
£50+	London Stock	British, Modern	3	3	3
	Olympic Studios	"	2	2	3
	The Telegraph	"	3	4	5
	The Plough	British, Traditional	2	2	3
	Smoke & Salt	"	5	4	3
	Cent Anni	Italian	3	3	3
	Lina Stores	"	2	2	3
	Made in Italy	"	3	2	2
	Little Taperia	Spanish	3	4	4
	Naughty Piglets	Steaks & grills	5	4	4
	MEATliquor	Burgers, etc	3	2	2
	Bravi Ragazzi	Pizza	4	2	2
	Zia Lucia	"	3	3	2
	Diba	Persian	2	2	2
	Kashmir	Indian	3	4	2
	Kricket	"	5	4	4
	Oka	Japanese	3	4	2
	Tsunami	"	3	2	3
£40+	Noci	Italian	3	2	3
	Rosmarino	"	3	3	3
	Soffice London	"	3	3	2
	Black Bear Burger	Burgers, etc	4	3	2
	Patty and Bun	"	3	2	2
	Yard Sale Pizza	Pizza	3	4	2
	Orange Pekoe	Sandwiches, cakes, etc	3	4	3
	Meza Trinity Road	Lebanese	3	3	3
	Black Salt	Indian	4	4	3
	Chook Chook	"	4	3	4
	Postbox	"	3	4	3
	Bone Daddies	Japanese	3	2	2
	Hoshi	"	3	3	2
	Tomoe	"	4	4	2
	Hare & Tortoise	Pan-Asian	2	3	2
	Cher Thai	Thai	3	4	3
	Kaosarn	"	3	4	3
	Bao Battersea	Taiwanese	3	4	4
£35+	Amrutha	Vegan	3	4	2
	Three Uncles	Chinese	5	2	2
	Balham Social	Indian	3	4	2
	Ela & Dhani	"	3	4	2
	Holy Cow	"	3	3	2
	Sushi Revolution	Japanese	4	4	2
	Taro	"	3	3	2
	Awesome Thai	Thai	3	3	2
£30+	Ploussard	British, Modern	4	3	3
	Indian Ocean	Indian	3	3	3

	Daddy Bao	*Taiwanese*	4	3	3
£25+	Milk	*Sandwiches, cakes, etc*	3	2	3
	Mirch Masala	*Pakistani*	4	2	2
£20+	Dropshot Coffee	*British, Modern*	3	4	4
	Thai Tho	*Thai*	3	3	3
£15+	Meiwei	*Chinese*	3	3	2
	Roti King	*Malaysian*	5	2	2

Outer western suburbs
Kew, Richmond, Twickenham, Teddington

£120+	Petersham Nurseries Cafe	*British, Modern*	2	2	5
£110+	Scott's Richmond	*Fish & seafood*	2	3	4
£90+	The Dysart Petersham	*British, Modern*	5	4	4
£80+	The Ivy Café	*British, Modern*	1	1	2
	Steven Edwards	"	4	2	4
	The Petersham	"	2	2	4
£70+	Le Salon Privé	*French*	3	3	3
	A Cena	*Italian*	4	4	3
	Bacco	"	3	3	2
£60+	The Fat Badger	*British, Modern*	3	2	2
	Hawthorn	"	3	5	3
	Petit Ma Cuisine	*French*	3	4	3
	Tapas Brindisa	*Spanish*	2	2	2
	Rock & Rose	*Pan-Asian*	2	2	3
£50+	Black Dog Beer House	*British, Modern*	3	3	3
	Four Regions	*Chinese*	3	3	3
£40+	Newens	*Afternoon tea*	3	4	3
	Dastaan	*Indian*	5	4	3
£15+	Kiss the Hippo	*Sandwiches, cakes, etc*	3	4	3

EAST

Smithfield & Farringdon (EC1)

Price	Restaurant	Cuisine	Ratings
£220+	The Clove Club	British, Modern	3 3 2
£170+	Restaurant St. Barts	British, Modern	5 4 5
£160+	Club Gascon	French	4 3 3
	Tehran Berlin	Persian	3 4 4
	Sushi Tetsu	Japanese	5 5 4
£110+	Anglo	British, Modern	5 4 3
£100+	NEST	British, Modern	4 3 3
	The Quality Chop House	British, Traditional	3 2 3
£90+	Luca	Italian	4 4 4
£80+	Compton	British, Modern	3 4 2
	St John Smithfield	British, Traditional	4 4 3
	Bouchon Racine	French	5 5 3
	Smiths of Smithfield	Steaks & grills	3 3 3
£70+	The Coach	British, Modern	3 3 3
	The Jugged Hare	"	3 2 4
	Daffodil Mulligan	Irish	4 4 3
	Apulia	Italian	2 2 3
	Macellaio RC	"	2 2 3
	Moro	Spanish	4 4 3
£60+	Granger & Co	Australian	2 2 3
	Caravan	British, Modern	2 2 2
	Sessions Arts Club	"	3 4 5
	Vinoteca	"	2 2 2
	Bleeding Heart Bistro	French	3 3 4
	Café du Marché	"	3 4 5
	Ibérica	Spanish	2 2 2
	The Gate	Vegetarian	3 3 3
	Homeslice	Pizza	3 2 3
	Le Bab	Middle Eastern	4 3 2
	Berber & Q Shawarma Bar	"	5 4 3
£50+	Attica	Greek	2 3 3
	Trattoria Brutto	Italian	3 4 5
	Morito	Spanish	4 3 2
	Street Burger	Burgers, etc	3 2 2
	The Sichuan	Chinese	3 2 2
	Pham Sushi	Japanese	2 3 2
£40+	Taqueria	Mexican	3 3 3
	Fish Central	Fish & seafood	4 4 2
	Noci	Italian	3 2 3
	The Eagle	Mediterranean	3 3 4
	Black Bear Burger	Burgers, etc	4 3 2

	Bone Daddies	*Japanese*	**3** 2 2
	Cây Tre	*Vietnamese*	**3** **3** 2
£15+	Daddy Donkey	*Mexican*	**4** **3** 2
	Prufrock Coffee	*Sandwiches, cakes, etc*	**3** **3** **3**

The City (EC2, EC3, EC4)

£170+	La Dame de Pic	*French*	**4** **3** **3**
£120+	City Social	*British, Modern*	**3** **3** **4**
	Nobu Shoreditch	*Japanese*	– – –
£110+	Fenchurch Restaurant	*British, Modern*	**3** **3** **4**
	Angler	*Fish & seafood*	**3** **4** 2
	Coya	*Peruvian*	2 2 **3**
	Sushisamba	*Japanese*	2 2 **3**
£100+	Lutyens Grill	*Steaks & grills*	**3** **3** **4**
	Yauatcha City	*Chinese*	**3** 2 2
£90+	Duck & Waffle	*British, Modern*	2 2 **3**
	14 Hills	"	2 2 **4**
	Helix	"	**3** **3** **5**
	Leroy	"	**4** **4** **3**
	1 Lombard Street	"	2 2 2
	Sweetings	*Fish & seafood*	**3** 2 **4**
	Bob Bob Ricard City	*French*	2 **4** **4**
	Coq d'Argent	"	2 2 2
	Hawksmoor Guildhall	*Steaks & grills*	**3** **3** 2
	M Restaurant	"	2 2 2
£80+	CORD	*British, Modern*	**4** **3** **4**
	Darwin Brasserie	"	2 2 **4**
	The Ivy City Garden	"	2 2 **3**
	The Mercer	"	**3** **3** 2
	Cabotte	*French*	**3** **4** **3**
	Cecconi's	*International*	2 **3** **3**
	Manicomio City	*Italian*	2 2 **3**
	Bibo by Dani García	*Spanish*	2 2 **3**
	Hispania	"	**3** **3** **4**
	Goodman City	*Steaks & grills*	**3** **4** **3**
	The Ivy Asia	*Pan-Asian*	**3** 2 **4**
£70+	Santo Remedio Café	*Mexican*	**3** **3** 2
	Bread Street Kitchen	*British, Modern*	2 2 **3**
	High Timber	"	**3** **3** 2
	Paternoster Chop House	*British, Traditional*	2 **3** 2
	Vivat Bacchus	*International*	**3** **3** 2
	Piazza Italiana	*Italian*	**3** **3** 2
	Burger & Lobster	*Burgers, etc*	**4** **3** 2
	Pachamama East	*Peruvian*	**3** **3** **3**
	Brigadiers	*Indian*	**4** **3** **3**

£60+	Caravan	British, Modern	2 2 2
	Coppa Club	"	2 2 4
	Humble Grape	"	2 3 3
	Vinoteca City	"	2 2 2
	VQ	"	2 2 3
	Brasserie Blanc	French	2 2 2
	Gazette	"	2 2 3
	Caravaggio	Italian	2 3 2
	Gloria	"	2 3 5
	Obicà Mozzarella Bar	"	3 3 2
	Popolo	"	3 3 2
	Terra Rossa	"	4 4 4
	Ekte Nordic Kitchen	Scandinavian	3 2 2
	Camino Monument	Spanish	2 2 2
	José Pizarro	"	3 2 2
	Haché	Burgers, etc	3 3 2
	Homeslice	Pizza	3 2 3
	Haz	Turkish	3 2 2
	Cinnamon Kitchen	Indian	4 3 3
£50+	Los Mochis	Fusion	3 3 3
	The Wine Library	International	2 3 5
	Barbican Brasserie	Italian	3 3 3
	Eataly	"	2 2 3
	Lina Stores	"	2 2 3
	Manteca	"	5 4 4
	Casa do Frango	Portuguese	3 3 5
	Blacklock	Steaks & grills	3 4 4
	Le Relais de Venise	"	3 3 3
	temper Shoreditch	"	2 1 2
	Street Burger	Burgers, etc	3 2 2
	temper City	BBQ	2 1 2
	Shoryu Ramen	Japanese	3 2 2
£40+	Zapote	Mexican	4 4 4
	Padella Shoreditch	Italian	4 3 4
	Patty and Bun	Burgers, etc	3 2 2
	Ozone Coffee Roasters	Sandwiches, cakes, etc	3 3 3
	Koya	Japanese	4 4 3
	Hare & Tortoise	Pan-Asian	2 3 2
£35+	Flat Iron	Steaks & grills	3 3 3
	Three Uncles	Chinese	5 2 2
£25+	Bleecker Burger	Burgers, etc	4 2 2
£5+	Rosslyn Coffee	Sandwiches, cakes, etc	3 4 3

East End & Docklands (All E postcodes)

| £290+ | Da Terra | Fusion | 5 4 5 |
| £210+ | Cycene | Fusion | 5 4 4 |

Price	Restaurant	Cuisine			
£190+	The Water House Project	*British, Modern*	4	5	4
£170+	The Sea, The Sea	*Fish & seafood*	5	4	4
£140+	Behind	*Fish & seafood*	5	4	3
£120+	Galvin La Chapelle	*French*	4	4	5
£100+	Brat at Climpson's Arch	*British, Modern*	4	3	2
	Lyle's	*"*	5	3	2
£90+	Allegra	*British, Modern*	3	2	2
	Cornerstone	*Fish & seafood*	5	5	4
	Hawksmoor	*Steaks & grills*	3	3	2
	M Restaurant	*"*	2	2	2
	Roka	*Japanese*	3	2	3
£80+	Brat	*British, Modern*	5	4	3
	The Ivy in the Park	*"*	2	2	3
	Pidgin	*"*	–	–	–
	Smith's Wapping	*"*	4	3	4
	Planque	*French*	3	4	4
	Casa Fofó	*International*	4	3	3
	Canto Corvino	*Italian*	2	3	3
	Cecconi's Shoreditch	*"*	2	3	3
	Boisdale of Canary Wharf	*Scottish*	3	3	3
	Goodman	*Steaks & grills*	3	4	3
£70+	Big Easy	*American*	2	2	3
	Eline	*British, Modern*	4	5	3
	Elliot's	*"*	3	3	2
	The Gun	*"*	3	2	4
	Rochelle Canteen	*"*	2	3	3
	St John Bread & Wine	*British, Traditional*	4	3	3
	The Melusine	*Fish & seafood*	4	4	4
	Angelina	*Fusion*	5	3	4
	Six by Nico	*International*	3	3	3
	Super Tuscan	*Italian*	–	–	–
	Brawn	*Mediterranean*	5	5	4
	Oren	*"*	4	4	2
	Ottolenghi	*"*	3	3	3
	Haugen	*Swiss*	–	–	–
	Burger & Lobster	*Burgers, etc*	4	3	2
	Sticks'n'Sushi	*Japanese*	3	2	2
£60+	Barge East	*British, Modern*	4	3	5
	Cafe Cecilia	*"*	4	4	4
	Caravan	*"*	2	2	2
	The Culpeper	*"*	3	3	3
	The Duke of Richmond	*"*	3	3	3
	Humble Grape	*"*	2	3	3
	Jones & Sons	*"*	3	3	4
	Chez Elles	*French*	3	3	3
	Galvin Bistrot & Bar	*"*	3	4	2
	Il Bordello	*Italian*	3	3	4

Obicà Mozzarella Bar	"		3 3 2
Ombra	"		– – –
Ibérica	Spanish		2 2 2
Elis	Brazilian		4 4 2
Le Bab	Middle Eastern		4 3 2
Berber & Q	"		5 4 3
Haz	Turkish		3 2 2
Lahpet	Burmese		4 3 2
Royal China	Chinese		3 2 2
Café Spice Namaste	Indian		5 4 4
Gunpowder	"		4 3 3
Smoking Goat	Thai		5 3 3

£50+			
The Empress	British, Modern		3 3 4
Mare Street Market	"		3 2 4
Papi	"		4 2 3
Townsend	"		3 3 2
Capeesh	Italian		3 3 3
Emilia's Crafted Pasta	"		3 3 3
Morito	Spanish		4 3 2
Blacklock	Steaks & grills		3 4 4
Mildreds	Vegetarian		3 3 3
Ark Fish	Fish & chips		3 3 2
Pizza East	Pizza		3 2 3
Zia Lucia	"		3 3 2
Acme Fire Cult	BBQ		2 1 3
Smokestak	"		4 3 3
Delamina East	Middle Eastern		3 3 3
Dishoom	Indian		3 4 5

£40+			
Provender	French		3 4 2
Black Bear Burger	Burgers, etc		4 3 2
Burger & Beyond	"		3 2 2
Patty and Bun	"		3 2 2
Yard Sale Pizza	Pizza		3 4 2
Ozone Coffee Roasters	Sandwiches, cakes, etc		3 3 3
Chick 'n' Sours	Chicken		4 3 3
Bubala	Middle Eastern		4 4 3
Lucky & Joy	Chinese		4 3 3
Issho-Ni	Japanese		4 4 2
Koya Ko	"		4 4 3
Som Saa	Thai		4 3 3
Sông Quê	Vietnamese		3 2 2
Bao Noodle Shop	Taiwanese		3 4 4

£35+			
Maene	British, Modern		4 3 3
Flat Iron	Steaks & grills		3 3 3
Crate	Pizza		3 2 3
The Dusty Knuckle	Sandwiches, cakes, etc		5 2 3
Mangal 1	Turkish		5 3 2
Taro	Japanese		3 3 2
Lahore Kebab House	Pakistani		4 2 2
Tayyabs	"		4 3 2

£30+			
Alter	Vegan		4 3 2
Supa Ya Ramen	Japanese		3 3 2

| £25+ | Bleecker Burger | Burgers, etc | 4 2 2 |
| | Singburi Royal Thai Café | Thai | 4 2 2 |

| £20+ | E Pellicci | Italian | 3 5 2 |
| | Tofu Vegan | Chinese | 4 3 2 |

£15+	Homies on Donkeys	Mexican	4 4 4
	Laxeiro	Spanish	3 3 3
	The Duck Truck	Burgers, etc	4 3 2
	Smokoloko	BBQ	4 3 3
	Marugame Udon	Japanese	3 3 2

| £10+ | The Rib Man | Burgers, etc | 4 4 – |

| £5+ | Brick Lane Beigel Bake | Sandwiches, cakes, etc | 5 2 1 |

MAPS

MAP 1 – LONDON OVERVIEW

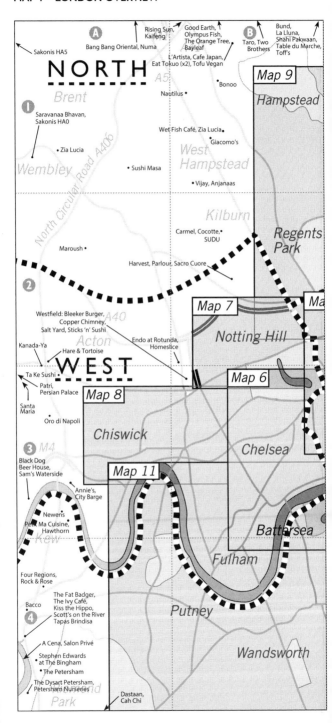

Bang Bang Oriental, Numa

Rising Sun, Kaifeng

Good Earth, Olympus Fish, The Orange Tree, Bayleaf

L'Artista, Cafe Japan, Eat Tokuo (x2), Tofu Vegan

Taro, Two Brothers

Bund, La Lluna, Shahi Pakwaan, Table du Marche, Toff's

Sakonis HA5

NORTH

Brent

Map 9

Hampstead

• Bonoo

• Nautilus

① Saravanaa Bhavan, Sakonis HA0

Wet Fish Café, Zia Lucia •

West Hampstead

• Giacomo's

• Zia Lucia

Wembley

• Sushi Masa

• Vijay, Anjanaas

North Circular Road A406

Kilburn

Carmel, Cocotte,• SUDU

Regents Park

• Maroush

Harvest, Parlour, Sacro Cuore

②

Ma

Westfield: Bleeker Burger, Copper Chimney, Salt Yard, Sticks 'n' Sushi

A40

Map 7

Notting Hill

Endo at Rotunda, Homeslice

Acton

Kanada-Ya

Hare & Tortoise

WEST

Map 6

Ta Ke Sushi

Patri, Persian Palace

Map 8

Santa Maria

Oro di Napoli

Chiswick

Chelsea

③ *M4*

Black Dog Beer House, Sam's Waterside

Map 11

Annie's, City Barge

Kew

Newens Peik Ma Cuisine, Hawthorn

Battersea

Fulham

Four Regions, Rock & Rose

Bacco

④ The Fat Badger, The Ivy Café, Kiss the Hippo, Scott's on the River Tapas Brindisa

Putney

A Cena, Salon Privé

Stephen Edwards at The Bingham

Wandsworth

• The Petersham

The Dysart Petersham, Petersham Nurseries

Dastaan, Cah Chi

MAP 1 – LONDON OVERVIEW

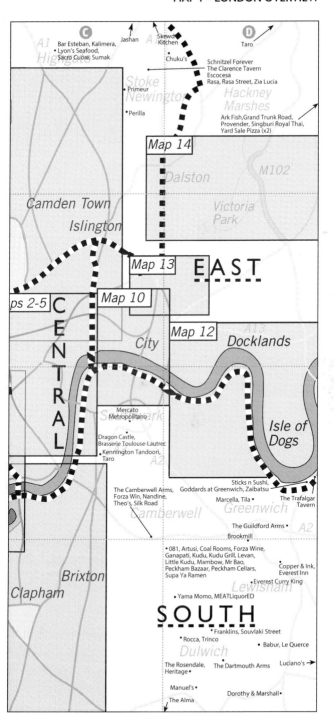

A1

Highgate

C

Bar Esteban, Kalimera,
• Lyon's Seafood,
Sacro Cuore; Sumak

Jashan

A

Skewd
Kitchen

Chuku's

D

Taro

Schnitzel Forever
The Clarence Tavern
Escocesa
Rasa, Rasa Street, Zia Lucia

Stoke
Newington

• Primeur

• Perilla

Hackney
Marshes

Ark Fish, Grand Trunk Road,
Provender, Singburi Royal Thai,
Yard Sale Pizza (x2)

Map 14

Dalston

M102

Camden Town

Islington

Victoria
Park

Map 13

E A S T

ps 2-5

C

Map 10

E

City

Map 12

Docklands

A13

N

T

R

Southwark

Mercato
Metropolitano

Dragon Castle,
Brasserie Toulouse-Lautrec
• Kennington Tandoori,
Taro

A

L

A2

Isle of
Dogs

The Camberwell Arms,
Forza Win, Nandine,
Theo's, Silk Road

Camberwell

Sticks n Sushi,
Goddards at Greenwich, Zaibatsu
• Marcella, Tila •

The Trafalgar
Tavern

Greenwich

The Guildford Arms •

A2

Brixton

Clapham

Brookmill

• 081, Artusi, Coal Rooms, Forza Wine,
Ganapati, Kudu, Kudu Grill, Levan,
Little Kudu, Mambow, Mr Bao,
Peckham Bazaar, Peckham Cellars,
Supa Ya Ramen

• Copper & Ink,
Everest Inn

Everest Curry King

• Yama Momo, MEATLiquorED

Lewisham

S O U T H

• Franklins, Souvlaki Street

• Rocca, Trinco

• Babur, Le Querce

Dulwich

The Rosendale,
Heritage •

The Dartmouth Arms

Luciano's

Manuel's •

The Alma

Dorothy & Marshall •

MAP 2 – WEST END OVERVIEW

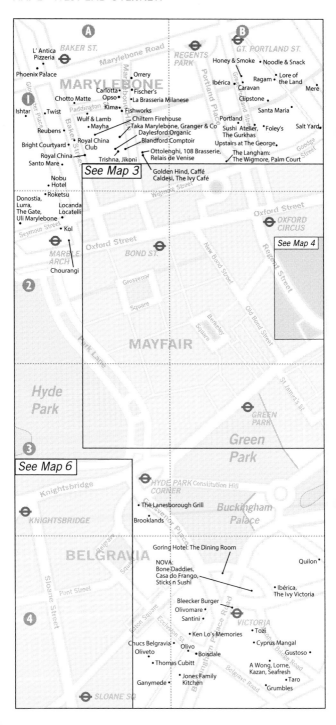

A

Baker St.

L'Antica Pizzeria
Phoenix Palace

Marylebone Road

MARYLEBONE

Orrery
Chotto Matte
Carlotta
Opso
Fischer's
La Brasseria Milanese
Kima
Ishtar
Twist
Paddington Street
Fishworks
Wulf & Lamb
Mayha
Chiltern Firehouse
Reubens
Taka Marylebone, Granger & Co
Daylesford Organic
Bright Courtyard
Royal China Club
Blandford Comptoir
Royal China
Trishna, Jikoni
Santo Mare
Ottolenghi, 108 Brasserie,
Relais de Venise
Nobu Hotel
Golden Hind, Caffè
Caldesi, The Ivy Café

REGENTS PARK

GT. PORTLAND ST.

Honey & Smoke • Noodle & Snack
Ibérica
Ragam
Lore of the Land
Caravan
Mere
Clipstone
Santa Maria
Portland
Sushi Atelier, Foley's
The Gurkhas
Salt Yard
Upstairs at The George.
The Langham:
The Wigmore, Palm Court

See Map 3

B

Donostia,
Lurra,
The Gate,
Uli Marylebone
Roketsu
Locanda
Locatelli
Kol
MARBLE ARCH
Chourangi

Seymour Street

Oxford Street

OXFORD CIRCUS

BOND ST.

See Map 4

Grosvenor Square

New Bond Street

Regent Street

Old Bond Street

2

Park Lane

MAYFAIR

Berkeley Square

St. James's St.

Hyde Park

GREEN PARK

3

Green Park

See Map 6

Knightsbridge

HYDE PARK CORNER
Constitution Hill

KNIGHTSBRIDGE

The Lanesborough Grill
Brooklands

Buckingham Palace

Goring Hotel: The Dining Room

BELGRAVIA

NOVA:
Bone Daddies,
Casa do Frango,
Sticks n Sushi

Quilon

Ibérica,
The Ivy Victoria

Bleecker Burger
Olivomare
Santini

Chucs Belgravia
Oliveto
Olivo
Boisdale
Ken Lo's Memories
Thomas Cubitt

Ganymede
Jones Family Kitchen

VICTORIA
Tozi
Cyprus Mangal
Gustoso
A Wong, Lorne,
Kazan, Seafresh
Taro
Grumbles

Sloane Street

Pont Street

Eaton Square

Eccleston St.

Belgrave Road

SLOANE SQ.

4

MAP 2 – WEST END OVERVIEW

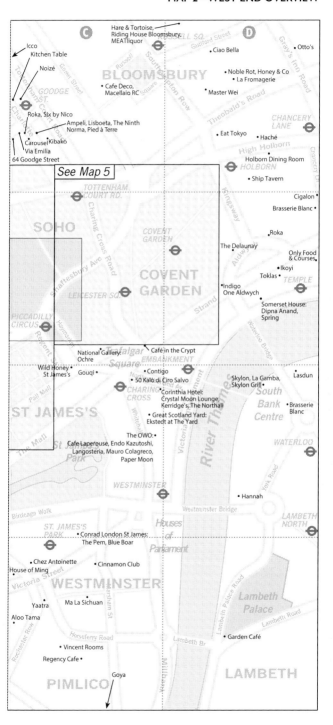

Hare & Tortoise,
Riding House Bloomsbury,
MEATliquor

Icco
Kitchen Table

Noizé

BLOOMSBURY

Cafe Deco,
Macellaio RC

Roka, Six by Nico

Ampeli, Lisboeta, The Ninth
Norma, Pied à Terre

Carousel Kibako
Via Emilia
64 Goodge Street

GOODGE

Ciao Bella

Otto's

Noble Rot, Honey & Co
La Fromagerie

Master Wei

CHANCERY
LANE

Eat Tokyo   Haché

Holborn Dining Room

HOLBORN

Ship Tavern

Cigalon

Brasserie Blanc

Roka

Only Food
& Courses

Ikoyi
Toklas

TEMPLE

Indigo
One Aldwych

Somerset House:
Dipna Anand,
Spring

The Delaunay

See Map 5

TOTTENHAM
COURT RD.

SOHO

COVENT
GARDEN

COVENT
GARDEN

PICCADILLY
CIRCUS

National Gallery
Ochre

Café in the Crypt

Wild Honey
St James's   Gouqi

Contigo

50 Kalò di Ciro Salvo

Corinthia Hotel:
Crystal Moon Lounge,
Kerridge's, The Northall

Great Scotland Yard:
Ekstedt at The Yard

The OWO:
Cafe Laperouse, Endo Kazutoshi,
Langosteria, Mauro Colagreco,
Paper Moon

ST JAMES'S

WESTMINSTER

Skylon, La Gamba,
Skylon Grill

Lasdun

South
Bank
Centre

Brasserie
Blanc

WATERLOO

Hannah

LAMBETH
NORTH

Conrad London St James:
The Pem, Blue Boar

Chez Antoinette

House of Ming

Cinnamon Club

WESTMINSTER

Yaatra

Aloo Tama

Ma La Sichuan

Lambeth
Palace

Garden Café

Vincent Rooms

Regency Cafe

Goya

PIMLICO

LAMBETH

MAP 3 – MAYFAIR, ST. JAMES'S & WEST SOHO

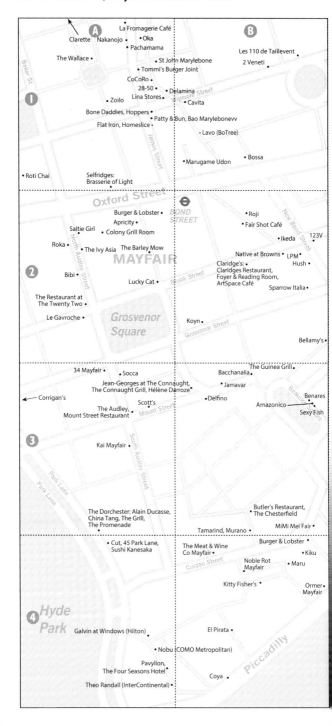

A

La Fromagerie Café
Clarette • Nakanojo • • Oka
• Pachamama

B

Les 110 de Taillevent
The Wallace • 2 Veneti •

St John Marylebone •
• Tommi's Burger Joint

CoCoRo •
28-50 • • Delamina
Lina Stores • • Cavita
• Zoilo
Bone Daddies, Hoppers •
Flat Iron, Homeslice •
• Patty & Bun, Bao Marylebonevv

1

• Lavo (BoTree)

• Bossa
• Marugame Udon

• Roti Chai

Selfridges:
Brasserie of Light

Oxford Street

BOND STREET

Burger & Lobster •
Apricity •
Saltie Girl •
• Colony Grill Room
Roka •
• The Ivy Asia The Barley Mow

• Roji
• Fair Shot Café
• Ikeda   123V •

MAYFAIR

Native at Browns • LPM •
Claridge's: Hush •
Claridges Restaurant,
Foyer & Reading Room,
ArtSpace Café
Sparrow Italia •

Bibi •

Lucky Cat •

The Restaurant at
The Twenty Two •

Le Gavroche •

Grosvenor
Square

Koyn •

2

Bellamy's •

34 Mayfair •
• Socca

The Guinea Grill •
Bacchanalia •

Jean-Georges at The Connaught,
The Connaught Grill, Hélène Darroze •

• Jamavar

Benares •

Corrigan's

The Audley •
Mount Street Restaurant •
Scott's •

• Delfino

Amazonico •

Sexy Fish •

3

Kai Mayfair •

The Dorchester: Alain Ducasse,
China Tang, The Grill,
The Promenade

Butler's Restaurant,
• The Chesterfield

Tamarind, Murano •

MiMi Mei Fair •

• Cut, 45 Park Lane,
Sushi Kanesaka

The Meat & Wine
Co Mayfair •

Burger & Lobster •
• Kiku

Noble Rot
Mayfair
• Maru

Curzon Street

Kitty Fisher's •

Ormer
Mayfair

4 Hyde
Park

Galvin at Windows (Hilton) •

El Pirata •

• Nobu (COMO Metropolitan)

Pavyllon,
The Four Seasons Hotel •

Coya •

Theo Randall (InterContinental) •

Piccadilly

MAP 3 – MAYFAIR, ST. JAMES'S & WEST SOHO

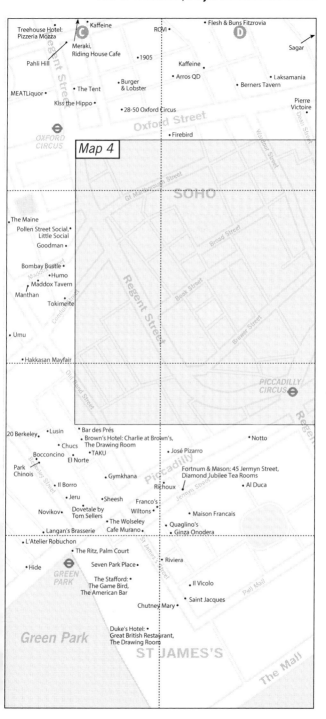

MAP 4 – WEST SOHO & PICCADILLY

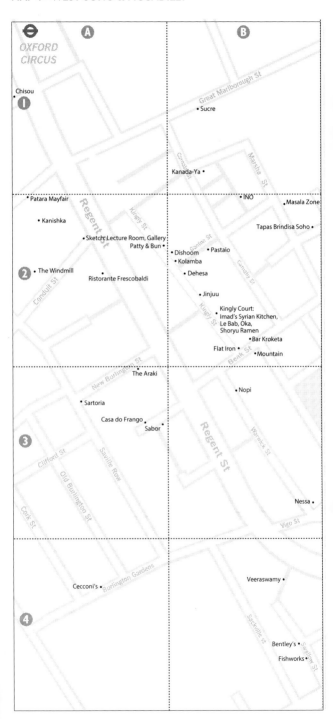

OXFORD CIRCUS

Chisou
1

Sucre

Canuda St

Great Marlborough St

Marble St

Kanada-Ya

INO
Patara Mayfair
Masala Zone

Kanishka

Regent St

Kingly St

Tapas Brindisa Soho

Sketch: Lecture Room, Gallery
Patty & Bun

Ganton St

Dishoom • Pastaio
Kolamba

Ganton St

2 The Windmill

Dehesa

Ristorante Frescobaldi

Jinjuu

Kingly St

Kingly Court:
Imad's Syrian Kitchen,
Le Bab, Oka,
Shoryu Ramen

Conduit St

Bar Kroketa
Flat Iron
Beak St
Mountain

New Burlington St

The Araki

Sartoria

Nopi

Casa do Frango
Sabor

Regent St

Warwick St

3

Clifford St

Old Burlington St

Saville Row

Cork St

Nessa

Vigo St

Burlington Gardens

Veeraswamy

Cecconi's

4

Sackville St

Bentley's
Swallow St

Fishworks

MAP 4 – WEST SOHO & PICCADILLY

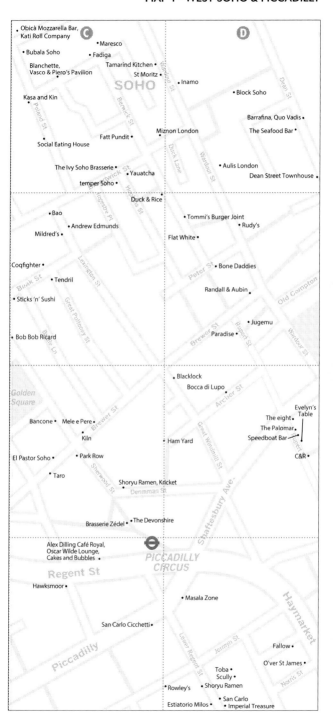

Obicà Mozzarella Bar,
Kati Roll Company • Ⓒ   Ⓓ

• Maresco

• Bubala Soho   • Fadiga

Blanchette,   Tamarind Kitchen •
Vasco & Piero's Pavilion   St Moritz •

SOHO   • Inamo

Kasa and Kin •   • Block Soho

                                    Barrafina, Quo Vadis •
                                    The Seafood Bar •

Fatt Pundit •   Miznon London •

Social Eating House •

The Ivy Soho Brasserie •   • Aulis London

temper Soho •   • Yauatcha   Dean Street Townhouse •

Duck & Rice

• Bao   • Tommi's Burger Joint
      • Andrew Edmunds   • Rudy's
Mildred's •   Flat White •

Coqfighter •   • Bone Daddies

      • Tendril

• Sticks 'n' Sushi   Randall & Aubin •

                        • Jugemu
• Bob Bob Ricard   Paradise •

                • Blacklock
                Bocca di Lupo •

Golden   Archer St   Evelyn's
Square   Table
                                  The eight •
Bancone • • Mele e Pere •   The Palomar •
      • Kiln   Speedboat Bar •
                  • Ham Yard   C&R •
El Pastor Soho • • Park Row

    • Taro

      Shoryu Ramen, Kricket •

    Brasserie Zédel • • The Devonshire

Alex Dilling Café Royal,
Oscar Wilde Lounge,   PICCADILLY
Cakes and Bubbles •   CIRCUS

Regent St

Hawksmoor •

                  • Masala Zone

    San Carlo Cicchetti •

                        Fallow •

                        O'ver St James •
                  Toba •
                  Scully •
            Rowley's • • Shoryu Ramen
      Estiatorio Milos • • San Carlo
                  • Imperial Treasure

MAP 5 – EAST SOHO, CHINATOWN & COVENT GARDEN

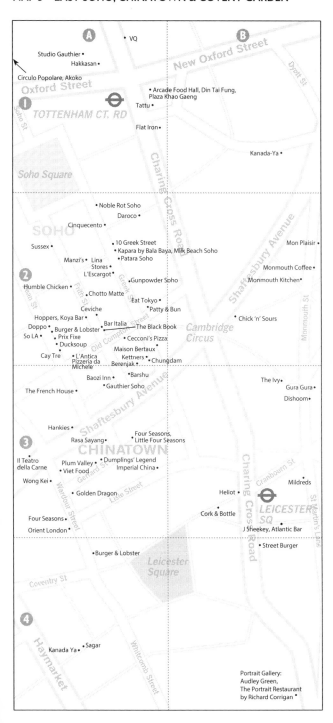

A

• VQ

Studio Gauthier •

Hakkasan •

Circulo Popolare, Akoko

B

New Oxford Street

Dyott St

Oxford Street

TOTTENHAM CT. RD

Soho St

• Arcade Food Hall, Din Tai Fung, Plaza Khao Gaeng

Tattu •

Flat Iron •

Kanada-Ya •

Soho Square

Charing Cross Road

SOHO

• Noble Rot Soho

Daroco •

Cinquecento •

Sussex •

• 10 Greek Street

Kapara by Bala Baya, Milk Beach Soho

Manzi's • Lina
Stores
L'Escargot •

• Patara Soho

Mon Plaisir •

Shaftesbury Avenue

Monmouth Coffee •

Monmouth Kitchen •

Monmouth St

Frith St

Greek St

Dean St

• Gunpowder Soho

Humble Chicken •

• Chotto Matte

Eat Tokyo •

Ceviche •

• Patty & Bun

Hoppers, Koya Bar •

Chick 'n' Sours •

Doppo •

• Burger & Lobster

Bar Italia — The Black Book

Cambridge
Circus

So LA •

• Prix Fixe

• Cecconi's Pizza

Old Compton St

• Ducksoup

Cay Tre •

• L'Antica
Pizzeria da
Michele

Maison Bertaux •

Kettners •

Berenjak •

• Chungdam

Baozi Inn •

• Barshu

The Ivy •

• Gauthier Soho

Gura Gura •

The French House •

Dishoom •

Shaftesbury Avenue

Hankies •

CHINATOWN

Rasa Sayang •

Four Seasons,
Little Four Seasons

Il Teatro
della Carne •

Plum Valley •

• Dumplings' Legend

Imperial China •

Charing Cross Road

Cranbourn St

St Martin's Lane

• Viet Food

Wong Kei •

Mildreds •

Wardour Street

Gerrard St

Little Street

• Golden Dragon

Heliot •

LEICESTER
SQ.

Four Seasons •

• Cork & Bottle

Orient London •

J Sheekey, Atlantic Bar •

• Street Burger

• Burger & Lobster

Leicester
Square

Coventry St

Whitcomb Street

Haymarket

• Kanada Ya • Sagar

Portrait Gallery:
Audley Green,
The Portrait Restaurant
by Richard Corrigan •

MAP 5 – EAST SOHO, CHINATOWN & COVENT GARDEN

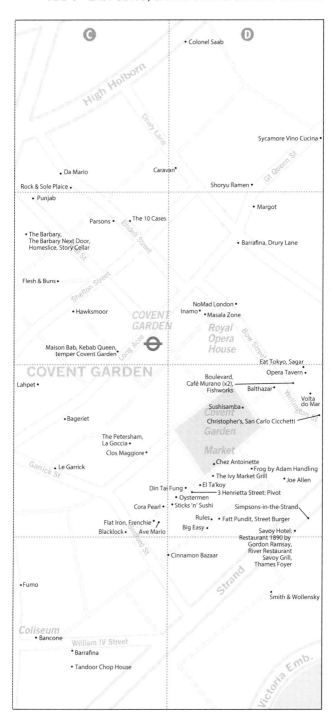

C

D

• Colonel Saab

High Holborn

Drury Lane

Sycamore Vino Cucina •

Gt Queen St

Caravan•

• Da Mario

Shoryu Ramen •

Rock & Sole Plaice •

• Punjab

• Margot

Parsons • • The 10 Cases

Endell Street

• The Barbary,
The Barbary Next Door,
Homeslice, Story Cellar

• Barrafina, Drury Lane

Flesh & Buns •

Shelton Street

• Hawksmoor

*COVENT
GARDEN*

NoMad London •
Inamo • • Masala Zone

Bow Street

*Royal
Opera
House*

Maison Bab, Kebab Queen,
temper Covent Garden•

Long Acre

Eat Tokyo, Sagar •

COVENT GARDEN

Opera Tavern •

Lahpet •

Boulevard,
Café Murano (x2),
Fishworks

Balthazar •

Wellington St

• Volta
do Mar

Sushisamba •

Covent

• Bageriet

Christopher's, San Carlo Cicchetti •

Garden

The Petersham,
La Goccia •

Market

Clos Maggiore •

• Chez Antoinette

• Frog by Adam Handling

• Le Garrick

Garrick St

• The Ivy Market Grill

• Joe Allen

Din Tai Fung •

• El Ta'koy

3 Henrietta Street: Pivot

Cora Pearl •

• Oystermen
• Sticks 'n' Sushi

Simpsons-in-the-Strand •

Flat Iron, Frenchie •
Blacklock • Ave Mario

Rules • • Fatt Pundit, Street Burger

Big Easy •

Savoy Hotel: •
Restaurant 1890 by
Gordon Ramsay,
River Restaurant
Savoy Grill,
Thames Foyer

Bedford St

• Cinnamon Bazaar

Strand

• Fumo

Smith & Wollensky •

Coliseum
• Bancone

William IV Street

Victoria Emb.

• Barrafina

• Tandoor Chop House

MAP 6 – KNIGHTSBRIDGE, CHELSEA & SOUTH KENSINGTON

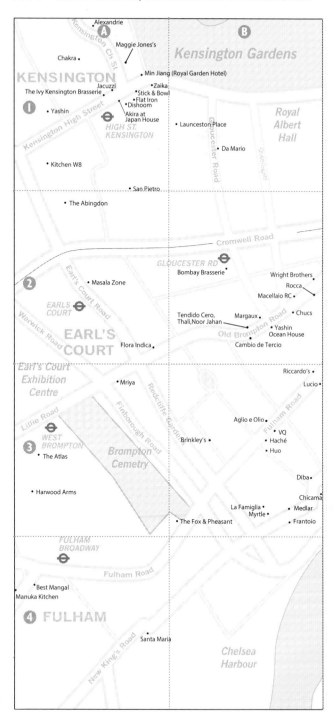

Alexandrie

A

B

Kensington Gardens

Maggie Jones's

Chakra

KENSINGTON

Min Jiang (Royal Garden Hotel)

Jacuzzi

The Ivy Kensington Brasserie

Zaika

Stick & Bowl

Flat Iron

Dishoom

Royal Albert Hall

1 Yashin

Akira at Japan House

HIGH ST. KENSINGTON

Launceston Place

Kitchen W8

Da Mario

San Pietro

The Abingdon

Cromwell Road

GLOUCESTER RD

2 Bombay Brasserie

Wright Brothers

Rocca

Masala Zone

Macellaio RC

Chucs

EARLS COURT

Tendido Cero, Thali, Noor Jahan

Margaux

Yashin Ocean House

EARL'S COURT

Flora Indica

Cambio de Tercio

Earl's Court Exhibition Centre

Riccardo's

Lucio

Mriya

Aglio e Olio

VQ

WEST BROMPTON

Brinkley's

Haché

3 The Atlas

Huo

Brompton Cemetery

Diba

Chicama

Harwood Arms

La Famiglia

Myrtle

Medlar

The Fox & Pheasant

Frantoio

FULHAM BROADWAY

Fulham Road

Best Mangal

Manuka Kitchen

4 **FULHAM**

Santa Maria

Chelsea Harbour

MAP 6 – KNIGHTSBRIDGE, CHELSEA & SOUTH KENSINGTON

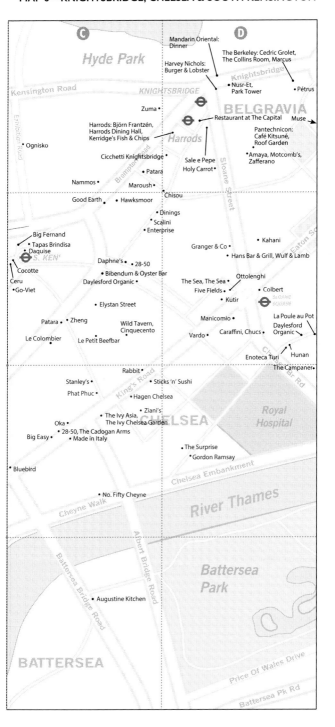

MAP 7 – NOTTING HILL & BAYSWATER

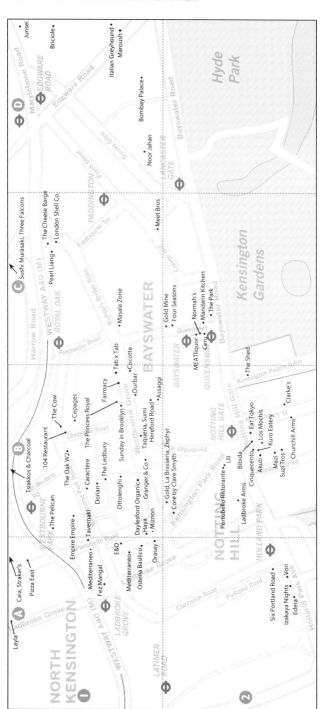

Junsel

Briciole

Italian Greyhound
Maroush

*Hyde
Park*

Bombay Palace

Noor Jahan

Sushi Murasaki, Three Falcons

The Cheese Barge
Pearl Liang • London Shell Co.

Meet Bros

BAYSWATER

Masala Zone

Gold Mine
Four Seasons   Normah's
Mandarin Kitchen
Cerru   The Park

*Kensington
Gardens*

Tàb x Tab
Cocotte
Farmacy   Durbar

The Cow

Cepages

The Princess Royal

104 Restaurant

Tsiakkos & Charcoal

The Oak W2   Caractere

The Pelican

Empire Empire   Tavernaki

Dorian

The Ledbury

Sunday in Brooklyn

Ottolenghi

Daylesford Organic

Haya   Granger & Co
Miznon

Assaggi

Taqueria, Sumi
Hereford Road

Gold, La Brasseria Zephyr
Core by Clare Smyth

MEATliquor

The Shed

**NOTTING
HILL GATE**

Portobello Ristorante • Uli

Ladbroke Arms

Cinquecento

Bibida

Eat Tokyo
Akub • Los Mochis
Mazi
Suzi Tros
Churchill Arms

Clarke's

E&O

Mediterraneo

Mediterraneo

Osteria Basilico •
Orasay

Fez Mangal

Layla

Caia, Straker's

Pizza East

**NORTH
KENSINGTON**

**NOTTING
HILL**

Six Portland Road

Izakaya Nights • Vori
Edera
Holland Park

MAP 8 – HAMMERSMITH & CHISWICK

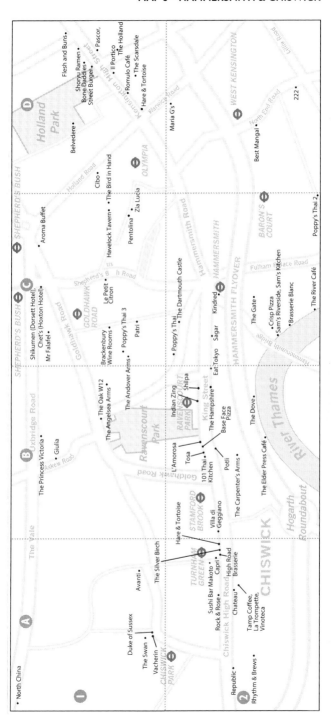

MAP 9 – HAMPSTEAD, CAMDEN TOWN & ISLINGTON

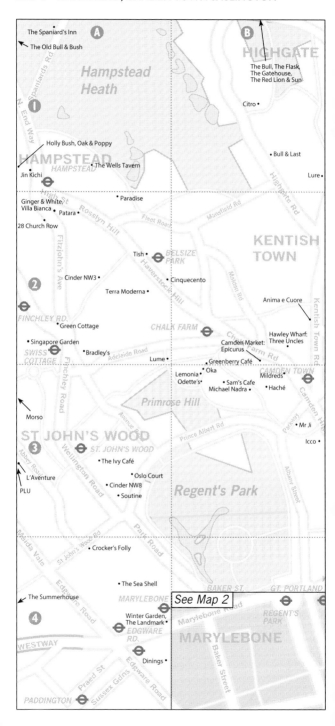

The Spaniard's Inn

The Old Bull & Bush

A

HIGHGATE

B

The Bull, The Flask,
The Gatehouse,
The Red Lion & Sun

Hampstead
Heath

Citro •

1

Holly Bush, Oak & Poppy

HAMPSTEAD

HAMPSTEAD

• The Wells Tavern

• Bull & Last

Jin Kichi

Lure •

Ginger & White,
Villa Bianca

• Paradise

Patara •

28 Church Row

**KENTISH
TOWN**

Tish •

DELSIZE
PARK

2

Cinder NW3 •

• Cinquecento

Terra Moderna •

FINCHLEY RD.

Anima e Cuore

Green Cottage •

CHALK FARM

Hawley Wharf:
Three Uncles

Singapore Garden •

SWISS
COTTAGE

• Bradley's

Camden Market:
Epicurus

Lume •

• Greenberry Café

• Oka

Lemonia •

Mildreds •

Odette's

• Sam's Cafe
Michael Nadra •

• Haché

Morso

Primrose Hill

• Mr Ji

ST JOHN'S WOOD

ST. JOHN'S WOOD

Icco •

3

L'Aventure

• The Ivy Café

PLU

• Oslo Court

Regent's Park

• Cinder NW8

• Soutine

• Crocker's Folly

• The Sea Shell

MARYLEBONE

The Summerhouse

BAKER ST.

GT. PORTLAND

See Map 2

4

Winter Garden,
The Landmark

EDGWARE
RD.

REGENT'S
PARK

MARYLEBONE

WESTWAY

Dinings •

PADDINGTON

MAP 9 – HAMPSTEAD, CAMDEN TOWN & ISLINGTON

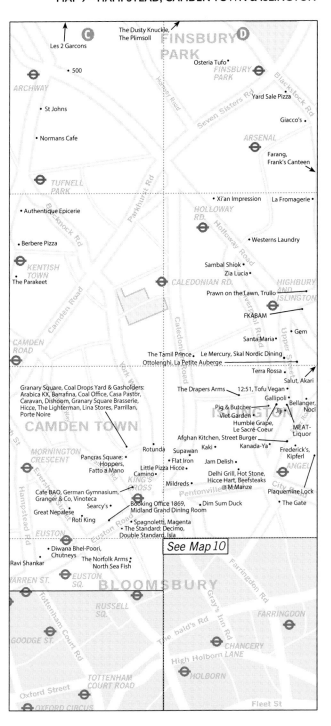

MAP 10 – THE CITY

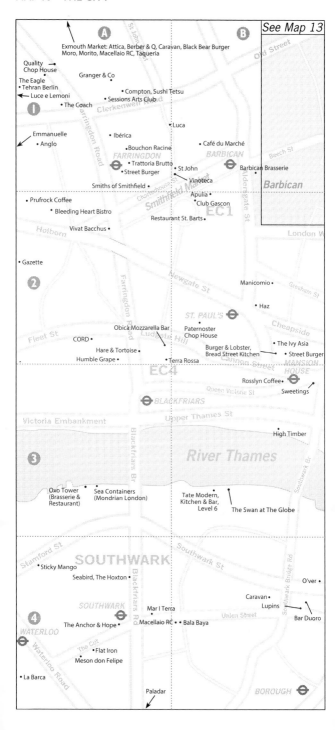

See Map 13

Exmouth Market: Attica, Berber & Q, Caravan, Black Bear Burger
Moro, Morito, Macellaio RC, Taqueria

A

B

Old Street

Quality Chop House
The Eagle
Tehran Berlin
Luce e Lemoni
The Coach

Granger & Co

Compton, Sushi Tetsu
Sessions Arts Club

Clerkenwell Rd

1

Farringdon Road

Luca

St John St

Emmanuelle
Anglo

Ibérica

Bouchon Racine

FARRINGDON

Trattoria Brutto
Street Burger

St John

Vinoteca

Café du Marché

BARBICAN

Beech St

Barbican Brasserie

Barbican

Smiths of Smithfield

Smithfield Market

Aldersgate St

Apulia
Club Gascon

EC1

London W

Prufrock Coffee
Bleeding Heart Bistro

Restaurant St. Barts

Holborn

Vivat Bacchus

Gazette

2

Farringdon Road

Newgate St

Manicomio

Gresham St

Haz

ST. PAUL'S

Cheapside

Fleet St

CORD

Hare & Tortoise

Humble Grape

Obica Mozzarella Bar

Ludgate Hill

Paternoster
Chop House

Terra Rossa

Burger & Lobster,
Bread Street Kitchen

Cannon Street

The Ivy Asia

Street Burger

MANSION
HOUSE

EC4

Rosslyn Coffee

Queen Victoria St

Sweetings

BLACKFRIARS

Upper Thames St

Blackfriars Br

High Timber

3

River Thames

Southwark Br

Victoria Embankment

Oxo Tower
(Brasserie &
Restaurant)

Sea Containers
(Mondrian London)

Tate Modern,
Kitchen & Bar,
Level 6

The Swan at The Globe

Stamford St

SOUTHWARK

Southwark St

Sticky Mango

Seabird, The Hoxton

Blackfriars Rd

SOUTHWARK

Mar I Terra

Southwark Bridge Rd

O'ver

Caravan
Lupins

WATERLOO

The Anchor & Hope

Macellaio RC

Bala Baya

Union Street

Bar Duoro

4

Waterloo Road

The Cut

Flat Iron
Meson don Felipe

La Barca

Paladar

BOROUGH

MAP 10 – THE CITY

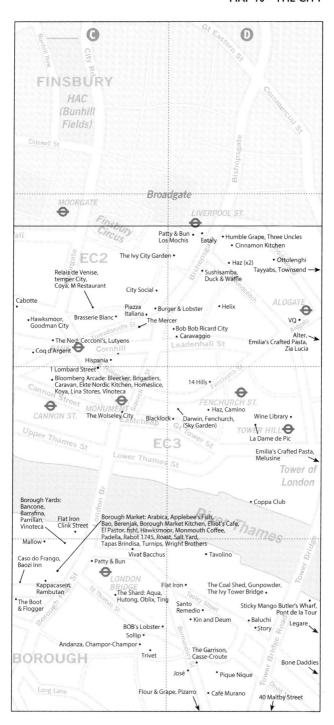

C

D

Gt Eastern St

FINSBURY

City Road

Bunhill Row

HAC
(Bunhill
Fields)

Commercial St

Chiswell St

Bishopsgate

Broadgate

MOORGATE

LIVERPOOL ST.

Finsbury Circus

Patty & Bun •
Los Mochis • Eataly •

Humble Grape, Three Uncles •
• Cinnamon Kitchen

EC2

The Ivy City Garden •

• Haz (x2)   • Ottolenghi

Relais de Venise,
temper City,
Coya, M Restaurant

• Sushisamba,
  Duck & Waffle

Tayyabs, Townsend →

Bishopsgate

Cabotte •

City Social •

ALDGATE

• Helix

• Hawksmoor,
  Goodman City

Piazza
Italiana •

• Burger & Lobster

Brasserie Blanc •

• The Mercer

VQ •

• The Ned: Cecconi's, Lutyens

• Bob Bob Ricard City
  • Caravaggio

Alter,
Emilia's Crafted Pasta,
Zia Lucia

• Coq d'Argent

Threadneedle St

Cornhill

Leadenhall St

Hispania •

1 Lombard Street •

• Bloomberg Arcade: Bleecker, Brigadiers,
  Caravan, Ekte Nordic Kitchen, Homeslice,
  Koya, Lina Stores, Vinoteca

14 Hills •

Fenchurch St

Cannon Street

MONUMENT

FENCHURCH ST.

CANNON ST.

The Wolseley City

• Haz, Camino

Eastcheap

Blacklock • • Darwin, Fenchurch,
              (Sky Garden)

Wine Library •

Upper Thames St

Gt Tower St

TOWER HILL

La Dame de Pic

EC3

Lower Thames St

Emilia's Crafted Pasta,
Melusine →

*Tower of
London*

London Br

River Thames

Borough Yards:
Bancone,
Barrafina,
Parrillan,
Vinoteca

• Coppa Club

Flat Iron
Clink Street

Borough Market: Arabica, Applebee's Fish,
Bao, Berenjak, Borough Market Kitchen, Elliot's Cafe,
El Pastor, fish!, Hawksmoor, Monmouth Coffee,
Padella, Rabot 1745, Roast, Salt Yard,
Tapas Brindisa, Turnips, Wright Brothers

Mallow •

Vivat Bacchus •

• Tavolino

Tower Bridge

Caso do Frango,
Baozi Inn

• Patty & Bun

LONDON
BRIDGE

Flat Iron •

The Coal Shed, Gunpowder,
The Ivy Tower Bridge

Borough High St

Kappacasein,
Rambutan

• The Shard: Aqua,
  Hutong, Oblix, Ting

Santo
Remedio •

Sticky Mango Butler's Wharf,
Pont de la Tour

St Thomas St

• The Boot
  & Flogger

• Baluchi
  • Story

Tooley St

• Kin and Deum

Legare →

Andanza, Champor-Champor •

BOB's Lobster •

Sollip •

Bermondsey St

Tower Bridge Road

Druid St

BOROUGH

• Trivet

The Garrison,
Casse-Croute

Bone Daddies →

Long Lane

José • • Pique Nique

Flour & Grape, Pizarro • • Café Murano

40 Maltby Street

MAP 11 – SOUTH LONDON (& FULHAM)

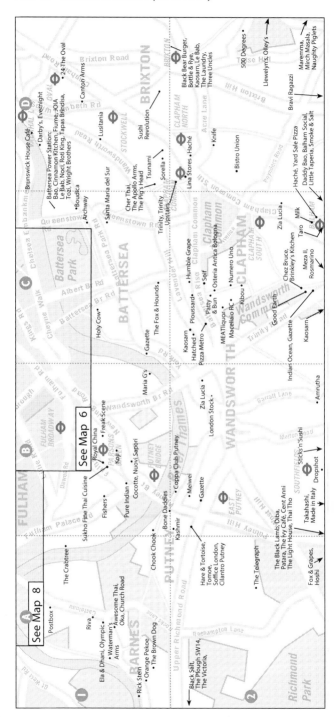

MAP 12 – EAST END & DOCKLANDS

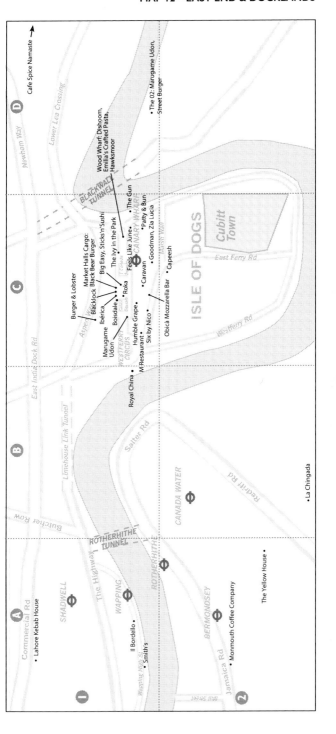

Cafe Spice Namaste

Newham Way

Lower Lea Crossing

D

• The O2: Marugame Udon,
Street Burger

Wood Wharf: Dishoom,
Emilia's Crafted Pasta,
Hawksmoor

BLACKWALL TUNNEL

• The Gun

CANARY WHARF

• Patty & Bun

Cubitt
Town

Big Easy, Sticks'n'Sushi

Market Halls Cargo:
Black Bear Burger

The Ivy in the Park

Feels Like June

Burger & Lobster

Blacklock

Ibérica

Boisdale

• Roka

• Caravan

• Goodman, Zia Lucia

ISLE OF DOGS

East Ferry Rd

Marugame
Udon

Humble Grape

Obica Mozzarella Bar

• Capeesh

Aspen Way

WESTFERRY
CIRCUS

M Restaurant

Six by Nico

Westferry Rd

East India Dock Rd

G

• Royal China

Limehouse Link Tunnel

Salter Rd

CANADA WATER

Redriff Rd

B

Butcher Row

ROTHERHITHE
TUNNEL

ROTHERHITHE

• La Chingada

The Highway

A

SHADWELL

WAPPING

Commercial Rd

• Lahore Kebab House

Wapping High St

• Il Bordello

• Smith's

BERMONDSEY

Jamaica Rd

The Yellow House •

• Monmouth Coffee Company

2

MAP 13 – SHOREDITCH & BETHNAL GREEN

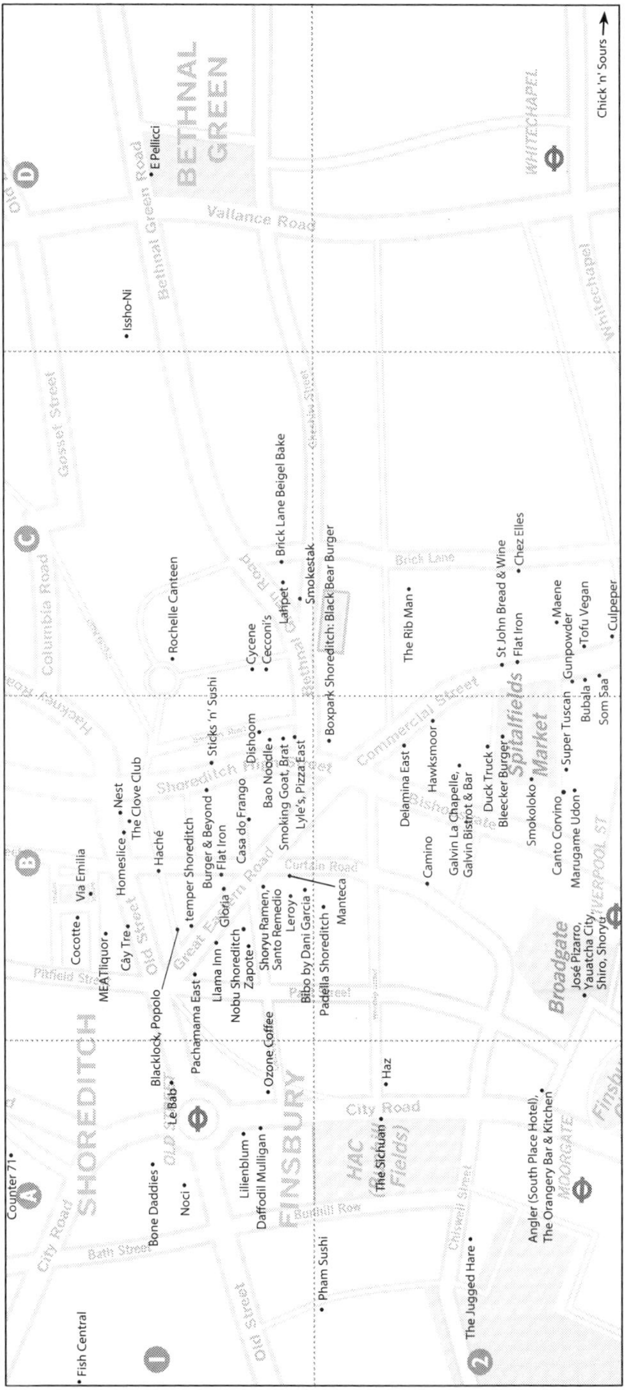

BETHNAL GREEN
E Pellici
Bethnal Green Road
Vallance Road
WHITECHAPEL
Chick 'n' Sours →
Whitechapel
Issho-Ni
Gosset Street
Columbia Road
Hackney Road
Rochelle Canteen
Brick Lane Beigel Bake
Brick Lane
Smokestak
Lahpet
Cycene
Cecconi's
Boxpark Shoreditch: Black Bear Burger
The Rib Man
Commercial Street
St John Bread & Wine
Chez Elles
Flat Iron
Maene
Gunpowder
Tofu Vegan
Culpeper
Super Tuscan
Bubala
Som Saa
Spitalfields Market
Sticks 'n' Sushi
Dishoom
Bao Noodle
Smoking Goat, Brat
Lyle's, Pizza East
Shoreditch High Street
Delamina East
Hawksmoor
Galvin La Chapelle,
Galvin Bistrot & Bar
Duck Truck
Bleecker Burger
Smokoloko
Canto Corvino
Marugame Udon
LIVERPOOL ST
José Pizarro,
Yauatcha City,
Shiro, Shoryu
Broadgate
Camino
Nest
The Clove Club
Homeslice
Haché
temper Shoreditch
Burger & Beyond
Flat Iron
Casa do Frango
Great Eastern Road
Curtain Road
Via Emilia
Cocotte
MEATliquor
Cây Tre
Old Street
Gloria
Shoryu Ramen,
Santo Remedio
Leroy
Bibo by Dani Garcia
Manteca
Padella Shoreditch
Llama Inn
Nobu Shoreditch
Zapote
Pachamama East
Pitfield Street
Blacklock, Popolo
Ozone Coffee
SHOREDITCH
FINSBURY
Le Bab
OLD ST
Haz
City Road
Lilienblum
Daffodil Mulligan
The Sichuan
HAC (Artillery Fields)
Counter 71
Bone Daddies
Noci
Bunhill Row
Bath Street
City Road
Angler (South Place Hotel),
The Orangery Bar & Kitchen
MOORGATE
Finsbury
Chiswell Street
Pham Sushi
The Jugged Hare
Fish Central
Old Street
A
B
C
D
1
2

MAP 14 – EAST LONDON

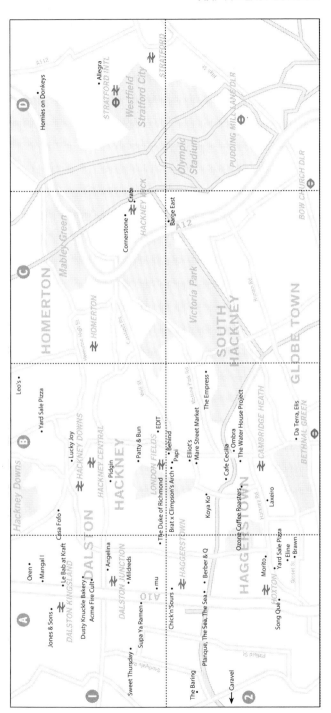